'Stay me with flagons, comfort me with apples:'

Song of Solomon

Produced by the Publishing Division of
The Automobile Association

Original research: David Hancock

Editor: Rebecca King

Contributors:
Richard Cavendish
Richard Dawes
Susan Gordon
David Hancock
Daphne Jolley
Denise Laing
Giala Murray
Nia Williams

Cover Design: The Paul Hampson Partnership, Southampton

Cover photograph: White Horse at Chilham

Photography: David Noble for the AA

A CIP catalogue record for this book is available from the British
Library.

AMERICAN EXPRESS ® is the registered trademark of American
Express Company

Published by The Automobile Association, Fanum House,
Basingstoke, Hampshire RG21 2EA

ISBN 0 7495 0685 7
AA Ref 19033

Printed by Wm Clowes Limited, Beccles and London

Colour repro by BTB

Contents

USING THE GUIDE

The Choice of Pubs All the pubs included in this guide have been visited by researchers commissioned by the AA, but the fact that a pub is listed does not of itself imply that it has been inspected or classified under any AA scheme, although this may in some instances be the case.

Selecting the pubs for the guide was not an easy task and a pub that appeals to one person may not do so to another. However, what they all have in common is at least one factor that makes them special, whether it be atmosphere, location, individuality, good food and drink or comfortable, value-for-money accommodation.

How The Pubs Are Listed The book has been divided into eight chapters - South West England, Southern England, London, East Anglia & East Midlands, Central England, Northern England, Wales and Scotland - and the counties within each region are arranged alphabetically. Within each county the pubs are listed alphabetically according to the village or town in which they are situated. (In London they are grouped according to their postal address, Central, North, South, East and West.) Please note that pubs are listed under their true location rather than the county designated in their postal address.

Opening Hours These vary considerably, but there are a few general points of law worth noting. Pubs in England and Wales are permitted to stay open all day - 11am to 11pm - from Monday to Saturday if they wish. The hours kept within these times are entirely up to the landlord. On Sundays the standard hours allowed are 12 noon to 3pm and 7pm to 10.30pm. Some establishments have a supper licence allowing them to stay open - serving food and alcohol - all afternoon on a Sunday.

In Scotland pubs are permitted to stay open all day on

Sundays, but generally the hours are 12 noon to 2.30pm and 6pm to 11pm. During the week, all-day opening is more common than in England and Wales, and pubs often obtain a licence to stay open until 12 midnight or 1am on certain nights of the week.

Food Every effort has been made to ensure that the information given about food and the times it is available is accurate, but changes are frequently made, especially with regard to menus and prices, so examples given should be taken as guidelines only. Information or opinions given about food are based on the experience of the researcher on the occasion of the visit.

Accommodation No attempt has been made in this guide to categorise the quality of the accommodation offered in the pubs selected - although it is always acceptable - and the facilities offered necessarily vary. Mention of accommodation in this guide does not imply AA inspection or recognition, although establishments may have an AA classification. A quick reference list of pubs offering accommodation is given on page 494.

Children Here again there are few hard and fast rules regarding children, and landlords are increasingly making provision for them.

Children under 14 years must always be accompanied by an adult, must not sit near the bar and are not allowed to buy drinks of any sort at the bar. Children over 14 years are not legally restricted from entering a pub, although alcohol cannot be served to persons under 18 years of age.

In this guide we indicate whether children are welcome inside the pub and whether there are any restrictions. It is assumed that children are always permitted outside.

Appletise Symbol ☻ This guide has been produced in association with Appletise plc and those establishments which stock Appletise bear this symbol in front of their name.

Every country has its drinking houses, but the pub is an institution deeply rooted in British social life and tradition. People go to a pub not only - or perhaps even mainly - to drink. They go for company and talk, though the 'silent regular' is a recognised phenomenon. They go for sympathy and laughter, to meet friends and the opposite sex, for neighbourliness, to play games and compete, to escape from the pressures of job and home, and to be taken, ostensibly at least, at their own valuation. People act roles in a bar and in each pub a kind of local soap opera unfolds, with the staff and regular customers in the leading parts.

In the 1930s a study of pub life in an industrial town in the north of England by Mass Observation found that what people mainly did in pubs was: drink, talk, think and smoke. They talked about betting, sport, work, people, drinking, the weather, politics and sex. They also played games (cards, dominoes, darts, quoits), made bets and

THE BRITISH PUB: TRADITION AND CHANGE

The Cherub in Dartmouth claims to be the oldest building in the town; it is certainly one of the prettiest

collected their winnings, sang or listened to singing or piano playing, bought bootlaces, hot pies, black puddings and embrocation, and occasionally quarrelled and fought.

Times change, however, and eating is now one of the chief activities in pubs. In the early 1990s pubs served up more than three and a half million meals a day and, along with real ale and atmosphere, good food has become one of the principal attractions of a good pub. Another major change has been the gradual disappearance of the old distinction between the Public Bar, which was for labourers, and the Saloon Bar for those further up the social ladder. Many pubs no longer have separate bar areas at all and most have lost that exclusively masculine atmosphere that once pervaded drinking houses.

In their role as meeting places and social centres pubs join in their neighbourhood's life and entertainment. Auctions and sales are often held in country hostelries; pubs are used for parties and celebrations, wedding breakfasts and Christmas and office outings. Games are still played in them, but nowadays these include slot machines and video games as well the more traditional ones. Many pubs relay piped music, some host live jazz and folk groups. Karaoke became a craze in the late 80s, and so did quizzes which remain a popular weekly event in many pubs. Pubs still run savings clubs or act as headquarters for benefit societies, and they were so closely connected with the ealy days of the trade union movement that a 'local' can mean a trade union branch as well as a pub.

For largely financial reasons pubs have been closing in shoals in recent years, but nevertheless there are still some 60,000 of them in Britain and one adult in three goes to a pub once a week or more. More than 29 million pints of beer go down the hatch in Britain every year, with an average consumption in 1990 of 194 pints a year per head of population (down from 208 pints a decade earlier). Of this, 51 per cent was lager, whose sales have outgrown those of the traditional beer, and pubs take wine and soft drinks more seriously these days, too.

Some of the famous names in Britain's brewing history go back for centuries, but since 1945 most of them have been swallowed up by the industry's 'big six': Bass, Allied, Elders (which includes Courage),

Grand Metropolitan, Whitbread and Scottish and Newcastle. The big brewers have been fiercely criticised for denaturing British beer and for spoiling too many pub interiors and after a Monopolies Commission report in 1989 they were made to prune their holdings of 'tied houses' (pubs which only sell one brewer's products). Whether competitiveness has really improved as a result is extremely doubtful, but this book amply demonstrates that the best pubs continue to play their time-honoured part in British life and leisure and that the spirit of the traditional British pub still flourishes.

'There is nothing which has yet been contrived by man
by which so much happiness is produced
as by a good tavern or inn'

Samuel Johnson,
Boswell's Life of Johnson

'Whoe'er has travell'd life's dull round,
Where'er his stages may have been,
May sigh to think he still has found
The warmest welcome at an inn.'

William Shenstone,
'At an Inn in Henley'

'Then to the spicy nut-brown ale
With stories told...'

Milton,
'L'Allegro'

'Say, for what were hop-yards meant,
Or why was Burton built on Trent?
Oh many a peer of England brews
Livelier liquor than the Muse,
And malt does more than Milton can
To justify God's ways to man.'

A E Housman,
'The Welsh Marches'

'What two ideas are more inseparable than
Beer and Britannia'

Revd Sydney Smith
The Smith of Smiths

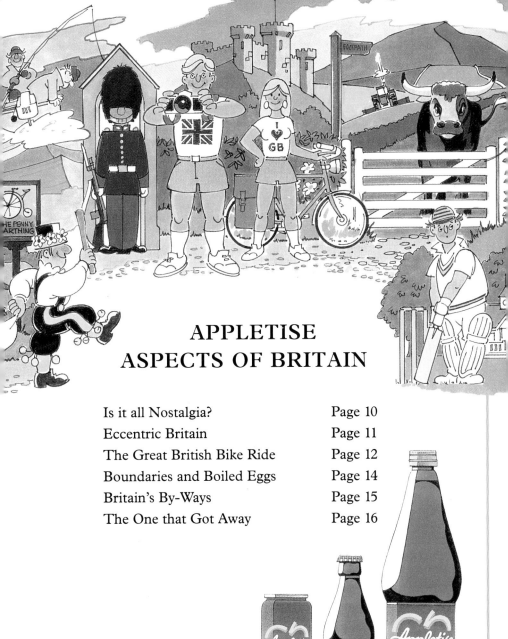

APPLETISE
ASPECTS OF BRITAIN

IS IT ALL NOSTALGIA?

There is the story of the American tourist talking to the Englishman - in a pub of course, where else?

"Tell me," said the American, "what's the best way to see your country?"

"Over a five-barred gate," replied the Englishman.

You can, of course, see his point. The countryside has always been one of Britain's traditional glories. Like village cricket, the pub, Edinburgh Castle and the changing of the guard.

But after a generation of intensive farming, with fields and hedgerows giving way to prairie-like tracts of wheat and barley, five-barred gates are disappearing into the nostalgic past.

Nevertheless, there is still a tremendously rich enjoyment to be had from Britain's landscape and traditions.

In the pages that follow, Appletise plc - the providers of that most genial of English drinks - make some constructive suggestions on the gentle art of enjoying Britain. On foot, on a cycle, on a village green, - or even in a car if you must.

Wherever your tastes take you, may we return to the original question and offer an answer that is perhaps more in keeping with today...

"What is the best way to see our country?"

"Over a glass of Appletise."

Made from apple juice, with just a light, refreshing sparkle added - and nothing else. Not sugar, not colouring, not preservatives. As in the countryside itself, good things come naturally.

ECCENTRIC BRITAIN

"The 25th Olympiad of the Modern Era." It has an impressive ring.

Yet did you realise that Britain got there first? Our own "Cotswold Olimpicks" were started in 1612 by Captain Robert Dover on a hillside above Chipping Campden (where Shakespeare could have seen them in his retirement). They continued till 1852, and were revived in 1963, to be held each year on the Friday of Spring Bank Holiday week.

At Appletise we like to think this is typical of Britain's love affair with things eccentric. Name a British tradition and you'll find someone zealously guarding it. Morris dancing, bluebell railways, Black Rod, real tennis, caber tossing, skittle alleys, knightly tourneys...All over Britain, traditional ways of life from the past are being devoutly preserved.

Eccentricities they may be. Irrelevant they may be in our hard, technological age. Yet all are flourishing to satisfy the eccentric in all of us. They are even being added to. In village fetes and county shows up and down the country, the wellie throwing contest and the donkey derby are becoming regular fixtures. As is lawn mower racing, made famous at Wisborough Green. In times to come maybe our descendents will be just as enthusiastically chucking space helmets and cheering robot races. One can only hope so.

Meanwhile, if you would like to enjoy your favourite eccentricity in action, a call to the relevant regional tourist authority or a visit to the local Tourist Information Centre will bring you details of dates and places.

And while we are on the subject of establishing traditions, may we add a particularly wholesome one. Appletise, the perfect refreshment for the whole family. Made only from apples, with nothing added apart from a delicate sparkle. Like our valued eccentricities, good things come naturally.

THE GREAT BRITISH BIKE RIDE

There are those who see it as quite an achievement to pedal a couple of miles to one of the pubs in this book and impress fellow drinkers with their performance in the saddle. Others put in 30 miles before breakfast and think nothing of it.

Whatever your inclination, cycling - quiet and fume-free as it is - must be one of the best ways of touring the intricate network of country lanes that meander through Britain.

A cyclist's experience of the countryside is immediate and vivid. You can hear the liquid notes of the skylark. You can delight in the fragrance of a bean field in flower. At the drop of a hat you can stop and examine a rare orchid, examine the carved Norman doorway of a village church. You can feel the sun on your back, the wind in your hair. You are part of everything around you.

And of course you feel justified, after all that fresh air and exercise, in working your way through a pub lunch menu. And if, after a generous main course, the pudding still looks wickedly seductive, well, who's counting the calories?

It makes a wonderful day out - and an even better holiday. One of our associates recently joined 150 other cyclists of all ages for The Great British Bike Ride: a three-week tour from Land's End to John O' Groats. Here's her account of the trip...

"Some kind of magic must have been at work," she says, "for almost all the way up this lovely island, from the winding lanes of the West Country to the mountains of Scotland, the sun shone!

"Minor roads led us through remote moorland, lush river valleys, tranquil farmland, spectacular mountains, and along by the sea. We low-geared gently up inclines and revelled in the exhilaration of swift descents. We explored impossibly pretty villages, gems of ancient churches, elegant towns. We heard accents change with every passing day and enjoyed the variety of the cottages, from picturesque cob through mellow brick to rugged granite.

"Our lunchtimes were dedicated to an unstinting and exhaustive study of the interior architecture of wayside pubs and inns (drinking, need we say, Appletise).

"And there were many moments of great humour. One evening we were at a pub in Much Wenlock, one of Shropshire's prettier villages. The entertainment was provided by Gus, one of our more splendidly built cyclists - a sort of Queen of Tonga in pink lycra. As he strutted and gyrated singing 'Not Fade Away' (as if he could) the stage finally gave up the unequal struggle and collapsed beneath him.

"As Gus sank, he showed a momentary flicker of surprise before his professionalism reasserted itself. With scarcely a pause, he continued his performance with just his head and shoulders visible through the hole in the stage. The crowd went wild of course. Gus's comment: 'It was just a stage I was going through at the time!'

"Sharing highs and lows and swapping our life stories with all these erstwhile strangers, we continued north. The beauty of the landscapes, the invigorating exercise and the feeling of achievement were an intoxicating combination, culminating in high euphoria at John O' Groats, where we celebrated with hugs, tears and promises.

"The Great British Bike Ride is a perennial favourite among cycle tourists. If you've never tried it, give it a whirl. Life will never be quite the same again."

Try this, or some of the other cycling holidays in the Bike Tours Brochure, available from Bike Tours Limited, PO Box 75, Bath, Avon BA1 1BX. Or call them on 0225 480130.

And when you set off, don't forget the essential luggage: Appletise. A deliciously different drink produced from fine apples and nothing else, apart from a light, refreshing sparkle to add power to your pedal. No added sugar, colouring or preservative. As with the scenery you cycle through, good things come naturally.

BOUNDARIES AND BOILED EGGS

"The smith a mighty man is he..." Everyone knows the scene: the massive frame lumbering up over the slope to hurl a bouncer with awesome velocity at the hapless curate the other end. Back in the pavilion (or rather, shed) the squire's wife winces as she butters the scones for tea.

That is our cherished concept of village cricket, the most levelling of games. But like everything else it has developed over the years. Parish still pits itself against parish and blacksmiths still no doubt terrorise the innocents the length and breadth of the land. But it has become more organised. Nowadays there is a national knock-out village championship, with the final played at the Holy of Holies itself: Lord's. Interestingly, one of the recent finalists was Hambledon, where some say the game first started.

But it remains a perfect partner to that other Great British institution, the picnic. The square leg boundary is one of the most idyllic alfresco spots you will find, though naturally there are countless others. National Trust sites abound in them, as does Britain's hospitable coastline. Though to get there you may well tangle with a further Great British institution, The Traffic Jam. Better stick to village cricket!

If you want to know more about village fixtures contact The Cricketer Magazine on 0892 740256. Or for more information about picnics and where to have them, the National Trust on 071-222 9251 can put you on to excellent and attractive facilities.

Meanwhile, whether your sustenance is a packet of cheese sandwiches or a Knightsbridge hamper, give a thought to what you're going to wash it down with. May we suggest yet another Great British Institution: Appletise. Deliciously different because it is made solely from the juice of fine apples. No added sugar, or anything else for that matter. Except, importantly, the light sparkle that makes it so refreshing. Like the squire's wife's scones, good things come naturally.

BRITAIN'S BY-WAYS

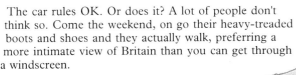

The car rules OK. Or does it? A lot of people don't think so. Come the weekend, on go their heavy-treaded boots and shoes and they actually walk, preferring a more intimate view of Britain than you can get through a windscreen.

As a pastime walking has many advantages. It is healthy, companionable and needs very little equipment. Also, it allows you to be as ambitious or as modest as you want to be.

You can tramp your ten miles a day through Snowdonia or the Cairngorms. You can go on a walking holiday. You can even grit your teeth for the daunting Fell Walk (allow at least a week and don't forget a tent, a map and a reliable compass).

Or at the other end of the scale you can enjoy a gentle three or four miles through the fields and woods on a Sunday morning - ending up at the kind of pub you'll find in this book. Then if you like you can get the bus back for your roast beef and Yorkshire.

However you do it, walking is the best way to be at one with the countryside. And in fact you will be doing Britain a favour. Look at a large scale Ordnance Survey map and you will see it criss-crossed with footpaths, many of them through farmland. They are public rights of way, which unfortunately are more popular with the public than they are with farmers. Some of them are unscrupulous enough to have shut them off. But you can still use them. If you do they stay open. If not, the right of way lapses.

So get on to your local Rambling Club, or call the Rambling Association on 071-582 6878 or 6826 - and start walking!

You may find it thirsty work. In which case we have a wholesome and deliciously different remedy:
Appletise. Apple juice with nothing added, apart from a refreshing sparkle to put a spring into your step. As in the fields and woods, good things come naturally.

THE ONE THAT GOT AWAY

We live, it is said, in the age of the spectator. Most sports have plenty of fans and not too many players. Angling stands unique as the most popular participating sport in Britain. It is probably also the most solitary.

At Appletise we take our hats off to the angler. He is active rather than passive. And no one can call it either a comfortable or a convenient sport. It seems to entail being at your chosen venue at 6 am at the latest in order to get the morning rise. And preferably there should be some rain about, because this brings down the insects and encourages the fish to the surface. What more could a fly fisherman want?

Alternatively you can fish from a boat - out on a lake, or, if it's close enough, the sea. Either way the early morning rule still applies. And the rain. Plus the extra hazard of the waterborne queasiness that afflicts a surprising number of these hardy spirits.

Every weekend sees the arrival of hundreds of them at the salmon pools of Scotland, the prime reaches of the Test and countless local streams, reservoirs and canals. Adverse conditions are not compulsory, of course. Many an angler is happy to sit dreaming away a summer's afternoon in soporific contentment. And who cares about the one that got away?

If you fancy getting hooked, start by calling your local Water Authority. They'll tell you where you pay and where you don't; where angling is permitted and where it isn't.

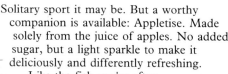

Solitary sport it may be. But a worthy companion is available: Appletise. Made solely from the juice of apples. No added sugar, but a light sparkle to make it deliciously and differently refreshing. Like the fish you're after, good things come naturally.

It's easy to recognise a good place when you see one.

American Express Cardmembers have been doing it for years.

The secret? Instead of just relying on what they see in the window they look at the door. If there's an American Express Blue Box on it, they know they've found an establishment that cares about high standards.

Whether it's a place to eat, to sleep, to shop, or simply meet, they know they will be warmly welcomed.

So much so, they're rarely taken in by anything else.

Always a good sign.

SOUTH WEST ENGLAND

Avon

❖

Cornwall

❖

Devon

❖

Dorset

❖

Somerset

❖

AVON

CROWN
Bathford Hill, Bathford, near Bath BA1 7SL. Tel 0225 852297

Bathford

This large, elegant building on the edge of town, rebuilt in 1904, is a cross between a traditional pub and a café. Its relaxed and friendly atmosphere attracts a complete cross-section of customers - the provision of a magician at Sunday lunchtime presumably contributing to this! A comfortable bar adorned with an assortment of bric-à-brac has Ushers, Courage and Bass beer on draught, and a good range of international bottled beers and wines - the ideal accompaniment to a menu of stylishly presented and generously served dishes that includes lentil nut casserole (£3.95) as well as the more usual choices like steak, mushroom and ale pie (£7.25), chicken Kiev (£8.50) or pan-fried rainbow trout (£7.25); those requiring a lighter meal might prefer a toasted sandwich or jacket potato (from £3.25). A garden and terrace at the rear of the pub offer pleasant alternative seating for fine days.

Brewery: Ushers
Licensees: Gregg and Angela Worrall
Opening hours: 11am-2.30pm, 6.30-11pm; closed Mon lunchtimes except BHs; Sun 12-3pm, 7-10.30pm
Bar food: As opening hours; Sun 12-3pm only
Children: Welcome in family room; children's menu and half portions available; magician Sun lunchtime
Credit Cards: AMERICAN EXPRESS® Access, Visa

CROWN INN
The Batch, Skinners, Churchill, Bristol BS19 5PP. Tel 0934 852995

Churchill

Set beside a country lane, with gardens both in front and behind, this 400-year-old pub offers a full range of international beers as well as Cotleigh Batch, Palmers Tally Ho!, Eldridge Pope Thomas Hardy Country and Butcombe; there is also a short but carefully chosen wine list that includes English country wines. The interior of the building, though very bare with exposed stone walls, is made homely by open fires and an interesting assortment of randomly collected nicknacks. Untouched by the modern preoccupation with piped music and electronic games, the bar has only such traditional amusements as darts and dominoes, and the food served in it (at lunchtime only) is simple but excellent, with jacket potatoes at £2.50, sandwiches of rare roast beef (£2.50) or salmon (£2.20), for example, and a vegetarian option always available.

Brewery: Free house
Licensee: Tim Rogers
Opening hours: 11.30am-3.30pm, 5.30-11pm; Sun 12-3pm, 7-10.30pm
Bar food: 12-3pm only
Children: Welcome in back room away from bar; outdoor play area

⊕ BLACK HORSE
Clevedon Lane, Clapton in Gordano, near Portishead BS20 9RH.
Tel 0275 842105

Clapton in Gordano

As close to a traditional ale house as can be found nowadays, this gem of a pub is tucked away down a tiny lane, with ivy and roses climbing the walls to complete the idyll. Although often busy, with many customers travelling a considerable distance, it is mercifully free from the noise of games and piped music, although solo musicians and duets perform on Monday evenings. The mellow bar of this 14th-century pub, with its flagstone and quarry tile floor, huge inglenook, winged settles and narrow oak tables, is the ideal place for a relaxing drink. Courage Best, Boys Bitter and a guest beer, as well as scrumpy, are on sale. But as for food, EC regulations demand changes to the kitchen which clash with the building's listed status, so at present only ploughman's is available. In addition to the bar there is a Snug with a window which is still barred, from the time when the room was a Petty Sessions gaol, and a family room. Outside is a large garden with a barbecue.

Brewery: Courage
Licensee: Tina Hutcheson
Opening hours: 11am-2.30pm
(Sat 3pm), 6-11pm; Sun 12-3pm,
7-10.30pm
Bar food: 12-2pm, (except Sun)
Children: In family room only;
outdoor play area

⊕ WHEATSHEAF
Combe Hay, near Bath BA2 7EG. Tel 0225 833504

Combe Hay

A low building, dating from the 16th century and distinguished by the dovecotes set into its front, the Wheatsheaf is set back from the road in large gardens overlooking the surrounding countryside. Three traditional bars with settles and open fires are hung with old photographs and prints on local themes; electronic games and piped music are conspicuously absent here, only the sounds of shove halfpenny punctuating the hum of conversation. The choice of draught beverages features different guest beers as well as Courage and Smiles, and there is an extensive wine list. Good food is served in both an eating area in farmhouse kitchen style and a separate restaurant, notable dishes including marinated pigeon breasts (£5.50) and medallions of pork with Stilton in oyster sauce (£7). Game is the establishment's speciality.

Brewery: Courage
Licensees: Mike and Sue Taylor
Opening hours: 11am-2.30pm,
6.30-10.30pm (Fri and Sat 11pm);
Sun 12-3pm, 7-10.30pm
Bar food: As opening hours
Children: Welcome in front area
away from bar

Dominoes

Dominoes came to Britain from the Continent at the end of the 18th century, perhaps brought back by British soldiers serving in the Napoleonic Wars. French prisoners-of-war made sets of dominoes, not only for their own amusement but to sell to the British. Though scorned by sophisticates - a writer in 1801 dismissed the game as 'very childish' - dominoes caught on. Many different varieties are played in pubs besides the standard block game, and some pubs belong to domino leagues.

⊜ RING O' BELLS
Compton Martin, near Bristol BS18 6SE. Tel 0761 221284

Compton Martin

A traditional pub which stoutly maintains its character whilst providing modern comforts, the Ring o' Bells stands at the village centre surrounded by a car park, a pleasant little garden and a good play area. Three traditionally styled bars with wood panelling and open fires include Butcombe, Wadworth and Bass among their draught beers, also offering the region's own cider, Mendip Magic, and a reasonable range of wines. Quality dishes like Butcombe beef (£4.75) or mariner's pie (£4.25) are generously served and there is always a vegetarian option. Such time-honoured pursuits as darts, shove halfpenny and bar skittles vie for popularity with electronic games.

Brewery: Free house
Licensee: David Walter
Opening hours: 11.30am-2.30pm, 6.30-11pm; Sun 12-3pm, 7- 10.30pm
Bar food: As opening hours
Children: Welcome; award-winning family room converted from old barn; outdoor play area

⊜ CROWN INN
Kelston, near Bath BA1 9AQ Tel 0225 423032

Kelston

This 16th-century roadside inn of much character is predominantly a beer-drinking pub, with Smiles, Butcombe, Wadworth, Bass and Guinness on draught, though a good range of blended whiskies is also sold. Bar food - available at lunchtimes only - will include a vegetarian dish alongside such established favourites as steak and ale pie (£4.20), and a separate restaurant operates at weekends. The candlelit bars with their dark woodwork and flagstone floors feature some ancient beer pumps and an array of old bottles, entertainment being confined to such traditional pursuits as dominoes, shove halfpenny and cards.

Brewery: Free house
Licensees: Messrs. Steele and Jackson
Opening hours: 11.30am-3pm, 5-11pm; Sun 12-3pm, 7-10.30pm
Bar food: Mon-Sat 12-2pm
Restaurant: Thu, Fri and Sat 7.30-9pm
Children: Not permitted inside

⊜ CATHERINE WHEEL
High Street, Marshfield, near Chippenham SN14 4BS. Tel 0225 892220

Marshfield

An elegant stone building dating back in part to the 16th century and looking more like a private home or small hotel, this friendly pub boasts a distinctive interior in country house style; its attractive courtyard, surrounded by old stonework, provides a popular meeting place during the summer months. The old-fashioned bar, well decorated with all sorts of memorabilia and disturbed only by a game of darts or the occasional Thursday 'singalong', offers a wide range of good-value wines and bottled beers like Diamond White as well as the draught Wadworth 6X, Courage Best and Smiles. An extensive selection of excellent home-cooked food - served in large portions and accompanied by a variety of vegetables - always includes a vegetarian choice as well as

Brewery: Free house
Licensees: Carole and Royston Elms
Opening hours: 11am-3pm, 6-11pm; closed Mon lunchtime; Sun 12-3pm, 7-10.30pm
Bar food: 12-2pm (except Mon), 7-10pm; Sun 12-2pm, 7-9pm
Restaurant: 7-10pm only; Sun 12-2pm, 7-9pm
Children: Welcome in eating area; half portions available

dishes like home-made cannelloni (£3.75), pork Marsala (£6.90) and braised venison with port and redcurrant sauce (£5.95).Accommodation will be available in the near future.

⊛ ANCHOR INN
Church Road, Oldbury-on-Severn BS12 1QA. Tel 0454 413331

Oldbury-on-Severn

Raised in the 17th century on the site of an old mill house, this mellow stone, wisteria-clad building became a public house during the village's seafaring days, when barges pulled up alongside it. The clientele is largely business people and retired folk, and for those whose appetite is whetted by Butcombe, Theakston Best, Bass from the barrel or Marston Pedigree, an extensive, daily changing menu is on offer. With a reputation for quality and value for money, the main courses include boozy beef pie at £4.35, fresh fillet of haddock Florentine at £5.25, lamb in cream and garlic sauce at £4.75 and leek and potato bake with salad at £3.95. Sweets include pie-in-the-sky and Oldbury mud pie, both at £2.10, and home-made shoofly pie at £2.05. There are 35 wines to choose from (ten by the glass), and an exceptional 75-plus malt whiskies. Both the Public Bar and the Lounge are furnished simply - the first with settles and benches, the second, whose walls are lined with original oils of country scenes, with an assortment of tables and chairs, high-back settles and easy chairs. Outside there is a large garden with picnic benches where pétanque can be played.

Brewery: Free house
Licensees: Michael J Dowdswell and Alex De La Torre
Opening hours: 11.30am-2.30pm, 6.30-11pm; Sat 11.30am-3pm, 6-11pm; Sun 12-3pm, 7-10.30pm
Bar food: 11.30am-2pm, 6.30-9.30pm; Sun 12-2pm, 7-9.30pm
Children: In dining area only
Credit cards: Access, Visa

⊛ SOMERSET INN
Bath Road, Paulton, near Bristol BS18 8PS. Tel 0761 412828

Paulton

Once a mine checking-house and now a friendly little 'restaurant' pub boasting real ale, real food and real fires, this early 19th-century building with a pleasant rear garden stands outside the small town of Paulton. Old mining equipment and local photographs from days long past adorn the homely, candlelit bar where taped classical music provides a relaxing background to the appreciation of a range of beverages including Ushers, Courage and Guinness among the draught beers; patrons can enjoy live folk music on Wednesday evenings, and there is often Morris dancing (particularly at weekends). Exceptional bar food - all cooked by the landlady - offers very good value for money in such original dishes as Porlock pie (salmon and bacon) at £7.25 and yokel pudding (apples, walnuts and cider) at £2.50, and a limited but carefully selected wine list is available.

Brewery: Ushers
Licensees: Ian and Yvonne MacFarlane
Opening hours: 12-2.30pm, 7-11pm; Sun 12-3pm, 7-10.30pm
Bar food: As opening hours (except Sun evening)
Children: One family table available

CORNWALL

⊕ OLD FERRY INN
Bodinnick-by-Fowey PL23 1LX. Tel 0726 870237

Bodinnick by Fowey

With its peaceful hillside position overlooking the Bodinnick ferry and its model ship, seafaring photographs, ships' lamps and other nautical artefacts, this handsome stone pub, built some 400 years ago, is made for lovers of the sea. As well as the inevitable yachting types, a good mix of locals and holidaymakers enjoys the two bars, both of which have black-painted half-panelling and historic local prints and photographs. One bar has stone flags, Windsor chairs and a settle, while the Lounge Bar offers captain's chairs around Victorian-style tables and displays a huge stuffed pike. Available on tap are St Austell Tinners Ale, Flowers Original and Murphy's Stout. Simple and reasonably priced, the bar food includes fisherman's lunch at £3.55, while the restaurant, from where there is a splendid view over the estuary, offers a fixed price menu at £16. There are 13 double rooms, again with a fine outlook, and built into the rock face is a family room equipped with children's games.

Brewery: Free house
Licensee: Simon Farr
Opening hours: 11am- 3pm, 6-11pm; Sun 12-3pm, 7-10.30pm
Bar food: 12-2pm, 6-9pm; Sun 12-2pm, 7-8.30pm
Restaurant: 7.30-8.15pm (one sitting)
Accommodation: (Price per room) double £60-£82; family room available
Children: In family room only
Credit cards: Access, Visa

⊕ CADGWITH COVE INN
Cadgwith, Ruan Minor, near Helston TR12 7JX. Tel 0326 290513

Cadgwith

An unspoilt fishing hamlet of thatched cottages is the appealing setting for this pub, three centuries ago the haunt of smugglers. In front of the plain, whitewashed building a small, thatched portal gives on to a sunny patio with views of a cove. Furnished simply and decked with mementoes of bygone seafaring days, the two bars , both with log fires, serve Cornish Original, Flowers IPA and Original, Marston's Pedigree and Murphy's on draught. Although largely standard pub fare, the menu can nevertheless pride itself on its fish, all the fresher for being landed just across the road. Three double rooms are available, furnished in simple, traditional style.

Brewery: Devenish
Licensees: Brian and Margaret Chivers
Opening hours: 12-3pm (winter 2.30pm), 6.30- 11pm (winter 7pm); Sun 12-3pm, 7-10.30pm
Bar food: 12-2pm, 7-9.00pm
Restaurant: 7-9.30pm; closed in winter
Accommodation: (Price per person) double £16; no children under five years
Children: In left-hand bar only; not permitted under 14 years after 8pm

✇ MALTSTERS ARMS
Chapel Amble, near Wadebridge PL27 6EU Tel 0208 812473

Chapel Amble

Foremost among the attractions of this 16th-century village pub is the food. In addition to a set menu at £15.95, there is a good choice of imaginative starters, including Mediterranean fish soup and duck breast marinated in soy sauce and stir-fried with spring onion, ginger and courgettes, both at £4.10, followed by main courses like beef in red wine at £7.95 and pan-fried scallops in a cream and Noilly Prat sauce at £9.95. As well as various char-grilled meat dishes, there is a good selection of salads and vegetarian meals. Wines by the bottle cater for all tastes, and 13 are served by the glass. The mainly well-heeled diners can choose where to eat, enjoying attentive service in both of the dining rooms. The smaller is half-panelled, with floral seats and wheelback chairs, and old photographs and prints on the wall, while the other is furnished more plainly. Although the bar is lively, with piped music and board games, and a quiz on Sunday evenings, overall a pleasant balance is struck between the eating and drinking areas. For those who prefer to sit outside in the summer, benches are set out in front and to the side of the white-painted, stone-built pub.

Brewery: Free house
Licensees: Jeffrey and Vivienne Pollard
Opening hours: 11.30am-2.30pm, 6.30-11pm; Sun 12-3pm, 7-10.30pm
Bar food: Summer 12-3pm, 6.30-9pm; winter 12-2pm, 7-9pm (flexible); Sun 12-2.30pm, 7-9pm
Children: Only if eating; children's menu available
Credit cards: Access, Visa

EARL OF ST VINCENT
Egloshayle, near Wadebridge PL27 6HT. Tel 0208 814807

Egloshayle

Built in the heart of a typical Cornish village as a boarding house for the men working on the church over 500 years ago, this pub was later named after an admiral who served under Nelson. Blessed with a good local trade, it has an Aladdin's cave of a main bar, with prints, paintings and sketches filling the walls, and china and clocks of all kinds, each one in working order, displayed on every available surface. The furniture is an appealing mix of honey-coloured church pews, pine settles, cosy armchairs and modern dark wood tables, while the Snug, adorned like the main bar with clocks and pictures, offers seating on antique carved chairs. St Austell Tinners Ale and Hicks Special Draught are on sale, and the food includes a good selection of grills from £8, several fish and seafood dishes, such as lemon sole at £6.50, and breast of chicken filled with lobster and prawns at £8.50. Behind the white-painted stone building is a prize-winning little terraced garden.

Brewery: St Austell Brewery
Licensees: Anne and Edward Connolly
Opening hours: 11am-3pm, 6.30-11pm; Sun 12-3pm, 7-10.30pm
Bar food: 12-2pm, 7.30-9.30pm; Sun 12.30-2pm
Children: Only if eating and well behaved; half portions available

CROWN
Goldsithney, Penzance TR20 9LG. Tel 0736 710494

Goldsithney

Hanging baskets, potted plants and vines lend a splash of colour to this 17th-century grey-stone pub in Goldsithney's busy main street. Its charming frontage and the relaxed atmosphere draw regulars and holidaymakers alike to the open-plan bar, which is simply furnished and decorated with local scenes and offers St Austell Hicks Special Draught and Bosun's Bitter, XXXX Mild and Guinness. In summer the patio, with its benches set among an array of flowers, is especially attractive. Home cooking is available in the bar and the separate restaurant. Good-value seafood and meat dishes are served - for example, crab or prawn salad at £4.25, deep-fried cod at £3.50 and beef curry at £3.25 - as well as a daily vegetarian dish. On Wednesday and Thursday a lunch of roast beef with vegetables and an excellent pudding costs just £2.50. The two double rooms are small but fresh and comfortable.

Brewery: St Austell Brewery
Licensees: Ken and Heather Wood
Opening hours: 11am-3pm, 6-11pm; Sun 12-3pm, 7-10.30pm
Bar food: 12-2pm, 6.30-9pm; Sun 12-2pm, 7-8.30pm
Restaurant: 7-9pm; Sun 12-1.30pm
Accommodation: (Price per room) £25
Children: Only if eating and only in restaurant
Credit cards: Access, Visa

SHIPWRIGHTS ARMS
Helford, near Helston TR12 6JX. Tel 0326 231235

Helford

A beautiful, tranquil setting giving views over the Helford River is no small part of the appeal of this 17th-century thatched and whitewashed pub. Traditional in character, with its wall seats, fishing prints and nautical mementoes, the single bar incorporates an eating area with modern settles. At the black-panelled bar Castle Eden Ale, Flowers IPA and Guinness are dispensed to a clientele of locals, yachting and angling types and holidaymakers. Visitors to the area may want to try their hand at euchre, a traditional Cornish card game. There is a covered patio and running down to the creek is a tiered terrace with plants and benches with umbrellas - an ideal spot for a drink on a summer evening, when barbecues also prove popular. Served daily, the bar food includes charcoal-grilled pork escalope (£6.25) and steak (from £7.40), beef in beer at £6.25, ploughman's lunch from £3.50, fresh, imaginative salads from £5.50 and a choice of sweets at £2.50.

Brewery: Whitbread
Licensee: Charles Herbert
Opening hours: 11am-2.30pm, 6-11pm ; Sun 12-2.30pm; 7-30.30pm
Bar food: 12-2pm, 7-9pm
Children: Welcome anywhere

⊛ BLUE ANCHOR
50 Coinagehall Street, Helston TR13 8EL. Tel 0326 562821

Helston

A real find for beer fanatics, this narrow, stone-built, thatched, town-centre pub has a great atmosphere and its brewhouse, dating back to the 15th century, may well be

Brewery: Free house, own brew
Licensees: Sidney and Patricia

one of the country's oldest. Blue Anchor Spingo ales (middle, best, special and extraspecial) are the only beers on sale here. Inside the pub, the two main bars lead off a stone-flagged passageway, and there are also a separate family (games) room and skittle alley; at the back of the pub is the brewhouse, which customers can visit at lunchtime, and a small terrace area. There is a limited range of bar snacks.

Cannon
Opening hours: 11am-4pm, 6-11pm; Sun 12-3pm, 7-10.30pm
Bar food: As opening hours
Children: In family room only

⊕ MEXICO INN
Long Rock, near Penzance TR20 8JL. Tel 0736 710625

Long Rock

Named after Bill Trewarthen, a miner who returned from Mexico in 1794 to set up a silver mine near by, this pub was originally the counting house which paid the miners as well as dispensing ale. Situated in a village not far from the picturesque St Michael's Mount, the pub is of granite, with a gravelled area with picnic benches at the back. Fresh flowers, old photographs and local artists' prints offset the traditional plainness of the bar, with its stone walls and plank and beam ceiling, where a clientele of locals, tourists and business people mingle. Bass and Worthington Best are the draught beers on offer, and there is a wide-ranging menu. Mainly home-cooked, dishes are available from the menu or as daily specials, and include cod Valentino at £5.60, chilli con carne at £4.70 and Phoodina lamb - marinated and spicy - at £5.50. Vegetarian dishes, and traditional sweets like apple pie at £1.95, are also served.

Brewery: Free house
Licensees: Bob and Pat Owen
Opening hours: 12-2.30pm (Sat 3pm), 6-11pm; Sun 12-2.30pm, 7-10.30pm
Bar food: 12-2pm, 6.30-9.30pm (Sun 7pm)
Children: Welcome anywhere if well behaved

ROYAL OAK INN
Duke Street, Lostwithiel PL22 1AO. Tel 0208 872552

Lostwithiel

In addition to being some 700 years old, this unassuming, stone-built, town-centre pub has the romantic cachet of being reputedly linked by a smugglers' tunnel to Restormel Castle, a mile distant, pictures of which can be seen inside. The carpeted eating area is furnished with captain's chairs and modern tables and chairs, cushioned wall benches and a gas-effect fire, while a jukebox makes the Public Bar, with its stone floor, pine wall benches and tables, rather livelier. Outside, in the sheltered patio and garden, picnic benches with umbrellas are provided. The clientele of locals and holidaymakers choose from a wide range of beers, including Jolly Roger Flagship, Marston's Pedigree and Flowers Original, and from the 35 bins on the wine list. Generous, home-cooked dishes include oak-style Barbary duck at £9.50, cow pie at £4.50 and avocado and orange salad for £2.45. Six double rooms are available.

Brewery: Free house
Licensees: Malcolm and Eileen Hine
Opening hours: 11am-3pm, 5.30-11pm; Sun 12-3pm, 7-10.30pm
Bar food: 12-2pm, 6.30-9.30pm (Sun 7pm)
Accommodation: (Price per room) single £24-£26, double £42-£46
Children: Only in function room and only if eating
Credit cards:
AMERICAN EXPRESS® Access, Visa, Diners

⊕ WHITE HART
Ludgvan, near Penzance TR20 8EY. Tel 0736 740574

Ludgvan

Its grey stone set off by baskets and beds of flowers, this unspoilt 13th-century pub stands next to the village church. Cosy rooms and nooks and crannies conjure up the past with their rustic furniture, blue and white china, paraffin lamps and a large kitchen range, while low, black beams contrast with ochre-coloured walls adorned with tasteful prints and bric-à-brac. A sizeable sheltered garden at the rear offers picnic benches and bench seats are also available in front of the pub. Locals are willing to travel some way for the combination of Flowers IPA, Cornish Original and Newquay Steam Pils, with entertainment in the form of quiz nights, a male-voice choir most Monday evenings and a pianist on Wednesdays.

Brewery: Devenish
Licensees: Denis and Julie Churchill
Opening hours: 12-2.30pm, 6-11pm; Sun 12-3pm, 7-10.30pm
Bar food: 12-2pm, 7-9pm
Children: Welcome in rooms other than bar, but must be supervised

⊕ HERON INN
Malpas, near Truro TR1 1SL. Tel 0872 72773

Malpas

Blessed with superb views of the confluence of the Truro and Tresillian R ivers and their wooded valleys, this substantial, whitewashed pub was built 150 years ago and served as a hotel until 1946. At lunchtime it is a glorious suntrap, with benches and umbrellas on the terrace and further seating across the lane. With plush wall seats and covered stools around modern tables, and in winter the comfort of two gas-effect log fires, the spacious, open-plan bar absorbs a mix of boating types, holidaymakers and business people from Truro. Conversation pieces include a heron in a glass case, trophies and photographs of sporting car trials - the landlord's passion - and scenes of bygone river life. As a complement to the standard bar meals, there is a choice of beers which includes St Austell Hicks Special Draught and Tinners Ale, and a dozen wines.

Brewery: St Austell Brewery
Licensee: Calvin Kneebone
Opening hours: 11am-3pm, 6-11pm; Sun 12-3pm, 7-10.30pm
Bar food: 12-2pm, 6.30-9.30pm; Sun 12-2pm, 7-9.30pm summer only
Children: Welcome anywhere

Toby Jugs

Toby jugs grin cheerfully from their vantage points in many a pub interior. They were first made in the Staffordshire Potteries in the 18th century and the standard figure wears a black tricorn hat, holds a foaming jug of beer and sits in a chair whose sides are covered by the skirts of his ample topcoat. This is the Ordinary Toby, but connoisseurs distinguish between the Long Face, the Sharp Face and the Roman Nose variations. Numerous variants include the Sailor, the Squire, the Tipsy Man and the Drunken Parson. Other jugs represent famous figures of history or literature, from Nelson and Mr Gladstone to Falstaff and John Bull, while modern examples include Winston Churchill and Clark Gable. There are a few female Tobies, but essentially the jugs depict the jovial male toper, benevolent and beery.

NEW INN
Manaccan, Helston TR12 6HA. Tel 0326 231323

Manacan

This really friendly, thatched village pub, has only one traditionally furnished bar, decorated with paintings (many for sale) and stands in a large garden, looking out over countryside. The 'new' of its name seems rather a misnomer since it was known to exist in Cromwell's day (and to be out of bounds to his soldiers). Apart from its peaceful setting, what draws the customers is the excellent quality of the fresh fish on the daily changing bar menu. Starters range from asparagus soup at £1.50 to crab pâté at £3.50; main dishes from John Dory at £6, or fillets of brill for £5.50, to macaroni Bolognese at £5. With prior notice you can even have lobster and oysters in season. There is a very good wine list to do justice to the food, and draught beers include Marston's Pedigree and Cornish Original straight from the barrel, also Guinness, Heineken and Newquay Steam Lager on draught. You can play dominoes, shove halfpenny, chess, backgammon and a local card game, euchre, if you know the rules.

Brewery: Devenish
Licensee: Patrick Cullinan
Opening hours: 11am-3pm, 6-11.30pm; Sun 12-3pm, 7-10.30pm
Bar food: 12-2.30pm, 7-9.30pm
Children: Very welcome

☙ MINERS ARMS
Mithian, near St Agnes TR5 0QF. Tel 087255 2375

Mithian

The local tin-mining industry inspired the name of this 400-year-old inn, which displays a number of mining artefacts inside. Situated at the heart of a quiet village, the part-white-rendered stone building is fronted by a fine cobbled courtyard with picnic benches and hanging baskets, and has a sheltered garden at the rear. Among the surviving original features are a 16th-century mural, ceiling mouldings of the same period, a penance cupboard and a secret passage leading to a manor house opposite. In addition to the main bar, with its beamed ceiling, log fire and cushioned wall seats, three other rooms are available to customers. These are a half-panelled lounge area with sofas and armchairs and embellished with original friezes and local paintings, an upstairs bar and dining area with stools and cushioned wall benches, and a Cellar Bar with games. Locals, business people and holidaymakers enjoy good, home-cooked food here, such as crab bake at £3 or steak and kidney pie at £4.95, washing it down with Marston's Pedigree, Boddingtons Best Bitter, Newquay Steam Pils or Scrumpy Jack.

Brewery: Devenish
Licensees: David and Dilys Charnock
Opening hours: 12-3pm, 6-11pm; Sun 12-3pm, 7-10.30pm
Bar food: 12-2pm, 6.30-10pm (approx); Sun 12-2pm, 7-9.30pm
Children: In Cellar Bar only; outdoor play area

⊜ BUSH INN
Crosstown, Morwenstow EX23 9SR. Tel 028883 242

Morwenstow

Built as a chapel in 950 - a Celtic cross still stands outside - this remote pub did not become an inn until 700 years later.With an invigorating coastal path near by, it attracts walkers and tourists, as well as farmers and other locals. Flagstones, beams, granite walls and inglenooks and ancient settles preserve the unspoilt character of the two bars, which are adorned with copper and brassware and local scenes. On display is the propeller from the plane in which, in 1930, Amy Johnson was the first woman to fly solo from England to Australia. St Austell Hicks Special Draught, Cotleigh Old Buzzard, Bass and Exmoor Best are on sale, along with ten or so malt whiskies. Reasonably priced and filling, the simple country fare includes home-made vegetable and meat soup at £1.30, beef stew at £2.75, and fresh crab and a selection of pies, all at £3. Outside, there are seats on the front lawn, giving a view out to sea, and in the courtyard.

Brewery: Free house
Licensee: Jim Gregory
Opening hours: 12-3pm, 7-11pm; closed Mon Oct-Jan; Sun 12-3pm, 7-10.30pm
Bar food: 12-2.30pm (flexible) (except Sun)
Children: Not permitted inside

SHIP
Harbourside, Mousehole, near Penzance TR19 6QX. Tel 0736 731234

Mousehole

A quayside setting in a pretty little fishing port grants visitors to this pub fine views across the sea to the Lizard. Dating from the 16th century, the grey-stone building has a welcoming stone-flagged bar with low black beams and panelling. Maritime prints, photographs and bits and bobs complete the nautical picture. Deep window seats and stools around low tables cater for those among the mix of regulars, fishermen and holidaymakers who prefer to sit over a drink; St Austell Tinners Ale, Hicks Special Draught and Bosun's Bitter are the beers on offer. Or they can bask in the sun on the terrace behind the pub. Bar food is served at lunchtime as well as in the evening, when the separate restaurant is open. Three double rooms are available.

Brewery: St Austell Brewery
Licensee: Michael Maddern
Opening hours: 10.30am-11pm ;Sun 12-3pm, 7-10.30pm
Bar food: 12-2.30pm, 6-9.30pm; Sun 12-2.30pm, 7-9.30pm
Restaurant: 6-9.30pm (except Sun)
Accommodation: (Price per person) £20; children under 14 years not permitted
Children: In rooms away from the bar only

PANDORA INN
Restronguet Creek, Mylor Bridge, near Falmouth TR11 5ST. Tel 0326 372678

Mylor Bridge

Parts of this historic, thatched pub date back to the 13th century, and though its riverside setting, separate restaurant overlooking the river, and floating pontoon make it popular with yachting types and tourists as well as local villagers, it has kept a rustic atmosphere in its three bars which are furnished with wooden benches, stools and shipping memorabilia. Owned by the local St Austell

Brewery: St Austell Brewery
Licensees: Roger and Helen Hough
Opening hours: 12-2.30pm, 6.30-11pm (summer 11am-11pm); Sun 12-10.30pm (no alcohol 3-7pm)

brewery, its beers include Hicks Special Draught, Tinners Ale, Bosun's Bitter and Bass; there are also about ten malt whiskies. Bar food offers a number of seafood specialities - for example, Restronguet fish pie or mussels at £4.50, crab salad at £7.75 and a range of soups and club sandwiches, as well as a daily vegetarian dish. Morning coffee and, in summer, afternoon tea are also available.

Bar food: 12-2pm (2.30pm summer), 6.30-9.30pm (10pm summer);
Sun 12-2.30pm, 7-9.30pm
Restaurant: 7.15pm-10pm
Children: Welcome in most rooms and restaurant, but not near bar
Credit cards: Access, Visa

⊜ TRENGILLY WARTHA INN
Nancenoy, near Falmouth, TR11 5RP. Tel 0326 40332

Nancenoy

With its cream-painted exterior, vine-covered pergola and neat garden this smart country inn , set in a quiet valley off the beaten track, but close to the tourist attractions of the Helford River, makes an ideal retreat for a country holiday. As well as the large main bar, decorated in traditional style, there is a cosy lounge bar and a games room, ideal for children. Up to six regularly changing real ales and two local ciders are served and around eight wines from the extensive wine list are available by the glass to accompany the varied bar menu which may include starters such as Greek salad, £3.50, and spring vegetable and herb soup; main courses like Trengilly cassoulet, £5.00, lemon sole, £6.00, with a home-made tart, for example pear and almond, £1.70, for dessert. The separate restaurant offers an interesting fixed-price, three-course menu for £18. In summer barbecues are held in the garden. There are six comfortable modern bedrooms.

Brewery: Free House
Licensees: Nigel Logan and Michael Maguire
Opening hours: 11am-2.30pm, 6-11pm
Bar food: 12-2.15pm, 6.30-9pm
Restaurant: 7.30-9pm
Accommodation: (Price per room) single £38-£42, double £49-£55; children welcome
Children: In family and games room only
Credit cards:
AMERICAN EXPRESS® Access, Visa

⊜ CORNISH ARMS
Pendoggett, near Port Isaac PL30 3HH. Tel 0208 880263

Pendoggett

Standing in the heart of a village a mile from a rugged stretch of coast, this 16th-century former coaching inn offers a choice of bars, a separate restaurant and accommodation comprising seven attractively furnished double rooms. The front bars, with stone flags, a dark, wood-panelled ceiling and antique furniture, are brightened by fresh flowers, gleaming copper and brass and hunting prints. Locals tend to drink in the busy Public Bar, however, where there is music and diversions which include darts, dominoes and the old Cornish card game euchre. Bass, Pendoggett Special and, in summer, Flowers IPA and Courage Directors are on sale, as well as snacks and bar meals. Elegant with its linen and silver cutlery, the restaurant offers starters and

Brewery: Free house
Licensees: John Robinson, Mervyn Gilmour and Paul Stewart
Opening hours: 11am-11pm;
Sun 12-3pm, 7-10.30pm
Bar food: 12.30-2pm, 6.30-9.30pm
Restaurant: 7-9pm
Accommodation: (Price per room) single from £36, double from £56
Children: In family room only; half portions available

main courses with an emphasis on fish and seafood - for example, seafood crêpe at £2.50 and coquille St Jacques Mornay at £11 - and a wide-ranging list of over 90 wines. Across the road from the white-painted building, which has a slate roof and slate tiles to most of the upper portion, is a garden for customers.

Credit cards:
AMERICAN EXPRESS® Access, Visa, Diners

ROSELAND INN
Ruan High Lanes, Philleigh, near Truro TR2 5NB. Tel 0872 580254

Philleigh

A peaceful setting near the village church, a rose-clad frontage and an unspoilt bar with a homely atmosphere combine with excellent cooking to make this 17th-century pub a real find. Scrupulously clean and decked with fresh flowers, the low-ceilinged main bar is furnished with old-fashioned seats set around sturdy tables and an ancient settle. From the eating area, with its huge hearth and gleaming brass, a stable door gives on to a suntrap of a terrace with tables and chairs set out among flowers. As it serves as a clubhouse for the local rugby club, the pub is decorated with mementoes of the sport, and of gig-racing, along with local scenes. The bar food, including daily blackboard specials like lamb curry at £3.75, is freshly prepared and good value, as are the evening meals - for example, entrecôte au poivre at £8.75, scampi Provençale at £8.25 and vegetarian Stroganoff at £6.50. On tap are Cornish Original and Flowers IPA.

Brewery: Devenish
Licensee: Graham Hill
Opening hours: 11.30am-3pm, 6-11pm; Sun 12-3pm, 7-10.30pm
Bar food: 12-2.15pm, 6.30-9.15pm; Sun 12-2pm, 7-9.15pm summer only
Children: Welcome anywhere

RASHLEIGH INN
Polkerris, near Par PL24 2TL. Tel 072681 3991

Polkerris

Its situation on the beach in a tiny fishing hamlet is what first attracts the visitor to this large, whitewashed pub, built as a fishermen's tavern in the1920s. With its huge bow window, the bar gives a splendid vista of St Austell Bay, while up some steps a plusher room and a separate restaurant also offer a fine outlook. Outside, three terraces with picnic benches and garden furniture provide equally attractive views. A standard but dependable bar menu is supplemented by daily changing blackboard specials and a good local reputation is deservedly enjoyed by the restaurant, which offers a choice of three dozen wines. Beer drinkers can sample Fergusons Dartmoor Best, St Austell Hicks Special Draught and Burton. In winter quiz nights are held and all year round on Friday and Saturday a pianist spices up the evening.

Brewery: Free house
Licensees: Bernard and Carole Smith
Opening hours: 11am-2.30pm, 6-11pm (Jul-Aug 11am-11pm); Sun 12-3pm, 7-10.30pm
Bar food: 11am-2pm, 6-10pm; Sun 12-2.30pm, 7-9pm
Restaurant: Wed-Sat 7-9.30pm
Children: In eating area only
Credit cards: Access, Visa

⊕ BLUE PETER
The Quay, Polperro PL13 2QZ. Tel 0503 72743

Polperro

Possibly dating from the 16th century and tucked into a cliff facing the harbour, this traditional little fishermen's pub is full of character. Outside, whitewashed walls are set off by blue window frames; inside, black woodwork and exposed beams, wooden settles, polished pews and two log fires create a cosy atmosphere in the dimly lit bar full of fishing paraphernalia. Upstairs, a room equipped with children's games makes this an ideal pub for families at any time of year. Blue Peter Ale, brewed specially for the pub, is on offer, as well as St Austell Hicks Special Draught and Exmoor Gold. A fitting complement to these and the strong, locally produced St Veeps Farmhouse Cider is the hearty, home-made fare, which includes fish in the peak of condition from the quay outside and vegetarian dishes. There is live entertainment once a fortnight during the winter.

Brewery: Free house
Licensee: Tim Horn
Opening hours: 11am-11pm;
Sun 12-3pm, 7-10pm
Bar food: 12-3pm, 7-9.30pm
Children: In family room only

PORT GAVERNE HOTEL Port Gaverne *see page 34*

FIVE PILCHARDS
Porthallow, St Keverne TR12 6PP. Tel 0326 280256

Porthallow

This plain, stone-built and half-tiled pub has been run by the same landlord, born and bred in the village, for the last 28 of its 300 years. Situated right beside the beach in a tiny fishing community, it faithfully pursues a nautical theme with its ship's wheel and lamps, lobster pots and seafaring prints. With its rustic tables, wall seats and stools, the single bar remains an unspoilt and friendly place, with the additional welcome in winter of a woodburning stove. Not surprisingly, the clientele comprises locals, fisherfolk and holidaymakers. Outside is a small, sheltered courtyard with tables and chairs. A free house, the pub serves Greene King Abbot Ale, Cornish Original and Flowers Original, scrumpy, Penzance Cornish Mead and a range of country wines. The lunch menu, based around good, fresh fish and seafood, changes daily according to what is available, and on Sunday a roast is served. Ploughman's lunch and sandwiches are also available.

Brewery: Free house
Licensee; Mr D Tripp
Opening hours: 12-3pm, 6.45-11pm; Sun 12-3pm, 7-10.30pm
Bar food: 12-2pm; Sun 12-1.45pm
Children: In courtyard only

⊜ PORT GAVERNE HOTEL
Port Gaverne, near Port Isaac PL29 3SQ. Tel 0208 880244

Port Gaverne

This white-painted pub and hotel, dating back to 1608, benefits from being set in a secluded cove. The bar, half-panelled, with a slate floor, wall benches and an open fire, serves St Austell Hicks Special Draught and Flowers IPA. Old photographs decorate the walls, along with watercolours of local scenes which are for sale. A Snug with cushioned wall seats, seafaring photographs and blue and white china, leads into another tiny room with a ship's table and a captain's chair, and some fascinating dioramas. At lunchtime a reasonably priced hot and cold buffet is available, including sandwiches, ploughman's and hot food such as Cornish crab soup at £2.35 and cottage pie at £2.50. In the evening there is a choice of a bar meal or eating in the restaurant. Complemented by a list of over 60 wines, the à la carte menu offers starters like French onion soup at £2.25 and fresh langoustines with home-made mayonnaise at £5.50, main courses such as goujons of monkfish diable and escalope of pork Marsala, both at £9.75, and a selection of vegetarian dishes, with appetizers at £2.25 and main courses at £8.75. Nineteen pleasant and well furnished double rooms are available, plus seven restored fishermen's cottages.

Brewery: Free house
Licensees: Fred and Midge Ross
Opening hours: 11am-2.30pm, 6-11pm; Sun 12-3pm, 7-10.30pm
Bar food: Summer 12-2pm, 7-10pm; winter 12-2pm, 7-9pm
Restaurant: Summer 7-9.30pm; winter 7-9pm
Accommodation: (Price per person) £36-£38. Cottages (price per week) £126-£497; BH weekends (price per day) £72
Children: Welcome anywhere away from bar; children's menu and half portions available
Credit cards: AMERICAN EXPRESS® Access, Visa, Diners

⊕ SHIP INN
Porthleven, near Helston TR13 9JS. Tel 0326 572841

Porthleven

Set into a cliff and reached by a flight of stairs, this 17th-century harbourside pub is the oldest building in the village. With sea views from every window, drinking or dining in this popular pub is a pleasure, especially in the evening, when the harbour is lit up. Nautical artefacts, including gleaming brassware and ship's lanterns, decorate the stone and wood-floored bar, which is furnished with pews and stools and has log fires in winter. A tiered terrace with bench seating climbs the cliff and the thatched Old Smithy serves as a family room. The clientele of locals, business trade, retired people and in summer tourists, partner the standard bar fare with Ushers, Directors or Courage Best Bitter, or choose from a range of draught lagers and ciders, among them Scrumpy Jack.

Brewery: Ushers
Licensee: Colin Oakden
Opening hours: 11.30am-3pm, 7-11pm; Jul-Aug 11am-11pm; Sun 12-3pm, 7-9.30pm
Bar food: 12-2.30pm, 7-9.30pm
Children: In family room only

⊕ OLD INN
St Breward, Bodmin Moor PL30 4PP. Tel 0208 85071

St Breward

The highest pub in Cornwall, at 825 feet, this moorland inn has a bar which dates back 1,000 years, to when it was a beer house for the builders of the nearby church. In addition to this bar, which has beams and slate floor, there is the main bar, likewise slate-floored, and with part-exposed stone walls and a granite fireplace, and a games room with a pool table. Picnic benches are set out in the walled garden. Tools, traps, horse-brasses and slate paintings, the latter for sale, enhance the pub's rural character, while a piano, and live country and folk music on some evenings, add to the friendly atmosphere generated by a mix of locals, among them farmers and walkers. Ruddles, Wadworth 6X, Bass and John Smith's are on tap, to complement home-cooked dishes from the menu, like the pub's speciality, moorland grill, at £6.75. Also served are blackboard specials and snacks, all good value for money, as well as sweets like banoffi pie at £1.85.

Brewery: Free house
Licensees: Iain and Ann Cameron
Opening hours: 12-3pm, 6-11pm; Sun 12-3pm, 7-10.30pm
Bar food: 12-2pm, 6-10pm (winter 6.30-9.45pm)
Restaurant: Times as bar food
Children: In restaurant and games room only; children's menu available

RISING SUN
The Square, St Mawes TR2 5DJ. Tel 0326 270233

St Mawes

Built a century ago and expanded recently to offer a choice of nine double and two single rooms, this pub-hotel offers locals, yachting types and holidaymakers the choice of two bars. There is a new conservatory at the front, with modern cane furniture and copious brass, as well as a small, homely Public Bar with photographs of old St Mawes

Brewery: St Austell Brewery
Licensees: Colin Phillips and Bryan Davies
Opening hours: Summer 11am-11pm; winter 11am-2.30pm, 6-11pm ; Sun 12-3pm,

and a popular window seat which gives a view of the picturesque harbour opposite. Occasional live music, quiz nights and, in winter, darts, also pull in the customers. In summer breakfast is served, in addition to the morning coffee, lunch and dinner available all year round. Good value for money, as is the menu as a whole, are moules marinières at £3.75, medallions of pork at £5.75 and poached salmon steak at £7.95, while the wine list is better than that of the average restaurant. The beers on offer are St Austell Hicks Special Draught and Bosun's Bitter. A good standard of accommodation is available in light, airy and comfortably furnished rooms, some with a fine sea view.

7-10.30pm
Bar food: 12-2.30pm, 6-9.30pm; summer barbecue 9.45-10.45pm; Sun 12-2pm, 7-9pm
Restaurant: 7.30-9.30pm; Sun 12.30-2pm, 7-9pm
Accommodation: (Price per person) £25-£39.50
Children: In conservatory bar and restaurant only
Credit cards:
AMERICAN EXPRESS ® Access, Visas

⊜ FALCON INN
St Mawgan, near Newquay TR8 4EP. Tel 0637 860225

St Mawgan

A terraced garden entered through a rose-covered arch is a major feature of this 16th-century pub. Set in the heart of the village, opposite the church, the large, stone building, draped with wisteria, has one main bar. Customers can eat in the separate dining area, with its flagstone floor, oriental rugs, and pine dresser, or in the award-winning garden. Good food served promptly is the order of the day, accompanied by wine from the 20 bins listed or by St Austell Hicks Special Draught or Tinners Ale. Two double rooms and one single are available. Throughout the winter there are regular quiz nights.

Brewery: St Austell Brewery
Licensees: Andy and Helen Banks
Opening hours: 11-3pm, 6-11pm; Sun 12-2.30pm, 7-10.30pm
Bar food: 11.30-2pm, 7-9.30pm; Sun 12-2pm, 7-9.30pm
Accommodation: (Price per person) double £17-£21; no children under 14 years
Children: In eating area only

⊜ FOX AND HOUNDS
Scorrier, near Redruth TR16 5BS. Tel 0209 820205

Scorrier

O riginally three cottages, this substantial, whitewashed pub lies back from the main road and is adorned with flower boxes, baskets and tubs. Its large sign depicts a hunting scene and inside, a stuffed fox in a case and a collection of prints continue the theme. Modern red-plush seating surrounds copper-topped tables, there are two large open fires and the front extension is designated a non-smoking area. On the terrace outside picnic benches with umbrellas are set amid an array of flowers. This busy pub serves Flowers IPA, Boddingtons Bitter and 13 wines, but its popularity is at least as much due to an imaginative menu. In addition to standard pub lunches, dishes from around the world are served - for example, Lebanese kofta, chicken tikka masala and mousaka, each at £4.30. The portions are generous and there is a good choice of vegetarian dishes.

Brewery: Devenish
Licensees: David and Linda Halfpenny
Opening hours: 11am-2.30pm, 6.30-11pm; Sun 12-2.30pm, 7-10.30pm
Bar food: 12-2pm, 7-10pm; Sun 12-1.45pm, 7-10pm
Children: Not permitted inside

ELIOT ARMS
Tregadillett, near Launceston PL15 7EU. Tel 0566 772051

Tredagillett

Long ago known as the Square and Compass, this creeper-clad, 14th-century pub is situated in the village centre. Slate floors, an assortment of furniture and 69 clocks, the majority antique, as well as endless brass and copper ornaments, banknotes and shelves of books, make the pub a fascinating treasure trove. This unspoilt warren, in addition to a choice of drinking and dining areas, has a separate Snug for families, and across the lane is a small, sheltered garden with benches. A good trade is provided by locals and the many customers who travel some way to eat here. The food, good value for money and served in generous portions, is available from an extensive printed menu which offers, for example, hot chicken satay with peanut sauce and cream curried prawn cocktail, both at £2.95, Louisiana lemon and pepper fish fillet at £6.95 , as well as charcoal grills like a 16oz Scotch rib steak at £8.95. Sandwiches, salads and a variety of ploughman's lunches are also served, while the sweets include banana cream crunch and fruit salad, both at £1.75. Two double rooms are available.

Brewery: Free house
Licensee: John Cook
Opening hours: 11am-2.30pm, 6-11pm; Sun 12-2.30pm, 7-10.30pm
Bar food: 12-2pm, 7-9.30pm
Accommodation: (Price per room) single £18, double £32
Children: Welcome anywhere away from bar; half portions available; outdoor play area

LOGAN ROCK INN
Treen, near Penzance TR19 6LG. Tel 0736 810495

Treen

Logan Rock is the best known of Cornwall's rocking stones, so called because, although it weighs over 60 tons, the slightest touch will set it teetering. In 1824 a naval lieutenant succeeded in levering the huge stone from its resting place but, following a local outcry, was forced by the Admiralty to restore it to its original position at a cost to himself of £130. This intriguing episode is brought to life by an unusual pub sign and by a set of pictures displayed inside the stone-built, 16th-century inn. Close also to some of Cornwall's finest coastline, in summer the pub is popular with holidaymakers, as well as having a regular, year-round clientele. There are two bars, the larger one low-ceilinged and rustic in character, the other more comfortably furnished, and a dining-cum-children's room. Picnic benches are set out in the sunny, cobbled courtyard at the front of the pub and on the secluded patio at the back. Standard bar food is supplemented daily by home-cooked specials, and on tap are St Austell Hicks Special Draught and Tinners Ale.

Brewery: St Austell Brewery
Licensees: Peter and Anita George
Opening hours: Jun-Sep 10.30am-11pm; Oct-May 10.30am-3pm, 5.30-11pm; Sun 12-3pm, 7-10.30pm
Bar food: Jun-Sep 12-9.30pm; Oct-May 12-2.30pm, 7-10pm; Sun 12-2.45pm, 7-9.30pm
Children: In children's room and patio only

TINNERS ARMS
Zennor, near Penzance TR26 3BY. Tel 0736 796927

Zennor

Originally built to house masons working on the 14th-century village church opposite, this grey-stone, slate-roofed pub is typical of this former tin-mining area. While retaining its traditional character, it has the further blessing of being in good walking country - as witness the clientele, among whom ramblers outnumber locals. In addition to the main bar, low-ceilinged with plain, rustic decor and furniture, two other rooms are open at busy times. Tables and chairs are set out in the sheltered courtyard in front of the pub, and at the rear there is a patio with access to a children's room. St Austell Hicks Special Draught is served, and there is a daily changing blackboard menu.

Brewery: Free house
Licensee: David Care
Opening hours: 10.30am- 3pm, 6.30-11pm; Jun-Sep 11am-11pm; Sun 12-3pm, 7-10.30pm
Bar food: 12- 3pm, 6.30 - 9.30pm, but flexible; Sun 12-2.30pm, 7- 10pm
Children: Not in bar, but two other rooms available if family is eating

DEVON

Bigbury-on-Sea *see Burgh Island*

⊛ MASONS ARMS
Branscombe, near Seaton EX12 3DJ. Tel 029780 300

Branscombe

Flanked by a roadside terrace with thatched canopies, this 14th-century inn at the centre of the village combines the style of yesteryear with modern standards of excellence. Both holidaymakers and locals are attracted to the traditional bar, with its open fire and no diversions more intrusive than shove halfpenny or darts. Food available at the bar ranges from soup of the day at £1.50 to duck and bacon pie or steak and kidney pudding, both at £5.25; no vegetarian option is guaranteed - though this is always available in the separate restaurant. Bass, Wadworth 6X and Dartmoor Best are available on draught. Accommodation is provided in elegant, tastefully decorated bedrooms.

Brewery: Free house
Licensee: Mrs J B Inglis
Opening hours: 11am-2.30pm (Sat 3pm), 6-11pm; Sun 12-3pm, 7-10.30pm
Bar food: 12-2pm, 7-9.30pm
Restaurant: 7.15-9.00pm; Sun 12-2.30pm
Accommodation: (Price per person) £22-£40
Children: In accommodation only

🍺 DREWE ARMS
Broadhembury, near Honiton EX14 0NF. Tel 040484 267

Broadhembury

Part-thatched and attractively set at the centre of the village, the Drewe Arms is a very good example of the traditional English pub at its best. A busy, friendly bar with old woodwork and settles offers the time-honoured pastimes of skittles and shove halfpenny, and a display of prints and photographs evokes memories of a bygone era. Both a selection of real ales (Otter Bitter, Whitbread, Murphy's, Bass, Fergusons Dartmoor Strong and Cotleigh Tawny, plus a guest beer) and an extensive wine list are available, while excellent, freshly cooked bar meals include good puddings as well as such main course choices as mushroom, Stilton and garlic bake (£3.95) and lemon sole at £7.25; meals are also served in a separate restaurant.

Brewery: Free house
Licensee: Mrs Kerstinburge
Opening hours: 11am-2.30pm, 6-11pm; Sun 12-2.30pm, 7-10.30pm
Bar food: 12-2pm, 7-10pm (Mon 9pm); Sun 12-2pm only
Restaurant: 7-10pm (except Sun)
Children: Permitted inside only when eating with parents; outdoor play area

🍺 PILCHARD INN
Burgh Island, near Bigbury-on-Sea TO7 4AU. Tel 0548 810344

Burgh Island

Set on an island linked to the mainland by sand causeway at low water and tractor ferry (adults 50p, children 25p, car park £1.50) at other times, this small 14th-century pub is of particular interest to holidaymakers - the beach providing an excellent play area for children. Two bars with a seafaring atmosphere and ancient exposed timbers are furnished with old wooden settles, and here you can either relax to a background of piped blues music or enjoy a game of darts, cards, shove halfpenny or Trivial Pursuit. Bar food is simple, being confined to a selection of huge rolls (£2.50 to £3.50) and salads (£3.75-£4.25), and Beamish, Webster's Yorkshire, Wadworth 6X and Ushers Best are served on draught.

Brewery: Free house
Licensee: T Porter
Opening hours: Summer 11am-11pm; Sun 12-3pm, 7-10.30pm; in winter telephone to enquire
Bar food: As opening hours
Restaurant: 10am-9pm; closed in winter
Children: Welcome in back bar

🍺 TUCKERS ARMS
Dalwood, near Axminster EX13 7EG. Tel 040488 342

Dalwood

Children are positively welcomed at this part-thatched 13th-century pub decked with speciality hanging baskets and set at the centre of a beautifully kept village; there are both a family room and a small paved and grassed area to the rear of the building where they can be with their parents. Two beamed bars with stone floors, massive fireplaces and wooden settles offer such traditional pursuits as darts and skittles, and a vast collection of spirit miniatures is attractively displayed. Boddingtons, Whitbread, Parish Poachers, Guinness, Murphy's, Flowers, Wadworth 6X and Bass beers are available on draught. A menu of home-

Brewery: Free house
Licensee: Mr D Beck
Opening hours: 11am-3pm, 7-11pm; Sun 12-3pm, 7.30-10.30pm
Bar food: 12-2pm, 7-9.30pm
Accommodation: (Price per room) single from £25, double from £40
Children: Welcome in family room
Credit Cards: Access, Visa

cooked bar meals features imaginative dishes at reasonable prices, encompassing potato skins with dips at £2.55, deep-fried hake at £3.95 and a pillow of puff pastry filled with baked avocado, peppers and mushrooms at £6.95. A modern annexe provides well equipped double bedrooms, including one family room with additional facilities for two children.

CHERUB
Dartmouth

13 Higher Street, Dartmouth TQ6 9NR. Tel 0803 832571

R eal ale (Original Burton, Wadworth 6X and Blackawton) and a selection of whiskies so large that you could choose a different one each week of the year play their part in attracting an across-the-board clientele to this delightful half-timbered pub dating back to 1380 and set at the centre of old Dartmouth. An exterior festooned with colourful hanging baskets gives on to a bar where wooden furniture and traditional brasses are set against ancient woodwork, and here (or in the separate restaurant) the good food enthusiast can enjoy a variety of high quality dishes - prices ranging from £3.75 for thatched pie to £10.50 for tuna steak Provençale, for example.

Brewery: Free house
Licensee: J Hill
Opening hours: 11am-3pm, 5-11pm; Sun 12-3pm, 7-10.30pm
Bar food: As opening hours
Restaurant: 7-10pm
Children: Welcome to eat in restaurant or downstairs room
Credit Cards: Access, Visa

Curiouser and Curiouser

Some pub names are exceedingly odd, and the suggested explanations often odder still. The Goat and Compasses is most unlikely to be a corruption of a supposed Puritan slogan 'God encompasses us', the Bag o' Nails to come from the Bacchanals of the Roman wine god or the Pig and Whistle from Old English words for 'pail' and 'health'. The Cat and Fiddle may come from the nursery rhyme, but then where did the nursery rhyme image itself come from? The device of the Elephant and Castle is known in heraldry and was the badge of the Cutlers Company, so there is no need to find an Infanta of Castile to derive it from.

Many strange names are the product of humour and sarcasm, such as the Quiet Woman (she has no head), the Honest Lawyer (also beheaded), the Drop Inn, Nog Inn and Never Inn. Others, like the Case Is Altered, the Who'd Have Thought It, the Live and Let Live, the Labour In Vain and the World Turned Upside Down are creations of rich and philosophical whimsy.

⊜ NOBODY INN
Doddiscombleigh

Doddiscombleigh, near Exeter EX6 7PS. Tel 0647 52394

T he combination of a range of 260 whiskies, a superior wine list, Nobody Beer, Bass, a guest beer and local farm cider should cater for most tastes, and all these - as well as good food and accommodation - are provided by this quality village pub. Brass, copper and silverware gleam in the beamed, traditionally furnished bar where you can enjoy well

Brewery: Free house
Licensees: P Bolton and N F Borst-Smith
Opening hours: 12-2.30pm, 6-11pm; Sun 12-3pm, 7-10.30pm
Bar food: 12-2pm, 7-10pm

cooked and reasonably priced favourites like cottage pie at £2.90, fish and potato pie at £3.90 or chicken in cream with rice for £4.90; vegetarian options are also available. Bedrooms, like the bar, are traditionally furnished, two being particularly spacious.

DREWE ARMS
Drewsteignton, near Exeter EX6 6QN. Tel 0647 21224

Drewsteignton

Though largely the haunt of locals and regulars from the surrounding country areas, this 300-year-old thatched pub at the centre of the village is well worth seeking out - not, perhaps, for the usual reasons, but because stepping through its doors brings an uncanny sense of entering a timewarp! Peeling brown paint, threadbare carpets and a generally down-at-heel air create an atmosphere reminiscent of the Public Bars of the 1920s; no amusement more sophisticated than darts is on offer, the only food available is a range of sandwiches, and the choice of beverages is confined to Flowers and Whitbread draught beer and West Country cider.

Brewery: Whitbread
Licensee: Mrs M I Mudge
Opening hours: 11.30am-2.30pm, 6-11pm; Sun 12-2.30pm, 7-10.30pm
Bar food: As opening hours
Children: Welcome in room off bar; not permitted under 14 years in bar

DOUBLE LOCKS
Canal Banks, Exeter EX2 6LT. Tel 0392 56947

Exeter

Difficult to find but well worth the effort involved for the connoisseur of real ale (Greene King Abbot Ale, Adnams Broadside, Everards Old Original, Exmoor Ale and Smiles are among the beers on draught), this good, simple and traditional pub dating back to the 1820s enjoys an unspoiled setting beside the canal; the large, grassed area to its rear incorporates a spacious and well equipped play area for children. The bar, which retains not only its old pine woodwork but also much of the character and atmosphere of a bygone era, boasts an extensive range of real ales and features jazz on Wednesday and Thursday evenings. Hot, freshly cooked bar meals are served in generous portions (and can be enjoyed in separate rooms away from the bar), and the interesting menu includes such options as Stilton, leek and courgette filo pie and a crêpe with mushroom, bacon and Vermouth sauce (both at £4.35) as well as the more straightforward shepherd' s pie at £3.30.

Brewery: Free house
Licensee: Mr P J Stuart
Opening hours: 11am-11pm; Sun 12-3pm, 7-10.30pm
Bar food: 11am-10.30pm; Sun 12-2pm, 7-10pm
Children: Welcome in separate family room; outdoor play area

TURF
Turf Lock, Exminster EX6 8EE. Tel 0392 833128

Exminster

Ideal for families and river-users, served by ferries from Exmouth, Topsham, Exeter and Starcross, an informal pub run by a charming couple enjoys a tranquilly beautiful setting on the Exe estuary, at the entrance to the Exeter Channel. Musak of a high standard provides a relaxing background in the simply decorated bar with its bare wooden floor and pine panelling; here you can enjoy a game of darts, cribbage or dominoes - or choose from a range of superb home-cooked dishes that represent excellent value for money with a Stilton and celery quiche or vegetable beanfeast at £3.95 and chicken curry at £5.50, for example. Marston's Pedigree, Boddingtons, Flowers IPA, Whitbread Best and Murphy's are all on draught. A unique grassy peninsula is set with picnic tables, and an extensive outdoor barbecue menu is available during the warmer months. Accommodation is provided in three double bedrooms which, though simple, are pleasantly decorated and comfortable. Both morning coffee and afternoon tea are served.

Brewery: Free house
Licensees: Clive and Virginia Redfer
Opening hours: Jul-Aug 11am-11pm; Apr-Jun and Sep 11am-3pm, 6-11pm (Sat 11am-11pm); Sun 12-3pm, 7-10.30pm; closed Jan and Feb; Mar, Oct-Dec lunchtimes only
Bar food: 12-2pm, 6-9pm (Sun 7pm)
Accommodation: (Price per person) from £22.50
Children: Welcome in eating areas, but not permitted under 14 years in bar; outdoor play area

CHURCH HOUSE INN
Harberton, near Totnes TQ9 7SF. Tel 0803 863707

Harberton

Attractive hanging baskets deck the walls of this friendly, traditional, slate-roofed pub at the centre of the village. Dating back to the 13th century, it still features some interesting interior architecture, and the massive beamed ceiling and huge stone fireplace of the bar are effectively set off by superb curved settles. Here you can enjoy a good and reasonably priced selection of both traditional and more adventurous dishes - liver, bacon and onion casserole, for example, appearing alongside spinach and broccoli cheesebake (both at £3.95) and prawn curry (£5.95). Toby, Beamish, Worthington, Bass, Courage and guest beers are served. Live jazz is featured on the last Thursday of each month.

Brewery: Free house
Licensee: Mrs J E Wright
Opening hours: 12-2.30pm, 6-11pm; Sun 12-2.30pm, 7-10.30pm
Bar food: As opening times
Children: Welcome in family room

⊜ TALLY HO
14 Market Street, Hatherleigh EX20 3JN. Tel 0837 810306

Hatherleigh

Both its dynamic landlord and a central market town position help to draw 'regulars' from the surrounding country areas to this interesting and varied pub. The chief attraction, however, may well be a selection of real ales which are brewed on the premises, and the pleasant little

Brewery: Free house
Licensees: Gianni and Annamaria Scoz
Opening hours: 11am-2.30pm, 6-11pm; Sun 12-2pm, 7-10.30pm

garden affords fascinating glimpses of the brewery at work. The bar, with its large fireplace, partial brick flooring and old woodwork, offers electronic games as well as more traditional pursuits like darts, dominoes and shove halfpenny. Meals represent good value for money, an excellently cooked range of Italian dishes - pasta Bolognese at £3.95 or fritto misto at £7.95, for example - being accompanied by an extensive wine list specialising in Italian labels; Wednesday is pizza evening and on summer Thusdays there is a barbecue. Accommodation is of an extremely high standard, the rooms furnished in stripped pine and those at the front of the building effectively soundproofed by double glazing.

Bar food: 11.30am-2pm, 7-9pm; Sun 12-2pm
Restaurant: Mon, Tue, Fri, Sat 7-9.30pm; Wed pizza evening; Thu barbecue; booking necessary
Accommodation: (Price per room) single from £28, double from £40; children under eight years mot permitted
Children: In accommodation only
Credit Cards: Access, Visa

⊜ ROCK INN
Haytor Vale, near Newton Abbot TQ13 9XP. Tel 0364 661305

Haytor Vale

High standards of accommodation in country style are provided by this 200-year-old slate-roofed inn set in a wooded village on the edge of Dartmoor and popular with holidaymakers, one room boasting a four-poster bed. Seating both in the grassed garden and on a smart terrace opposite enables guests to take advantage of the pub's pleasant surroundings, and inside, in bars undisturbed by musak or electronic games, they can enjoy Guinness, Eldridge Pope Royal Oak, Thomas Hardy Country and Dorchester Bitter, Bass and Fergusons Dartmoor Strong. Meals are prepared from fresh ingredients and served hot; beef and venison pie and vegetable curry represent good value for money at £4.95, while a brunch of steak and salad in a toasted pitta costs £5.95.

Brewery: Free house
Licensee: G F H Craves
Opening hours: 11am-2.30pm, 6.30-11pm; Sun 12-2.30pm, 7-10.30pm
Bar food: 12-2pm, 7-9.30pm
Restaurant: 12-2pm, 7-9.30pm
Accommodation: (Price per person) single from £37.95, double £24.95-£37.50
Children: Welcome in side room and restaurant at lunchtime; not encouraged in the evening
Credit Cards: AMERICAN EXPRESS®, Access, Visa

⊜ELEPHANTS NEST
Horndon, near Mary Tavy, Tavistock PL19 9NQ. Tel 082281 0273

Horndon

Ideal for a family visit, boasting both a family room and a play area as well as a rear garden surrounded by rabbits, ducks and horses, this rural white-painted stone pub dates from the 16th century: beware the low doorway! The bar, comfortably furnished with cushioned settles, holds a collection of elephant ornaments, and the pub's name has been written on the ceiling beams in a variety of languages; darts, Shut the Box or cards are available, and a folk club meets on the second Tuesday of each month. A good choice of beers (Boddingtons, Webster's Yorkshire, Palmers IPA,

Brewery: Free house
Licensees: Nick and Gill Hamer and Peter Hughes
Opening hours: 11.30am-2.30pm, 6.30-11pm; Sun 12-3pm, 7-10.30pm
Bar food: As opening hours, but last orders 2pm and 10pm
Accommodation: (Price per person) single or double from £15

St Austell Hicks Special Draught, plus a guest beer) and a comprehensive wine list is matched by a menu offering a good variety of unusual dishes, well presented and sensibly priced; paprika mushrooms with tagliatelle at £3.40, for example, or local game pie at £5 might be followed by treacle walnut tart or choc-rum trifle, both at £1.80. Accommodation is provided in cottagey double bedrooms.

Children: Welcome in family roomsn but not permitted in bar under 14 years; outdoor play area

ROYAL INN
Horsebridge, near Tavistock PL19 8PJ. Tel 082287 214

Horsebridge

An ancient, foliage-clad inn, set in the depths of the country close to a superb 15th-century bridge over the River Tamar, now operates as a friendly, family-run, rural pub of the best sort, featuring its excellent own-brewed beer as well as serving Bass, Marston's Pedigree, Eldridge Pope Royal Oak and Guinness on draught and attracting a wide-ranging but discerning clientele. Old farming implements are displayed in two slate-floored bars furnished with settles and offering such traditional amusements as darts and bar billiards; piped classical music provides an unobtrusive background to conversation, and an innovative range of high-quality bar meals includes such appetising options as sherried kidneys (£5.95), seafood lasagne (£5.50) and mushroom and nut fettucini (£5.20).

Brewery: Free house
Licensee: Terence Wood
Opening hours: 12-2.30pm, 7-11pm (Sun 10.30pm)
Bar food: 12-2pm, 7-9pm; Sun 12-2pm
Children: Not permitted inside

DUKE OF YORK
Iddesleigh, near Winkleigh EX19 8BG. Tel 0837 810253

Iddesleigh

Mainly local customers frequent this unpretentious, traditional pub which has stood at the village centre since the 15th century. Its one bar reflects the country style, with plain wooden furniture and huge open fireplaces; the real ale enthusiast (Cotleigh Tawny and Hook Norton Old Hooky served, as well as Trophy Bitter) will overlook the lack of any form of entertainment! Bar meals represent good value for money, straightforward dishes such as smoked turkey and salad (£4.80), fresh poached salmon (£5.95) and rump steak (£7.95) being attractively presented. Accommodation is provided in simply appointed bedrooms which overlook a small garden at the rear of the building.

Brewery: Free house
Licensees: Mr and Mrs King and Martin Gent
Opening hours: 11.30am-3pm, 6.30-11pm; Sun 12-3pm, 7-10.30pm
Bar food: As opening hours, but lunchtime only on Sun
Restaurant: Times as bar food
Accommodation: (Price per person) single or double from £20
Children: Not permitted under 14 years in bar; family room

⊛ BARN OWL INN
Aller Mills, Kingskerswell, near Newton Abbot TQ12 5AN. Tel 0803 872130

Kingskerswell

High standards and superb accommodation in spacious, individual and beautifully decorated bedrooms are the hallmarks of this slate-roofed roadside pub dating back to the 16th century. Within easy reach of the town, it nevertheless retains its rural atmosphere in a display of old farm implements and the country-style furnishings of the three beamed bars with their upholstered settles. Here you can enjoy a selection of such tasty, well prepared and fairly priced dishes as cod and prawn Mornay or chicken Bombay at £5.50 and vegetarian chilli (£5.25); there is also a separate restaurant, and a rear garden contains tables. On draught are Fergusons Dartmoor, Burton Ale, Guinness, Tetley and Ansells.

Brewery: Free house
Licensees: Margaret and Derek Warner
Opening hours: 11.30am-2.30pm, 6.30-11pm; Sun 12-3pm, 7-10pm
Bar food: 11.30am-2pm, 6.30-10pm; Sun 12-2pm, 7-10pm
Restaurant: 6.30-9.45pm (except Sun); booking essential
Accommodation: (Price per person) single from £47.50, double £27.50-£37.50
Children: Not permitted under 14 years inside
Credit Cards:
AMERICAN EXPRESS®, Access, Visa

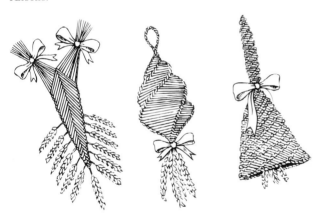

⊛ OLD RYDON INN
Rydon Road, Kingsteignton, near Newton Abbot TQ12 3QG. Tel 0626 54626

Kingsteignton

This part-16th-century inn - well managed in traditional style and popular with both locals and the business fraternity - is well worth visiting for its interesting internal architecture. Set in a residential estate on the edge of the town, it boasts not only a garden but also a secluded play area to one side and a very pleasant glazed terrace with vine. A bar with many nooks and an unusual gallery serves Wadworth 6X, Bass and a guest beer on draught plus quality food at reasonable prices. Imaginative dishes include local smoked trout and egg mayonnaise at £2.60, lasagne gratin (£4.85) and liver casserole (£5.25); a vegetarian option is also available.

Brewery: Free house
Licensees: Hermann and Miranda Hruby
Opening hours: 11am-3pm, 6-11pm; Sun 12-3pm, 7-10.30pm
Bar food: As opening hours
Restaurant: 7-12pm (except Sun)
Children: Welcome in all areas except bar; outdoor play area
Credit Cards:
AMERICAN EXPRESS®, Access, Visa, Diners

⊜ MASONS ARMS
Knowstone, near South Molton EX36 4RY. Tel 0398 4231

Knowstone

Real ales (Hall & Woodhouse Badger Best and Cotleigh Tawny) and a very good wine list account in part for the popularity of this lovely thatched stone pub in traditional country style, set at the heart of the isolated little hamlet of Knowstone and dating from the 13th century. The stone-floored bar, with its massive fireplace and wooden settles, displays collections of old bottles and agricultural implements, and - as well as darts, billiards and shove halfpenny - there are play readings every second Sunday. Good-value home-cooked bar meals offer, for example, rabbit pie or vegetable mousaka for £3.95 and sea trout at £5.95. Pretty, cottagey bedrooms are available, and a secluded garden enjoys rural views.

Brewery: Free house
Licensees: David and Elizabeth Todd
Opening hours: 11am-3pm, 7-11pm; Sun 12-3pm, 7-10.30pm
Bar food: 12-2pm, 7-9.30pm
Restaurant: 7-9pm; Sun 12.30-2pm
Accommodation: (Price per person) single or double £20-£24
Children: Welcome in lower bar and family room

LUPPITT INN
Luppitt, near Honiton EX14 0RT. Tel 0404 891613

Luppitt

Two back rooms in a 19th-century farmhouse, furnished in utilitarian style, this inn might well be described as an anachronism - but it is an anachronism which makes this small village well worth a visit. Locals congregate in a bar Spartanly equipped with stools and formica-topped tables; darts and cards provide the only entertainment, food is not served, and the choice of beverages is limited to Otter Beer and a local farm cider (Clayhyndon). There is no provision for children here - not even a garden.

Brewery: Free house
Licensee: Mrs M Wright
Opening hours: 7-11pm; closed Sun. Will open at other times if people call
Children: Not permitted inside

⊜ RISING SUN
Harbourside, Lynmouth EX35 6EQ. Tel 0598 53223

Lynmouth

Picturesquely thatched and set beside the harbour, this 14th- century smugglers' inn has a charm which attracts holidaymakers as well as locals. Equally appealing are the low ceilings, beams, sloping floors and wonderful sea views. The panelled bar is simple in the extreme, with cushioned settles, wooden tables and pictures of old Lynmouth. Draught beers on offer are Ushers Best, Ruddles County and Best and Webster's Yorkshire; bar meal menus (available at lunchtime only - a separate restaurant operates in the evenings) offer dishes as varied as garlic mushrooms (£3.55), steak, mushroom and Guinness pie (£3.85) and seafood platter (£5.95). Well appointed accommodation reflects the character of the establishment, and the garden is reserved for residents' use.

Brewery: Free house
Licensee: Hugo Jeune
Opening hours: 11am-3pm, 6.30-11pm; Sun 12-3pm, 7-10.30pm
Bar food: 12-2pm; residents only in evening
Restaurant: 7-9pm
Accommodation: (Price per person) single or double £38-£46
Children: Not permitted under 14 years in bar unless eating; welcome in restaurant if eating
Credit Cards: Access, Visa

Pins and Firkins

Brewing has a rich store of technical terms and old-fashioned measures. The conventional container for draught beer - for centuries made of wood, but nowadays of metal - is called a cask. A barrel in brewing terminology is a 36-gallon cask, and a keg is a sealed metal container for beer that has been filtered, sterilised and pressurised before leaving the brewery. British beer in pubs still comes in pints or half-pints and pubs still order their beer using the old-style cask measures, which follow a scale of nine.

> *pin   4 1/2 gallons*
> *firkin   9 gallons*
> *kilderkin   18 gallons*
> *barrel   36 gallons*
> *hogshead   54 gallons*

Two obsolete cask sizes are the butt of 108 gallons and the tun, which held varying quantities above 200 gallons. A yard of ale is a glass tube 3ft long and containing up to 3 pints, now only used in drinking contests.

ROYAL OAK
Meavy, near Yelverton PL20 6PJ. Tel 0822 852944

Meavy

Competitively priced food and a range of interesting dishes play no small part in attracting a regular local clientele to this unspoiled 16th-century pub, but its pleasant setting beside the green in a village on the edge of Dartmoor is also a powerful factor. Traditionally furnished bars - one with a huge stone fireplace - offer such old-established pastimes as darts, dominoes, euchre and cribbage, with live folk music on the first Saturday of each month. Bar meal menus feature some imaginative recipes, including chicken flamed in Cognac (£5.25) and home-made cheesy aubergine bake with garlic bread or a fruity vegetable curry with pilau rice and mango chutney (both at £3.50); tables set in the cobbled courtyard provide a pleasant eatingvenue, weather. permitting. There is an interesting range of ciders available, plus Flowers Original, Whitbread Castle Eden, Boddingtons and Guinness on draught.

Brewery: Free house
Licensee: G Wilson
Opening hours: 11am-2.30pm, 6-11pm; Sun 12-3pm, 7-10.30pm
Bar food: 12-2pm, 7-9pm
Children: Not permitted inside

⊜ RING OF BELLS
North Bovey, near Newton Abbot TQ13 8RB. Tel 0647 40375

North Bovey

Regulars and holidaymakers alike flock to this quality inn which commands lovely views from a setting at the centre of the pretty Dartmoor village. An exterior of white-painted stone walls topped by immaculate thatch houses two beamed bars, one of them featuring an interesting long-case clock built into a niche; darts, pool, electronic games and occasional live music are provided for guests' entertainment,

Brewery: Free house
Licensee: Tony Rix
Opening hours: 11am-3pm, 6-11pm; Sun 12-3pm, 7-10.30pm
Bar food: 12-2pm, 6.30-9pm; Sun 12-2pm, 7-9pm
Restaurant: 7-9pm

and 15 to 20 malt whiskies are available. Whitbread, Guinness, Fergusons, Wadworth, Bass and Burton beers are on draught. Well cooked bar meals represent sound value for money, including such dishes as lasagne verde at £4.25 and casserole of local rabbit in cider at £7.50. Accommodation is available in spacious, comprehensively equipped bedrooms, two of which have four-posters. A garden at the rear of the pub contains a swimming pool which casual visitors as well as residants may use, while that at the front is set with umbrella-shaded tables and a swing.

Accommodation: (Price per person) single or double from £25
Children: Welcome in Lounge and restaurant; outdoor play area

PETER TAVY INN
Peter Tavy, near Tavistock PL19 9NN. Tel 0822 810348

Peter Tavy

Its lovely setting and friendly landlord make this small, unpretentious village pub worth seeking out. Parts of the building date back to the 15th century, and the rear car park opens on to a paved patio and a hedged garden area with tables. In the traditionally furnished bars with their beamed ceilings and slate floors you can enjoy a game of darts - or perhaps concentrate on the appreciation of a good range of regularly changing real ales which might include, for example, Butcombe Bitter, Palmers and Fergusons Dartmoor Strong. Once a month there is entertainment in the form of live music. An interesting variety of freshly prepared bar food represents good value for money; the emphasis (with positively no chips!) being on wholefood and vegetarian dishes like Peter Tavy crunchy nut pasta (£3.50), though old favourites like cottage pie are also available (again, at £3.50). A separate restaurant operates during the evening.

Brewery: Free house
Licensee: Mr Hawkins
Opening hours: 11.30am-2.30pm, 6.30-11pm; Sun 12-3pm, 7-10.30pm
Bar food: As opening hours
Restaurant: 7-9.30pm
Children: Welcome in side room, Snug and in restaurant if eating
Credit Cards: Access, Visa

⊜ CHURCH HOUSE INN
Rattery, near South Brent TQ10 9LD. Tel 0364 42220

Rattery

This pleasant old pub, dating back to the 11th century and attractively located beside the village church, is fronted by a paved terrace set with umbrella-shaded tables. In its beamed, stone-walled bar, undisturbed by musak or electronic games, visitors can enjoy Guinness, Flowers, Ind Coope, Fergusons and Ansells beers. Tasty, attractively presented and generously portioned meals are served at a fair price - a locally smoked mackerel ploughman's, for example, costing £3.50, the famous Church House fry-up £4.65 and duckling with gooseberry sauce £6.25. A vegetarian option is always available, and there is an extensive wine list.

Brewery: Free house
Licensees: B and J J Evans
Opening hours: 11am-2.30pm, 6-11pm; Sun 12-2.30pm, 7-10.30pm
Bar food: 12-2pm, 7-9.30pm
Restaurant: Times as bar food
Children: Welcome in dining room and small bar area
Credit Cards: Access, Visa

⊜ JACK-IN-THE-GREEN
Rockbeare, near Exeter EX5 2EE. Tel 0404 822240

Rockbeare

Named after the popular leaf-clad jester of pre-Christian spring rites, this quality pub beside the A30 is much appreciated by travellers on that road as well as by 'regulars' both from Exeter and the village itself. Built over 400 years ago as a farmhouse, it now offers two bars which have recently been renovated to a high standard; featuring open fires and furnished with reproduction pieces, they serve Wadworth 6X, Courage Directors, Eldridge Pope Royal Oak and Thomas Hardy Country, Ruddles Best, John Smith's and Guinness from the tap. A list of 35 wines (eight of them available by the glass) accompanies a bar menu of imaginative dishes ranging in style from the old-fashioned bubble-and-squeak with sausages at £3.95 to a less traditional fresh pasta with smoked chicken and thyme sauce at £4.25. The same selection is featured in the restaurant at £9.50 for a two-course, £11.50 for a three-course meal.

Brewery: Free house
Licensees: Paul Parnell, Charles Manktelow, Michael Beckett
Opening hours: 11.30am-2.30pm (Fri and Sat 11am-3pm), 6-11pm (Fri from 5.30pm; Sun 3pm, 7-10.30pm
Bar food: 12-2pm (Fri 2.30pm), 6.30-9pm; Sat 11.30am-2.30pm; Sun 12-2.30pm, 7-9pm
Restaurant: Times as bar food
Children: Permitted in restaurant if eating; family room
Credit Cards: Access, Visa

TOWER INN
Slapton, near Kingsbridge TQ7 2PN. Tel 0548 580216

Slapton

Despite the drawbacks of hidden access and difficult parking, this white-walled 14th-century pub decked with hanging baskets attracts seasonal visitors as well as 'regulars' to its sleepy village setting. Not only the delightful atmosphere of the beamed bar serving Exmoor, Palmers, Wadworth 6X, Hall & Woodhouse Tanglefoot, Eldridge Pope Royal Oak and Gibbs Mew Bishop's Tipple, plus the local Staincombe cider, but also a range of tasty and original bar meals at reasonable prices make it well worth a visit. Dishes might include Gorgonzola pasta (£4.95), pizza Napolitana (£4.80) or seafood risotto (£7.20). Accommodation is simple but adequate, two of the three bedrooms having a pleasant outlook over the gardens. Occasionally live bands can be heard of an evening.

Brewery: Free house
Licensee: K Romp
Opening hours: 11.30am-2.30pm, 6-11pm; Sun 12-3pm, 7-10.30pm
Bar food: 12-2pm, 7-9.15pm
Accommodation: (Price per person) single and double from £17
Children: Welcome in family rooms; outdoor play area

⊜ MILLBROOK INN
South Pool, near Kingsbridge TQ7 2RW. Tel 0548 531581

South Pool

White-painted under its natural slate roof, and attractively set in a pretty village at the head of a tidal creek, this small pub dating back 400 years offers a friendly welcome to locals and holidaymakers alike. No electronic games or musak disturb the peace of the two traditional bars

Brewery: Free house
Licensee: A K Spedding
Opening hours: 11am-3pm, 5.30-11pm; Sun 12-3pm, 7-10.30pm

with their displays of horse-brasses and clay pipes - though a friendly game of darts is in order! Locally brewed cider (Churchwards) could provide an interesting accompaniment to a reasonably priced range of good, home-cooked bar meals which offers such alternatives as a Stilton and broccoli quiche at £3.30, prawns in a crowd at £5.95 and Millbrook crab salad at £6.25. Beer drinkers can choose from Ruddles Best, Worthington, John Smith's Best or Bass. On a fine day you might care to eat at one of the front terrace tables, or relax whilst watching the ducks on the stream that flows past the small back patio.

Bar food: 12-2pm, 6.30-9pm (Sun 7pm)
Children: Permitted in separate bar if eating

☕ OXENHAM ARMS
South Zeal, Okehampton EX20 2JJ. Tel 0837 840244

South Zeal

This unspoiled village pub - an ivy-clad stone inn dating from the 12th century - tends to attract the upper end of the market. A bar furnished in keeping with the style and age of the building and exhibiting some interesting architectural features offers no entertainment other than the traditional darts, dominoes, cards and shove halfpenny; St Austell Tinners Ale and Bass are on draught, and the range of reasonably priced bar meals includes such dishes as spaghetti Bolognese at £3.75, cauliflower and prawn Mornay at £3.95 and steak and kidney pie at £4.25 (a vegetarian option always being available). Both morning coffee and afternoon tea are served, and you can enjoy these in the pretty rear garden, weather permitting.

Brewery: Free house
Licensee: J H Henry
Opening hours: 11am-2.30pm, 6-11pm; Sun 12-2.30pm, 7-10.30pm
Bar food: As opening hours; last orders 9.30pm
Restaurant: 12.30-2pm, 7.30-9pm
Accommodation: (Price per person) single £40-£45, double £40- £60
Children: Not permitted under 14 years in bar; welcome in small family room
Credit Cards: Access, Visa

☕ KINGS ARMS INN
Stockland, near Honiton EX14 9BS. Tel 040488 361

Stockland

The cheap beer (Ushers Best, Exmoor Ale, Hall & Woodhouse Badger Best, Ruddles County, Webster's and Guinness) and five draught lagers of the Farmer's Bar, combined with food magnificent enough to satisfy a gourmet draws visitors to the area, as well as regulars, to the part-thatched 17th-century inn at the centre of this lovely village. Sensitive owners have preserved many original features in two bars where classical music provides a relaxing background - except on Sundays, when there is live entertainment in country and western or traditional style. Over 40 malt whiskies are on sale at any one time, and an excellent wine list is available to accompany excellent quality

Brewery: Free house
Licensees: H Kiefer and P Diviani
Opening hours: 12-3pm, 6.30-11pm; Sun 12-3pm, 7-10pm
Bar food: 12-2pm, 6.30-9pm; Sun 7-9pm only
Restaurant: 7-9pm
Accommodation: (Price per person) single from £20, double from £15
Children: In extension and

dishes as varied as king prawn Thermidor (£9.50), chicken Masala (£6.50) and vegetarian pancake (£3.50). The accommodation is spacious, airy and comfortable.

games area only if under 16 years

THELBRIDGE CROSS INN
Thelbridge, near Witheridge EX17 4SQ. Tel 0884 860316

Thelbridge

In a part of the county poorly off for pubs, this former coaching inn, dating from around 1700, is worth knowing about - not least because of the accommodation. Its seven double rooms are clean, comfortable, pleasantly furnished and offer good facilities. Set back from the main road, the long, white building has a lawn to one side where children can play. Locals and tourists mingle in the carpeted, open-plan bar, where Bass, Butcombe Bitter and Wadworth 6X are on tap. The restaurant serves traditional food - steak and kidney pie and roast lamb, both at £4.50, for example - as well as dishes like salmon Thelbridge at £8.50.

Brewery: Free house
Licensees: Bill and Ria Ball
Opening hours: 11.30am-3pm, 6.30-11pm; Sun 12-2pm, 7-10.30pm
Bar food: 12-2pm, 6.30-9.30pm (Sun 7pm)
Restaurant: Times as bar food
Accommodation: (Price per person) single £30-£35, double £25-£30
Children: In family room and dining area only; children's menu available; outdoor play area
Credit cards: AMERICAN EXPRESS®, Access, Visa

START BAY INN
Torcross, near Kingsbridge TQ7 2TQ. Tel 0548 580553

Torcross

Brewery: Heavitree
Licensees: Paul and Fay Stubbs
Opening hours: 11.30am-2.30pm, 6-11pm; Sun 12-2.30pm, 7-10.30pm
Bar food: 11.30am-2.30pm, 6-10pm; Sun 12-2pm, 7-10pm
Children: Welcome in family room; beach very close

A traditional seaside pub popular with holidaymakers - not least for good-value, generously served bar meals making excellent use of locally caught fish - the Start Bay Inn has a pleasant terrace overlooking the sea and set with umbrella-shaded tables. Here, or at the bar's wooden tables, you can enjoy a large selection of dishes which includes skate wing in batter at £4.70, lemon sole at £6.95 or seafood platter at £7.50; a vegetarian option can always be supplied. Murphy's, Guinness, Whitbread, Flowers and Marston's Pedigree are the beers on draught. The beach, just a pebble's throw away, provides the ideal play area for children, while the bar offers electronic games.

⊕ OTTER
Weston, near Honiton EX14 0NZ. Tel 0404 42594

Weston

Brewery: Free house
Licensees: Brian and Susan Wilkinson
Opening hours: 11am-3pm, 6-11pm; Sun 12-3pm, 7-10.30pm
Bar food: 12-2pm, 6.30-10pm; Sun 12-2pm, 7-9.30pm
Children: Not permitted near fruit machines; family room; outdoor play area
Credit Cards: Access, Visa

Children are welcome at this friendly family pub whose extensive gardens run beside the shallow waters of the Otter. Set off the road, it enjoys delightful rural surroundings relatively unchanged since the 14th century when it began life as a cider house. Now, Eldridge Pope Thomas Hardy Country, Flowers IPA, Bass, Guinness and Murphy's can be enjoyed at the bar. Beamed and air-conditioned, it offers fruit machines and every amusement from skittles to Trivial Pursuit as well as occasional live Country and Western music and quizzes. Excellently cooked bar meals range from a Stilton and mushroom jacket potato at £2.70 to a home-made steak and oyster pie at £6.95, and include a vegetarian option. The superior wine list features one with the pub's own label.

⊕ RUGGLESTONE INN
Widecombe in the Moor, near Newton Abbot TQ13 7TF. Tel 03642 327

Widecombe in the Moor

Brewery: Free house
Licensee: L A Ensor
Opening hours: 11am-3pm, 6-11pm; Sun 12-3pm, 7-10.30pm
Bar food: 12-2pm, 6-9pm; Sun 12-2.30pm, 7-9pm
Children: Not permitted inside

Snacks are now served at this simple, 200-year-old pub which stands by the roadside near the well-known village of Widecombe in the Moor and for years provided neither food nor accommodation. Behind its granite and slate exterior (whose wonderful window lintels will be appreciated by lovers of moorland architecture) there survives, however, a totally unspoiled bar with old beams, wooden settles and a large fireplace, and here regulars still enjoy the 19th-century card game of euchre while supping the local farm-brew cider or Bass beer which are still served in time-honoured fashion from barrels in the back scullery.

⊕ POLTIMORE ARMS
Yarde Down, near South Molton EX36 4DA. Tel 0598 710381

Yarde Down

High up on the edge of remote Exmoor, this white, pebble-dashed pub has served as such ever since it was built, over 300 years. ago. A clientele consisting mainly of farmers, huntsmen and tourists can choose between Cotleigh Tawny Bitter and Courage Directors in the main bar, with its wall benches and assortment of chairs and its huge fireplace and wood-burning stove. Not surprisingly for a pub which has its own team, cricketing pictures decorate the walls, alongside hunting scenes. There is also a simply furnished Lounge and a family room, and benches are set out on the grass outside. Standard pub fare, although very good value for money, is on offer, including ploughman's at £3, steak and kidney pie and lasagne, both at £3.90, and rump steak at £5.80.

Brewery: Free house
Licensees: Mike and Mella Wright
Opening hours: 11.30am-2.30pm, 6.30-11pm; Sun 12-2pm, 7-10.30pm
Bar food: 11.30am-2pm, 6.30-9.30pm; Sun 12-1.30pm, 7-9pm
Children: In family room only; children's menu available

DORSET

ILCHESTER ARMS
Abbotsbury, near Weymouth DT3 4JR. Tel 0305 871243

Abbotsbury

Tourists and walkers, as well as a regular clientele, are attracted by the charm and character of this welcoming 17th-century coaching inn, set at the heart of a picturesque village and handy for the nearby swannery and abbey gardens. Well equipped, comfortable bedrooms - named after flowers and individually decorated in their colours - offer excellent value for money, including three with four-poster beds and a honeymoon suite. As well as three beamed bars (the Swan and Public displaying an enormous collection of hunting, shooting and fishing memorabilia) there are two dining rooms, a conservatory containing a huge oak table, and a terrace where meals can be taken on pleasant days; drinks and snacks can also be enjoyed at picnic benches in the little garden's grassed area which looks across to St Catherine's Chapel on the hill. A list of some 38 wines accompanies a restaurant menu which features a three-course Sunday lunch for £7.95 and offers such dishes as fillet of beef with black pepper and brandy sauce (£9.95) and lemon sole (£8.50) while bar meals include old favourites like home-made steak and kidney pie (£4.50), deep-fried chicken (£4.95) and gammon steak (£6.95). Beer drinkers have the choice of Flowers Original, Wadworth 6X and Boddingtons Bitter.

Brewery: Devenish
Licensee: A A F Doyle
Opening hours: 11am-11pm; bar closed 3-7pm (open for teas only); Sun 12-3pm, 7-10.30pm
Bar food: 12-2pm, 7-9pm
Accommodation: (Price per person) single £30, double £25
Children: Not permitted in bars
Credit Cards: Access, Visa

☺ SPYWAY INN
Askerswell, near Bridport DT2 9EP. Tel 030885 250

Askerswell

Spyway Bar, distinctively furnished with high-backed settles, scrubbed tables and a grandfather clock, is augmented by a pleasant second bar decked with farm memorabilia; there is also a dining area in farmhouse kitchen style, with china-laden dresser and quarry-tiled floor. The bar menu is standard, but its reliable home-cooked dishes represent excellent value for money, with a good range of ploughman's (woodman's, farmer's, squire's) from £2.25, salads from £2.95 and steaks at £7.50. A quiet garden with superb views includes a children's play section as well as paved and lawned areas set with picnic tables.

Brewery: Free house
Licensees: Don and Jackie Roderick
Opening hours: 11am-2.30pm, 6-11pm; Sun 12-3pm, 7-10.30pm
Bar food: 12-2pm, 6.45-9.15pm (Sun 7pm)
Children: Welcome in eating area of bar, but not under ten years; outdoor play area

☺ GEORGE HOTEL
4 South Street, Bridport DT6 3NQ. Tel 0308 23187

Bridport

Standing opposite the Guildhall in the town centre, the handsome Georgian exterior of this building gives little hint of the lively atmosphere inside. Morning coffee, served by the large cup and enjoyed to a background of classical and operatic music, has a French feel to it, though the evenings - with games of bagatelle, and a quiz night on Sundays in winter - are uncompromisingly English. The food and drink available at the bar are similarly diverse, beer ranging from Palmers Bridport Bitter and Tally Ho! and Guinness to Kronenbourg 1664, and dishes from Welsh rarebit (£2.50) and pigeon pie (£3.50) to crudités (£3) and mousaka (£3.75); all meals are prepared in an open-view kitchen. A tiled entrance hall leads to the main bar with its open fire, Regency stripe wallpaper and fine selection of paintings and prints, while a smaller bar features a wooden floor, old paintings and mirrors and a Victorian fireplace.

Brewery: Palmers
Licensee: John Mander
Opening hours: 9am-11pm; Sun 12-3pm, 7-10.30pm
Bar food: 12-2.30pm, 7-9.30pm (Fri and Sat evenings only in winter)
Accommodation: (Price per person) £18 sharing double room
Children: Permitted in bar to the left
Credit Cards: Access, Visa

☺ NEW INN
Cerne Abbas, near Dorchester DT2 7JF. Tel 0300 341274

Cerne Abbas

The Cerne Abbas Giant, believed to be a Bronze Age fertility symbol, is among various attractions not far from this village-centre pub. A former coaching inn, built in the mid-16th century in stone, flint and brick, with a stone roof and a cobbled courtyard, it has a single large bar with an open fire. With tapestry-covered wall benches and stools for seating, the carpeted bar is decked with traps, horse-brasses and harnesses. Customers can choose from Eldridge Pope Dorchester Bitter, Thomas Hardy Country and Royal Oak, or

Brewery: Eldridge Pope
Licensees: Helen and James Smith
Opening hours: Summer 11am-11am; winter 11.30am-2.30pm, 6-11pm (Sat 11am-11pm); Sun 12-3pm, 7-10.30pm
Bar food: 11.30am-2.30pm, 6.30-9.30pm; Sun 12-3pm, 7-9pm

from a wide selection of French, German, Italian and Spanish wines, or champagne. Good, home-cooked food, from the menu and as daily specials, is the order of the day - for example, steak and kidney pudding at £5.50 and braised duckling at £8.50, and raspberry and hazelnut meringue at £3. Five double rooms, each with a television, are available.

Accommodation: (Price per room) single £25, double £40
Children: In seating area away from bar only; half portions available
Credit cards: Access, Visa

Badger Country

Soon after a farmer's son named Charles Hall founded his brewery in 1777 he secured the contract to supply beer to a military camp established near Weymouth against invasion by the French. The soldiers' morale was no doubt raised, the French were deterred and the fortunes of Hall & Woodhouse were made. The Woodhouses married into the Hall family two generations later. With its brewery at Blandford Forum, the firm is known for its Badger beers in Dorset, Somerset and Wiltshire.

⊕ ANCHOR
Seatown, near Chideock DT6 6JU. Tel 0297 89215

Chideock

Superbly set on a coastal footpath beside the beach, this attractive cream-painted pub with front terraces is popular with both locals and holidaymakers. Morning coffee and afternoon tea are served, sandwiches are available all day in summer, and good-value bar meals include such dishes as lasagne or bacon and cheese carbonara at £4.25 and vegetables au gratin at £3.95, excellent locally caught fish also being well represented; Palmers IPA, Bridport Bitter and Tally Ho! and Guinness are on draught, and a list of 14 wines accompanies the food. Bars display a fine selection of pictures and prints, piped music providing a relaxing background, and the food service area doubles as a family room.

Brewery: Palmers
Licensees: David and Sadie Miles
Opening hours: 11am-2.30pm, 7-11.30pm; Whit-early Sep 11am-11pm; Sun 12-3pm, 7-10.30pm
Bar food: 12-2pm, 6.30-9.30pm; Sun 12-2pm, 7-9.30pm (winter 12-2pm only)
Children: In family room only

⊕ FOX INN
Corscombe, near Dorchester DT2 0NS. Tel 0935 891330

Corscombe

Built in 1640 as a cider house on the old droving route to Yeovil, the Fox still stands isolated on the outskirts of the village, by the stream where the sheep used to be dipped. A local cider from Bridge Farm is still served, and Exmoor Ale and Green King Abbot Ale are on draught. Thatched and cream painted, with hollyhocks and roses climbing its stone walls, the pub is backed by a paved courtyard with huge oak tables, vines and flower-filled tubs and urns; a small garden offers seating near the river. The interior is tastefully decorated - the entrance lobby boasting

Brewery: Free house
Licensee: Martyn Lee
Opening hours: 12-2.30pm, 7-11pm; Sun 12-3pm, 7-10.30pm
Bar food: 12-2pm (Sun 2.30pm), 7-9pm
Children: In family room only

a fine mural of wild flowers and ivy, while the dining room and a Public Bar with old scrubbed pine tables and a grandfather clock retain ancient oak beams and flag-stoned floors. Both have open fires and display collections of banknotes and copper as well as hunting memorabilia; neither has machines or music. A further room with stone walls, beams and a tiled floor is equally comfortable with farmhouse kitchen chairs and a settle. A good, though short bar menu offers quality fresh produce cooked in country style and representing value for money in straightforward dishes like lemon sole (£7.50) and beef stew (£5.25). There is always a vegetarian dish.

⊛ FLEUR DE LYS
Cranborne, near Wimborne Minster BH21 5PP. Tel 07254 282

Cranborne

This fine old inn, half covered by creepers and set at the heart of a pretty village, has a loyal clientele of regulars. One attractive feature is the paved terrace, its pergola covered in wisteria and honeysuckle, and a small lawned area with picnic tables and swings is ideal for children. A carpeted, well modernised Lounge Bar with light oak panelling and a huge inglenook where horse-brasses, plates and straw dollies are displayed has a separate dining area in which reliably good food is served. Here, traditional dishes like rabbit pie and braised faggots (both at £4.65) are supplemented by a range of vegetarian options and a display of daily changing specials. There are also a separate restaurant and a heavily beamed Public Bar with round pub tables and a wall painting of the village over the fireplace. Hall & Woodhouse Badger Best, Tanglefoot and Guinness are served. Comfortable overnight accommodation is provided in eight cottagey bedrooms with floral wallpaper and chintz curtains.

Brewery: Hall & Woodhouse
Licensees: Charles and Ann Hancock
Opening hours: 10.30am-2.30pm, 6-11pm; Sun 12-2.30pm, 7-10.30pm
Bar food: 12-2pm, 7-9.30pm
Restaurant: Times as bar food
Accommodation: (Price per room) single £24-£35, double £36-£50
Children: Welcome in eating area; outdoor play area
Credit Cards: Access, Visa

⊛ ACORN INN
Fore Street, Evershot, near Dorchester DT2 0JW. Tel 0935 83228

Evershot

Window boxes and hanging baskets of flowers make bright splashes of colour in summer against the 16th-century stone exterior of this good country inn which, attactively set at the heart of a quaint, historic village, provides an excellent base from which to tour Dorset. Individually decorated bedrooms are clean and comfortable, and there are two bars - the Lounge, incorporating a dining area adorned with hunting prints and glass cages of stuffed birds and animals, and the Public, with its dark wood

Brewery: Free house
Licensees: Denise and Keith Morley
Opening hours: 11am-3pm, 6.30-11pm; Sun 12-3pm, 7-10.30pm
Bar food: 12-2pm, 6.30-10pm; Sun 12-2pm, 7-9pm
Restaurant: Times as bar food

furniture and wood-burning stove; a separate games room houses fruit machines and a juke box as well as the more traditional amusements like darts, skittles and pool. Such dishes as haddock au gratin (£4.95), pork chop in cider (£5.95) or game hotpot (£6.95) can be enjoyed in either the bar or restaurant, and there is a separate vegetarian menu. Two guest beers are always available, along with the regular Wadworth 6X, Palmers IPA, Bass and four draught lagers.

Accommodation: (Price per person) standard rooms £30-£32; other rooms £37-£50; supplements for single occupancy; reduced rates for more than two nights
Children: Welcome in Village Bar and if eating; must leave restaurant by 8pm; half portions available
Credit Cards: Access, Visa

🍺 MUSEUM HOTEL
Farnham, near Blandford Forum DT11 8DE. Tel 0725516 261

Farnham

Imaginative meals, prepared from fresh, quality ingredients and attractively presented, bring an 'upmarket' clientele from far and wide to this hotel dating back to the days of Cromwell. At lunchtime, for example, a home-made orange and carrot soup (£1.95) might be followed by pork, wild mushroom and apricot pie (£4.95), with a fresh strawberry mousse (£2.75) to finish; real ale is served (Smiles, Hall & Woodhouse Badger Best and Adnams) and local country wines are featured in an excellent list which includes a good range of French labels and a choice of half bottles. For a summer meal, the conservatory and its terrace provide a pleasant alternative to the more formal setting of a small dining room. Coopers Bar retains a traditional atmosphere in keeping with its beamed ceiling and old brick inglenook (still containing the original bread oven), while the livelier Woodland Bar houses a selection of pub games, and a lawned garden with children's play area provides additional seating. Old stables have been converted into double bedrooms, one of which boasts a four-poster bed. The hotel stands in a predominantly thatched village, and many of the local prints hanging on the bar walls are available for purchase.

Brewery: Free house
Licensee: John Barnes
Opening hours: 11am-3pm, 6-11pm; Sun 12-3pm, 7-10.30pm
Bar food: 12-1.45pm, 7-9.30pm
Accommodation: (Price per room) single from £36, double from £50
Restaurant: Times as bar food; booking essential
Children: Welcome in restaurant, games room and Woodland Bar; outdoor play area
Credit Cards: Access, Visa

🍺 SCOTT ARMS
West Street, Kingston, near Corfe Castle BH20 5LH. Tel 0929 480270

Kingston

An 18th-century coaching inn set high in the Purbeck Hills and much loved by film-makers commands outstanding views from its terraced lawns. Picturesque surroundings and tasteful furnishings make it an attractive place in which to eat, and a menu supplemented by good, daily changing specials allows guests to enjoy dishes ranging from an oven-baked potato at £2 to more exotic dishes like fishpot Creole at £4.95; Ringwood Best and Fortyniner and Wadworth 6X are available on draught. This well modernised and efficiently run establishment offers three bars, the one formerly used by local quarrymen complementing its woodblock floor, beams and exposed stone walls by collections of fishing rods and Toby jugs, while the Lounge - in whose huge stone fireplace a real fire burns during the colder months - includes old local photos and prints among its memorabilia.

Brewery: Devenish
Licensee: Mr M Ralph
Opening hours: 11-2.30pm, 6-11pm; Sun 12-3pm, 7-10.30pm
Bar food: 12-2pm, 6.30-9pm; Sun 12-2pm (all year), 7-9pm (summer only)
Children: Welcome except in Quarry Bar; children's menu available
Credit Cards: Access, Visa

🍺 ELM TREE
Langton Herring, Weymouth DT3 4HU. Tel 0305 871257

Langton Herring

This old, whitewashed pub in a peaceful village setting close to the Dorset Coast Path and Chesil Beach is a popular eating place, offering an excellent choice of home-cooked, generously served dishes which includes cheesey ham and spinach lasagne at £5.99, rump steak au poivre at £7.25 and Scotch salmon steak at £7.50. Sandwiches (from £1.20) and ploughman's lunches (from £3.75) are on offer for those requiring a lighter snack, a vegetarian dish is always available and children can choose from their own menu (this being very much a family pub). One of a selection of country wines could provide an interesting accompaniment to your meal, and Boddingtons Bitter and Whitbread Royal Wessex are available on draught. The smaller of the bars - which retains such original features as a low, beamed ceiling, a large inglenook fireplace and a flagstone floor in front of the bar - houses a collection of Toby jugs, while brass and copper gleam in the larger, with its red leatherette stools and modern central fireplace; there is also a long, low, traditionally furnished extension in keeping with the original style of the building. Flower tubs and trellis-supported climbing plants enhance an outside area given over to picnic benches, and there is a lawned area to the side of the pub.

Brewery: Devenish
Licensees: Antony and Karen Gurracci
Opening hours: 11-2.30pm, 6.30-11pm; Sun 12-3pm, 7-10.30pm
Bar food: 12-2pm, 6.30-10pm (Sun 7pm)
Children: Welcome anywhere, family room; children's menu available
Credit Cards: Access, Visa

🍺 HAMBRO ARMS
Milton Abbas, near Blandford Forum, DT11 OBP. Tel 0258 880233

Milton Abbas

A thatched, whitewashed inn dating from 1773, set at the top end of this historic and very attractive village's main street, offers accommodation in two pleasant double bedrooms. A range of bar food supplemented by specials includes such snacks as Dorset pâté (£2.25) alongside heartier options like beef and oyster pie at £6.95 or a 16oz rib steak at £12.95, and the wine list offers 22 choices; there is a separate restaurant, except on Sundays, when only a carvery is provided. A Lounge Bar, where open fires burn on colder days, displays collections of jugs and plates as well as prints against its exposed brickwork, while the Public Bar contains a pool table, juke box and fruit machines. Boddingtons Bitter and Flowers Original are on draught. Live jazz is featured from time to time, and Sunday night is quiz night during the winter months.

Brewery: Devenish
Licencees: Ken and Brenda Barne
Opening hours: 11am-2.30pm (Sat 3pm), 6.30-11pm; Sun 12-3pm, 7-10.30pm
Bar food: 12-2pm, 7-9.30pm; Sun as opening times
Restaurant: 12-2pm, 7-9.30pm; Sun Carvery 12-2pm
Accommodation: (Price per person) single £30, double £25; children over 13 years only
Children: In Public Bar and in restaurant if eating
Credit Cards: Access, Visa

🍺 THREE ELMS
North Wootton, near Sherborne DT9 5JW. Tel 0935 812881

North Wootton

A choice of nine real ales, including Oakhill Bitter, Greene King Abbot Ale, Smiles Best and Wadworth 6X, a wide range of unusual bottled beers and lagers, and good bar food all combine to make this erstwhile cider house beside the A3030 difficult to pass by! Visitors can enjoy a snack of Dorset liver pâté for £2.95 or the more substantial mixed grill at £9.75, and an excellent vegetarian choice is always available. A fascinating collection of model vehicles provides an additional attraction, and the huge bar offers a selection of board games for patrons' entertainment. The garden backs on to farmland and contains a picnic area.

Brewery: Free house
Licensees: Eileen and Howard Manning
Opening hours: 11am-2.30pm, 6.30-11pm (Fri and Sat from 6pm); Sun 12-3pm, 7-10.30pm
Bar food: 12-2pm, 6.30-10pm (Sun 7pm)
Accommodation: (Price per person) £17.50
Children: Inside only if eating; outdoor play area; half portions available

---

Country Matters
Country occupations and pursuits provide many inns with their names. The Wheatsheaf, the Barley Mow, the Haywain, the Dun Cow, the Heifer, the Plough (sometimes the constellation) and the Harrow recall the farming year's immemorial round. Horses, long essential to agriculture, communications and sport, figure frequently - the Black Horse, the Nag's Head, the Grey Mare and many more. The Bull and the Bear are often related to the once popular sport of baiting the animals with dogs. The Dog is usually a sporting dog and hunting has supplied many names, from the Fox and Hounds and the Hare and Hounds to numerous deer (also from heraldry), including the Stag and Hounds, the White Hart and the Roebuck. There are signs related to angling, too, such as the Angler and the Trout, and there are Jolly Cricketers and even Jolly Farmers.

POACHERS INN
Piddletrenthide, near Dorchester DT2 7QX. Tel 03004 358

Piddletrenthide

Background music and electronic games are provided as well as the traditional darts in the bar of this much modernised inn, a long white building dating from the 16th century and set at the heart of the village with lawns running down to the banks of the River Piddle. Exposed stone walls, red plush furnishings and old prints strike a less modern note, and an old farm plough introduces a reminder of rural life in simpler days which is echoed in the menu's inclusion of such country dishes as steak and kidney pie (£3.75) and poached salmon (£6.95); the bar menu also caters for vegetarians. Tetley Bitter and John Smith's beers are on draught. Clean and comfortable accommodation is popular with tourists, who find this a good base from which to tour the area, and the inn's amenities include a swimming pool.

Brewery: Free house
Licensees: Stephen Fox and Peter Hickey
Opening hours: 12-2.30pm, 6.30-11pm; Sun 12-3pm, 7-10.30pm
Bar food: 12-2pm, 6.30-9.30pm; Sun 12-2pm, 7-8.30pm
Accommodation: (Price per person) single £28, double £21
Children: Welcome anywhere; half portions available
Credit Cards: Access, Visa

🍽 BRACE OF PHEASANTS
Plush, near Dorchester DT2 7RQ. Tel 03004 357

Plush

D ating from the 16th century and originally the old village forge plus two cottages, the white-painted thatched pub of this isolated hamlet stands on a quiet country lane; its tranquil setting in good walking country and its suitability for families - the large, secluded rear garden housing animals and an aviary as well as the more predictable climbing frame and picnic tables with their red-checked cloths - attracts an across-the-board clientele. Good food is an additional attraction, the lunchtime bar selection (ranging from a ploughman's at £3.25 to duck with apple and Calvados sauce at £10.50) being supplemented by the restaurant's slightly more elaborate evening menu. There is always a vegetarian option, puddings include old favourites like apple crumble and strawberries and cream, and a list of 27 wines is available, as are Wadworth 6X, Bass, Butcombe Bitter and Guinness.

Brewery: Free house
Licensees: Geoffrey and Jane Knights
Opening hours: 11.30am-2.30pm, 7-11pm; Sun 12-3pm, 7-10.30pm
Bar food: 12-2pm, 7-10pm; Sun 12-1.45pm, 7-9.45pm
Restaurant: Times as bar food
Children: Welcome in family room; outdoor play area; own menu available
Credit Cards: Access, Visa

🍽 THREE HORSESHOES INN
Powerstock, near Bridport DT6 3TF. Tel 030885 328

Powerstock

S olidly old-fashioned, this popular dining pub in Victorian style (rebuilt from local stone after a fire in 1906) stands near the church at the heart of a peaceful village tucked into the folds of the Dorsetshire downs. Three-quarter-acre gardens commanding fine views over the surrounding countryside, together with an attractive interior with simple country furnishings, open fires and a relaxed atmosphere, attract an 'upmarket' clientele from miles around; well stocked bars offer a wide selection of wines and spirits as well as Palmers Bridport Bitter and IPA and draught scrumpy, while a reliably good restaurant serves an interesting range of home-cooked meals that includes a Sunday roast. Good use is made of fresh local fish in such dishes as baked cod with chopped tomato, onion and herbs at £7.25, lobster grilled with garlic butter at £12.50 and seafood grill at £15.50. Four traditional bedrooms enjoy a very pleasant outlook.

Brewery: Palmers
Licensee: Pat Ferguson
Opening hours: 11am-3pm, 6-11pm; Sun 12-3pm, 7-10.30pm
Bar food: 12-2pm, 7-10pm; Sun 12-3pm, 7-9pm
Restaurant: 7-10pm; bookings only in winter
Accommodation: (Price per room) single £24-£30, double £44- £55
Children: Welcome except by the bar
Credit Cards: AMERICAN EXPRESS®, Access, Visa

🍽 PYMORE INN
Pymore, near Bridport DT6 5PN. Tel 0308 22625

Pymore

A n across-the-board clientele favours this pub on the outskirts of Pymore near Bridport, its simple rustic building - once a shop and stables - dating from the end of

Brewery: Free house
Licensee: Valerie and Mark Burdon

the Georgian era. Today it is popular for honest, excellent value, home-cooked meals based on good fresh ingredients. The midday menu includes a range of sandwiches (from £1), ploughman's lunches (from £2.60), salads (from £4.50) and steaks (£8.95) in addition to such perennial favourites as cottage pie at £4.20 or poached salmon at £6.25 and a tempting range of puddings; a more extensive evening menu introduces dishes like braised duck (£7.50) and venison in red wine (£6.20). Food is served either in the half-panelled bar (serving Fuller's London Pride, Wadworth 6X and Murphy's on draught), with its two open fires and dark wooden furniture, or in a small, intimate dining room. On a lawned area to the side of the building there are tables, chairs and picnic benches.

Opening hours: 11am-2.30pm, 6.30-11pm; closed Mon in winter; Sun 12-2pm, 7-10.30pm
Bar food: 12-1.30pm, 7-9.30pm (Sun 9pm)
Children: Welcome in dining area if eating

⊕ SHAVE CROSS INN
Shave Cross, Marshwood Vale, near Bridport DT6 6HW. Tel 0308 68358

Shave Cross

Surrounded by an award-winning garden and set in a remote spot at the heart of Marshwood Vale, this thatched cob-and-flint inn offers a classic Public Bar with huge beams (that over the fireplace hung with copper and brass), a lovely old flagged floor, and settles on each side of the inglenook fireplace; the atmosphere is unspoiled by electronic games or piped music, the only amusements being the traditional ones of skittles, darts, dominoes and cards. The long, low lounge/dining area is similar in style, while a children's room at the rear is functionally furnished with standard pub tables and chairs. Bar menus, too, are fairly standard, offering such dishes as lasagne at £3.75 and chicken, ham and leek pie or trout fillet ploughman's at £4.25 - though the range is extended in the evenings by char-grilled specialities, and there is always a vegetarian option. Eldridge Pope Royal Oak, Bass, Hall & Woodhouse Badger Best and Guinness are on draught. No dogs are permitted.

Brewery: Free house
Licensees: Ruth and Bill Slade
Opening hours: 12-3pm, 7-11pm; Sun 12-2.30pm, 7-10.30pm; closed Mon except BHs
Bar food: 12-2pm, 7-9.45pm; Sun 12-1.45pm, 7-9.30pm
Children: Not permitted under 14 years in bars; outdoor play area

---

LANGTON ARMS
Tarrant Monkton, near Blandford Forum DT11 8RX. Tel 025889 225

Tarrant Monkton

This fine, thatched, 17th-century pub, peacefully and picturesquely set opposite the village church and reached by driving through a shallow ford, has two cosy bars serving Wadworth 6X, Bass, Smiles Best and Exhibition and Murphy's, and a huge skittle alley which is also used as a function room and children's playroom - electronic games and a juke box offering an alternative to more old-fashioned amusements like darts, dominoes, cribbage and shove

Brewery: Free house
Licensee: Michael Crook
Opening hours: 11am-3pm, 6-11pm; Sun 12-3pm, 7-10.30pm
Bar food: 11am-2.30pm, 6.30-9.30pm; Sun 12-3pm, 7-9.30pm
Restaurant: 7-30-9pm; Sun 12.15-3pm only

halfpenny. Food is served in all bars both at lunchtime and in the evenings, dishes ranging from filled jacket potatoes (£2.95) and steaks (£6.95) to chilli or lasagne at £4.25, and there is always at least one vegetarian dish. A traditional roast lunch is available, Friday night is pizza night, and an Italian menu is served on Tuesdays in the restaurant - a converted stable witha large log fire. Puddings include a selection of home-made ices. Outside the pub is an expanse of lawn with picnic benches and a play area for children, and a purpose-built single-storey extension with its own courtyard offers good clean accommodation which makes provision for the needs of both family parties and wheelchair users.

Accommodation: (Price per room) single £28-£32, double £40-£48
Children: In separate family room only; outdoor play area
Credit Cards: Access, Visa

⊜ ROSE AND CROWN
Trent, near Sherborne DT9 4SL. Tel 0935 850776

Trent

U nspoiled and welcoming, this tranquil village pub near the church was, until the 1950s, a farmhouse licensed to sell alcohol. Today its trade is more sophisticated, the humbler draught beverages, which include Fuller's London Pride, Hook Norton Best and Marston's Pedigree, augmented by a list of some 35 wines (eight available by the glass), while an imaginative range of hearty home-cooked dishes, freshly prepared from local produce, is served in the character bars, frequently varied menus featuring such established favourites as lamb casserole or seafood pancakes at £5.50 and chicken curry at £4.95; both vegetarians and children are catered for, and home-made puddings (all at £2.25) include old-fashioned treacle tart, crème caramel and a chocolate and brandy mousse. This is a particularly pleasant place to visit in summer, with picnic benches among the flower tubs and hanging baskets that brighten the front of the mellow 500-year-old building, and fine views from the crazy-paved terrace and lawned area at its rear.

Brewery: Free house
Licensee: Charles Crawford
Opening hours: 12-2.30pm, 7-11pm; Sun 12-2.30pm, 7-10.30pm
Bar food: 12-2pm, 7-9.30pm; Sun 12-2.30pm (no food in the evening except for parties over six)
Children: Welcome in conservatory or Barrow Room if eating
Credit Cards: Access, Visa

SQUARE AND COMPASS
Worth Matravers, near Swanage BH1 93LF. Tel 0929 439229

Worth Matravers

T he name and sign of this pub honour all those who once cut marble from the nearby quarries - the square and compass being the mason's tools. Slate-roofed and built in the 17th century from local stone, the pub itself pays testimony to their art, and a flagged terrace with stone tables and benches completes the theme. An elevated position on the edge of the village, looking out to sea, makes it popular with both tourists and walkers, as does its unspoiled interior,

Brewery: Whitbread
Licensee: Ray Newman
Opening hours: 11am-3pm, 6-11pm; Sun 12-3pm, 7-10.30pm
Bar food: 11am-3pm, 6-11pm; Sun 12-3pm (sandwiches and rolls only)
Children: In smaller room only

the painted wood-panelled walls of the traditional main bar hung with old prints and photographs, the exposed stone walls of the smaller forming the background to a collection of ancient bottles and stone jugs; the absence of video games and juke box (the only pub game in evidence being dominoes) adds to the timeless ambience. Strongs Country, Castle Eden Ale, Pompey Royal, Marston's Pedigree and Guinness are served on draught, while bar food is limited to rolls, pasties, sausages, pies, fresh crab sandwiches (a glass case houses a huge crab!) and occasionally cockles. As the family who have owned the Square and Compass for the last 85 years know, however, it is the pub's originality that is its real and abiding attraction, not the facilities it offers.

SOMERSET

⊕ ASHCOTT INN
Bath Road, Ashcott, near Bridgwater TA7 9QH. Tel 0458 210282

Ashcott

Fresh fish, well cooked, is the speciality of this 17th-century pub, which stands at the edge of the village. Ten or so varieties of fish are on offer, including brill, turbot, plaice, lemon sole and monkfish, the latter served with prawns at £12.50, while fish pie costs £6.95. Also served are traditional favourites such as cottage pie at £3.50 and treacle tart at £2.35. French windows look on to a walled garden where children can safely play. The two carpeted, stone-walled bars are furnished traditionally with oak and elm tables, and among the choice of games is a skittle alley. Eldridge Pope Thomas Hardy Country Bitter and Marston's Pedigree are the beers on offer.

Brewery: Heavytree
Licensee: A K Porter
Opening hours: 11am-2.30pm, 5.30-11pm; Sun 12-2.30pm, 7-10.30pm
Bar food: 12-2pm, 6.30-9.30pm (Sun 7pm)
Restaurant: Times as bar food
Children: Welcome if eating
Credit Cards: Access, Visa

⊕ NEW INN
Dowlish Wake, near Ilminster TA19 0N2. Tel 0460 52413

Dowlish Wake

Perry's cider is brewed in the quiet village containing this pub, and the stone-built, 17th-century inn sells this local speciality, along with Wadworth 6X, Butcombe and Theakston Old Peculier and some 25 malt whiskies. A mixed clientele creates a pleasant atmosphere in the two bars, which are carpeted and have cushioned settles and other traditional pub furniture. An unusual feature is the long skittle alley, while behind the pub, in the attractive, secluded garden, there is a climbing frame to keep young children occupied. Food, of good quality and value for money, is

Brewery: Free house
Licensees: D C Smith and T A A Boosey
Opening hours: 11am-3pm, 6-11pm; Sun 12-3pm, 7-10.30pm
Bar food: 12-2pm, 6.30-9pm; Sun 12-2pm
Children: In family room only; outdoor play area

available from a bar menu which offers the famous Bellew sausage at £2.75 and stand-bys like steak and kidney pie, at £4.25, as well as in the restaurant. Available in the evenings and by request at lunchtime, the à la carte menu includes starters such as carpaccio at £4 and main courses like braised duck mandarin at £8.75 and fillet steak with oyster meat at £9.25.

🍺 HORSE AND GROOM
East Woodlands, near Frome BA11 5LY. Tel 0373 462802

East Woodlands

Dating from 1677 but not used as a public house until a century later, this whitewashed stone pub numbers among its attractions a remote setting near the popular Longleat Estate. Another draw is the beer, for the changing selection embraces Hook Norton Best, Bateman XXXB, Butcombe, Brakspear Special, Wadworth 6X and Fuller's London Pride. Some 40 wines are available to complement the food, which includes a wide choice of starters, and fresh-fish specialities like shark steak at £7.95 and whole sea bass at £10.95. Steak and chicken, as well as vegetarian main courses, are also served. The main bar has a flagstone floor and a large fireplace, with settles and stools for seating, and there is a separate dining room, which is a non-smoking area, and a conservatory.

Brewery: Free house
Licensee: C J Marshman
Opening hours: 12-2.30pm (closed Mon lunchtime), 6-11pm; Sun 12-3pm, 7-10.30pm
Bar food: 12-2pm, 7-9.15pm (except Mon); Sun 12-2pm
Restaurant: 12-2pm, limited menu (except Mon), 7-9pm; Sun 12-2pm
Children: In conservatory and in dining room if eating
Credit Cards: Access, Visa

🍺 TUCKERS GRAVE INN
Faulkland, near Radstock BA3 5XF.Tel 0373 834230

Faulkland

Edward Tucker, who hanged himself in a nearby barn in 1747, bequeathed his name to this country pub, built as a farm cottage in the 16th century and in use as an inn since around 1800. Cheddar Valley and Thatcher's ciders are the speciality of the house, although Bass and Butcombe are also served, likewise straight from the barrel. Sandwiches and ploughman's, and morning coffee, are available, but no hot meals. Unspoilt and blessed with a friendly atmosphere, the pub consists of two simple rooms: a tiny bar with wooden benches and a room with settles and an open fire. Tables and chairs are set out on the lawn at the back.

Brewery: Free house
Licensees: Ivan and Glenda Swift
Opening hours: 11am-3pm, 6-11pm; Sun 12-3pm, 7-10.30pm
Bar food: As opening hours (Sun ploughman's only)
Children: Welcome anywhere but at lunchtime only

POULETT ARMS
High Street, Hinton St George, near Crewkerne TA17 8SE. Tel 0460 73149

Hinton St George

Restaurant-quality food at pub prices is the prime attraction of this friendly, 17th-century former coaching inn, patronised mainly by well-heeled regulars. Among the home-cooked dishes served in the separate dining room are steak and kidney pie at £4.25 and chicken Cotswold at £4.50, with game available in season, and treacle and walnut tart at £2.20. Fuller's London Pride and ESB, Butcombe and Eldridge Pope Thomas Hardy Country Bitter are on offer, while the extensive wine list includes items from Australia and South Africa. Stone-built, with a slate and tile roof, the pub has two carpeted bars with cushioned chairs around small tables and open fireplaces in each, and a garden. A double room, furnished in cottage style and with tea-making facilities, is available for either one or two guests.

Brewery: Free house
Licensee: Mr Chisnall
Opening hours: 11am-3pm, 7-11pm; Sun 12-3pm, 7-10.30pm
Bar food: 12-2pm, 7-9.30pm
Accommodation: (Price per room) single £20, double £40
Children: Welcome anywhere away from bar
Credit Cards: Access, Visa

ROSE AND CROWN
Huish Episcopi, near Somerton TA10 9RA. Tel 0458 250494

Huish Episcopi

Otherwise known as Eli's, in memory of the present licensee's father, this highly individual pub has been in the same family for 125 of its more than 300 years. Thatched and with church-like windows and a stone floor, it is an unspoilt gem, and all the more unusual for having no bar. Boddingtons, Bass, Oakhill and Butcombe, and Burrowhill farmhouse cider, are served straight from barrels in a central still room which links the plainly furnished front parlours. Outside is a lawn with tables and chairs. Sandwiches, ploughman's and snacks like baked beans on toast are the only food available, but morning coffee is served, and tea throughout opening hours.

Brewery: Free house
Licensee: E M Pittard
Opening hours: 11.30am-2.30pm, 5.30-11pm (Fri, Sat and BHs 11am-11pm); Sun 12-3pm, 7-10.30pm
Bar food: As opening hours
Children: Welcome anywhere

Down on the Farm

Cider has been drunk in Britain since before Roman times and was originally made of fermented crab apple juice. Farmers made their own, especially in the West Country, and by the 17th century about 350 varieties of cider apple tree were cultivated, with names like Redstreak and Kingston Black, Sweet Coppin and Handsome Maud.

The basic process of cider-making is to crush apples in a press, run off the juice and leave it to ferment naturally in casks for four months or so. The Industrial Revolution, however, transferred cider from the farm to the factory and by the 1960s the major producers were following the same path as the brewers and efficiently turning out a standardised product - weak, sweet and fizzy - that had only a distant resemblance to the powerful 'rough cider' or 'scrumpy' of earlier days. Fortunately, a draught cider renaissance has followed in the wake of the real ale revival, and one of the Campaign for Real Ale's aims is to prevent the disappearance of rough cider and perry.

⊜ HOOD ARMS
Kilve, near Bridgwater TA5 1EA. Tel 027874 210

Kilve

Particularly popular with the over-35s, this 17th-century pub enjoys a friendly atmosphere in its two comfortable bars and garden. Boddingtons, Flowers and Whitbread are on sale, as well as a large selection of whiskies, and bar food is served, including scrumpy pork casserole and spinach and garlic lasagne, both at £4.50, and home-made sweets at £1.60. The separate restaurant, with its own menu, is open in the evenings in the latter half of the week. Three double rooms and two singles with twin beds are available, comfortably furnished in cottage style.

Brewery: Free house
Licensee: C R Rutt
Opening hours: 10.30am-2.30pm, 6-11pm; Sun 12-2pm, 7-10.30pm
Bar food: 12-2pm, 6.30-10pm; Sun 12-1.30pm, 7-9.30pm
Restaurant: Wed-Sat 7-9pm
Accommodation: (Price per person) single £34, double £28
Children: In restaurant only, and not under seven years
Credit Cards: Access, Visa

⊜ RISING SUN
Knapp,, near North Curry TA3 6BG. Tel 0823 490436

Knapp

Tucked away in a remote village near the walking country of the Somerset Levels, this whitewashed Somerset longhouse offers a warm welcome and a relaxed atmosphere to a mixed bag of customers. Dating from 1480, it was a cider house for 200 years and still has its Cider Room. A beamed ceiling, stone walls and two inglenook fireplaces stamp a traditional rural character on the bar, which by way of seating offers benches, cushioned settles and armchairs. Decoration is provided by *Punch* cartoons, prints and horse-brasses. Exmoor Ale, Boddingtons and Bass are on tap, and the wine list offers a choice of 23 bins to complement the constantly changing menu, which specialises in fresh-fish dishes of good quality and representing value for money. A Sunday roast lunch is also served. Jazz or folk can be heard every so often on a Sunday evening, and for those who like to drink outside in warm weather there is a patio, and flower gardens at front and rear.

Brewery: Free house
Licensee: Tony Atkinson
Opening hours: 11.30am-2.30pm, 6.30-11pm; Sun 12-3pm, 7-10.30pm
Bar food: 12-2pm (Sun ploughman's only)
Restaurant: 12-2pm, 7-9.30pm; Sun 12-2pm (roast only)
Children: In Cider Room only; half portions available
Credit Cards: Access, Visa

⊜ THREE HORSESHOES
Langley Marsh, near Wiveliscombe TA4 2UL. Tel 0984 23763

Langley Marsh

Beers like Palmers IPA, Ringwood Best, Shepherd Neame Spitfire Ale and Master Brew, Thompson's Best and Oakhill are among the frequently varied selection of beers in this 17th-century, stone-built pub. Locals and business people mingle in the bar, with its stone flags, cushioned settles, open fires, nicknacks and pictures of cars and planes,

Brewery: Free house
Licensee: J Hopkins
Opening hours: 12-2.30pm, 7-11pm: Sun 12-3pm, 7-10.30pm
Bar food: As opening hours
Children: Welcome anywhere

in a relaxed atmosphere which is helped along by piped jazz and, on some evenings, live improvised music. All home-cooked, the food includes starters such as garlic mushrooms at £2.90, main courses like Somerset fish pie at £4.95 and courgette and mushroom bake at £3.95, as well as a selection of puddings at £1.85. Outdoor seating is provided on the veranda and in the garden, where there are children's playthings.

away from bar if well behaved; outdoor play area

ROYAL OAK
Luxborough, near Watchet TA23 0SH. Tel 0984 40319

Luxborough

Its appealing situation, tucked away in a secluded valley, ensures that this 18th-century pub enjoys a good trade. The clientele consists of regulars willing to travel some distance and, particularly in summer, discerning tourists, while the enclosed garden is ideal for visitors with children. Stone-built and L-shaped, the cottage-like pub has two unspoilt bars with simple rustic furniture and a floor of slate flags, and two double rooms are available upstairs. Exmoor Gold, Bateman XXXB, Cotleigh Tawny Bitter and Flowers IPA are on sale, as well as a choice of local ciders. Bar food is served, and includes pâté at £3.25 and beef and Beamish pie at £4.45. Alternatively, there is a separate restaurant menu and wine list, with starters such as king prawns and cucumber at £5.65 and main courses like leg of lamb at £8.85 and fillet of pork at £9.25. On Tuesday evenings there is a quiz and on Fridays folk music can be heard.

Brewery: Free house
Licensee: Robin Stamp
Opening hours: 11am-2.30pm, 6-11pm; Sun 12-3, 7-10.30pm
Bar food: 12-2pm, 7-10pm (Sun 9.30pm)
Restaurant: Times as bar food
Accommodation: (Price per person) £13
Children: In restaurant only

NOTLEY ARMS
Monksilver, near Taunton TA4 4JB. Tel 0984 56217

Monksilver

A good selection of beers, wholesome home cooking and soft classical music combine to produce a relaxed atmosphere in this beamed pub. The well-assorted clientele can choose from Ushers Best, Theakston Best, Wadworth 6X and Ruddles County, or sample the local fruit wines. Good value for money, the food includes pitta bread, cheese and salad at £1.95, home-made pasta at £3.75 and traditional-style lamb casserole with dumplings at £4.50. Among the sweets on offer are treacle tart and fresh fruit crumble, both at £1.95. A collection of old plates, local paintings and a wood-burning stove lend a homely feel to the large bar, a separate family room is available and trestle tables are set out in the garden.

Brewery: Grand Metropolitan
Licensees: Sarah and Alistair Cade
Opening hours: 11.30am-2.30pm, 6.30-11pm; Sun 12-2.30pm, 7-10.30pm
Bar food: 12-2, 7-9.30 (Sun 9pm)
Children: Welcome anywhere away from the bar if eating; family room

KINGS ARMS INN
Bishopston, Montacute, near Yeovil TA15 6UU. Tel 0935 822513

Montacute

Families, business people and a large proportion of older customers make up the clientele of this village-centre pub. Stone-walled and traditional in style - the pub dates from 1545 - the carpeted bar is nevertheless comfortable, while the lounge, with its sofas and tables, has the feel of a hotel. Outside are a patio with tables and a lawn with further seating. Worthington and Bass are the beers on offer, and there is a comprehensive choice of wines to accompany the food. In addition to bar meals, a cold buffet is served, with a large selection costing £5.10 and a small £4.10. Regularly revised, the à la carte menu includes starters such as avocado turnover at £2.50 and main courses like breast of duck at £11.60 and fresh local veal at £12.40. Eight double and three twin rooms are available.

Brewery: Free house
Licensee: S D Price
Opening hours: 11am-2.30pm, 6-11pm; Sun 12-2pm, 7-10.30
Bar food: 12-2pm, 7.30-9.30pm
Restaurant: Times as bar food
Accommodation: (Price per room) single £46, double £64
Children: Welcome anywhere away from bar
Credit Cards:
AMERICAN EXPRESS® Access, Visa, Diners

GEORGE INN
Norton St Philip, near Frome BA3 6LH. Tel 0373 834224

Norton St Philip

Erected in 1223 to house wool and cloth merchants trading with nearby Hinton Priory, this evocative, village-centre pub has served as an inn for the past six centuries. Built of stone and wood, it has an imposing half-timbered and galleried courtyard, mullioned windows, a massive oak door set beneath a stone porch and an external Norman stone stair-turret. A mixed clientele, united by a fascination with the character of the place, frequents the main bar, which is furnished in traditional style with settles and substantial tables, and the lounge, which is beamed and oak-panelled. Bass and Wadworth 6X and Old Henry's IPA are on offer, along with food which includes starters like snails at £3.50 and goujons of plaice at £3 and main courses like fillet steak at £10.50 and Dover sole at £12.50.

Brewery: Wadworth
Licensee: M Moore
Opening hours: 10am-3pm, 5-11pm; Sun 12-3pm, 7-10.30pm
Bar food: 12-2.30pm, 6.30-10pm; Sun 7-10pm
Restaurant: 12.30-2pm, 7-10.30pm; Sun 12-3pm
Children: In restaurant and separate room away from bar only; half portions available
Credit Cards:
AMERICAN EXPRESS®, Access, Visa, Diners

ROYAL OAK
Over Stratton, near Petherton TA13 5LQ. Tel 0460 40906

Over Stratton

A large, well equipped play area with a trampoline and a children's assault course as well as seating, draws families to this village pub, although it attracts a mixed clientele. Alternative outdoor seating is available on the patio and the gravelled sitting-out area. A stone and thatch building, formerly three cottages, the pub was built 400 years ago and the two spacious bars retain great character, with their exposed beams, rough walls, flagstone floor and granite

Brewery: Hall & Woodhouse
Licensee: Lyn Holland
Opening hours: 12-2.30pm, 7-11pm; Sun 12-2.30pm, 7-10.30pm
Bar food: 12-2pm, 7-10pm
Restaurant: Times as bar food (Sun 9.30pm)

bar tops. The beers are Badger Best, Tanglefoot and Hard Tackle, all brewed by Hall & Woodhouse, and there is a wide choice of malt whiskies and a wine list of over 100 bins from all around the world. Inventive starters are on offer, such as pineapple and prawns at £4.95 and frogs' legs in Pernod sauce at £5.25, while main courses include veal escalopes in Calvados at £11.95 and Neptune's platter at £13.95.

Children: In dining room only; children's menu available; outdoor play area
Credit Cards: Access, Visa

⊕ NEW INN
Priddy, near Wells BA5 3BB. Tel 0749 676465

Priddy

The highest pub in Somerset, this stone-built village inn combines a main part from the 17th century with a farmhouse some 200 years older and a Lounge added in the 1970s. The latter, with a stone and carpeted floor, offers seating on upholstered benches and plain wooden chairs, while the inner bar, with a fine old fireplace, has padded benches. Locals, retired folk and business people make up the clientele, and can choose between Wadworth 6X, Marston's Pedigree and Eldridge Pope Thomas Hardy Country Bitter, or enjoy a meal in the dining room, perhaps with a bottle of wine from the good list. Among a number of dishes incorporating the local speciality are lamb's liver marinated in cider and pork chops with cream and cider. Also served are vegetarian dishes and traditional sweets like Spotted Dick. In front of the pub a terrace looks on to the green, while at the rear there is a garden where children can play. Six double rooms are available, each neat and furnished simply.

Brewery: Free house
Licensee: Douglas Weston
Opening hours: 11.30am-2.30pm, 7-11pm; Sun 12-2.30pm, 7-10.30pm
Bar food: 12-2pm, 7-10pm (Sun 9.30pm)
Accommodation: (Price per room) single £18.50, double £29.50
Children: In dining room only; outdoor play area.

✇ FULL MOON
Rudge, near Frome BA11 2QF. Tel 0373 830936

Rudge

At one time a cider house, this 17th-century pub, despite being extended in recent years, retains considerable character thanks to its small, cottage-style rooms and stone floor. In addition to the bar there is a spacious new restaurant and two other dining areas where bar-style meals are served, one of which doubles as a family room (food is not served in the main bar). Bass, Butcombe and Wadworth 6X are served to an assorted clientele, who can also enjoy a snack or a main course like tortellini or cod hot pot, both at £3.25, and on Sundays, when the Carvery is in action, a traditional roast at £3.95. Skittles and shove halfpenny are available and on Sunday evenings during the winter country music can be heard. A small front garden and a sheltered garden at the rear provide an alternative to eating and drinking inside. Six comfortably furnished double rooms are available.

Brewery: Free house
Licensee: Pat Gifford
Opening hours: 11am-3pm, 6-11pm; closed Mon lunchtime; Sun12-3pm, 7-10.30pm
Bar food: 12-2.30pm, 6.30-9.30pm; Sun sittings at 12 and 1.45pm
Accommodation: (Price per room) single £25, double £36
Children: In family room only; half portions available; outdoor play area

GREYHOUND
Staple Fitzpaine, near Taunton TA3 5SP. Tel 0823 480227

Staple Fitzpaine

A good choice of beers - Flowers IPA and Original, Marston's Pedigree, Exmoor Ale and Boddingtons is served in this creeper-covered village pub. It was constructed in1640 by a local lord as a hunting lodge, and its traditional character survives in the flagstone floor, stone walls with partial wood panelling and solid wooden tables. A mixed clientele frequents the two bars, which are freshened by flowers and candles and have log fires in the winter. In warmer weather a few seats are set out in the gravelled stable yard at the side of the pub, while for children there is a climbing frame, a slide and a Wendy house. Bar billiards, darts and skittles are on offer, and on Thursday evenings live blues can be heard. Meals are served in the restaurant and bar - for example, fresh crusty mushrooms at £2.75 and, both at £7.25, grilled local farm trout and medallions of pork. The restaurant offers charcoal grills in the evening and a special written menu on Sundays. On Wednesday evenings a candlelit set meal, at £15.95 for two, is served in the bar.

Brewery: Free house
Licensee: Steven Watts
Opening hours: 11am-3pm, 5-11pm; Sun 12-3pm, 7-10.30pm
Bar food: 12-2pm, 7-10pm
Restaurant: Times as bar food
Children: Welcome anywhere; outdoor play area
Credit Cards: Access, Visa

Tried and True
England's only brewery with a stretch of thatched roof has been producing good beer since 1794 and is little changed outwardly since then. It stands where two streams, the Asker and the Brit, join forces at Bridport in Dorset, and has been run by the Palmer family since 1896. They like the tried and true, and for more than 60 years until his death in his 80s in 1987 employed the same pub sign artist, George Biles. The pubs are mostly in Dorset and Devon.

⊜ ROSE AND CROWN
Wood Hill, Stoke St Gregory, near Taunton TA3 6EW. Tel 0823 490296

Stoke St Gregory

Two talking points of this 300-year-old village pub are Bonnie, a ghost dressed in grey with a bonnet, and a 60ft well in use in the bar until 1948 and rediscovered in 1982. But equally interesting is the food, with its emphasis on fresh fish. Home-cooked bar meals like whole plaice and grilled skate wings, both at £4.95, are served, as well as non-fish dishes like scrumpy chicken at the same price. The separate restaurant offers items like seafood risotto and nut roast at £5, and on Sundays there is a set lunch at £7. Two house wines bottled by Eldridge Pope feature on the wine list. Beers on sale in the low-beamed bar, which is hung with paintings by the landlord, include the same brewery's Royal Oak and Thomas Hardy Country Bitter, Exmoor Ale and Bass Toby Bitter. A mixed clientele of regulars, families and business people enjoys a pleasant atmosphere which is helped along by unobtrusive classical music and, on Saturday evenings, a pianist. One double and two twin rooms are available. To the front of the pub there is a pretty terrace with seating.

Brewery: Free house
Licensees: Ron and Irene Browning
Opening hours: 11am-2.30pm, 7-11pm; Sun 12-2.30, 7-10.30pm
Bar food: 12-2pm, 7-10pm
Restaurant: Times as bar food
Accommodation:(Price per room) single £18.50, double £34
Children: In restaurant only; half portions available
Credit Cards: Access, Visa

Shades and Grades

A distinction between beer and ale used to be drawn centuries ago. Ale was the old British brew made without hops. Not until the 15th century did the use of hops spread to Britain from the Continent and the suspect, newfangled, bitterer drink was called beer. Ale is no longer made and the two words are now used indiscriminately. Bottled beer is distinguished from draught beer from a cask, keg or tank, but a more useful dividing line may be the one between real ale, which matures in the cask, and keg or bottled beer that does not.

Bitter is the classic British draught beer, brewed with plenty of hops.

Mild, less heavily hopped and less sharp in taste, is most often found in the Midlands and the North West of England.

Old ale usually means stronger mild, matured longer.

Light ale or pale ale is bottled beer of a lightish colour.

Lager is lighter and blander still, in a bottle or on draught. Brewed in Germany originally, it now accounts for more than half the beer sold in Britain.

Brown ale is a darker, richer bottled beer, and porter is richer still.

Stout is the blackest and richest of all.

Strong ale or barley wine has a higher alcohol content than the others, or should have.

⊕ ROYAL OAK INN
Withypool, near Minehead TA24 7QP. Tel 064383 236

Withypool

With its decoration of hunting prints and stags' heads, this 300-year-old moorland pub, stone-built and slate-roofed, has something of the atmosphere of a hunting lodge. Hunting and shooting types, walkers and tourists mingle in the beamed lounge, with its comfortable wall benches and raised log fire, and in the simply furnished Rod Room bar, which likewise has a welcome open fire. Further tables are set out on the raised flagstone patio. Ushers Best, Exmoor Ale and Webster's are the beers, and the bar food, in addition to blackboard specials, includes dishes such as red mullet at £5.75, snails at £6 and duck at £9. The restaurant offers a daily changing set menu, with three courses at £19 and four at £21. Eight rooms are available - seven double and one twin.

Brewery: Free house
Licensees: M Bradley and T Lucas
Opening hours: 11-2.30pm, 6-11pm; Sun 12-2.30pm, 7-10.30pm
Bar food: 12-2pm, 6.30-9.30pm; Sun 12-1.30pm, 7-9pm
Restaurant: 7-9pm
Accommodation: (Price per person) £30
Children: Not permitted under 14 years in bar
Credit Cards:
AMERICAN EXPRESS® Access, Visa, Diners

SOUTHERN ENGLAND

Berkshire

❖

Hampshire

❖

Isle of Wight

❖

Kent

❖

Surrey

❖

Sussex

❖

Wiltshire

❖

BERKSHIRE

⊕ BELL INN
Aldworth, near Reading RG8 9SE. Tel 0635 578272

Aldworth

This pub, established in 1314 and run by the same family for 200 years, makes very few concessions to modernity and yet, despite its age, remains in good condition. In the original, stone-floored taproom can be seen a 300-year-old, one-handed, long-case clock. There is a separate smoke room. An attractive garden, full of roses in summer, backs on to open fields and provides seating at benches and tables. A good choice of beers is on offer - Arkells Bitter and Kingsdown, Hall & Woodhouse Badger Best, Morrell Dark Mild and Hook Norton Best Bitter - but the bar food is rudimentary: hot, crusty rolls with various fillings. People come from far and wide to this fascinating pub - visiting cards from all over the world decorate the wall - but they will be happier if their face fits, since the owner is somewhat forthright.

Brewery: Free house
Licensee: Heather Macaulay
Opening hours: 11am-3pm, 6-11pm; closed Mon, except BHs; Sun 12-3pm, 7-10.30pm
Bar food: As opening hours
Children: Welcome if well behaved

⊕ DEW DROP INN
Honey Lane, Batts Green, near Hurley SL6 6RV. Tel 0628 824327

Batts Green

A secluded woodland setting 1½ miles off the main road makes this 250-year-old pub rather difficult to find. But the regulars, truly a mixed bunch, will confirm that the effort is rewarded by the warm welcome, the quality of dishes like seafood creole at £3.25 and tagliatelle at £4.25, and the overall appeal of the place - not least due to the pleasant furnishings (golf memorabilia reflects the owner's fondness for the game). Brakspear Ordinary and Old are on tap, as are Guinness, Scrumpy Jack and two lagers. The children's play area in the garden is small but makes up for it with a tree swing.

Brewery: Brakspear
Licensee: Michael Morris
Opening hours: 11am-2.30pm, 6.15-11pm; Sun 12-2.30pm, 7-10.30pm
Bar food: 12-2.30pm
Children: Welcome anywhere; outdoor play area

⊕ BELL
Lambourn Road, Boxford, near Newbury RG16 13DD. Tel 048838 721

Boxford

Built in Tudor times, this is a roomy pub with an open fire and an unusual old range in the corner. The bar, which is furnished with settles and chairs, both cushioned, echoes the pub's name with prints of bells and a collection of handbells of various sizes. Outside, a small patio with benches fronts the road, while behind the pub is an attractive garden.

Brewery: Free house
Licensee: Paul Lavis
Opening hours: 11am-2.30pm, 6-11pm; Sun 12-3pm,7-10.30pm
Bar food: As opening hours
Restaurant: Times as bar food

Whitbread Best Bitter, Flowers Original, Boddingtons Bitter and Wadworth 6X are on offer, along with Scrumpy Jack and Red Rock cider, a reasonable list of French and German wines and non-alcoholic wine. Daily blackboard specials complement regular dishes, both of which can be eaten either in the bar or in the small but comfortable restaurant. Eight double and two single rooms are available, all furnished in modern country style. Occasional jazz evenings take place when the races are on at nearby Newbury.

Accommodation: (Price per room) single £32.50 (£56 weekends), double £48 (£68 weekends)
Children: Welcome anywhere; outdoor play area
Credit cards: AMERICAN EXPRESS®, Access, Visa, Diners

CARPENTERS ARMS

Harts Lane, Burghclere, near Newbury RG15 9JY. Tel 0635 27251

Burghclere

A mix of country regulars and business people provides the major part of this pleasant little pub's trade. Dating from the early 19th century, it has a conservatory used as a restaurant at the rear and at one side a patio equipped with garden furniture and beyond that a small garden with benches. Inside there are interesting prints and plates, and in winter there is a welcoming open fire. A good choice of ales is served, among them Morland Old Speckled Hen and Original, Hampshire King Alfred's, Fuller's London Pride and Guinness, while the food embraces sandwiches, blackboard specials and regular dishes.

Brewery: Free house
Licensee: John Evanson
Opening hours: 11am-2.30pm, 6-11pm; Sun 12-3pm, 7-10.30pm
Bar food: 12-1.45pm, 7-9.30pm
Restaurant: 12-2.30pm, 7-9.30pm
Children: Welcome anywhere
Credit cards: Access, Visa

⊛ IBEX

Chaddleworth, near Newbury RG16 0ER. Tel 04882 311

Chaddleworth

High on the list of attractions of this 16th-century pub is a beautiful and tranquil village setting. In addition, it has an interesting link with the world of horse racing, the landlord having been the rider of Desert Orchid. Images of the sport decorate the walls of the three small bars, and one room is devoted to mementoes of the world-renowned 'Dessie'. The pub attracts all types, and beer drinkers among them have the choice of Morland Old Speckled Hen, Original, Old and Keg, plus Guinness. The imaginative, home-cooked menu includes broccoli, Stilton and port soup at £1.95 and chicken livers in mustard and cream sauce at £3.25.

Brewery: Morland
Licensee: Colin Brown
Opening hours: 11.30am-2.30pm (Sat 3pm), 7-11pm; Sun 12-3pm, 7-10.30pm
Bar food: As opening hours but last orders 9.30pm and no food Sun evening
Restaurant: Times as bar food
Children: In family room only; outdoor play area
Credit cards: AMERICAN EXPRESS® Access, Visa

SWAN
East Ilsley, near Newbury RG16 0LF. Tel 063528 238

East Ilsley

This roomy 16th-century coaching inn benefits from a peaceful village location, a pleasant, spacious garden with a slide and a swing and an ample car park. Traditional favourites - for instance, steak and kidney pie and cottage pie, both at £4 - and daily specials can be enjoyed in the bar or the small dining room. To complement the food there is the choice of Morland or Charles Wells beer as well as a selection of popular French and German wines. Country regulars and business people mingle in the bar, where naval pictures, prints and memorabilia recall the owner's time at Portsmouth. The accommodation comprises seven double and three single rooms, all furnished in simple country style.

Brewery: Free house
Licensees: Michael and Jenny Connolly
Opening hours: 10.30am-2.30pm, 6-11pm; Sun 12-3pm, 7-10.30pm
Bar food: 12-2pm, 6.15-10pm (Sun from 7pm)
Accommodation: (Price per room) single £21.50-£32.50, double £42-£49
Children: Welcome anywhere; outdoor play area
Credit cards: Access, Visa

⊕ POT KILN
Frilsham, near Yattendon RG16 0XY. Tel 0635 201366

Frilsham

This secluded, 17th-century pub has been updated without being prettified by the present owners who have been here 12 years (prior to that the pub had been in the same family for 185 years), and so remains a traditional country inn, albeit with a modern emphasis on vegetarian food alongside meat dishes. Of the three bars, one is a small restaurant whose lack of space makes booking necessary. The others are well equipped for winter, one with an open fire, the other with a stove. Locals, visitors, business people and families make up the clientele, and have a choice of Arkells, Morland Bitter or Old Speckled Hen to sup with their meal. Darts and a selection of pub games are to hand, and there is a good chance of a hearty sing-along.

Brewery: Free house
Licensee: Philip Gent
Opening hours: 12-2.30pm, 6.30-11pm; Sun 12-2.30pm, 7-10.30pm
Bar food: 12-1.45pm (rolls to 2pm), 7-9.45pm; Sun and Tue 12-2pm, 7-10pm (rolls only)
Children: Welcome anywhere; outdoor play area

⊕ WHITE HART INN
Hamstead Marshall, near Newbury RG15 0HW. Tel 0488 58201

Hamstead Marshall

This smart, well-run pub has an Italian owner and the cooking of that country is its speciality. Five kinds of fresh pasta are on offer at £6.50, as well as more elaborate dishes, Italian and international - for example, duckling at £12.50 and Dover sole at £14.50. There is also a good wine list. Quietly situated in the heart of the village, the 16th-century building is well cared for and has the benefit of a pretty garden full of roses in summer. A clientele comprising mainly regulars and business people relaxes in a pleasant bar

Brewery: Free house
Licensees: Nicola and Dorothy Aromando
Opening hours: 11.30am-2.30pm, 6.30-11pm; closed Sun and three weeks in Aug
Bar food: As opening hours
Accommodation: (Price per

which serves Wadworth 6X and Hall & Woodhouse beers and is comfortably furnished with cushioned chairs and settles and a log fire in winter. Four double and two single rooms are available, all well furnished in country style.

room) single £35, double £35-£50
Children: Welcome if well behaved
Credit cards:
AMERICAN EXPRESS®, Access, Visa

⊜ BEAR
Bath Road, Hungerford RG17 0EL. Tel 0488 682512

Hungerford

This traditional country pub forms part of a sizeable hotel with 38 double and three single rooms. With a small river running through the garden and ducks on the lawn, the 700-year-old establishment is pleasantly situated and quiet, despite being on the main road. The service and the quality of the food - the menu includes goujons of plaice at £5.75, rabbit casserole at £3.85 and turkey, ham and pork pie at £5.25 - are matched by an impressive wine list, rated tenth best in the country. Wines from the list are also served in the comfortable bar, along with Guinness,Wadworth 6X, Bass and Worthington Best Bitter. Like the bar, the attractive, beamed accommodation is furnished with antique pieces. Afternoon tea is served.

Brewery: Free house
General manager: Frank Adams
Opening hours: 11am-3pm, 6-11pm; Sun 12-3pm, 7-11pm
Bar food: 12.30-2pm, 7.30-9.30pm (Fri and Sat 10pm)
Restaurant: Times as bar food
Accommodation: (Price per room) single £65-£95, double £75-£120
Children: Welcome anywhere; outdoor play area
Credit cards:
AMERICAN EXPRESS® Access, Visa, Diners

DUNDAS ARMS
53 Station Road, Kintbury RG15 0UT. Tel 0488 58263/58559

Kintbury

The Kennet and Avon Canal runs beside this picturesque, 200-year-old pub, and pictures of the waterway decorate the bar, which while not large is comfortable. Apart from the location - plenty of tables and chairs are set out invitingly in the small garden by the water's edge - a major attraction for the predominantly business clientele is the wine list, ranging from house wine at £7, through a wide choice in the £40 to£60 bracket, to the most expensive item at £180. Beer drinkers can choose from Morland Original, Eldridge Pope Thomas Hardy and Charles Wells Bombardier. A fairly standard menu is offered in the bar and the separate restaurant, with dishes such as scampi, chips and salad (£5.25) and steak and chips (£10.50). Pudd ings include chocolate brandy cake and summer pudding. Five rooms are available as either single or double accommodation.

Brewery: Free house
Licensee: David A Dalzell-Piper
Opening hours: 11am-2.30pm, 6.30-11pm; Sun 12-2.30, 7-10.30pm
Bar food: As opening hours (except all day Sun and Mon evening)
Restaurant: Times as bar food
Accommodation: (Price per room) £55-£65
Children: Welcome anywhere
Credit cards:
AMERICAN EXPRESS ® Access, Visa

⊜ SWAN
Lower Inkpen, near Hungerford RG15 0DX. Tel 0488 668326

Lower Inkpen

Dating from the 17th century, this pub is blessed with a peaceful situation in the depths of the country. But for some its appeal surely lies in the combination of an imaginative menu - offering, for example, fried prawns in chilli sauce (£7.15), lamb keema (£5.55) and beef rendang (£6.85) as main courses, with starters at around the £4 mark - and a selection of exotic beers such as Tsing Tso from China, Singha from Thailand and Tiger from Singapore, as well as Singapore Slings. For the draught-beer enthusiast, however, there is a reassuring choice of Brakspear Bitter, Worthington, Hook Norton Brewery and Ringwood. Families, regulars and business people mingle in the softly lit bar, which, like the restaurant, gains from having good-quality furniture and decorations. In summer, benches are set out on the flower-filled patio in front of the pub.

Brewery: Free house
Licensee: John Scothorne
Opening hours: 1.30am-2.30pm, 6.30-11pm; closed all day Mon (except BHs) and Tue lunchtime; Sun 12-3pm, 7-10.30pm
Bar food: 12-2pm, 7-9.30pm
Children: Welcome anywhere
Credit cards: Access, Visa, Diners

⊜ BULL
High Street, Sonning RG4 0UP. Tel 0734 693901

Sonning

Although rather cramped inside and tucked away at the end of the high street, this 600-year-old town pub is attractively furnished, with a penny farthing standing in the corner. During the summer it is all the more engaging for a riot of hanging baskets and window boxes. The food, apart from jacket potatoes with various fillings, is basically a cold buffet offering a good choice of cold meats, cheeses and salads - but no sandwiches. Vegetarian meals can be ordered by prior notice. On tap are Whitbread, Brakspear Special, Marston's and Flowers Original. Two double and two single rooms are available, all furnished to an acceptable standard.

Brewery: Whitbread
Licensee: D T Catton
Opening hours: 10am-2.30pm, 5.30-11pm; Sun 12-3pm, 7-10.30pm
Bar food: 12-2pm (no hot food Mon and Sun)
Restaurant: 7-9pm (except Sun and Mon)
Accommodation: (Price per room) £35-£65
Children: Not permitted inside under 14 years

⊜ BULL COUNTRY INN
Stanford Dingley, near Reading RG7 6LS. Tel 0734 744409

Stanford Dingley

A quiet village setting, bar food a cut above the average and a friendly welcome combine to make this pub a real pleasure to visit. Brakspear Ordinary and Bass Charrington IPA are on offer to a well-assorted clientele in the two pleasantly furnished bars. Those so inclined can try their hand at the ancient pub game of Ring the Bull, in which the object is to swing a nose ring on a string over a wall-mounted bull's horn. Tasty, unpretentious and well presented, the

Brewery: Free house
Licensees: Trudi and Patrick Langdon
Opening hours: 12-3pm, 7-11pm; closed Mon lunchtime; Sun 12-3pm, 7-10.30pm
Bar food: As opening hours
Children: Welcome anywhere

food includes French onion soup at £2, shepherd's pie at £3.95 and toffee pudding in butterscotch sauce at £2.10, and there are usually three vegetarian dishes on the menu. Tables and benches are set out in front and on a small lawn to one side of the 15th-century building.

⊜ HARROW
West Ilsley, near Newbury RG16 0AP. Tel 0635 28260

West Ilsley

An imaginative menu, offering sensibly priced country dishes like local rabbit pie with herbs and bacon at £4.25 and venison pie with mushrooms in red wine at £5.25, as well as vegetarian food and home-made bread, draws regulars and business people alike to this attractive pub. The choice of Morland Original, Old Masters and Old Speckled Hen must also have something to do with its appeal. Some 600 years old and situated in the village itself, it is a handsome building, made all the more attractive in summer by window boxes and tubs. The bar is comfortable without being fussy, and there is further seating in the flower-filled garden.

Brewery: Morland
Licensee: Heather Humphreys
Opening hours: 11am-3pm, 6-11pm; Sun 12-3pm, 7-10.30pm
Bar food: 12-2.15pm, 6-9.15pm (Sun from 7pm)
Children: Welcome anywhere
Credit cards: Access, Visa

⊜ ROYAL OAK
The Square, Yattendon, near Newbury RG16 0UF. Tel 0635 201325

Yattendon

The most impressive feature of this 400-year-old pub facing the village square is undoubtedly the restaurant, among the best in the area and boasting an extensive list of wines from France, Germany, Italy, Spain, Australia, the USA and Chile ranging from £12 to £175. High-quality ingredients, good cooking and friendly and efficient service justify prices such as £7.50 for half a dozen Loch Fyne oysters, £11.95 for grilled calves' liver and bacon and £10.50 for half a guinea fowl in red wine sauce. Apart from the restaurant, the well-heeled clientele can avail themselves of a comfortable bar with cushioned settles and chairs, side rooms with additional tables and chairs or, weather permitting, the attractive garden with its profusion of flowers. There is occasional live entertainment. Beer drinkers' needs are catered for by Guinness, Wadworth 6X, Adnams Bitter and Hall & Woodhouse Tanglefoot, plus a range of draught and bottled lagers. Five double rooms, one of which is the charming Bridal Room, and five singles are available. The rooms are furnished to a high standard.

Brewery: Free house
Licensee: Mr O Williams and Miss J Huff
Opening hours: 11am-3pm. 6.30-11pm; Sun 12-3pm, 7-10.30pm
Bar food: 12-2.00pm, 7-10pm; Sun 12-2pm, 7.30-9.30pm
Restaurant: 12-2.00pm, 7-10pm; Sun 12-2pm only
Accommodation: (Price per room) single £60-£70, double £70-£80
Children: Welcome anywhere
Credit cards: AMERICAN EXPRESS® Access, Visa, Diners

HAMPSHIRE

MILBURYS
Beauworth, near Cheriton SO24 0PB. Tel 0962 771248

Beauworth

A choice of 80 wines and 15 country wines, as well as a range of draught beers that includes John Smith's Yorkshire Bitter, Courage Directors, Gale's HSB, King Alfred's Hampshire Bitter and Ruddles County, is listed by this unique, characterful pub. Two open fires warm the bar, with its flagged floor and old wooden tables, while the Wheel Room - which features the original waterwheel and a covered 300ft well - boasts a minstrels' gallery that can seat 20 people. Dishes on a regularly changing specials board offer snacks and salads alongside main dishes like grilled salmon and vegetables at £5.95 and puddings such as apple and raspberry crumble at £2.95, vegetarians and children both being catered for. The pub's isolated position, high on downland, commands extensive views of Hampshire's rolling countryside which make the large garden's picnic tables popular during the summer months. One double bedroom in rustic style is available for the use of overnight guests.

Brewery: Free house
Licensees: Jan and Len Larden
Opening hours: 10.30am-2.30pm, 6-11pm; Sun 12-3pm, 7-10.30pm
Bar food: 12-2pm, 7-10pm
Restaurant: 12-2pm, 7-10pm; Sun set lunch at 12 and 1.30pm, 7.30-9.30pm
Accommodation: (Price per person) single £28.50, double £38.50
Children: Not permitted in main bar; outdoor play area
Credit Cards:
AMERICAN EXPRESS®, Access, Visa

SUN
Bentworth, near Alton GU34 5JT. Tel 0420 62338

Bentworth

This delightful unspoiled country pub dating from 1635 is not easy to find, set as it is beside a lane just outside the straggling village. Here, an across-the-board clientele congregates to enjoy a range of draught beers that includes Bass, Wadworth 6X, Courage Best, Ruddles and Marston's Pedigree, plus regular guest beers; a good choice of Gale's country wines is also featured. Very good meals, well cooked and attractively presented, offer imaginative dishes like sweet and sour chicken (£6.50) or fillet pork Stroganoff (£7.50) alongside the more mundane - but, nevertheless, good - beef stew or ham, egg and chips at £5.50, and there will always be something suitable for vegetarians. Pleasant bar areas with wood-burners, brick and wooden floors and low, beamed ceilings are adorned with an effectively natural accumulation of bric-à-brac and furnished with large, kitchen-style tables bearing vases of flowers. Limited outside seating is available.

Brewery: Free house
Licensees: Richard and Jan Beaumont
Opening hours: 12-3pm, 6-11pm; Sun 12-3pm, 7-10.30pm
Bar food: 12-2pm (2.30pm Sat), 7-9.30pm
Children: Not permitted inside and no garden

Country Matters

Country occupations and pursuits provide many inns with their names. The Wheatsheaf, the Barley Mow, the Haywain, the Dun Cow, the Heifer, the Plough (sometimes the constellation) and the Harrow recall the farming year's immemorial round. Horses, long essential to agriculture, communications and sport, figure frequently - the Black Horse, the Nag's Head, the Grey Mare and many more. The Bull and the Bear are often related to the once popular sport of baiting the animals with dogs. The Dog is usually a sporting dog and hunting has supplied many names, from the Fox and Hounds and the Hare and Hounds to numerous deer (also from heraldry), including the Stag and Hounds, the White Hart and the Roebuck. There are signs related to angling, too, such as the Angler and the Trout, and there are Jolly Cricketers and even Jolly Farmers.

⚘ THREE HORSESHOES
Bighton, near Alresford SO23 9RE. Tel 0962 732859

Bighton

Visitors to this delightful country inn, set back from a quiet lane in the village centre, are assured of both a warm welcome and good service from its ex-policeman landlord. First referred to as an ale house in 1615, it stood beside an old coaching route, providing refreshment for weary travellers; today, however, it meets the needs of a clientele of local regulars, serving Scrumpy Jack cider, a choice of lagers and a range of draught beers from Gale's. The brewery's country wines are also available. Small, simply furnished but comfortable bars - the tiny, carpeted Lounge Bar having an open fire and the Public Bar being fitted with a wood-burner - display rural tools and traps alongside a few police mementoes. Entertainment is limited to the traditional darts, dominoes, cards and shove halfpenny, accompanied by piped musak, while bar snacks are modest, nothing more elaborate than chilli, quiche or ham and eggs with chips (all at £3) augmenting the basic sandwiches, rolls and ploughman's ranging from £1 to £2.50. Picnic benches are provided on a sheltered, peaceful lawn to one side of the pub.

Brewery: Gale's
Licensees: Arthur and Norma Hayward
Opening hours: 11am-2.30pm, 6-11pm; Sun 12-2pm, 7-10.30pm
Bar food: 12-2pm (except Sun) only
Children: Welcome lunchtime and early evening (if well behaved)

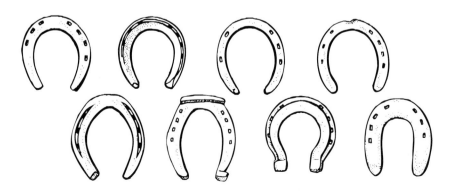

⊛ RED LION
Boldre, near Lymington SO41 8NE. Tel 0590 673177

Boldre

An old cart decked with flowers stands outside this well-modernised 17th- century pub - once three houses but mentioned as an ale house as long ago as Domesday Book - in the village centre opposite the green; a characterful stable area retains much of the atmosphere of the original buildings. Two peaceful bars, free of music or any other entertainment and adorned with old household items, provide a pleasant dining venue where reliable dishes include farmhouse soup at £2, vegetable casserole at £4.50 and partridge in white wine at £8.50 as well as ploughman's (£3.50) and sandwiches (from £2). The choice of draught beers is restricted to Eldridge Pope Hardy Country, Royal Oak and Dorchester Bitter. Outdoor seating is provided on a patio at the side of the building, and there is a pleasant lawned area to the rear.

Brewery: Eldridge Pope
Licensees: John and Penny Bicknell
Opening hours: 10am-3pm, 6-11pm; Sun 12-3pm, 7-10.30pm
Bar food: 11am-2.30pm, 6-10.30pm; Sun 12-2pm, 7-10pm
Children: Not permitted inside
Credit Cards: Access, Visa

FOX Bramdean *see page 85*

⊛ FIVE BELLS
High Street, Buriton, near Petersfield GU31 5RX. Tel 0730 263584

Buriton

This 16th-century brick and stone pub is set above the main lane of the attractive South Downs village of Buriton; outdoor seating is provided on the terrace and on a lovely lawn where trellises bear vines and climbing roses. Charmingly refurbished bars, with open fires and pine furniture, offer not only the old-fashioned pastimes of darts, cards, dominoes and board games but also a relaxing background of piped music - except for live jazz once a month and folk, country and western each Wednesday. A mixed clientele, including walkers from the South Downs Way, can enjoy draught Murphy's, Friary Meux Best, Tetley Bitter, Ballard's Best, Ringwood Old Thumper and Burton Ale, but many come primarily to dine - the wide-ranging menu supplemented by blackboard specials offering something to suit most tastes, including a good vegetarian choice. Excellent fish dishes (trout with almonds or salmon steak with prawns and chives, for example, both at £7.50) are worthy of note.

Brewery: Free house
Licensees: John and Oliver Ligertwood
Opening hours: Summer 11am-11pm; winter 11am-2.30pm (Sat 3pm); Sun 12-3pm, 7-10.30pm
Bar food: 12-2pm, 7-10pm (Fri and Sat 6.30pm)
Restaurant: 12-2pm (Sun only), 7-10pm
Children: Permitted in small bar (but not under 14 years) if permission asked
Credit Cards: Access, Visa

⊜ FOX
Bramdean, near Alresford SO24 0LP. Tel 0962 771363

Bramdean

With a wine list of some 31 bins, this popular dining pub set beside the A272 on the edge of the village is less strong on draught beverages, Strongbow cider, Stella Artois and Heineken lager, Guinness, Marston's Pedigree and Best Bitter being the only ones on sale. Imaginative bar food menus - with the emphasis on fresh fish and good vegetables and salads - offer quality home-cooked dishes such as quiche or game pie at £5.50, poached salmon (£5.95) and fresh lobster (£10.95), with at least one vegetarian alternative each day; there is also a good range of starters: grilled sardines or smoked trout mousse, for example, at £3.95, or pâté at £3.50. Though its building dates back to the 17th century, the Fox's bar avoids the self-conscious olde worlde style, being furnished with a comfortable mixture of seating, its walls hung with an assortment of plates, prints and mirrors. The larger part provides a smart eating area, while the small public bar section is lively with electronic games, piped music and the occasional Race Night. A small patio is set with garden furniture, and there are umbrella-shaded benches in the large rear garden.

Brewery: Marston's
Licensee: Jane Inder
Opening hours: 10.30am-3pm, 6-11pm; Sun 12-3pm, 7-10.30pm
Bar food: 12-2pm, 7-9pm (Sun 8.30pm)
Children: Not permitted inside; outdoor play area
Credit Cards:
AMERICAN EXPRESS®, Access, Visa

JOLLY SAILOR
Land's End Road, Bursledon, near Southampton SO3 8RN. Tel 0703 405557

Bursledon

Built around 1700 as a shipbuilder's house - a fact reflected in the carved figureheads that adorn it - the Jolly Sailor stands on the banks of the River Hamble, still serving the boating fraternity who were largely responsible for its transition into a pub. Picnic tables at the water's edge command spectacular views, set on the terrace that runs the length of the building. Businessmen and locals, as well as tourists and yachtsmen, frequent the traditional bars that display nautical bric-à-brac, many attracted by the wide selection of draught beers (Hall & Woodhouse Tanglefoot and Badger Best Bitter, Wadworth 6X, Gale's HSB, Jolly Sailor Bitter and Mauldons Black Adder), but others tempted by a menu of home-cooked bar food with daily changing specials. Fillet steak in red wine or duck breast in Tia Maria sauce are both offered at £9.95, alongside vegetarian options like courgette quiche (£4.85).

Brewery: Hall & Woodhouse
Licensees: Ron and Anne May
Opening hours: 11am-2.30pm, 6-11pm (Sat 11am-11pm); Sun 12-3pm, 7-10.30pm
Bar food: 12-2pm, (Sat 2.30pm) 6.30-9.30pm; Sun 12-2pm, 7-9pm
Restaurant: 7-9.30pm (except Sun)
Children: Welcome in dining area
Credit Cards: AMERICAN EXPRESS®, Access, Visa

RED LION
Chalton, near Horndean PO8 0BG. Tel 0705 592246

Chalton

This beautifully timbered and thatched pub - a typical Hampshire cottage, reputedly built in the 12th century as dwellings for the craftsmen building St Michael's Church - stands at the heart of the quaint village, opposite the lych-gate. Tourists and walkers, as well as businessmen, are attracted to its old-fashioned bars - not least by the range of 50 malt whiskies that augments a choice of draught beers (Gale's Best, Butser Brew and HSB), and a selection of country and fruit wines. A large dining room in the modern extension offers a menu (plus daily changing specials) featuring popular dishes like macaroni cheese (£3.75), pan-fried liver and bacon (£4.65) and steak au poivre (£6.50). Both Public and Lounge Bars are contained in the original building, the high-backed settles of the former providing a perfect foil to the black beams and huge inglenook of what is reputedly the oldest pub in the county.

Brewery: Gale's
Licensee: Michael Gerard McGee
Opening hours: 11am-2.30pm, 6-11pm; Sun 12-3pm, 7-10.30pm
Bar food: 12-2pm, 6.30-9.30pm; Sun 12-2.30 only
Children: Welcome if eating in family dining area
Credit Cards: Access, Visa

FLOWER POTS
Cheriton, near Alresford S024 0QQ. Tel 0962 771318

Cheriton

Guinness, Archers Village Bitter, Hop Back Summer Lightning, Smiles Best Bitter and a guest ale are all available here, and the pub should be offering its own brew by the beginning of 1993. Set back from a quiet lane on the

Brewery: Free house
Licensees: Paul Tickner andJoanna and Patricia Bartlett
Opening hours: 11.30am-

edge of lawns and camping fields, this unspoiled local has been lucky enough to have a long-standing proprietor enthusiastic enough to upgrade its facilities whilst not insensitive to the value of traditional features and a relaxed atmosphere. A simply furnished bar with a tiled floor and a huge open fireplace reflects the building's 19th-century origins as a farmhouse, and old-fashioned games like dominoes, darts, cribbage and shove halfpenny provide appropriate entertainment in these unsophisticated surroundings; the Lounge Bar is more formal, its striped wallpaper, sofa and wall settles reminiscent of a drawing room. Locals, visitors to the area and walkers are attracted by a straightforward menu of honest, home-cooked bar snacks - sandwiches from £1.30, filled jacket potatoes from £1.66 and sweet and sour chicken or beef stew at £3.30 all representing excellent value for money. A renovated barn provides bedrooms which are airy and modern, though cottagey in style, two of them equipped with sofa beds.

2.30pm, 6-11pm; Sun 11.30am-3pm, 7-11pm
Bar food: 12-2pm, 7-9.30pm; Sun 12-2.30pm, 7-9pm
Accommodation: (Price per person) double £18-£22
Children: Welcome in children's room (sofas, books and television); half portions available

Chilbolton

MAYFLY
Chilbolton, Testcombe, near Stockbridge SO20 6AZ. Tel 0264 860283

B uilt 150 years ago as a riverkeeper's cottage, this red-brick pub right by the River Test is extremely popular with an across-the-board clientele. Though the swans still glide majestically by, however, it is not an idyllic setting for contemplation at weekend, both the conservatory extension and outdoor seating often becoming very crowded. While cottagey in style, its rough plastered walls above tongue-and-groove half-panelling hung with bird prints, the bar features both electronic games and piped music, and food - although perfectly acceptable for quality - is of the standard 'look and choose' variety (with either chicken Tandoori or baked sugared ham at £3.40, for example, and a good selection of salads and desserts). An unusual feature is the wide range of cheeses on offer. Six malt whiskies are available, while draught beers include Flowers IPA, Gale's Winter Royal and Brakspear.

Brewery: Whitbread
Licensees: Wayside Inn (managers Barry and Julie Lane)
Opening hours: 11am-11pm; Sun 12-3pm, 7-10.30pm
Bar food: As opening hours
Children: Welcome in dining area and in conservatory
Credit Cards: Access, Visa

Crondall

⊕ CASTLE
Croft Lane, Crondall, near Farnham GU10 5QF. Tel 0252 850892

T his friendly Victorian pub, facing the church on the edge of the village, attracts both regulars and visitors with its enticing menu and peak-condition Fuller's London Pride and ESB. Appetising, well presented and good value for money, typical main courses are swordfish steak at £5, lamb curry

Brewery: Fuller's
Licensee: Kenneth James Tracey
Opening hours: 12-2.30pm, 6-11pm; Sun 12-3, 7-10.30pm
Bar food: 12-2.30pm, 7-9.30pm (except Mon evening)

and nan bread at £4.75 and guinea fowl at £6.50. Scrumpy Jack cider is on sale, as well as a wide range of whiskies. Carpeted and well looked after, the bar is decorated in Victorian style and has a skittle alley, while there is additional seating on the terrace in front of the pub.

Children: Only if eating; outdoor play area

WHITE HORSE
South Hill, Droxford SO23 1PB. Tel 0489 877490

Droxford

At least 500 years old, this coaching inn was originally a courthouse; hangings took place on the beams outside, leaving rumours of ghosts to this day! The pub stands on the edge of Droxford village, beside the A32, its whitewashed brick façade sporting flower baskets - as does the courtyard set with picnic tables behind the building. A complete mix of customers is usually to be found here, though bikers tend to congregate in the Public Bar with its inglenooks, antique furniture and Hogarth prints, while more upmarket clients favour the Lounge area or a third bow-windowed bar. Bass, Morland Old Speckled Hen, Gale's HSB, King & Barnes Sussex Bitter and Wadworth 6X are all on draught, and ten malt whiskies are featured as well as an extensive wine list (including Gale's country wines). Home-cooked bar food menus augmented by specials provide, for example, steak, onion and mushroom pie (£7.15) or salmon (£8.95) followed by sherry trifle or cherry pie (£2). Overnight accommodation comprises two simply furnished rooms in the roof, and one has a half-tester bed.

Brewery: Free house
Licensee: Sidney Higgins
Opening hours: 11am-2.30pm, 6-11pm; Sun 12-3pm, 7-10.30pm
Bar food: 12-2pm, 7-9.45pm
Restaurant: Times as bar food
Accommodation: (Price per room) double £40-£50
Children: Welcome in restaurant and family room; children's menu and half portions available
Credit Cards: Access, Visa

HAMPSHIRE BOWMAN
Dundridge, near Bishops Waltham SO3 1GD. Tel 0489 892940

Dundridge

Set beside a country lane, this unassuming Victorian pub dating from 1860 remains a typically old-fashioned local, its beamed, simply furnished and brick-floored bar providing a delightful atmosphere in which to relax over a game of dominoes, cribbage, shove halfpenny or bar skittles. Draught beers on stillage behind the bar include a guest ale such as Hampshire King Alfred's as well as King & Barnes Sussex and Festive and Archers Village and Golden, a good selection of whiskies and Gale's country wines also being on sale. Value-for-money bar meals are an added inducement, offering sandwiches from £1.50 as well as dishes like chicken curry (£3.95), lasagne (£4.95) or sirloin steak (£6.95); traditional puddings (treacle sponge and custard at £1.95, for example) are also available. The Bowman's name derives from the fact that an area of land used for archery forms part of its grounds.

Brewery: Free house
Licensee: Tim Park
Opening hours: 11am-2.30pm, 6-11pm; Sun 12-3pm, 7-10.30pm
Bar food: 12-2pm, 7-9pm (except Mon); Sun 12-2.30pm only
Children: Permitted in lower part of the bar if not busy; children's menu available; outdoor play area

⊕ FOX
Green Lane, Ellisfield, near Basingstoke RG25 2QW. Tel 0256 381210

Ellisfield

A choice of draught beers including Hall & Woodhouse Badger Best and Tanglefoot, Theakston Old Peculier, Hampshire King Alfred's, Fuller's London Pride, Gale's HSB, Marston's Pedigree, Wadworth 6X and Guinness must figure high among the attractions of this warm, comfortable country pub on the edge of the village. The bar menu is fairly standard, with chilli at £4.50 (very hot), rainbow trout at £6.95 and Scotch fillet steak at £10.95, but dishes are reliably good, well cooked and attractively presented; a vegetarian option is always available, and those requiring something light can choose from a range of snacks and sandwiches. The carpeted main bar is pleasantly uncluttered, with light wood panelling and pine tables, while an open fire, fresh flowers and newspapers add to the relaxed atmosphere. Darts, electronic games and a juke box provide entertainment in the Public Bar, and there is a pleasant garden with bench seats.

Brewery: Free house
Licensees: Ray and Glenys Bull
Opening hours: 11am-2.30pm, 6.30-11pm; Sun 12-3pm, 7-10.30pm
Bar food: 12-2pm, 7-9.30pm (except Mon evening); Sun 12-1.45pm, 7-9pm
Children: Not permitted inside
Credit Cards: Access, Visa

NEW FOREST INN
Emery Down, near Lyndhurst SO43 7D. Tel 0703 282329

Emery Down

A reputation for good, reliable food and efficient but friendly service, combined with an attractive wooded setting on the edge of a New Forest village, make this rambling, smartly painted inn near Lyndhurst popular with local families as well as holidaymakers. Old photographs of the area can be seen on the walls of the busy open-plan bar with its three fireplaces, but electronic games supplement traditional pursuits like darts and shove halfpenny, and modern seating offers an alternative to the older wall benches. Wadworth 6X, Guinness, Flowers Original and Strongs Country Bitter are all available on draught, and a good choice of well presented bar dishes - generously served and including regularly changed specials - features veal à la king, salmon tart in white wine or sauté lamb Provençale (all at £6.75) followed by puddings like strawberry meringue or summer pudding at £2.50. Based on a cottage built in 1710 and extended after the Second World War by the incorporation of the cottages on either side, the inn boasts a very pleasant covered courtyard and peaceful terraced lawns with flower borders and picnic benches; bed and breakfast accommodation can be provided throughout the year.

Brewery: Whitbread
Licensees: Sue and Nick Emberley
Opening hours: 11am-2.30pm, 6-10.30pm (Fri and Sat 11pm); Sun 12-2.30pm, 7-10.30pm
Bar food: 12-2pm, 6-9.30pm; Sun 12-1.30pm, 7-9pm
Accommodation: (Price per person) double room £25-£50
Children: Welcome anywhere; half portions available
Credit Cards: Access, Visa

⊜ JOHN O' GAUNT
Horsebridge, near Stockbridge SO20 6PU. Tel 0794 388394

Horsebridge

Friendly owners offer a warm welcome to this simple rural pub, a whitewashed brick building dating from the 19th century, when it was a railway inn; picnic tables outside take advantage of its setting near the bridge in a hamlet bordering the River Test. Walkers from the Test Way as well as locals are drawn to a simply furnished but comfortable bar which is warmed by two open fires and provides a good choice of generously served, home-cooked bar meals - representing excellent value for money in, for example, filled rolls at 75p, liver and bacon casserole at £3.50 or steak and kidney pie at £4.25, and always including a vegetarian alternative (though there will not necessarily be anything suitable for children). Ringwood Fortyniner, Palmers IPA, Adnams Bitter and Guinness may be obtained on draught to a background of darts and shove halfpenny enlivened by a juke box.

Brewery: Free house
Licensees: Mike and Mary Gilbert
Opening hours: 11.30am-2.30pm (Sat 11am-3pm), 6-11pm;
Sun 12-3pm, 7-10.30pm
Bar food: 12-2pm, 7-9.30pm (except Tue evening)
Children: Not permitted inside

ROYAL OAK
19 High Street, Langstone, near Havant PO9 1RJ. Tel 0705 483125

Langstone

Waterside benches at the front of this 16th-century pub - a white-painted brick building with hanging baskets - enjoy fine views across the landlocked natural harbour; the garden is ideal for children, featuring goats. rabbits, caged birds and a pot-bellied pig and also containing a lovely lawned area with picnic benches. The interior of the building is remarkably unspoiled, the main bar with its flagstones, beams and open log fire augmented by a small room with an old floor of polished pine, a wood-burning stove and a display of paintings of the area (the latter for sale). A range of amusements includes occasional theme evenings. Patrons can enjoy a selection of excellent country wines as well as a range of draught beers which includes Castle Eden Ale, Boddingtons Bitter, Gale's HSB and Flowers Original. A menu with daily changing specials offers such dishes as beef au poivre (£4.75), braised pork in hot chilli sauce (£4.50) and turbot with lemon parsley butter (£9.50); meals are taken in the comfort of a pleasant separate dining area near the food servery.

Brewery: Whitbread
Licensee: Hilary Wallace
Opening hours: 11am-11pm;
Sun 12-3pm, 7-10.30pm
Bar food: 12-2pm (Sat and Sun 2.30pm), 7-9.30pm
Children: Welcome if dining, in areas away from bar; half portions available; interesting garden with animals
Credit Cards: Access, Visa

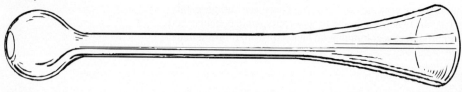

⊕ PLOUGH
Longparish, near Andover SP11 6PB. Tel 0264 72358

Longparish

Part brick-built, part tile-hung and covered with Virginia creeper, this popular dining pub stands at the heart of the village, its secluded garden attractively screened by trellis-work supporting climbing roses and clematis. A combined restaurant and bar in traditional style, displaying hunting prints, brass and copperware, attracts good business trade with its daily changing blackboard menu of home-cooked fare, the selection always offering a vegetarian option as well as excellent pies (served with fresh vegetables) at £4.65, and dishes like Madras curry or fillet of cod in cheese sauce for £4.95; draught beers include Castle Eden Ale, Boddingtons Bitter, Flowers Original and Strongs Country Bitter.

Brewery: Whitbread
Licensees: Carole and Kevin Lockstone
Opening hours: 11am-3pm, 6-11pm; Sun 12-3pm only
Bar food: 11.30am-2.30pm, 7-10.15pm; Sun 12-2.30pm only
Restaurant: Times as bar food
Children: Welcome if eating; half portions available
Credit Cards: Access, Visa

⊕ YEW TREE
Lower Wield, near Alresford SO24 9RX. Tel 0256 389224

Lower Wield

Country regulars and local businessmen alike are attracted to this pleasant rural pub, the original part of which dates back about 300 years. Set in an isolated position beside a country lane, it commands views over open fields from a garden which provides a children's slide and swings as well as bench seating. A narrow-beamed bar with a dartboard, its walls part brick, part plastered, serves Hampshire King Alfred's and Bunces as well as John Smith's Yorkshire Bitter, Stella Artois and Fosters lager and Strongbow cider, and a wide-ranging list offers some 30 wines including examples from the New World. The other bar is primarily a restaurant area, featuring an open fire and beams, and here you can enjoy a range of good-quality dishes in comfort which, though not cheap, are well worth the price. The same menu is also available in the bar and includes steak and kidney pie at £5.35, a bap filled with smoked chicken at £3.50 and escargots baked in garlic and parsley butter at £4.75.

Brewery: Free house
Licensees: Mick and Ann Ferguson
Opening hours: 12-3pm, 6-11pm; Sun 12-3pm, 7-10.30pm
Bar food: 12-2.30pm; 7-9.45pm (except Sun and Mon evenings)
Restaurant: Times as bar food
Children: Welcome anywhere if eating; outdoor play area
Credit Cards: Access, Visa

Jingle Bells

Teams of flower-bedecked Morris dancers, bells a-jingle and handkerchiefs a-flutter, have become a familiar sight outside many a pub as the revival of affection for this ancient pastime or ritual has gathered strength. It had almost completely died out by the 1890s, when the folk-dance enthusiast Cecil Sharp began to record the surviving examples in the Cotswolds. The earliest reference to 'the moreys dance' comes from London in 1458, but it is thought to go much further back, to pagan fertility ritual.

⊕ RED LION
Church Road, Mortimer West End, near Reading RG7 2HU. Tel 0734 700169

Mortimer West End

Dating from 1575, the Red Lion stands on the edge of the village, fronted by a courtyard with picnic tables and window boxes. Inside, the bar is made up of two rooms (the main with exposed brick walls, beamed ceiling and log fire) and a dining area with dark wood tables and old local photographs. Despite the open-plan layout, the atmosphere is intimate and relaxing, backgammon, chess and Sunday night quizzes taking the place of amplified music and electronic games. Draught beers like Hall & Woodhouse Tanglefoot and Badger Best, Gribble Ale and Mauldons Black Adder maintain a loyal following, while reliable bar food features blackboard specials like sirloin with green peppercorn sauce (£10.50) or steak, kidney, oyster and Guinness pie (£6.95), with a vegetarian alternative like vegetable gnocci (£4.95) always available.

Brewery: Free house
Licensee: Sam Hall
Opening hours: 11am-11pm; Sun 12-3pm, 7-10.30pm
Bar food: 12-2pm, 6.30-10pm; Sun 12-2pm, 7-9.30pm
Children: Welcome in dining areas if eating; half portions available
Credit Cards: Access, Visa, Diners

BUSH INN
Ovington, near Alresford SO24 0RE. Tel 0962 732764

Ovington

This old-fashioned pub on the Pilgrims' Way enjoys an idyllic setting close to the gently flowing River Itchen (some of the picnic tables in its tranquil rear garden actually standing beside a stream) in a winding country lane at the edge of the tiny village. A whitewashed cottage exterior fronted by colourful flower beds and festooned with roses and honeysuckle hides softly lit bars with open fires, bottle-green walls and scrubbed tables; here, ranges of malt whiskies and country wines supplement draught beers like Wadworth 6X, Gale's HSB, Flowers Original and Whitbread Pompey Royal. The weekly bar menu offers sandwiches as well as salads (ranging from £4.95 to £8.95) and hot dishes like home-made chilli con carne with crusty bread at £5.50, grilled Itchen trout at £5.95 and sirloin steak with mushrooms at £8.95.

Brewery: Free house
Licensees: G M and S Draper
Opening hours: 11am-2.30pm, 6-11pm; Sun 12-3pm, 7-10.30pm
Bar food: 12-2pm, 6.30-9.45pm; Sun 12-2pm, 7-9pm
Restaurant: 7.30-9.30pm
Children: Permitted at lunchtime only in bottom bar; children's menu available
Credit Cards: Access, Visa

SHIP INN
Owslebury, near Winchester SO21 1LT. Tel 0962 777358

Owslebury

Set beside a quiet country lane on the edge of the village, its tile-hung façade brightened by flower tubs and baskets, this 300-year-old pub boasts a large garden which incorporates a cricket practice area, bowling green and children's play area with swings; rabbits, caged birds and a goat provide additional attractions. Two comfortable beamed

Brewery: Marston's
Licensees: Clive and Angela Mansell
Opening hours: 11am-2.30pm, 6-11pm; Sun 12-2pm, 7-10.30pm
Bar food: 12-2pm, 6-9.30pm; 12-

bars displaying nautical artefacts and cartoons alongside photographs of past cricket XIs feature quiz nights and unusual events throughout the year as well as the more standard pursuits of darts and cribbage. Draught beverages include Strongbow cider, Stella Artois and McEwans lager, Marston's Pedigree and Murphy's, while bar meals - at present limited to a standard pub menu which ranges from jacket potatoes (£2.75) to sirloin steak (£8.50) plus a few specials - should offer an extended range of home-cooked dishes when planned improvements provide a new kitchen.

2pm, 7-10pm
Children: Welcome in early evening if eating; children's menu available; outdoor play area

---

WHITE HORSE
Priors Dean, near Petersfield GU32 1DA. Tel 042058 387

Priors Dean

Known as 'the pub without a name' - there being no sign in the cradle on the nearby road - this low, white-painted building is extremely difficult to find, though the views from its setting deep in the country, on one of the county's highest spots, make the effort worthwhile. First mentioned as a pub in 1620, it has over the years both housed a blacksmith's shop and served as a coaching inn, and its exceptionally charming antique-furnished bars retain a timeless ambience that is very relaxing. In the Edward Thomas Bar (named after the poet who used to drink here until he died in the First World War) a farmhouse chair stands in front of a log fire and the smoke-blackened walls are hung with hunting prints, while in the other room the ticking of a grandfather clock and the gentle motion of two rocking chairs transport the visitor to a bygone age. A choice of country wines augments an excellent range of real ales including Ballard's Best Bitter, King & Barnes Broadwood, Ruddles County, Courage Best and Directors and Theakston Old Peculier. Hearty snacks provide good value for money in hot specials like cottage pie (£3.40) or chicken lasagne (£3.95), a vegetarian alternative always being featured.

Brewery: Free house
Licensee: Jack Eddleston
Opening hours: 11am-2.30pm (Sat 3pm), 6-11pm; Sun 12-3pm, 7-10.30pm
Bar food: 12-2pm only at present
Children: Not permitted inside; outdoor play area

⊜ COACH AND HORSES
The Street, Rotherwick, near Basingstoke RG27 9BG. Tel 0256 762542

Rotherwick

A beer drinker's paradise - offering three regularly changing guest beers as well as nine regulars which include Hall & Woodhouse Badger Bitter, Mauldons Black Adder, Gribble Inn Reg's Tipple and Gribble Ale - this basically unspoiled 300-year-old pub at the centre of the village also serves hand-pumped Taunton Traditional cider as well as the full range of Hofbrau lager on draught. A selection of fairly standard but reasonably priced bar dishes,

Brewery: Free house
Licensee: Ian Wilson
Opening hours: 11am-11pm; Sun 12-3pm, 7-10.30pm
Bar food: 11am-3pm, 6-10pm; Sun 12-2pm (Carvery only), 7-9.30pm
Restaurant: Fri and Sat 7-

in generous portions, includes home-made pizzas at £3, vegetarian samosa at £3.25 and traditional bubble and squeak with cold meat and pickles at £4.25; a separate Carvery operates on Friday and Saturday evenings and at lunchtime on Sundays. No games disturb the three seating areas with their exposed brick walls, slate-tiled and wooden floors and open log fires, the only entertainment being a quiz on Sunday evenings. Outdoor seating is provided at bench tables set on a patio in front of the attractive, creeper-clad building next to the road and car park.

9.45pm; Sun 12-2pm (Carvery)
Children: Welcome in rooms away from the bar
Credit Cards: Access, Visa

WHITE LION
Soberton, near Bishop's Waltham SO3 1PF. Tel 0489 877346

Soberton

Set near the church and opposite the village green, this is a traditional country pub. A 17th-century building, it has a cream-painted façade brightened by flower tubs and hanging baskets; a side patio and secluded rear garden provide outside seating. The wood-floored Public Bar is rustic in style, with a wood-burner and a piano, the Lounge carpeted and decorated with a range of prints and warmed by an open fire; both maintain a tranquil atmosphere - darts being the only entertainment available. A mixed clientele enjoys draught Morland Old Speckled Hen, Wadworth 6X, Marston's Pedigree, Murphy's and Fremlins Bitter, and the restaurant (which caters for functions during the week) offers a Friday and Saturday bar menu of tasty home-cooked dishes which includes some particularly good pasta specialities. A typical meal might include zucchini soup (£1.50), fresh grilled tuna steak (£7.25) and raspberry russe.

Brewery: Whitbread
Licensees: Rod and Joan Johnson
Opening hours: 11am-2.30pm (Sat 3.30pm), 6-11pm; Sun 12-3pm, 7-10.30pm
Bar food: 11am-2.30pm, 6-11pm; Sun 12-2pm, 7-9pm
Restaurant: Fri and Sat only, times as bar food
Children: Welcome in lower lounge area; outdoor play area; half portions available

---

Tudor and Stuart Hostelries

After the closing down of the monasteries, prosperity and increasing travel brought a rise in the number and standards of inns. By Elizabeth I's time there were hostelries big enough to lodge 300 people and their horses. Inns were commercial centres for local merchants and traders, some were 'posthouses' for the developing mail service and in the 17th century smart shops appeared in the largest inns.

The introduction of hops was stoutly resisted. Henry VIII would drink only hopless ale and the brewers were castigated for ruining the traditional drink. Beer brewed with hops kept better for longer, however, which stimulated the development of large-scale breweries and both inns and alehouses gradually gave up brewing their own.

Alehouses were growing steadily less primitive. The main drinking room might still be the kitchen, for warmth. Furniture would be simple - a few trestle tables, benches and stools. As the number of people on the roads grew, alehouses began to offer a night's lodging, though in the poorer ones the traveller might sleep on the kitchen table or in bed with the landlord and his wife. Games were played just outside the house - quoits, skittles, bowls - and customers relieved themselves there too.

HARROW
Steep, near Petersfield GU32 2DA. Tel 0730 262685

Steep

A totally unspoiled rural gem, this tile-hung cottage pub enjoys almost as tranquil a setting now (despite the new A3) as it did when it was built between 400 and 500 years ago - the lane beside which it stands narrowing until it is merely a footpath to the stream. Customers come from far and wide, and it is nearby Bedales School's local. The delightful, secluded garden is bright with flowers in spring and summer, and outdoor seating is provided in front of the building. Attractive wild flower arrangements are a feature of the interior - hops as well as dried flowers adorning the Public Bar with its barrels and huge inglenook fireplace - and photographs of local characters and bygone years hang in both bars; undisturbed by piped music or the noise of electronic games, the only amusements being the traditional ones of cribbage and dominoes, books and newspapers, patrons can enjoy a fairly limited range of draught beers (Strongs Country Bitter, Boddingtons Bitter or Flowers Original). Hearty, wholesome pub food is featured on a menu consisting of soup (£2.10), sandwiches (from £1.60), salads (with cheese at £6 or ham at £7, for example) and a hot dish like lasagne (£4.75). Free range eggs are usually for sale.

Brewery: Free house
Licensee: Edward McCutcheon
Opening hours: 11am-2.30pm (Fri and Sat 3pm), 6-11pm; Sun 12-3pm, 7-10.30pm
Bar food: 12-2pm, 6-11pm (flexible)
Children: Not permitted inside

⊜ FOX
Tangley, near Andover SP11 0RU. Tel 0264 70276

Tangley

This 300-year-old white-painted brick and flint cottage - a pub since 1830 - stands in an isolated position at the fork of two country lanes, flower tubs and hanging baskets brightening its façade. Two bars well furnished in rustic style (both with open fires) serve Guinness, Courage Best, Eldridge Pope Royal Oak and Bass, and an excellent wine list is available. A largely upmarket local and business clientele appreciates the hearty but imaginative home-cooked bar meals, lunches representing particularly good value for money. The menu is augmented by a daily changing specials blackboard detailing such delights as poached salmon with hollandaise sauce or noisettes of lamb in red wine and mustard sauce (both at £8.50), and a vegetarian alternative can always be provided. Children will be served half portions - or an extra plate can be provided so that they may share their parents' meal.

Brewery: Free house
Licensees: Gwen and John Troke
Opening hours: 11am-3pm, 6-11pm; Sun 12-3pm, 7-10.30pm
Bar food: 12-2pm, 6.30-10pm (Sun 7pm)
Restaurant: Times as bar food
Children: Welcome anywhere; half portions available

TICHBORNE ARMS
Tichborne, near Alresford SO24 0NA. Tel 0962 733760

Tichborne

Set in an unspoiled village in the picturesque Itchen valley, this heavily thatched brick building was built at the beginning of the 17th century but not used as a pub until 1939 (the licence at first applying to the barn). Locals and businessmen relax both at the picnic tables in its well kept garden and in the two bars - the smaller wood-panelled and featuring old prints and local history, while the larger sports a darts board and electronic games; both are free of piped music. Courage Best and Directors, Flowers Original, Wadworth 6X, Guinness and Hampshire King Alfred's are all on draught, and the bar menu offers good portions of well prepared home-cooked food which includes daily changing specials such as carbonnade of beef (£4.65) and pork in cider (£4.95) together with vegetarian alternatives. There is a large, informal garden at the back.

Brewery: Free house
Licensees: Peter and Chris Byron
Opening hours: 11.30am-2.30pm, 6-11pm; Sun 12-3pm, 7-10.30pm
Bar food: 12-1.45pm, 6.30-9.45pm; Sun 12-1.30pm, 7-9.30pm
Children: Not permitted inside under 14 years

⊕HODDINGTON ARMS
Upton Grey, near Basingstoke RG25 2RL. Tel 0256 862371

Upton Grey

This is the only pub in the extremely pretty village of Upton Grey and it has gained a reputation for very good, imaginative and fairly priced food. Bar meals include such old favourites as corned beef hash (£3.95) alongside vegetarian alternatives like mushroom Yorkshire pudding with fresh vegetables (also at £3.95) and more adventurous dishes - red bream baked with fresh tomato sauce and Emmental cheese, for example, at £4.25. There is a separate restaurant menu, the main choices in its à la carte selection (priced at £6 to £11) being supplemented by regularly changing specials. A range of Morland draught beers plus a guest beer are served in the pleasant, comfortable, beamed bars; the dining area is carpeted and has an open fire, whereas there are darts and electronic games in the other bar. Bar billiards are an attraction in the separate family room and there is a spacious back garden with a swing tucked away at the far end.

Brewery: Morland
Licensee: Ian Fisher
Opening hours: 11am-2.30pm, 6-11pm; Sun 12-2.30pm, 7-10.30pm
Bar food: 12-2pm, 7.30-9.30pm
Restaurant: Times as bar food; booking necessary for Fri and Sat evening
Children: Permitted in family room only; outdoor play area
Credit Cards: Access, Visa

GEORGE
Vernham Dean, near Andover SP11 0JY. Tel0264 87279

Vernham Dean

Marston's Pedigree, Best Bitter and Mild are served in the busy bars of this unspoiled 16th-century pub at the centre of an idyllic thatched village. There is no separate restaurant, but the range of good-value bar snacks and country dishes is popular with a largely local clientele who enjoy meals like leek and potato soup (£1.50) followed by spiced beef salad (£4) and raspberry and apple pie (£1.50); a blackboard menu allows for daily variations and there is always at least one vegetarian dish. Pleasant first impressions created by the George's fine brick and timber exterior, decked with hanging baskets, will be reinforced by a beamed three-room bar warmed by open fires, comfortably furnished and carpeted and including a huge inglenook with seating inside. Outdoor seating is provided both in front of the attractive building and in a sheltered garden to its rear.

Brewery: Marston's
Licensees: Philip and Mary Perry
Opening hours: 11am-2.30pm
(3pm Sat), 6-11pm; Sun 12-3pm,
7-10.30pm
Bar food: 12-2pm, 7-9pm; Sun
12-1.45pm only
Children: Well behaved children
welcome in family room

CHEQUERS INN
Well, near Odiham RG25 1TL. Tel 0256 862605

Well

Boddingtons, Brakspear, Wadworth 6X, Flowers Original and Murphy's are the beers on sale in this white-painted, roadside pub, whose regulars include a fair number of well-heeled youngsters and which becomes very busy at weekends. Traditional in style, with beams, wooden flooring, tongue-and-groove-clad walls, an inglenook fireplace and pine tables, the bar is supplemented by a Continental-style seating area in front of the pub, beneath an overhanging vine which supplies wine for cooking purposes. The garden at the back overlooks farmland. Among the appetising blackboard specials are moules at £4.50, lamb stew at £5.75 and seafood lasagne at £4.95, while the quieter, wood-panelled restaurant offers a set meal at £18.50 per person and a good wine list, with last orders at 9pm (you can stay as long as you like).

Brewery: Free house
Licensees: Hugh Stanford and
Christopher Phillips
Opening hours: 11am-3pm,
5.30-11pm; Sun 12-3pm,
7-10.30pm
Bar food: 12-2.30pm, 7-10pm
Restaurant: 7.30-12.30pm
(except Sun)
Children: Welcome anywhere
Credit cards: Access, Visa

⊕ CARTWHEEL
Whitsbury, near Fordingbridge SP6 3PQ. Tel 07253 362

Whitsbury

Five real ales - Arkell's 3B, Eldridge Pope Thomas Hardy Country, Adnams Broadside, Smiles Exhibition and Ash Vine Bitter - are available on draught here, as well as Addlestone cider, a good choice of lagers and a range of country wines. A bar of character (where an old steam engine wheel divides the Public with its traditional games and simple wall-bench seating from the main area) sports

Brewery: Free house
Licensee: Jeanie McGragham
Opening hours: 11am-2.30pm,
6-11pm; Sun 12-3pm, 7-10.30pm
Bar food: 12-2pm, 7-9.30pm
Restaurant: 7.30-9.30pm
Children: Permitted in restaurant

prints and photographs of race horses, reflecting the proximity of the racing stables made famous by Desert Orchid, and the menus featured here and in the intimate dining room are both extensive and reliable. Sandwiches begin at £1.40, ploughman's at £2.20 and jacket potatoes at £2.90, while a more formal meal might follow a starter like Dorset liver pâté (£2.90) or seafood au gratin (£3.60) with chilli (£4.50), steak and kidney pudding (£4.70) or vegetarian alternatives always provided; the Cartwheel Special (a 12in deep pan pizza) provides a main course for two.

area only; outdoor play area
Credit Cards: Access, Visa, Diners

WYKEHAM ARMS
35 Kingsgate Street, Winchester SO23 9PE. Tel 0962 853834

Winchester

A fine 250-year-old brick building on a cobbled street at the heart of old Winchester, near the famous school and cathedral, the Wykeham Arms has an excellent reputation for good food and quality wines (about 22 of them available by the glass). The daily changing blackboard menu offers steaks from £9.50 as well as an imaginative range of well cooked and stylishly presented dishes like breast of duck with a ginger and plum glaze (£10.95) or pan-fried calves' liver with lime and sage butter (£10.75), and there is always a vegetarian option. Two characterful bars - originally a coach-house and the old college watchmaker's shop - attract businessmen, dons and clergy alike with their open fires and collected items of local interest; draught beers include Guinness, Eldridge Pope Dorchester Bitter, Thomas Hardy Country Bitter and Royal Oak, and patrons are assured of a warm welcome from the enthusiastic landlord. Tucked behind the building are a sheltered courtyard and a small garden, both offering outdoor seating for warmer days. Accommodation is provided in individually decorated, stylish bedrooms equipped with modern facilities and such thoughtful extras as fresh fruit and magazines.

Brewery: Eldridge Pope
Licensees: Graeme and Anne Jameson
Opening hours: 11am-11pm; Sun 12-3pm, 7-10.30pm
Bar food: 12-2.30pm, 6.30-9pm (except Sun)
Accommodation: (Price per room) single £59.50, double £69.50
Children: Not permitted under 14 years inside

Darts

Although darts is now regarded as the archetypal pub game, its history is shrouded in almost total obscurity and it may not have entered the pub scene until well into the 19th century. The original board may have been the end of a barrel, with the doubles ring as its outer rim. The accepted arrangement of numbers round the rim dates from the 1890s, but there are variant types of board in different areas of the country. The Yorkshire board, for instance, has no trebles ring. Nor does the Lancashire or Manchester board, which has a very narrow doubles ring and is customarily kept soaked in beer when not in use. The media did not become interested in darts until after the First World War and not until the 1970s did television take it up.

ISLE OF WIGHT

WIGHT MOUSE INN
Chale PO38 2HA. Tel 0983 730431

Chale

This pub is part of the Clarendon Hotel, a former 17th-century coaching inn with superb sea views. The large, rambling bar is decorated with plates, prints and photographs, musical instruments, farming implements, oars and walking sticks. This is very much a family pub, with a play area and a pets' corner in the garden, regular Punch and Judy shows and other children's activities arranged, as well as games like pétanque, dominoes, shove halfpenny, etc. Bar food is available all day, with popular family dishes such as deep fried chicken for £3.80, fisherman's platter for £6.60, quiche for £3.60, treacle tart for £1.70 and a large selection of local ice creams from £1.20. The draught beers include Wadworth 6X, Marston's Pedigree, Fuller's Chiswick, Boddingtons, Morrells Strong Country, Murphy's Stout, Guinness, with Wight Mouse as an occasional guest beer, and there is an extraordinary range of whiskies - one for every day of the year. A high standard of accommodation is available in the hotel, which has excellent family facilities.

Brewery: Free house
Licensees: John and Jane Bradshaw
Opening hours: 11am-11pm; Sun 12-3pm, 7-10.30pm
Bar food: 12-10pm; Sun 12-2.30, 7-9.30pm
Accommodation: (Price per person) single £36, double £39
Children: In any of the three family rooms; outdoor play area
Credit cards: Access, Visa

SUN INN
Hulverstone PO30 4EH. Tel 0983 740403

Hulverstone

This pretty, thatched pub has a history going back more than 600 years, and in former times a light would be put in a window to give the 'all clear' to smugglers waiting out at sea to bring in their contraband - there was even a secret tunnel to the coast. The bar now has rugs on the flagstone floor, two open fires, cushioned seating, flowers, pictures and books. The delightful garden with its roses and terraced lawns has won awards and has wonderful views over the coast towards the Needles. Gale's HSB and Butser Brew are served from the barrel, and the excellent-value, high-quality food is very popular. The menu changes daily and, in addition to snacks like filled jacket potatoes from £2, or mushroom broth at £1.60, might include steak and ale pie and haggis with red wine, both at £4.95, and fresh trout baked in a clay oven over the fire. There are regular quiz nights and a guitarist entertains on Friday nights.

Brewery: Gale's
Licensees: Mr and Mrs F P Bore
Opening hours: Winter 11am-3pm, 7-11pm; summer 11am-11pm; Sun 12-3pm, 7-10.30pm
Bar food: 12-2.30pm, 6.30-9pm (winter 7.30pm); Sun 12-2pm, 8-9.30pm
Children: Not permitted inside; outdoor play area

BUDDLE INN
St Catherines Road, Niton PO36 2NE. Tel 0983 730243

Niton

This old stone farmhouse standing close to the cliff path at the southernmost tip of the island dates back in parts to the 16th century and has been licensed as an inn since 1850. The bar has kept its traditional character and appeal, with a flagstone floor, huge inglenook fireplace and exposed stone walls. It is a good pub for families with children because there is a games room housed in an old barn, a lovely garden with sea views and good walking country all around. Beers on draught are Brakspear, Boddingtons, Bass and Flowers IPA, and bar food includes dishes such as vegetable crumble for £4.25, lasagne for £4.45 and hot chocolate fudge cake for £2.25.

Brewery: Whitbread
Licensees: Pat and John Bourne
Opening hours: Summer 11am-11pm; winter 11am-3pm (Fri and Sat 11am-11pm); Sun 12-3pm, 7-10.30pm
Bar food: 11.30am-2.30pm, 6-10pm; Sun 12-2pm, 7-9.30pm
Children: In games room and away from the bar at the far end of dining area
Credit cards: Access, Visa

⊜ SEAVIEW HOTEL
The High Street, Seaview PO34 5EX. Tel 0983 612711

Seaview

Built in 1820, this seafront hotel has two bars decorated on a nautical theme. The Pump Bar is the public, with wooden floors and furniture, nautical pictures, old oars, masts and ships' wheels, while the carpeted Ward Room sports marine prints and photographs. The sea air can be enjoyed from the hotel's two attractive terraces. Beer on draught is limited to Flowers IPA and Guinness, but the bar food is good and includes lots of fish dishes, and popular

Brewery: Free house
Licensees: Nicholas and Nicola Hayward
Opening hours: 11-3pm, 6-11pm; Sun 12-2.30pm, 7-10.30pm
Bar food: 12-2.30pm, 7-9.30pm; Sun 12-2pm, 7-9.30pm

snacks such as seafood quiche for £4.95, and soup for £1.95. There is also a separate restaurant.The bedrooms are all most attractive and individually decorated; some have antique furniture, two have their own patios and there is one private suite.

Restaurant: 12.45-1.30pm, 7.30-9.30pm (except Sun evening)
Accommodation: (Price per person) single £48.50-£58.50, double £30-£39.50
Children: Welcome away from the bars and in the restaurant if eating with parents; not permitted under five years in the restaurant in the evenings
Credit cards: AMERICAN EXPRESS®, Access, Visa

⊕ NEW INN
Shalfleet, near Newport, PO34 NS. Tel: 0983 78314

Shalfleet

B uilt in 1746 on the site of an old church house, this lovely cream-painted stone pub with its small garden, stands in the village centre on the main road between Yarmouth and Newport. The Public Bar, with its inglenook fireplace, flagstone floor, and wood panelling has kept its pubby atmosphere, and the Lounge Bar/dining area is neat and bright with blue-flowered tablecloths. Excellent fresh fish may include lemon sole, plaice, halibut, sea bass, and crab, priced from £6.25 to £12; other dishes might be chicken and ham pie (£3.95), pork and leek sausages (£2.75), and raspberry Pavlova and apple pie, both at £1.95. You are advised to book a table in the dining room at weekends and in summer. Draught beers include Wadworth 6X, Flowers Original, Murphy's and Morrells Strong Country.

Brewery: Whitbread
Licensees: David and Jane Thomas
Opening hours: summer 11am-11pm; winter 11am-3.30pm, 6-11pm; Sat 11am-11pm; Sun 12-2pm, 7-10.30pm
Bar food: 12-2.30pm, 7-10pm; winter 7-9pm
Restaurant: Times as bar food
Children: Welcome anywhere
Credit cards: Access, Visa

⊕ CROWN INN
Shorwell PO30 3JL.Tel 0983 740293

Shorwell

S itting next to a trout stream in the middle of the village, this 16th-century, slate-roofed, stone building has always been a pub. The two bars are given a countrified atmosphere with beams, exposed brick and stone walls, wood panelling, large fireplaces and fine old furniture, notably an antique carved dresser with a collection of blue and white china. The garden is complete with dovecote. A varied choice of bar food is available, such as crab cocktail at £3.50, steak and kidney pie at £3.95, fresh mackerel at £4.25 and pizzas and pasta dishes from £3. More elaborate dishes are served in the evenings, including chicken breast Alexander for £5.95 and steak Diane for £7.95. Draught beer is limited to Flowers Original and a guest beer.

Brewery: Whitbread
Licensee: Michael Grace
Opening hours: 10.30am-3pm, 6-11pm; Sun 12-2pm, 7-10.30pm
Bar food: 12-2.30pm, 6-10pm; Sun 12-2.15pm, 7-9.45pm
Children: In the lounge if eating; outdoor play area

SPYGLASS INN
Esplanade, Ventnor PO38 1JX. Tel 0983 855338

Ventor

Its superb location on the sea front of an attractive resort town have made the Spyglass a favourite with holidaymakers. Its terrace is on the sea wall, and has an enclosed veranda so that guests can enjoy the sea air in comfort; on stormy days the sea can break over the wall. Inside, the bar consists of five interconnecting rooms, some tiled, some flagstoned and some carpeted, all with collections of nautical artefacts, model ships, oars, prints and photographs. Though quite modern, the inn is full of character and has a warm, welcoming atmosphere. Draught ales are few - Guinness, Burton and Spyglass Kingrock. Bar meals feature such popular dishes as lasagne and chilli, both at £3.95, and live entertainment is provided every night during the holiday season.

Brewery: Free house
Licensees: Neil and Stephanie Gibbs
Opening hours: Summer 10.30am-11pm; winter 11am-3pm, 7-11pm
Bar food: 12-2.15pm, 7-9.30pm (Sun 9pm)
Children: Not permitted in main bar area

KENT

LITTLE GEM
19 High Street, Aylesford ME20 7AX. Tel 0622 717510

Aylesford

This is claimed to be the smallest pub in Kent and traces its origins back to 1106. Fame has not spoiled it, however, and it is still an excellent local. The tiny whitewashed building with its moss-covered roof is easy to overlook as you walk down the high street, but despite its size, the one bar, with its low beams, crooked walls and cast-iron tables, is not cramped. Stairs lead up to a gallery where children are permitted (although families might be wise to choose a larger pub). There is a choice of nine beers on draught - Fuller's ESB and London Pride, Theakston Old Peculier, Draught Bass, Wadworth 6X, Harveys Sussex Best Bitter, Shepherd Neame Spitfire and Marston's Owd Rodger, plus a guest beer. Bar food is available.

Brewery: Free house
Licensee: Maria Brenchley
Opening hours: 11am-3pm, 6-11pm; Sun 12-3pm, 7-10.30pm
Bar food: 12-2pm (except Sun)
Children: In gallery only

⊜ KING WILLIAM 1V
The Street, Benenden TN17 5DJ. Tel 0580 240636

Benenden

Sitting in the village centre, this small, creeper-clad pub, dating back to the 15th century, has two bars, Public and Saloon, and a pretty cottage garden, bright with hollyhocks in summer and provided with picnic tables. Low beams, old photographs, wooden pews and an inglenook fireplace lend

Brewery: Shepherd Neame
Licensee: Allan Roy Austin
Opening hours: 11am-3pm (Sat 11am-11pm); Sun 12-3pm, 7-10.30pm

character to the bars. The Public Bar, with its electronic games, is popular with the young. Draught beers are limited to Shepherd Neame Spitfire and Master Brew, and there are also two draught lagers and a cider. Bar meals are reasonably priced, and might offer whitebait for a starter at £2.20, followed by rabbit pie for £4.95 or chicken Wellington for £5.95, and perhaps finishing with Death by Chocolate for £1.95. Live music (keyboard, bottle-neck guitars) and Morris dancers provide entertainment two or three times a year.

Bar food: 12-2pm, Wed-Sat 7-9pm; Sun no food
Children: Welcome in half of the saloon bar

🍺 THREE CHIMNEYS
Biddenden, near Ashford TN27 8HA. Tel 0580 291472

Biddenden

This attractive, half-timbered, 14th-century pub sits at a fork in the road about a mile from Biddenden. The two bars (quite cramped, but very cosy) are simply furnished, with low ceiling, and exposed brick fireplaces, and have no electronic games, but shove halfpenny, cards and dominoes are freely available - if you can find room to play. Bar food has an excellent local reputation, and is both good value and delicious. Dishes include stuffed vine leaves at £2.75, bacon and mushroom quiche at £4.45 and raspberry fool for £2.75. Vegetarian meals can be provided on request. The garden room (unlicensed - collect drinks from the bar) doubles as a restaurant and its popularity makes it advisable to book. In the warm weather, the huge garden, well provided with tables, is also popular. Draught beers include the Kent-brewed Goacher's Maidstone, Fremlin's, Wadworth 6X, Harveys Sussex Best Bitter , Marston's Pedigree, and Adnams Bitter. There is also a wide range of wines from Australia, France and Spain.

Brewery: Free house
Licensee: C F W Sayers
Opening hours: 11-2.30pm, 6-11pm; Sun 12-2.30pm, 7-10.30pm
Bar food: 11.30am-2pm, 6.30-11pm; Sun 12-2pm, 7-10pm
Children: In garden room only

🍺 WOOLPACK INN
Brookland, Romney Marsh TN29 9TJ. Tel 0797 344321

Brookland

This small, low, white-painted pub has tremendous character and is tucked away in a quiet rural area, overlooking reedy marshland. Anyone who appreciates an authentic pub atmosphere will find the detour worth while. There are two bars, both equally appealing, one fairly simple with quarry-tiled floor, low beams and a massive inglenook fireplace; the other, the games bar, slightly more plush. Old brass pieces hang around the walls, and the bars are furnished with cushioned chairs, benches and barrel stools. For entertainment there are pool, darts, dominoes, shove halfpenny, crib and electronic games. There is also a small garden, patrolled by free-range chickens and geese.

Brewery: Shepherd Neame
Licensee: John Palmer
Opening hours: 11am-2.30pm, 6-11pm; Sun 12-3pm, 7-10.30pm
Bar food: 12-2pm, 6-9pm; Sun 12-2pm,7-9pm
Children: Welcome anywhere

Shepherd Neame Spitfire and Master Brew are on draught, and bar food is available every day, with dishes such as shepherd's pie at £2.25, rump steak at £6.75 and vegetables au gratin at £3.25.

CASTLE INN
Chiddingstone, near Edenbridge TN8 7AH. Tel 0892 870247

Chiddingstone

Tile-hung, with leaded lights and a pretty bow window, this attractive building at the heart of a village owned by the National Trust, has been an inn since 1752, although it was originally built three centuries earlier. There are two bars: the Public is more simply furnished and has a regular local clientele; the other has been modernised to appeal to a more comfort-loving type of customer; both can get very crowded during the summer. The garden is a delight, with lawn and patio areas, a rockery, a fish pond and a beautiful mature grape vine. The restaurant is very popular too, so it is advisable to book, although meals are available in the bars as well. Typical dishes include chilli con carne at £4.75, a daily pasta dish at £4.55, smoked salmon-trout salad at £7.65 and Dutch apple slice at £2.35. Larkins Sovereign Bitter from the local Edenbridge brewery heads the list of draught beers, followed by Shepherd Neame Master Brew and Harveys Sussex Best Bitter. There are also regularly changing guest beers, a good selection of low and no-alcohol drinks and a wide-ranging wine list.

Brewery: Free house
Licensee: Nigel Lucas
Opening hours: 11am-3pm, 6-11pm; Sun 12-3pm, 7-10.30pm
Bar food: Served until 15 minutes before closing time
Restaurant: 12-2pm, 7.30-10.30pm
Children: As the law permits
Credit cards: AMERICAN EXPRESS® Access, Visa, Diners (only accepted for food)

⊜ ROCK INN
Chiddingstone Hoath, near Edenbridge TN8 7BS. Tel 0892 870296

Chiddingstone Hoath

Hidden away in the depths of the countryside, this attractive pub, built in 1510, stands next to an even more ancient listed barn.With its peg-tile roof, leaded lights and mix of creepers and roses around the door, the Rock Inn promises to be a haven of unspoilt 'olde worlde' charm, and visitors will not be disappointed. The two bars, with brick floors and a collection of banknotes decorating the beamed ceilings, are cheerful and cosy, dominated by a vast inglenook fireplace, and above one comfortable armchair there hangs, rather menacingly, a bull's head - the object of a local pub game, Ringing the Bull. Other entertainment is provided by live music every month or so during the winter. Larkins Bitter from the local Edenbridge brewery, Guinness and a guest beer are served on draught, and traditional pub food includes lasagne at £3.75, chicken tikka masala at £4.75 and ploughman's from £2.75. A small fenced garden with a few picnic tables is a safe area for children.

Brewery: Free house
Licensee: R Mulrenan
Opening hours: 11.30am-11pm; Sun 12-3pm, 7-10.30pm
Bar food: 12-2pm (Sun 12.30pm), 7.30-9pm (except Wed evening); no hot food Sun lunchtime
Children: Welcome anywhere

WHITE HORSE
The Square, Chilham CT4 8BY. Tel 0227 730355

Chilham

This beautiful 15th-century pub (see the front-cover photograph) overlooks the centre of the lovely village of Chilham, one of Kent's most popular tourist attractions. There is only one bar, which has low beams, a huge inglenook fireplace and comfortable old sofas. A small area is set aside for diners and the lunchtime menu includes the usual pub favourites, while in the evening there is a short à la carte menu. On draught are various Whitbread beers as well as Wadworth 6X and Murphy's Stout. The pub also stocks six malt whiskies and some wines from local vineyards. There is also a small walled garden which is shaded by trees and safe for children.

Brewery: Whitbread
Licensee: Roy Terry
Opening hours: 11am-11pm; Sun 12-3pm, 7-10.30pm
Bar food: 12-3pm, 7-9pm (Fri and Sat 9.30pm); no food Tue evening; Sun 12-2.30, 7-9pm
Children: Not permitted inside
Credit cards: Access, Visa (only if eating)

COMPASSES INN
Sole Street, Crundale CT4 7ES. Tel 0227 700300

Crundale

Standing on a quiet road in a peaceful rural setting, this white-painted pub looks exceptionally pretty in summer, with wisteria climbing up the walls and colourful hanging baskets. Dating back to the 15th century, the building has been beautifully preserved and, with its many exposed beams, open fires, stone and board floors and interesting nooks and crannies, exudes character. The garden room, looking on to a lovely big garden with an aviary, is used for meals and the extensive menu includes tasty, good-value food such as home-made steak and kidney pie at £5.80, lentil crumble at £4.70 and lemon brûlée at £2.50. Beers on draught include Shepherd Neame Master Brew, Fuller's London Pride and ESB, Wadworth 6X, Whitbread Best, Fremlins, and Beamish Stout.

Brewery: Free house
Licensee: John Bennett
Opening hours: 12-2.30pm, 6.30-11pm;closed Mon; Sun 12-3pm, 7-10.30pm
Bar food: Mon-Sat 12-2pm; Mon-Thu 7-9.30pm; Fri-Sat 7-10pm; Sun 12-2.15pm, 7-9pm
Children: Welcome away from bar; family room; children's menu available; outdoor play area

CARPENTERS ARMS
The Street, Eastling, near Faversham ME13 0AZ. Tel 079589 0234

Eastling

Sitting in the centre of the village, this small brick and weatherboard pub has a history going back to the 14th century. The one bar smells fragrantly of woodsmoke from the fire in the inglenook fireplace, and garlands of hops hang from the low beams over the wooden pews and chairs. Traditional bar games include bar skittles, dominoes, shove halfpenny, cards and shuttlebox. Shepherd Neame Spitfire, Master Brew Bitter and Mild, plus Beamish, are on draught. Food consists of traditional favourites, home-cooked, very tasty and good value; the short menu may include an

Brewery: Shepherd Neame
Licensee: M A O'Regan
Opening hours: 11am-4pm, 6-11pm; Sun 12-3pm, 7-10.30pm
Bar food: 12-2.30pm, 6.30-10.30pm; Sun 12-1.30pm only
Restaurant: Times as bar food
Accommodation: (Price per room) single £32, double £40; no children under 12 years

excellent onion soup with croûtons and garlic bread at £1.50, home-cooked ham, egg and chips at £3, ploughman's at £2.50 and a range of toasted sandwiches. There is a separate restaurant for which booking is advisable at weekends. If you are looking for somewhere to stay for a night or two, there are three very attractive bedrooms with all modern comforts in an adjacent house.

Children: Welcome in the pub and in the restaurant if eating a full meal
Credit cards: AMERICAN EXPRESS®, Access, Visa

⊜ PEPPERBOX INN
Fairbourne Heath, near Ulcombe ME17 1LP. Tel 0622 842558

Fairbourne Heath

This white-painted pub in the centre of a hamlet dates back to the late 15th and early 16th centuries, has pretty roses growing round the door and a well-kept garden with a swing, a pond and attractive flower beds. There is only one bar, with low beams and a carpeted floor, to which the three-piece suite in front of the inglenook fireplace gives something of the feel of a family lounge. Three local Shepherd Neame beers are served - Master Brew, Bishops Finger and Spitfire - plus Beamish Stout. You are advised to book a table for the separate restaurant, but there is good food at the bar, where the menu offers a mixture of standard and more adventurous dishes. Soup at £1.80, or pâté at £2.90 make satisfying snacks or starters with main dishes like sole bonne femme at £6.90, or a vegetarian stuffed pancake at £5.20 as main dishes. On Sunday evenings there is live music.

Brewery: Shepherd Neame
Licensee: Geoff Pemble
Opening hours: 11am-3pm, 6.30-11pm; Sun 12-2.30pm, 7-10pm
Bar food: 12-2pm, 7-10pm (except Sun)
Restaurant: Times as bar food
Children: Welcome in the dining area at lunchtime; outdoor play area

---

⊜ CROWN
The Green, Groomsbridge TN3 9QH. Tel 0892 864742

Groomsbridge

Although it stands beside the main road, at the upper end of a rather long-drawn-out village, it is still pleasant in summer to sit outside this 400-year-old pub and look out over the old churchyard and green. Of the two bars the Snug is the quieter, while the main bar, with its open fire and low, beamed ceiling decorated with pewter and other drinking jugs, combines a lively local atmosphere with a cheerful welcome for strangers; in the evenings double doors close part of it off as a restaurant. Beers on draught include Webster's Yorkshire Bitter, Adnams Bitter, Harveys, and Wadworth 6X. The bar menu sticks firmly to tried and tasty pub favourites, but it is good value with main dishes from about £4. There is a separate restaurant-style à la carte menu in the evening, for which it is advisable to book a table. For overnight stays, the pub also has four quite small bedrooms with beamed ceilings and steeply sloping floors.

Brewery: Free house
Licensee: Mr and Mrs W B Rhodes
Opening hours: 11am-2.30pm (Sat 3pm), 6-11pm; Sun 12-3pm, 7-10.30pm
Bar food: 12-2pm, 7-9.30pm (except Sun evening)
Restaurant: 7-9.30pm (except Sun)
Accommodation: (Price per room) single £19, double £35; no children under four years
Children: Welcome anywhere except in the main bar
Credit cards: Access, Visa

⊜ ARTICHOKE INN
Park Road, Hamptons, near West Peckham TN11 9SR. Tel 0732 810763

Hamptons

Originally built in 1483, this attractive white-painted pub sits by the side of a quiet road, isolated in the depths of the Kentish countryside. Striped awnings shelter some outside seating and there is more on the other side of the road. The two bars have low beams, pleasingly erratic plasterwork and a snug, friendly atmosphere, much appreciated by lots of regulars who come from miles around. Draught beers are Fuller's London Pride, Greene King Abbot Ale and Young's Special. Dishes available at the bar offer fair value for money and prices range from £1.75 for French onion soup to £4.95 for lasagne and £5.50 for vegetable pie, with puddings at around £2.25. On Friday and Saturday evenings there is also a separate restaurant.

Brewery: Free house
Licensee: T Simmonds
Opening hours: 11.30am-2.30pm, 6.30-11pm; Sun 12-3pm, 7-10.30pm; closed Sun evenings Oct-Easter
Bar food: 12-2pm, 7-9.30pm (except Sun in winter)
Restaurant: 7-9.30pm Fri and Sat only
Children: Welcome in Snug if eating

DUKE WILLLIAM INN
The Street, Ickham, near Canterbury CT3 1PQ. Tel 0227 721308

Ickham

Though the pub was in fact built in the early 17th century, the etched-glass windows overlooking the main village street give it a 19th-century feel. There is just one bar, a cosy, slightly chintzy, room with an inglenook fireplace and beamed ceiling where the amiable landlord and landlady create a friendly atmosphere. Caricatures of regulars are dotted around the walls, and there are also collections of old rifles and farming implements. A conservatory acts as a family room, and there is also a well kept garden where there are ponds and (beware, said our researcher) a finger-eating parrot. The long menu includes popular bar snacks and such dishes as mussels Provençale at £6.95, chilli con carne at £4.75 or cheese omelette at £3.95 and is both enjoyable and good value for money. There is also a separate restaurant for which booking is advisable. Draught beers include Young's Special, Fuller's London Pride, Shepherd Neame Master Brew, and Adnams Bitter. The pub has a list of about 100 wines, 15 of which are, commendably, served by the glass.

Brewery: Free house
Licensees: Alistair and Carol McNeill
Opening hours: 11am-3pm, 6-11pm; closed Mon lunchtime (inc BH Mons); Sun 12-3pm, 7-10.30pm
Bar food: 11am-2.30pm, 6-10pm; Sun 12-5pm (supper licence)
Restaurant: Times as bar food
Children: Welcome in eating areas and conservatory; outdoor play area
Credit cards:
AMERICAN EXPRESS®, Access, Visa, Diners (only if eating)

Horse-brasses

Delightful and attractive as they are, horse-brasses are nothing like as old as is generally believed. The working horse in a harness gleaming with ornamental hanging brasses is a creature of the period since 1850. The brasses were mass-produced folk art, following the earlier precedent of the heraldic badges worn by the carriage horses of aristocratic families. Favourite symbols include the sun, the moon, stars and such heraldic creatures as the lion, the stag, the unicorn and the eagle, as well as railway locomotives and ships.

⊕ HARROW
Common Road, Ightham Common TN15 9ER. Tel 0732 885912

Ightham Common

Situated in a quiet village, this 19th-century pub with its ivy-covered walls and colourful umbrellas, sheltering outdoor tables, is a welcoming sight. Inside, the two bars with their brick floors and varnished wood-boarded walls, decorated with stuffed fish and birds, make the perfect setting for browsing through the newspapers or 'library' of old books. Friendly staff help the relaxing atmosphere along and the finishing touches in the evenings are provided by open fires and flickering candles. King & Barnes Festive and Sussex Bitter, Fuller's London Pride, Beamish Stout and a guest beer are on draught. The freshly cooked bar meals are good value; typical dishes are pasta Milano at £4 and baked snapper with caper sauce at £6.50, with raspberry Pavlova roll at £1.75 to follow. Booking is advisable for the separate restaurant. A pub quiz on Thursday nights, and acoustic music, often jazz, on Friday nights, are popular crowd-pullers

Brewery: Free house
Licensee: Gerry Costello
Opening hours: 12-3pm, 6.30-11pm; Sun 12.30-3pm 7-10.30pm
Bar food: 12-2pm, 6.30-9pm; Sun 12.30-2.30pm
Restaurant: 12.30-2pm, 7.30-10pm; Sun 12.30-3.30pm
Children: At lunchtimes only; not permitted under four years
Credit cards: AMERICAN EXPRESS® Access, Visa (for orders over £20)

⊕ PLOUGH
Ivy Hatch, near Sevenoaks TN15 0NL. Tel 0732 810268

Ivy Hatch

Situated at a fork in the road at the heart of Ivy Hatch, with benches and tables outside, this 100-year-old pub has kept the style of a typical village local. Inside, what were once three rooms have been knocked into one rambling bar with part-boarded walls and beams in abundance. Customers can enjoy Murphy's Stout, Brakspear Bitter and Marston's Pedigree on draught, or the good wine list. There is a restaurant in the conservatory (booking advisable) and bar meals are good quality. Typical dishes include tagliatelle Bolognese for £5.50, crispy duck salad for £6.50, and venison casserole for £8.95.

Brewery: Free house
Licensee: Keith Edwards
Opening hours: 11am-3pm, 6-11pm; Sun 12-3pm
Bar food: 12-2pm, 7-10pm; Sun 12-2.15pm
Restaurant: Times as bar food
Children: In conservatory only; not permitted under eight years
Credit cards: Access, Visa

⊕ BROWN TROUT
The Down, Lamberhurst TN3 8HA. Tel 0892 890312/891066

Lamberhurst

Hard to miss at night with its floodlighting and fairy lights, this attractive, whitewashed pub is set back from the road on the outskirts of the village, with a large sloping lawn to the front and a garden to the rear. Inside, numerous polished brass jugs hang from the low beams, and though there is only one bar, cosy areas are easily found. Draught beers include Whitbread Mild and Best Bitter, Wadworth 6X, Fremlins Bitter, Bentley's Yorkshire Bitter and Murphy's Stout. There is a small range of malt whiskies and over 50

Brewery: Free house
Licensee: J Stringer
Opening hours: 11am-3pm, 6-11pm; Sun 12-3pm, 7-10.30pm
Bar food: 11.30am-2.30pm, 6-10pm; Sun 12-2.30pm, 7-9.30pm
Restaurant: Times as bar food
Children: Welcome anywhere;

wines. The food deserves its good local reputation, especially the fish dishes, which range from grilled sardines at £3 to skate wing at £5.95 and whole lobster salad at £11.95. There are meat dishes too, and a vegetarian menu. You are advised to book for the separate restaurant.

outdoor play area
Credit cards: Access, Visa

⊜ HARROW INN
Warren Street, Lenham, near Maidstone ME17 2ED.
Tel 0622 858727

Lenham

Although old, this isolated rural pub has been extensively renovated and extended. The one, very neat bar has low, beamed ceilings and an inglenook fireplace with a wood-burning stove. There is also a family room and, outside, the tidy patio and garden, remarkably, feature a waterfall. Booking is advisable in the restaurant at weekends, and the bar menus offer a fair choice of acceptable dishes - for example, stuffed baby squid for £2.25, stuffed aubergines for £5.95, steak and mushroom pudding for £7.65, and apple pie and custard for £2.95. Morning coffee and afternoon tea are available. Beers on draught include Crouch Vale Best, Guinness, Ruddles County, Shepherd Neame Master Brew and Tetley Bitter. There are 16 spacious and pleasantly furnished bedrooms. Live entertainment is provided on Sunday nights with a regular jazz slot.

Brewery: Free house
Licensees: Sheila Burns and Alan Cole
Opening hours: 11.30am-2.30pm, 7-11pm (Sat 6.30pm); Sun 12-3pm, 7-10.30pm
Bar food: Sun-Fri 12-2pm, 7-10pm; Sat 11.30am-2pm, 6.30-10pm
Restaurant: Times as bar food
Accommodation: (Price per room) single £35, double £45
Children: Welcome away from the bar area
Credit cards: AMERICAN EXPRESS®, Access, Visa

⊕ GEORGE INN
The Street, Newnham, near Sittingbourne ME9 0LL. Tel 0795 89237

Newnham

Dating back to Elizabethan times, this is an attractive pub, built in traditional Kentish style, in the centre of the village. Inside, a large inglenook fireplace divides the large bar into two areas with low, beamed ceilings, and period-style decor. The spacious garden at the back is overlooked by sheep in the neighbouring field, and shaded by a splendid beech tree. Draught beers include Shepherd Neame Master Brew and Spitfire, and Beamish Stout. The bar menu, short but of high quality, offers interesting dishes such as hare pudding at £6.75, courgette au gratin at £5.30, and soup or ploughman's for lighter snacks.

Brewery: Shepherd Neame
Licensee: Simon Barnes
Opening hours: 10.30am-3pm, 6-11pm; Sun 12-2pm, 7-10.30pm
Bar food: 12-2pm, 7.30-10pm (except Sun evening and all day Mon)
Children: Welcome if eating

SPOTTED DOG
Smart's Hill, Penshurst TN11 8EE. Tel 0892 870253

Penhurst

This lovely old pub is quite difficult to find, but there are signs at nearby road juctions and the effort is worth it. Look for a half-timbered, black and white Tudor building, set well back from the road. In summer there are lovely views from the two terraces on the hillside at the back of the pub, and there is also a large garden. Inside, the bar, rich in timbering and wood panelling, with no fewer than four open fires for winter warmth, exceeds one's expectations in every respect. The bar food, too, is of excellent quality, and dishes include soup for £1.85, pâté for £2.75, grilled sardines for £3.95, tagliatelle for £4.95, and poached salmon for £7.95. Booking is necessary for the restaurant. On draught are Old Spotty (a 1040 real ale brewed specially by Courage), King & Barnes Sussex Bitter, Wadworth 6X, and John Smith's Bitter.

Brewery: Free house
Licensee: Andy Tucker
Opening hours: 11am-2.30pm, 6-11pm; Sun 12-3pm, 7-11pm
Bar food: 12-2pm (Sun 2.30pm), 7-9.30pm
Restaurant: Wed-Sat 7.30-9.45pm
Children: Welcome away from the bar
Credit cards: Access, Visa

DUCK INN
Pett Bottom, near Bridge, Canterbury CT4 5PB Tel 0227 830354

Pett Bottom

This isolated pub lies between the A2 at Bridge and the B2068. A genuine well and forecourt-parking separate the low, 17th-century building from the road. Inside there are two quiet, cosy bars, unfussily decorated, with friendly service. At least two guest ales supplement the regular Greene King IPA and Abbot, which are gravity-drawn from the barrels. Bar service is available from the stable door into the tree-lined garden. Bar meals are delicious, attractively presented, and good value. Typical dishes include hot chilli at £4.65, steak and oyster pie at £6.20, with chocolate rum crunch tart and caramel walnut meringue, both at £2.10, for pudding. There is also a separate restaurant.

Brewery: Free house
Licensee: Ron Brown
Opening hours: 11.30am-3pm, 6.30-11pm; Sun 12-3pm, 7-10.30pm
Bar food: 12-2pm, 7-10pm (Mon 9pm); Sun 12-2.15pm, 7-9pm
Restaurant: 7.15-9.30pm
Children: Welcome in restaurant and small bar
Credit cards: AMERICAN EXPRESS® Access, Visa

⊜ RINGLESTONE INN
Ringlestone, near Maidstone ME17 1NX. Tel 0622 859900

Ringlestone

This beautiful 16th-century pub, in the depths of the countryside, is a rare example of how to be popular and successful without losing genuine character - 'a splendid pub' was our researcher's comment. The three bars, with their low beams, exposed brick and timber walls and plain brick floors offer what is possibly the best selection of real ales in Kent: Shepherd Neame Bitter and Theakston Bitter and Old Peculier are the regulars but there are always at least four other guest ales - examples are Cains Formidable (from Merseyside) and Harveys Sussex Bitter. There are also five draught lagers, the local Biddenden cider and 30 English country fruit wines and champagnes. Excellent buffet-style bar food includes dishes like lamb and Stilton pie for £2.85 and macaroni with tuna and clams for £4.25, plus many old favourites. Puddings - for example, brandy bread pudding and summer pudding - cost £2.85. Meals are popular, and it is a good idea to book. There is an attractive garden with waterfalls and a fountain and, in due season, intelligent wasps.

Brewery: Free house
Licensee: Mike Millington-Buck
Opening hours: 12-3pm, 6.30-11pm; Sun 12-3pm, 7-10.30pm
Bar food: 12-3pm, 7-9.30pm
Children: Welcome away from the bar area
Credit cards: AMERICAN EXPRESS®, Access, Visa, Diners

⊜ BELL
Bell Lane, Smarden TN27 8PW. Tel 023 337 0283

Smarden

Situated about a mile and a half from the village, this low, rambling pub dates back to the 15th century and has a garden filled with fruit trees at the back. Inside, the bars are a succession of rooms with brick and flagstone floors and low beams hung with hop garlands, a prevailing Kentish theme. One room, the candlelit Snug, is for non smokers, while another serves as a family room. Darts, pool, card and board games are available. A good selection of ales includes Ringwood Old Thumper, Harveys Sussex Best, Fuller's London Pride, Shepherd Neame Bitter, Fremlins, Flowers, and Murphy's Stout and there is a list of over 30 wines. Soup, ploughman's, pizza and steak are typical dishes on the bar menu; prices are not high. Overnight accommodation consists of three simply furnished, comfortable rooms, with tea trays and self-service Continental breakfast.

Brewery: Free house
Licensee: Ian Turner
Opening hours: 11am-2.30pm (Sat 3pm), 6-11pm; Sun 12-3pm, 7-10.30pm
Bar food: 12-2pm, 6.30-10pm, Sun 12-2.30pm, 7-10pm
Accommodation: (Price per person) £15-£16
Children: In family room only
Credit cards: Access, Visa

⊜ CHEQUERS
The Street, Smarden TN27 8QA. Tel 023377 0217/0623

Smarden

For centuries, this attractive pub has been a welcoming sight in Smarden's main street, with flowers growing round the door and up to the old peg-tile roof. There are two cosy, comfortable bars, with low ceilings and oak beams; considering the central location they are surprisingly quiet, as is garden at the rear with its large pond. The separate restaurant takes bookings and offers the same menu as the bar; for example, roulade of smoked salmon and prawns for £6.95, crispy roast duckling for £9.75, vegetable platter for £4.75, sherry trifle for £2.95 and chocolate truffle tart for £2.75. The choice of beers includes Bass Mild and cask-conditioned, Fuller's London Pride and Young's Special. More than 40 wines and 25 malt whiskies are also available. There are six fair-sized bedrooms.

Brewery: Free house
Licensee: Frank Stevens
Opening hours: 10am-3.30, 6-11pm; Sun 12-3pm, 7-10.30pm
Bar food: As opening hours; last orders for elaborate dishes 9.45pm
Accommodation: (Price per person) double £15.50-£16.50, single £19
Children: Welcome away from bar areas
Credit cards: Access, Visa

⊜ RED LION INN
Snargate, Romney Marsh TN29 9UQ. Tel 0797 344648

Snargate

It would be easy to pass by this isolated country pub, because from the outside it does not look particularly special, but this would be a mistake. The inside of the 16th-century building is beautifully preserved and the atmosphere totally unspoilt. There is one panelled, low-ceilinged, simply furnished bar, a family room, and a games room where bar billiards, Toad in the Hole, and Bat and Trap are played. In winter, fires blaze merrily in every room, while in summer, visitors share the cottage garden with the resident sheep and chickens. Though this is very much a local pub, the landlady extends a cheerful welcome to all visitors. No food is available here, but beers on draught include Bateman, Adnams Best Bitter and Beamish Stout, plus guest beers.

Brewery: Free house
Licensee: Doris Jemisom
Opening hours: 11am-3pm, 6-11pm; Sun 12-3pm, 7-10.30pm
Children: Welcome in family room and games room

⊜ TIGER INN
Stowting, near Ashford, TN25 6BA. Tel 0303 862130

Stowting

An isolated roadside pub, nominally at the centre of a scattered hamlet, the Tiger Inn dates back to the 16th century. A bit of its history is preserved on the exterior - embossed into the rendering are the words 'Mackeson Hyte Ales'. Creepers climb the side of the building, and there is also a wisteria-covered pergola on the front terrace. People tend to come here for the excellent bar food, especially at lunchtime, but the pub has lost none of its character. The one bar, with its exposed brickwork and wood panelling, is

Brewery: Free house
Licensees: Alan and Linda Harris
Opening hours: 12-3pm, 7-11pm; Sun 12-3pm, 7-10.30pm
Bar food: 12-2pm; 7-10pm (Sun 9.30pm)
Children: Welcome away from the bar area
Credit cards: Access, Visa

light and-airy with a comfortable, relaxing atmosphere. Typical dishes include cheesey smoked haddock and prawn pie, minty leg of lamb steak and steak, kidney and mushroom pie, all at £5.50, with apple pie for pudding at £2.50. Regular beers are Tetley Bitter, Burton Ale and Everards Tiger Best, plus two guest beers. A piano player entertains Sunday lunchers, and Monday evenings are dedicated to live jazz.

(accepted only for food orders over £10)

SHIP INN
Conyer Quay, Teynon, near Sittingbourne ME9 9HR. Tel 0795 521404

Teynon

A truly remarkable selection of beers, wines and spirits awaits those who venture to this fairly isolated quayside inn. Five real ales change regularly, and other draught beers include Ankerstein wheat beer and Kriek, a Belgian cherry beer. There is a list of 200 wines, 100 of which are available by the glass, 250 whiskies, 150 liqueurs, 50 brandies, 30 rums, 25 ports, and 60 bottled beers from 30 different countries. The building itself is 350 years old, and its shingle-covered terrace overlooks a working waterfront and the marshes. Inside, the bar is festooned with maps, fishing tackle and nautical equipment, and has a real quayside atmosphere. Booking is necessary for the Smuggler's Restaurant, but the inn also serves bar snacks, for example, lasagne and chips for £4.25, scampi and chips for £3.95 and soup for £2.25.

Brewery: Free house
Licensee: Alec Heard
Opening hours: 11am-3pm, 6-11pm; Sun 12-3pm, 7-10.30pm
Bar food: 12-2.30, 7-10.30pm
Restaurant: Times as bar food
Children: In restaurant only
Credit cards:
AMERICAN EXPRESS® Access, Visa

FOX AND HOUNDS
Toy's Hill, near Westerham TN16 1QG. Tel 0732 750328

Toy's Hill

When you arrive at this isolated country pub, its front doors may be locked, but don't turn away, just go round to the back door and you will find a small, welcoming bar, furnished with old sofas and odd chairs, and looking like a much-lived-in family sitting room. Since most of the customers, at least during the week, are both local and regular, and there are photographs of some of them on the walls, this cosy atmosphere is reinforced. Beers are limited to Greene King IPA and Abbot Ale, with Harp lager, Guinness, and Dry Blackthorne cider also on draught, and bar meals are not available on a regular basis. There is a garden and a veranda at the front .

Brewery: Greene King
Licensee: Hazel Canning
Opening hours: 11am-2.30pm, 6-11pm; Sun 12-2.30pm, 7-10.30pm
Children: As the law permits

⊕ PROVENDER
Pye Corner, Ullcombe, near Maidstone ME17 1EE. Tel 0622 850273

Ullcombe

Sitting by the roadside in an isolated position, this 16th-century brick-built and tile-hung pub has a cosy, welcoming atmosphere. There is one bar with exposed brickwork, a large inglenook fireplace and low beams. Beers on draught include John Bull and Double Diamond, with guest beers like Archers Golden Bitter. Bar food - mostly the standard favourites - is very reasonably priced, and a separate restaurant operates at the weekends, for which it is necessary to book. There is a large garden laid entirely to lawn and with three tables.

Brewery: Free house
Licensee: Martin Elster
Opening hours: 11am-3pm, 7-11pm; Sun 12-3pm, 7-10.30pm
Bar food: 11am-2.30pm, 8-10.30pm; Sun 12-1.30pm, 8-9.30pm
Restaurant: Fri and Sat 7-9.45pm
Children: In restaurant only

Smuggling and Skulduggery
All round Britain's coast an explosion of smuggling was the 18th-century response to high excise duties on goods imported from abroad. There were villages in Kent where people were said to wash their windows with smuggled gin, it was so cheap. Inns were often involved, because they had cellars where casks and bales could conveniently be hidden and they could sell smuggled drink. Smugglers were nothing like as romantic in real life as they are in fiction. Lawless and violent smuggling gangs could exercise a reign of terror. Other criminal activities were often associated with some of the rougher pubs, where thieves planned operations, the landlord fenced stolen goods and the 'gentlemen of the road' dropped in. Many a pub on the Great North Road claims the famous highwayman Dick Turpin as a habitué.

SURREY

⊕ ABINGER HATCH
Abinger Common, near Dorking RH5 6HZ. Tel 0306 730737

Abinger Common

This characterful, white-rendered building, a pub since 1850 but considerably older, is situated in a quiet village amid gentle, wooded countryside and so attracts walkers, as well as retired people, families, business trade at lunchtime and a younger clientele in the evenings. A good choice of beers is on offer, among them Hall & Woodhouse Tanglefoot and Badger Best, Gibbs Mew Bishop's Tipple and Wadworth 6X, in addition to 15 wines and Merrydown fruit wines. Like the roomy bar, which has a central fireplace and brick chimney, the dining room is simply furnished. The cosmopolitan menu embraces onion bhajees at £2.50 and, both at £4.50, tagliatelle with mushrooms in blue cheese and chicken, ham, leek and mushroom vol-au-vents. Picnic benches are set out in the pleasant garden to the side of the pub.

Brewery: Free house
Licensee: Charles Stewart
Opening hours: 11am-3pm, 6-11pm, Sun 12-3pm, 7-10.30pm
Bar food: 12-2.15pm, 6-9pm (flexible); Sun 12-2.30pm, 7-9pm
Restaurant: 12- 2.15pm, 7-9pm (except Mon); Sun 12-2.15pm only
Children: Only if eating and supervised

WILLIAM IV
Dark Lane, Albury Heath, near Shere GU5 9DB. Tel 048641 2685

Albury Heath

Those in the know travel some distance to rub shoulders with locals, retired folk, walkers and business people in this unspoilt country pub. Situated in a quiet, secluded hamlet, the 14th-century building has a cream-rendered frontage below dark bargeboards, and in front is a pretty, illuminated garden with trees and picnic benches. Low beams, stone flags, an inglenook fireplace, traps, foxes' heads and stuffed fishes and birds reinforce the traditional character of the friendly bar, which is divided into three separate drinking areas. Among the cask-conditioned beers on sale are Greene King Abbot Ale, Tetley Bitter and Young's Special, and Scrumpy Jack is also on offer. At the bar and in the upstairs dining room, home-made dishes are served, including mutton stew and dumplings and monkfish Stroganoff, both at £4.20, and, in winter, oxtail casserole at £4.50. An à la carte menu is served upstairs on Thursday, Friday and Saturday evenings, and 20 wines are available by the bottle. A seafood evening takes place on the first Saturday of each month, and a spit roast of lamb, pork, venison and wild boar on each third Saturday.

Brewery: Free house
Licensee: Michael Davids
Opening hours: 11am-3pm, 5.30-11pm; Sun 12-3pm, 7-10.30pm
Bar food: 12-2.30pm, 7-10pm (Sun 9pm)
Restaurant: Times as bar food
Children: Anywhere away from bar, but must be supervised

DOLPHIN
The Street, Betchworth, near Reigate RH3 7DW. Tel 0737 842288

Betchworth

Tucked away in a quiet village with a river meandering through it, this 16th-century pub is popular with locals, business people at lunchtime and, at weekends, daytrippers and walkers. White-rendered with black window frames beneath a deep, mellow-tiled roof, it is screened from the road by pollarded trees. There is ample seating outside, with benches at the front and in two separate gardens. A single bar serves three rooms: one with stone flags and a large inglenook fireplace, a second wood-panelled, carpeted and boasting a fine grandfather clock, and a third simply furnished and serving as a Snug. Young's Best, Special and, in season, Winter Warmer are on tap and there is a selection of French, German and Italian wines, as well as champagne by the glass. Daily blackboard specials - cannelloni verde with garlic bread at £3.95, for example - complement a menu which includes starters like mussels in garlic butter with a freshly baked roll at £3.55, main courses such as deep-fried calamari with French fries and side salad at £4.40, and traditional sweets like Spotted Dick with custard at £1.65.

Brewery: Young's
Licensee: George Campbell
Opening hours: 11am-3pm, 5.30-11pm; Sun 12-3pm, 7-10.30pm
Bar food: 12-2.30pm, 7-10pm
Children: Not permitted under five years in bar; outdoor play area

⊕ PLOUGH AT BLACKBROOK
Blackbrook Road, Blackbrook, near Dorking RH5 4DS. Tel 0306 886603

Blackbrook

L ittle more than a mile from a built-up area, this delightful pub nevertheless benefits from peaceful surroundings, being set back from a lane running through woodland. Behind the white-rendered, 16th-century building is a garden big enough to accommodate 60 people at picnic benches. Comfortable seating on cushioned benches and stools is provided in the two carpeted bars, one of which has handsome copper-topped tables, the other a collection of over 550 ties, a number of ancient sewing machines and a wood-panelled ceiling hung with old saws. The clientele of locals and, at lunchtime, business people have the choice of Sussex, Broadwood, Festive or Old, all from the King & Barnes range of beers, as well as Stowford Press cider, an unusually wide selection of European bottled lagers and about 20 traditional country wines. Extensive and cosmopolitan, the menu includes starters such as New England seafood chowder, taramosalata and pâté Provençale, all at £2.65, and main courses like beef loin in coconut curry at £5.75 and seafood Florentine at £6.95. Popular sweets include hot carrot pudding and apple, almond and caramel tart, both at £2.45.

Brewery: King & Barnes
Licensee: Robin Squire
Opening hours: 11am-2.30pm, 6-11pm; Sun 12-2.30pm, 7-10.30pm
Bar food: 12-2pm, 7-9.30pm (except Mon evening)
Children: Not permitted under 14 years in bar

⊕ WHYTE HARTE
Bletchingley, near Redhill RH1 4PB. Tel 0883 743231

Bletchingley

D ating from 1388, this long, white-rendered pub, set back from the wide main road through the village, is a fine example of a former coaching inn. Their black beams and ochre walls creating an attractive contrast, the four drinking and eating areas, one non-smoking, are served by a single bar. Here there is a rare chance to try the ancient game of Ring the Bull, the aim being to swing a nose ring on a string over a wall-mounted bull's horn. Old woodworking tools, prints and a model steam engine likewise add to the character of the place. At the rear are a garden with picnic benches, and stables where riders may tie up their horses. Beers from Benskins, Burton, Tetley and Adnams are on offer, and the enticing menu comprises home-made dishes such as Stilton and broccoli soup at £1.95, steak and ale pie at £4.95 and pork fillet in pepper sauce at £7.95. Two double rooms, one with a four-poster bed, and seven single rooms are available. Clean and comfortable, all are fitted out with modern pine furniture.

Brewery: Ind Coope
Licensees: David and Miriam Yarwood
Opening hours: 11-3pm, 5-11pm; Sun 12-3pm, 7-10.30pm
Bar food: 11.30am-2pm, 6-9.30pm; Sun 12-2pm, 7-9pm
Restaurant: Times as bar food
Accommodation: (Price per person) single £40, double £25-£30. Children are welcome but must not be left alone in the rooms
Children: Anywhere away from bar
Credit cards:
AMERICAN EXPRESS®, Access, Visa, Diners

VINE INN
Bridge Road, Chertsey KT16 8JH. Tel 0932 563010

Chertsey

A flourishing vine and a pretty little garden with swings and chickens to keep the children amused are but part of the appeal of this 400-year-old, brick-built pub, situated on the edge of town. Inside, old black and white photographs decorate the restful blue walls, a collection of ancient cameras and a pair of stuffed pheasants are on show and flowers adorn the dark tables. Customers of all ages mingle in the relaxed and friendly atmosphere of the carpeted bar, where Courage Directors, Guinness and Brakspear are the beers available and on Saturday evenings entertainment is on offer in the form of live bands and discos. There is an extensive menu of home-made food, including, in winter, shepherd's pie and chilli con carne at a reasonable £3.95 and in summer salads as well as hot meals.

Brewery: Courage
Licensee: Mrs P Doyes
Opening hours: 10am-3pm, 5-11pm; Sun 12-3pm, 7-10.30pm
Bar food: 12.30-2.30pm, 7-9.30pm
Children: Welcome if well behaved, but not after 9.30pm; half portions available; outdoor play area

CROWN INN
The Green, Petworth Road, Chiddingfold GU8 4TX. Tel 0428 682255

Chiddingfold

Originally a rest-house for travelling Cistercian monks, this fine wisteria-clad, timber-framed inn dates back to 1285. At that time the village was famed for its stained glass, fine examples of which grace Westminster Abbey and the pub itself. The spacious bar has dark beams, old oak tables surrounded by carvers and wheelback and tapestry-covered chairs, while a comfortable sofa beckons beside a huge, open, stone fireplace. Just outside the bar, a sedan chair houses a public telephone. The oak-panelled restaurant, whose versatile chef even bakes his own biscuits and crumpets, enjoys a high standing among the clientele of locals, business people and tourists. Imaginative dishes like tea-smoked quail at £4.50, grilled knot of sole and pink trout at £10.95 and baked banana martinique at £4.05 appear on an extensive menu which is complemented by over 50 wines. Bar meals are also available. The choice of beers is good, and includes Hall & Woodhouse Badger, Tanglefoot and Gribble (the latter brewed at a nearby pub) and Wadworth 6X. Benches are provided in the garden, which has a barbecue, and there is further seating on the patio and terrace. Seven comfortable rooms, six double and one single, are available - all with traditional dark furniture and three with four-poster beds.

Brewery: Hall & Woodhouse
Licensee: Mrs Terry Williams
Opening hours: 11am-11pm; Sun 12-3pm, 7-10.30pm
Bar food: 12-2.30pm, 7-9.30pm
Restaurant: Times as bar food
Accommodation: (Price per room) single £47, double £57-£90
Children: Welcome away from bar
Credit cards: AMERICAN EXPRESS®, Access, Visa, Diners

CRICKETERS
Downside, Cobham KT11 3NX. Tel 0932 862105

Cobham

Pretty and cottage-like with its white, ivy-clad exterior, this 16th-century pub attracts an upmarket clientele. But since it looks on to a common where children can play, and they are also allowed in the Stable Bar, it is suitable for families too. Ruddles County and Best, Courage Best and Webster's Yorkshire are served in the softly lit main bar, where cushioned settles, low beams and an exposed-brick inglenook fireplace contribute to an atmosphere of civilised calm - this is not a pub for gaggles of youngsters. Spacious and light, the restaurant extension is similarly peaceful and offers a table d'hôte lunch at £11.50, an à la carte menu with delights such as courgette and Stilton soup at £3.35 and smoked chicken tropicana at £5.95, and a regularly changing blackboard menu with, for example, mousaka at £4.35 and chicken chasseur at £4.85. In summer, white cast-iron tables and chairs are set out on the flowery patio at the front.

Brewery: Courage
Licensee: Brian Luxford
Opening hours: 11am-2.30pm, 6-11pm; Sun 12-2.30pm, 7-10.30pm
Bar food: 12-2pm, 7-10pm
Restaurant: 12-2pm, 7-10pm (except Sun evening and all day Mon)
Children: In Stable Bar only; half portions available; outdoor play area
Credit cards: AMERICAN EXPRESS®, Access, Visa, Diners

PLOUGH
Coldharbour Lane, Coldharbour, near Dorking RH5 6HD. Tel 0306 711793

Coldharbour

Situated among wooded hills, this white-rendered, 16th-century pub is the highest in the south-east, and attracts a mainly young clientele of mountain bikers, motorcyclists, walkers and riders, particularly at weekends, while in the week business people eat lunch here. The carpeted bar has black beams and red-ochre walls decorated with old guns, jugs and plates and a fearsome mantrap, and, like the adjoining eating area, is often full. A simply furnished family room is available, and in warm weather the patio or the garden, both with picnic benches and the latter with a pond and a fountain, are pleasant alternatives to being inside. The beers include Gibbs Mew Bishop's Tipple, Theakston Old Peculier, Hall & Woodhouse Badger, Ringwood Old Thumper, Adnams Broadside and Bateman XB and, in season, Winter Porter. French, German, Italian, Spanish, Californian and Australian wines, as well as a local white, are on sale. The home-cooked, traditional fare, which comes in generous portions, includes fish soup at £2.50, bacon pudding at £5.50 and apple, peach and apricot crumble at £2.25. Furnished in modern country style, two double rooms and a twin-bedded room are available.

Brewery: Free house
Licensees: Richard David Abrehart and Anna Josephine Abrehart
Opening hours: 11.30am-3pm, 6.30-11pm; Sun 12-3pm, 7-10.30pm
Bar food: 12-2.30pm, 7.30-9.30pm
Accommodation: (Price per person) single £20. (Price per room) double £40-£50; children under ten years not permitted
Children: In family room and eating area only and if supervised; half portions available

⊕ QUEENS HEAD
The Street, East Clandon, near Guildford GU4 7RY. Tel 0483 222332

East Clandon

An assorted clientele consisting mainly of older couples, tourists and, at lunchtime, business people, all find a warm welcome in this well-run village pub. The mellow brick-and-timber building, dating back to 1570, is quietly situated and has the further attractions of a large garden set out with picnic benches, a paddock with fruit trees where riders can tether their mounts and a patio with tables and chairs. Inside, a single bar with a flagstone floor serves four pleasant, carpeted rooms, all with black beams and ochre walls, while old guns and local prints add to the rural feel. Meals can be eaten in any of the four rooms, two of which are particularly cosy, thanks to a large inglenook fireplace in one and a smaller open fire in the other. The generous, home-cooked food includes Stilton and pork pâté and hot buttered shrimps, both at £3.75, and traditional main courses like rabbit and bacon pie at £5.95 and scrumpy chicken at £6.15. Fruit syllabub, at £2.75, is just one of several popular sweets on the menu. French, German, Italian and Spanish wines are available, while beer drinkers are catered for with ales from Friary Meux, Tetley, Burton and a guest beer.

Brewery: Ind Coope
Licensee: Christopher Green
Opening hours:11.30am-2.30pm (Sat 3pm), 6-11pm; Sun 12-3pm, 7-10.30pm
Bar food: 12-2pm, 7-10pm; Sun 7.30-9pm
Children: If eating and over eight years; outdoor play area
Credit cards: Access, Visa

⊕ WOOLPACK
The Green, Elstead, near Godalming GU8 6HD. Tel 0252 703106

Elstead

Dating back to the 14th century, the main part of this pub was much later augmented by a timber-clad extension which, happily, is in keeping with the building's original character. Reflecting the pub's name, implements of the wool trade are displayed in the spacious bar, which is carpeted and furnished with cushioned settles and spindle-back chairs. This pub is popular with business people at lunchtimes, families at weekends and regulars at any time - not least because of the food. As imaginative as that of many a good restaurant, the menu offers a wide choice which includes hot Camembert in cranberry sauce with salad at £3.95, duck breast in pear brandy and peppercorns and venison steak in port, mushroom and tarragon, both at £8.25, as well as traditional pies, steaks and sweets. Beers on draught include Burton, Friary Meux, and Greene King. At the rear is a garden with benches and a children's play area.

Brewery: Ind Coope
Licensees: Mr K W and Mrs J Macready
Opening hours: 11am-2.30pm, 6-11pm; Sun 12-3pm, 7-10.30pm
Bar food: 12-2pm, 7-9.45pm (Sun 7.30-9pm)
Restaurant: Times as bar food
Children: In family room and restaurant only; outdoor play area
Credit cards: Access, Visa

⊕ STEPHEN LANGTON
Friday Street, Abinger Common, near Dorking RH5 6JR. Tel 0306 730775

Friday Street

The plain appearance of this brick and timber pub, which is named after a 13th-century archbishop of Canterbury and replaced a much older inn in the 1930s, contrasts with the luxuriant setting. Undulating mixed woodland surrounds a secluded hamlet comprising a handful of cottages of local stone and timber cladding and a tranquil hammer pond. Customers find a warm welcome in the carpeted bar, with its cushioned wall seats and small open fire. At busy times a family room cum additional eating area is available, and in summer picnic benches are set out in front of the pub. Bass, Young's Special, Fuller's London Pride and two guest beers are on offer to accompany generous portions of traditional country fare - good value at, for example, £2.50 for home-made carrot and mint soup, £5 for rabbit pie and £5.25 for beef in ale.

Brewery: Bass
Licensee: Steve Duckett
Opening hours: 11am-2.30pm, 6-11pm; Sun 12-3pm, 7-10.30pm
Bar food: 12-2.30pm, 6-10pm; Sun 12-2.30pm, 7-10pm
Children: In family room only
Credit cards: Access, Visa

⊕ CITY ARMS
5-6 Portsmouth Road, Long Ditton, near Surbiton KT7 0XE. Tel 081 398 2471

Long Ditton

As well as prints of country scenes and copper pots and pans, this riverside pub boasts a collection of fire badges. In the early days of fire insurance, if a building was on fire but did not display such a badge, fire engines would drive straight by, to the next blaze. Nowadays, this unfriendly attitude is long forgotten in the comfortable bar and restaurant, with their clientele of local people in the evenings and largely business trade at lunchtime. Webster's Yorkshire, Courage Best, Wadworth 6X and a selection of imported lagers are on offer. In the non-smoking restaurant, which has its own bar, a menu and daily specials are available. All home-made, the dishes include devilled whitebait at £2.75 and steak and kidney pie and mushrooms at £3.95, and, on Sundays, a three-course lunch at £7.95.

Brewery: Free house
Licensee: D A Lehane
Opening hours: 11am-11pm; Sun 12-3pm, 7-10.30pm
Bar food: 11am-2.30pm, 5.30-10pm; Sun 12-2.30pm, 7-10pm
Restaurant: Times as bar food
Children: In restaurant only and if well behaved; children's menu available
Credit cards: Access, Visa

⊕ PUNCHBOWL INN
Oakwoodhill, near Ockley RH5 5PU. Tel 0306 627249

Oakwoodhill

Dating in part from the 14th century, this substantial, tile-hung pub is a good example of the Wealden style. The spacious bar, with inglenook fireplace, stone floor and cushioned settles at pine tables, adjoins an eating area which is popular with families as well as older customers. South African specialities like bobotjie (baked spicy minced beef with rice and sultanas) at £4.95 form part of a cosmopolitan

Brewery: Hall & Woodhouse
Licensees: Peter and Diana Watson
Opening hours: 11am-11pm; Sun12-10.30pm
Bar food: 12-2.30pm, 7-9.30pm
Children: In eating area only

menu that also offers Portuguese and Greek dishes as well as traditional English stand-bys such as Spotted Dick at £2.25. Hall & Woodhouse Badger and Tanglefoot, and Wadworth 6X, are the draught beers on sale, and there is a good selection of malt whiskies and South African wines. From time to time of an evening jazz can be heard in the separate function room. A few picnic benches are set out on the patio in front of the pub, which enjoys a quiet setting amid wooded farmland.

BELL INN
Outwood Lane, Outwood, near Redhill RH1 5PW. Tel 0342 844427/842989

Outwood

Tucked off a lane through a quiet village, this handsome17th-century pub, tile-hung over brick, is a pleasant haven, particularly for diners. The restaurant does a bustling trade with regulars, business people and well-heeled youngsters, serving starters such as garlic shrimps at £2.30 and scampi Kiev at £4, main courses including beef Wellington at £8.45 and sole Dieppe at £9.90, as well as a good selection of sweets. During the summer barbecues are held every weekday evening in the spacious garden, where there is a separate bar, and cream teas are served from 3 to 5pm. The welcoming, beamed bar and restaurant extension are carpeted, and the latter has comfortable tapestry-covered chairs around dark tables and attractive Holbein prints on the walls. Harvey's Best, Young's Special and Marston's Pedigree are among the beers on offer.

Brewery: Free house
Licensees: John Lane and Peter Austin
Opening hours: 11am-11pm; Sun 12-3pm, 7-10.30pm
Bar food: 12-2pm, 7-10pm
Restaurant: Times as bar food
Children: Welcome anywhere away from bar
Credit cards: AMERICAN EXPRESS®, Access, Visa

⊜ WHITE HORSE
Middle Street, Shere, near Guildford GU5 9HS. Tel 048641 2518

Shere

The heart of a pretty village, long popular with tourists and daytrippers, is the setting for this pub. Dating from 1475, the half-timbered and part tile-hung building has served as a pub for three centuries. In addition to the bar, with its open fire, black beams and wheelback and upholstered high-back chairs, there is a cosy dining room and a further drinking area. On tap are Webster's Yorkshire and Ruddles County and Best, and 20 wines are available to accompany the inventive, sensibly priced dishes. A typical starter is deep-fried Camembert in cranberry sauce at £2.80, while main courses include sausage and Stilton pie at £4.95 and the sweets, pecan pie for example, are all £1.50. In summer picnic benches are available in front of the pub, or drinkers can sit beside the nearby stream.

Brewery: Chef and Brewer
Licensee: Michael Wicks
Opening hours: 11.30am-2.30pm, (Sat 3pm), 6-11pm; Sun 12-3pm, 7-10.30pm
Bar food: 12-2pm, 7-9.30pm
Children: In dining room and other drinking areas, but not near bar
Credit cards: AMERICAN EXPRESS®, Access, Visa, Diners

⊜ THREE HORSESHOES
Dye House Road, Thursley, near Godalming GU8 6QU. Tel 0252 703268

Thursley

A quiet, secluded location and a spacious garden with a summer house, backing on to open country, are among the external attractions of this tile-hung, 17th-century pub. Inside, in addition to Gale's beer and guest ales, and the choice of five malt whiskies, the main draw is the restaurant's cosmopolitan menu: Italian starters at £2.50 to £4, Greek salad at £3.95, Indonesian chicken at £6.25 and various curries, as well as traditional main courses and sweets like treacle tart at £2.50. Simple bar food is also available. A good assortment of customers mingle in the comfortable, carpeted bar, with its wheelback chairs, two open fires and cartoons by Brockbank of *Punch* .

Brewery: Free house
Licensee: Steven Denman
Opening hours: 11am-2.30pm, (Fri and Sat 3pm); Sun 12-3pm, 7-10.30pm
Bar food: 12-2pm, 7-9.30pm (except Sun evening)
Restaurant: Times as bar food
Children: In restaurant during day only; outdoor play area
Credit cards: Access,Visa

SCARLETT ARMS
Walliswood Green Road, Walliswood, near Ockley RH5 5RD. Tel 0306 627243

Walliswood

O ak beams, a stone floor and a generous open fireplace give a homely feel to the front bar of this unspoilt and friendly country pub. The cosy back bar, carpeted and with delicate green wallpaper, serves as a dining room, and both bars are decked with locally dried flowers and corn dollies. The pleasant front garden, extending the width of the white-rendered, 16th-century building, faces a quiet road and is well supplied with picnic benches. Simple country cooking is the perfect complement to the King & Barnes beers on offer here - Broadwood, Sussex, Old Ale and Festive - and to Stowford Press cider. Regular dishes, which can be eaten in either bar, include rabbit pie, steak and kidney pie and pheasant casserole at £3.95, as well as popular sweets like Mississippi mud pie at £1.65.

Brewery: King & Barnes
Licensee: P A Haslam
Opening hours: 11am-2.30pm, 5.30-11pm; Sun12-3pm, 7-10.30pm
Bar food: 12-2pm, 7-9pm
Children: Not permitted inside

⊜ ONSLOW ARMS
West Clandon, near Guildford GU7 4TE. Tel 0483 222447

West Clandon

In the comfortable, beamed restaurant - the pub dates from 1623 - lit by candles and with original oil paintings lining the walls, diners can choose between the table d'hôte at £16.50 and an extensive à la carte menu. The latter offers imaginative starters such as torte filled with salmon with sole and turbot mousse and oyster sauce at £6.50 or home-made terrine at £2.95, followed by a wide and frequently changing selection of main courses, including sea bass at £9.85, tournedos at £10.25 and calves' sweetbreads at £9.95. Around 120 wines are available, ranging from £7.85 for the house wine to £85. With the onset of autumn the restaurant's large inglenook fireplace is pressed into nightly service for spit-roasting suckling pig. In addition, bar meals are served in the Carvery. In summer, when the pub's pretty, tile-hung frontage is decked with hanging baskets, sitting in the garden at the rear or in the covered arbour makes a pleasant alternative to drinking inside. A small helipad is available for those who wish to literally drop in for a drink or a meal. The choice of beers is broad, with 11 on offer, including Boddingtons, Bass, Young's Special and Wadworth 6X. An unusual item among the bottled beers is the German Weissbier. Brimming with character and with ancient guns, fresh flowers and gleaming copper everywhere, the bar is frequented by a mixed clientele, with the occasional celebrity to be spotted.

Brewery: Free house
Licensee: Alan Peck
Opening hours: 10.30-3pm, 5.30-11pm; Sun 12-3pm, 7-10.30pm
Bar food: 12-2pm, 7-9.30pm; Sun 12-2pm only
Restaurant: 12.30-2pm, 7-10pm (except Mon)
Children: In Carvery and restaurant only; outdoor play area
Credit cards: AMERICAN EXPRESS®, Access, Visa, Diners

BLEAK HOUSE
Chertsey Road, Horsell, Woking GU21 5ML. Tel 0483 760717

Woking

With children welcome as long as they are kept away from the bar, this is a good family pub, although the clientele is well assorted, comprising both younger and retired people, and business trade at lunchtime. Youngsters in particular are attracted by the jazz and blues bands which play here every Monday evening. A substantial, cream-painted building with a garden with picnic benches at the back, the pub dates from the last century. Recently renovated, the carpeted, part wood-panelled bar has a bright, new feel to it, having lost some of the character it had when, for example, part of *The War of the Worlds* was filmed here. All the same, the staff are committed and friendly and the food is good. Mainly home-made, this includes shellfish platter at £5.95 and steak and kidney pie at £4.10, with a list of 12 wines to complement them. Beer drinkers can choose from Tetley, Burton and Young's, or three draught lagers.

Brewery: Friary Meux
Licensee: Paul Staps
Opening hours: 11am-3pm, 5.30-11pm; Sun 12-2.30pm, 7-10.30pm
Bar food: 12-2pm, 7-9.30pm (except Mon evening)
Children: Welcome anywhere away from bar; children's menu available
Credit cards: Access, Visa

SUSSEX (EAST)

ROSE COTTAGE INN
Alciston, near Polegate BN26 6UW. Tel 0323 870377

Alciston

A welcoming landlord, good food and a setting at the foot of the Downs in ideal walking country make this inn popular with weekend hikers as well as a loyal local following. Attractive and cottagey, its white walls creeper-covered, it stands at the centre of the hamlet facing a large barn across a quiet road to nowhere. A small beamed bar displaying enamel advertising signs alongside animal traps and other paraphernalia of country life offers Merrydown local ciders and designer beers like Rolling Rock and Becks as well as draught Harveys Best, Young's Special and Guinness. Good-quality home-cooked meals, based on fresh ingredients and fairly priced, include some particularly tasty fish dishes - devilled crab and noodles at £5.25 or brill meunière at £7.95, for example - and there is always a vegetarian option; the restaurant, which at lunchtimes and on Sundays doubles as bar space, offers a more extensive evening menu.

Brewery: Free house
Licensee: Ian Lewis
Opening hours: 11.30am-2.30pm, 6.30-11pm; Sun 12-2pm, 7-10.30pm
Bar food: 12-2pm, 7-10pm; Sun 12-1.30pm, 7-9.30pm
Restaurant: 7-9pm (except Sun)
Children: Welcome as legally permitted

☕ YE OLDE SMUGGLERS INNE
Waterloo Square, Alfriston BN26 5UE. Tel 0323 870241

Alfriston

The sign of this weatherboarded two-storey pub which has overlooked the main square of the village since 1358 still displays the name by which it was known in its smuggling days - the Market Cross Inn. Informal and relaxed, it attracts locals and visitors alike, a walled courtyard with tables and aviary proving ideal for families with children. There is one rambling bar, the low-beamed main area with its inglenook fireplace displaying a collection of old kitchen utensils being augmented by a light, airy conservatory extension which provides a no-smoking area. Standard pub fare - of average quality and fairly priced - offers chips with everything from scampi (£3.90) to T-bone steak (£8.75), but there is always at least one vegetarian dish, and a range of sweets includes such temptations as treacle pudding and custard or Death by Chocolate (both £1.95). Some five or six malts are available, and several bottled beverages (Grolsch, Newcastle Brown, Real Budweiser, with Merrydown Vintage and Diamond White ciders) supplement a draught range which includes Courage Best and Directors, Harveys Best and John Smith's Keg.

Brewery: Free house
Licensee: Maureen Ney
Opening hours: 11am-2.30pm (3pm Sat), 6.30-11pm; Sun 12-3pm, 7-10.30pm
Bar food: 12-2pm, 7.30-9pm; Sat and Sun 12-2pm, 7-9pm
Children: Not permitted near bars

WHITE HORSE INN
Bodle Street Green, near Herstmonceaux BN27 4RE. Tel 0323 833243

Bodle Street Green

The house emblem painted on its roof a famous local landmark and its attractive white exterior enlivened by flower tubs, this 150-year-old inn has been double-glazed to combat the noise of the busy crossroads near which it stands. Carefully maintained, clean and welcoming, it appeals particularly to the older generation; certainly the only outside seating - a paved terrace alongside the road - is not safe for young children. The carpeted, beamed bar offers 20 malts, a range of draught beers that includes Harveys Best, Guinness, Toby, Worthington Best and Bass mild, and a very imaginative menu - standard choices like home-cooked ham salad at £4.50 and rump steak at £6.75 being supplemented by both a specials board and a range of vegetarian dishes.

Brewery: Free house
Licensee: Mr R Tiney
Opening hours: 12-2.30pm, 7-11pm; closed Mon; Sun 12-3pm, 7-10.30pm
Bar food: As opening hours; last orders 2pm and 9pm
Children: Not permitted inside

BELL INN
Burwash, near Etchingham TN19 7EH. Tel 0435 882304

Burwash

This pleasant pub, its solid-looking brick building dating from 1609, stands opposite the church at the centre of the village; etched glass windows, hanging baskets and a passion flower creeper combine to create an attractive frontage, and tables are set on the wide pavement dividing the inn from a busy road. A medium-sized but quite cosy bar, its low beams decked with hop vines, offers traditional amusements as well as serving generous portions of such dishes as steak and kidney with mushrooms and ale (£5.95) or grilled Rye Bay plaice (£6.50); draught beers include Harveys Best, Guinness and three guest beers. Accommodation - though perhaps somewhat lacking in elegance - is comfortable and clean.

Brewery: Beards of Sussex
Licensee: David Mizel
Opening hours: 11am-2.30pm, 6-11pm; Sun 12-3pm, 7-10.30pm
Bar food: 12-2pm, 7-9.30pm (except Sun evening)
Restaurant: Times as bar food
Accommodation: (Price per room) single from £25, double from £35
Children: Welcome in restaurant
Credit Cards: Access, Visa

On the Inside
The earliest pubs were people's homes and were furnished and decorated accordingly. It was not until the 1820s that the bar-counter made its appearance, but already a distinction had grown up between the taproom for labourers and poorer customers, and the parlour for the better-off. The taproom might have sawdust on the floor and simple, rough furniture, but the parlour began to sport carpets, pictures of the royal family and cases of butterflies or stuffed birds. The Victorian gin palaces introduced an altogether plushier style.

The big brewing chains have intruded a fake and regimented note into pub decor, but many pubs still nostalgically display Toby jugs or horse-brasses, agricultural bygones, ornamental brass plates or gleaming copper pans.

Some maintain their individuality with collections of oddities that have taken the landlord's fancy - police equipment or cigarette cards, neckties or man traps, or even fossilised hot cross buns.

⊕ YEW TREE INN
Chalvington, near Hailsham BN27 3TB. Tel 0323 811326

Chalvington

Small and intimate, this unspoiled country pub dating from the mid-1600s stands isolated beside a quiet back road, set in a small garden which opens on to a six-acre playing field where local football and cricket are played. Two quaint, low-ceilinged bars - peopled mainly by regulars - offer a fruit machine as well as traditional amusements like darts, pool and cards. A limited range of draught beverages includes Harveys Best beer, Heineken lager and Strongbow cider. Home-cooked bar food features old favourites such as cottage pie or macaroni cheese with French bread (both at £4.20) as well as sandwiches and ploughman's; small portions can be provided for children, but there will not necessarily be a vegetarian alternative.

Brewery: Free house
Licensee: R Coomber
Opening hours: 11am-2.30pm, 6-11pm; Sun 12-3pm, 7-10.30pm
Bar food: 12-2pm (except Sun)
Children: Welcome subject to legal restrictions; outdoor play area

⊕ SIX BELLS
The Street, Chiddingly, near Hailsham BN8 6HE. Tel 0825 872227

Chiddingly

This pleasant country pub with a friendly atmosphere is popular both for its good-value food and its weekend music - rock or blues on Friday, Saturday and Sunday evenings, and jazz at lunchtime on Sundays. A solid-looking, rectangular, brick building dating back to 1720, it stands at a quiet road junction in the village centre, the enclosed garden beside its car park set with tables and used for barbecues in summer. Three welcoming bars with panelled walls, brick floors and cushioned bench seating display old farm implements and an attractive collection of enamelled signs; beverages on sale include both the local Merrydown cider and a good range of lagers as well as draught Courage Best and Directors and John Smith's Keg. Bar meals make no pretension to haute cuisine, comprising generously served portions of such dishes as lasagne (£1.70), steak and kidney pie (£2.25) and chilli con carne (£3.75). At least three vegetarian options are available each day.

Brewery: Free house
Licensee: Paul Newman
Opening hours: 11am-3pm, 6-11pm; Sun 12-3pm, 7-10.30pm
Bar food: 11.45am-2.30pm, 6-10.30pm; Sun 12-2.30, 7-10pm
Children: Welcome away from the bar and in family room

⊕ OLD VINE
Cousley Wood, near Wadhurst TN5 6ER. Tel 0892 782271

Cousley Wood

Set at the centre of a rambling village, dating from 1515 and retaining much of its original old-world charm, this pleasant pub has achieved an excellent local reputaion. Its small, fenced beer garden will appeal to families with young children, while a bar with low oak beams and an inglenook is divided into cosy little areas by partitions and high pew seats;

Brewery: Whitbread
Licensee: Mr A Peel
Opening hours: 11am-2.30pm, 6-11pm; Sun 12-2.30pm, 7-10.30pm
Bar food: 12.15-2pm, 7-9.30pm

in its peaceful atmosphere (the only entertainment being live jazz on Monday evenings) customers are offered a choice of Flowers, Harveys Best and Fremlins draught beer. A good wine list accompanies a range of value-for-money home-cooked meals which includes such main courses as steak and kidney pie (£4) and chicken Kiev and chips (£5.25), a selection of starters (Parma ham and melon at £2.50, for example) and a trolley choice of sweets at £2.

(except Mon evenings)
Restaurant: Times as bar food
Children: Welcome in restaurant only
Credit Cards: Access, Visa, Diners

⊜ TIGER INN
The Green, East Dean, near Eastbourne BN20 0DA. Tel 0323 423209

East Dean

Popular with walkers, this cosy old pub - with roses round the door and window boxes making splashes of colour against its white-painted walls - provides a favourite coffee and lunch venue in the pleasant terrace overlooking the village green; though there is no actual road access, parking is available near by. A tiger's head adorns the oak-beamed bar, and beneath its gaze is served a selection of draught beers that includes Harveys Bitter and Worthington Keg. A list of half a dozen wines accompanies a bar menu offering such dishes as green pea and ham soup (£1.95), Dover sole meunière (£6.25), cauliflower cheese (£3.25) and cherry crumble (£1.75).

Brewery: Free house
Licensee: C Davies-Gilbert
Opening hours: 11am-2.30pm (3pm Sat), 6-11.30pm;
Sun 12-3pm, 7-10.30pm
Bar food: 12-2pm (Sat 2.30pm), 6.30-9pm; Sun 12-2.30pm only
Children: Welcome in family room

WHITE DOG INN
Village Street, Ewhurst Green, near Robertsbridge TN32 5TD.
Tel 0580 830264

Ewhurst Green

Its front separated from the road only by a terrace set with tables, this white-painted, tile-hung inn also has an enclosed rear garden where children can play safely. Despite later additions, parts of the original 15th-century buildings remain, features like the bar's low beams and polished brick floor still being very much in evidence. A good range of beers (including Newcastle Amber/Brown and Miller and draught Worthington, Harveys, Bass, Guinness and Fuller's London Pride) is available, and meals - though fairly standard pub fare - represent good value for money, with soup at £1.80, ploughman's at £3.75, macaroni cheese at £4.50 and chicken Kiev at £6.50.

Brewery: Free house
Licensees: Andy and Val Walters
Opening hours: 11am-3.30pm, 6-11pm; Sun 12-3pm, 7-10.30pm
Bar food: 12-2pm, 7-9pm (Fri and Sat 9.30pm, Sun 8.30pm)
Restaurant: Times as bar food
Children: Not permitted in bar; children's menu available
Credit Cards: Access, Visa

RAM INN
Firle, near Lewes BN8 6NS. Tel 0273 858222

Firle

Patrons from all walks of life are attracted to this quiet and friendly pub with its light, airy interior, sizeable side garden and views of the distant Downs. A traditional three-storey building which has stood at the centre of the village since the 17th century, it features a spacious, low bar with black beams and cream-washed walls adorned with photos of local interest. You won't find either electronic games or piped music here, but all the old-fashioned amusements - darts, dominoes, shove halfpenny and Toad in the Hole are available and there is a piano in the corner of the room; folk music evenings are held on the first Monday and first and third Wednesday of each month. A range of bar meals (the quality of which has earned the Ram second place in the Guinness Pub Food Competition) includes home-cooked ham salad at £4.95, hot smoked trout salad or macaroni cheese with garlic bread at £5.45 and banana toffee pie or apricot crumble at £2.75. Draught beers include Harveys Best, Charrington IPA and Guinness, there is a choice of four malts, and several wines can be purchased by the glass. Accommodation of a generally good standard is provided in large, plainly decorated bedrooms furnished with reproduction pieces.

Brewery: Free house
Licensee: Michael Wooller
Opening hours: 11.30am-3pm, 7-11pm; Sun 12-3pm, 7-10.30pm
Bar food: 12-2pm, 7-9pm
Accommodation: (Price per room) single from £25, double £45-£60; children not permitted under 14 years
Children: Permitted in Snug only
Credit Cards: Access, Visa

☺ GRIFFIN INN
Fletching, near Uckfield TN22 3SS. Tel 0825 722890

Fletching

This very pleasant 400-year-old pub opening directly on to the main street of the village has a particularly charming frontage, with its elegant porches, carved eaves and geranium-filled window boxes. The large, unfenced garden enjoys lovely views. Egon Ronay's Wine Pub of the Year, with about 70 bottles on its list, it also offers designer lagers like Becks, Rolling Rock and Stein in addition to draught beers featuring Harveys Best Bitter, King & Barnes Sussex, Fuller's London Pride and Hall & Woodhouse Tanglefoot. An excellent short menu is presented in both bar and restaurant, the latter also providing a wider à la carte choice in the evening; home-cooked food, expertly prepared and served with fresh seasonal vegetables represents sound value for money - a range of puddings (all at £2.95) forming part of a regularly changed blackboard display whose main courses (French bread pizza at £3.95, cheese quiche at £4.95 or fish pie at £5.25, for example) include a seafood special on Thursdays. Accommodation is provided in attractive beamed rooms, the doubles boasting four-poster beds.

Brewery: Free house
Licensee: David Pullan
Opening hours: 12-3pm, 6-11pm; Sun 12-3pm, 7-10.30pm
Bar food: 12-2.30pm, 7-9.30pm
Restaurant: Bar menu at lunchtimes, evening à la carte 7.30-9.30pm
Accommodation: (Price per room) single £40-£50, double £40-£70
Children: Welcome amywhere
Credit Cards: AMERICAN EXPRESS®, Access, Visa

⊕ ANCHOR INN
Church Street, Hartfield TN7 4AG. Tel 0892 770424

Hartfield

A very good selection of draught beers - Fremlins, Guinness, Flowers Original, Whitbread Best, Murphy's, Adnams, Harveys Sussex, and Marston's Pedigree - figures prominently among the attractions of this pleasant, unpretentious, village-centre inn, an ivy-clad 15th-century building with mock-Tudor extensions. The cosy, cheerfully noisy bar with its wood-burner, low oak beams and long-case clock provides adults with such traditional diversions as darts, dominoes and shove halfpenny, while swings and a climber in the large garden keep younger visitors amused. Bar meals like steak sandwich with chips (£4.75) or eels in red wine (£5.50) followed by lemon sorbet (£1.25) or French apple flan (£1.50), for example, always include vegetarian options, and accommodation is available in spaciously comfortable double bedrooms.

Brewery: Free house
Licensee: K J Thompson
Opening hours: 11am-11pm; Sun 12-3pm, 7-10.30pm
Bar food: 12-2pm, 6-10pm; Sun 12-1.45pm, 7-10pm
Restaurant: 7-9.30pm (except Sun)
Accommodation: (Price per room) single £25-£30, double from £35
Children: Welcome anywhere; outdoor play area
Credit Cards: Access, Visa

STAG INN
14 All Saints Street, Hastings TN34 3BJ. Tel 0424 425734

Hastings

A smuggling inn in the days when tunnels ran up the East Hill, this solid-looking pub is approached by a steep flight of steps off one of Hastings' most ancient streets, right in the middle of the old town; an equally steep garden, though unkempt, provides a safe play area for children. Unspoiled by tourism and retaining a core of local 'regulars', it offers a fair choice of draught beers (Shepherd Neame Best, Spitfire, Stock Ale and Master Brew, Eldridge Pope Thomas Hardy Bitter and Murphy's), Steinbeck and Hurlimann lager and Scrumpy Jack cider, as well as a wide selection of malts in two pleasant, welcoming bars with oak beams, waxed board floors - and a glass case of mummified cats said once to have been witches' familiars! Amusement as divergent as electronic games and chess co-exist happily, and standard bar menus include fairly priced dishes like chicken Kiev and lasagne at £3.70 or chilli con carne at £3.30. A vegetarian alternative is always included, but there will not neccessarily be anything suitable for children.

Brewery: Shepherd Neame
Licensee: Andrew Lipscombe
Opening hours: 11am-3pm, 6-11pm (Sat 11am-11pm); Sun 12-3pm, 7-10.30pm
Bar food: 12-2.30pm, 6-9.30pm (Sun 7pm)
Accommodation: (Price per room) single from £15, double from £25
Children: Permitted in back bar when drinks not being served; outdoor play area

---

Brewing on a Sussex Wharf
The majestic Victorian Gothic brewery on Bridge Wharf, with its own spring of water close to the River Ouse at Lewes in Sussex, dates from 1882. The firm of Harvey goes much further back, however, to 1790, when it was founded by John Harvey, a Sussex wine merchant. The brewery passed to the Smith family by marriage and for years was controlled by three Smith sisters, the last of whom retired in 1965. Harvey's has won many awards for its Elizabethan Ale and Sweet Sussex Stout.

⊜ JUGGS ARMS
The Street, Kingston, near Lewes BN7 3NT. Tel 0273 472523

Kingston

Excellent facilities for both parents and children are provided by this pleasant old pub at the centre of the village. The traditional Kentish-style building with low eaves and ivy-covered, tile-hung walls stands in a garden featuring not only attractive flower beds but also a good children's play area and a very extensive brick-paved section with seating at tables for up to 150 people. Fairly standard pub meals are served in a low-ceilinged, oak-beamed bar where the horse-brasses - which, together with harnesses, form part of a display of country artefacts - reflect the flames of an open fire; main courses range from scampi at £4.50 to fillet steak at £8.95, with a vegetarian choice always available; draught beers include Harveys Bitter and King & Barnes Broadwood and Festive. A similar menu is offered in the gas-lit restaurant (no smoking), and a good wine list currently features some 30 bottles, with an additional English selection promised for the near future.

Brewery: Free house
Licensee: Andrew Browne
Opening hours: 10am-2.30pm, 6-10.45pm (Fri and Sat 11pm); Sun 12-2.30pm, 7-10.45pm
Bar food: 12-2pm, 6-9.30pm (Sun from 7pm)
Restaurant: Times as bar food
Children: Welcome anywhere; own menu available; outdoor play area
Credit Cards: Access, Visa (five per cent supplement for credit cards)

ROSE AND CROWN INN
Fletching Street, Mayfield TN20 6TE. Tel 0435 872200

Mayfield

A welcoming atmosphere and quality accommodation are the hallmarks of this attractive, unspoiled, 16th-century pub on the outskirts of the village. The four linked rooms that make up the rambling, comfortable bar area are traditional in style, an inglenook fireplace and low beams forming the background to an array of pewter mugs and a collection of coins stuck to the ceiling. Some foreign lagers and designer beers are featured alongside good-value draught - Harveys Sussex Best, Greene King Abbot Ale, Courage Directors and Adnams Southwold; and a varied selection of home-cooked foods, served in generous portions, always includes a vegetarian option as well as dishes like steak and kidney pie at £4.95, lamb fillets with redcurrant and rosemary at £6.25 and salmon and scallops in pastry at £7.65. A rear garden, separated from the pub by a hedge, provides both a safe area for children to play in and pleasant seating, while tables at the front of the building enjoy the shade of a huge horse-chestnut tree.

Brewery: Free house
Licensee: Mr P Seely
Opening hours: 11am-3pm, 5.30-11pm; Sun 12-3pm, 7-10.30pm
Bar food: 12-2pm, 7-9.30pm
Restaurant: 12-3pm, 7-11.30pm
Accommodation: (Price per room) single from £38, double from £48
Children: Welcome but not permitted inside under nine years
Credit Cards: Access, Visa

⊛ BULL INN
Three Leg Cross, near Ticehurst TN5 7HH. Tel 0580 200586

Three Leg Cross

Cosy and friendly (even if a little slipshod, and adorned with an overabundance of brewery and beer advertisements!) this Kentish-style pub dating from 1385 stands in a quiet road half a mile from the village centre, near Bewl Water Reservoir. Outside seating is provided in a large garden complete with fishpond, and though there is no actual play area for children a 'bouncy castle' is set up during the summer months. Two low-ceilinged, oak-beamed bars decked with dried hops display rural artefacts, and open fires burn in the inglenook in winter. Chips are conspicuously absent from the menu, generously sized and fairly priced portions of dishes such as duck salad (£2.95), fillet in pastry (£8.50) or broccoli en croûte (£4.50) being followed perhaps by bread-and-butter pudding or sherry trifle (both at £2). Meals are also served in a separate restaurant (booking recommended). Scrumpy Jack, Taunton and Dry Blackthorn ciders are available on draught alongside Grolsch, Carling Black Label, Kronenbourg and Tennent Pils lagers and a choice of beers that includes Harveys Bitter, Morland Bitter, Charrington IPA and a guest beer.

Brewery: Free house
Licensee: Josie Wilson-Moir
Opening hours: 11am-3pm, 6-11pm; Sun 12-3pm, 7-10.30pm
Bar food: 12-2.30pm daily, 7-10.30pm (except Sun)
Restaurant: Times as bar food
Children: Welcome anywhere

DORSET ARMS HOTEL
Withyham, near Hartfield TN7 4BD. Tel 0892 770278

Withyham

The very friendly atmosphere pervading this comfortable, welcoming pub attracts customers from all walks of life. A front garden set with tables effectively isolates the white, tile-hung building from a fairly busy road that runs through this scattered village, but, being unfenced, it is not suitable for children. The slightly shabby bar with its big, old fireplace provides traditional amusements like darts, dominoes and cribbage as well as piped music and electronic games, and bar meals (though not notable) are fairly priced, with plaice and chips at £3.95 and steak and mushroom pie at £4.25. A vegetarian option is also available. Strongbow and Addlestone cask-conditioned cider, and Traditional Best, Mild and IPA are all available on draught.

Brewery: Harveys of Lewes
Licensee: Mr D T Young
Opening hours: Mon-Thu 11am-3pm, 5.30-11pm; Fri 11am-11pm; Sat 11am-3pm, 6-11pm; Sun 12-3pm, 7-10.30pm
Bar food: 12-2.30pm, 7-9.30pm (except Mon evening)
Children: Welcome anywhere

SUSSEX (WEST)

☕ FOUNTAIN INN
Ashurst, near Steyning BN44 3AP. Tel 0403 710219

Ashurst

The wide choice of real ales available at this charmingly unspoilt 400-year-old inn is listed on a board outside the entrance, tempting you in to try a beer from breweries like Bateman, Marston's, Young's, Whitbread or maybe Eldridge Pope and to unwind in the atmospheric and aptly named Inglenook Bar with its vast fireplace, low beams and scrubbed, flagged floor. A hatched bar allows service into a passageway which leads to the comfortable Lounge Bar where a blackboard menu announces dishes that offer excellent value for money. At lunchtime, there may be cheese and onion flan (£3.95), minced beef pie (£4.25) or mousaka (£4.25); in the evening, dishes range from vegetable and asparagus coulibiac, and steak and kidney pie, to salmon shantie, all at £5.95, while on summer evenings (Wed-Sat) and weekend lunchtimes a local Japanese lady prepares an oriental barbecue in the flower-bordered garden which has proved a great attraction. A further seating area is laid out beside a duck pond in the lovely garden. Morning coffee available.

Brewery: Free house
Licensees: Maurice and Jean Caine
Opening hours: 11am-2.30pm, 6-11pm; Sun 12-2.30pm, 7 10.30pm
Bar food: 12-2pm, 7.30-9.30pm (except Wed and Sun evening)
Children: In dining area only; outdoor play area

BLUE SHIP
The Haven, Billingshurst RH14 9BS. Tel 0403 822709

Billingshurst

The Victorian tile-hung, creeper-clad exterior conceals the true age of this unspoilt country pub, tucked away down a peaceful lane (off the A29 north of Billingshurst). At its core is a 14th-century, brick-floored room with vast inglenook fireplace, low heavy beams, pine tables and high-backed settles, leading to the small hatchway bar, which dispenses King & Barnes ales - Sussex Bitter and Broadwood - straight from the barrel. A stone-flagged passageway links the main bar to two other simply furnished rooms. A daily changing blackboard menu offers a good range of hearty dishes which may include tuna bake (£3.50), ratatouille au gratin (£3.85), ham, egg and chips (£4.20), with treacle tart, fruit crumble or 'grannies wedding cake' (home-made bread pudding, £1.85) for dessert. You can play bar-billiards, dominoes, crib and shove halfpenny in the separate games room. In summer, the pub's attractive garden and patio are popular for al fresco eating and drinking.

Brewery: King & Barnes
Licensees: John and Jenny Davie
Opening hours: 11am-3pm, 6-11pm; Sun 12-3pm, 7-10.30pm
Bar food: 12-2pm daily; Tue-Sat 7-9pm; Sun 12-2pm only
Children: In family room; outdoor play area

FOX
Bucks Green, Rudgwick, near Horsham RH12 3JP. Tel 0403 822386

Bucks Green

A unique feature of this attractive white-painted 16th-century cottage is the public bridleway that runs straight through the bar to the A281 Horsham-to-Guildford road beyond, and is kept open once a year by someone riding a horse in at one door and out through the other. On your way through though, stop for a well kept draught of Sussex-brewed King & Barnes ale - Sussex, Festive or Broadwood - and either relax among fox-hunting bits and pieces in the wood-floored and traditionally furnished main bar, sit in the tiny Saloon which is dominated by its vast inglenook fireplace, or, in summer, follow the path out into the fine garden. Sunday nights here are quiz nights and there is live music once a week. A wide range of standard pub food at fairly reasonable prices is available.

Brewery: King & Barnes
Licensees Charlie and Pauline Pulsford
Opening hours: 11am-2.30pm (Sat 3pm), 6-11pm; Sun 12-3pm, 7-10.30pm
Bar food: 12-2pm, 6.30-9pm; Sun 12-2pm
Children: Not permitted under 14 years in the bars; children's menu available; outdoor play area
Credit cards: Access, Visa

⊛ BLACK HORSE
Byworth, near Petworth GU28 0HO. Tel 0798 42424

Byworth

Supposedly built on the site of an old priory in a beautiful village setting, the pub's Georgian, three-storey, brick and stone frontage hides a much older interior dating back to the 14th century. Wooden floors and furniture, half-panelled walls and open fires characterise the three inter-connecting rooms, which lead to a flight of stairs up to a timbered Elizabethan dining room with magnificent views across the steeply terraced garden to a wooded valley beyond. A wide ranging and interesting menu may include French onion soup (£2.40), chicken sweet and sour (£6.55), lemon sole (£5.75), or a choice of steaks as well as some vegetarian dishes. Well kept Ballard's Best Bitter, Courage Directors and Young's Best Bitter are on handpump.

Brewery: Free house
Licensee: Paul Wheeler-Kingshott
Opening hours: 11am-2.30pm (11.30am winter), 6-11pm (6.30 pm winter); Sun 12-3pm, 7-10.30pm
Bar food: 12-1.45, 6-9.45pm; Sun 12-1.45pm, 7-9.45pm
Children: Welcome if well behaved
Credit cards:
AMERICAN EXPRESS®, Access, Visa, Diners

⊛ WHITE HORSE
Chilgrove, near Chichester PO18 9HX. Tel 0243 535219

Chilgrove

Renowned for its fine restaurant and splendid, award-winning cellar of wines - over 2000 bottles - this attractive old inn set in a lovely position at the base of the Sussex Downs also offers a short and imaginative bar menu, featuring a range of cold snacks as well as hot dishes such as roast Aylesbury duck (£6.95), venison casserole (£6.50), pot roast partridge (£10.95) and wild mushroom and leek pasta (£5.95). Sweets stray into the bar from the restaurant menu

Brewery: Free house
Licensees: Barry and Dorothea Phillips and Neil Rusbridger
Opening hours: 11am-2.30pm, 6-11pm; Sun 12-3pm (closed Sun evening, all day Mon, one week at end Oct and all Feb)

and may include rich chocolate terrine, treacle tart, apple and pear crumble or, as an alternative, a platter of English cheeses, all at £3.25. An excellent choice of 18 wines by the glass and (in summer only) a real ale - King & Barnes Festive - are available. Across the lane is a lawn for summer drinking. You may, incidentally, notice the inn sign, with its picture of a cat. The sign painter could not, when it came to the crunch, paint a convincing horse, but was good at cats.

Bar food: 12-2pm, 6-9pm; Sun 12-2pm
Restaurant: 12-2pm, 7-9.30pm; Sun
Children: Not permitted under 14 years inside
Credit cards: Access, Visa, Diners

⊜ COACH AND HORSES
The Square, Compton, near Chichester PO18 9HA. Tel 0705631 228

Compton

Situated in the heart of the village on the B2146, this white-painted, 15th-century coaching inn caters for all needs in its two bars and comfortable restaurant. As its name suggests, the half-panelled Village Bar is the public, where the locals gather, with bar billiards, juke box, a range of five real ales - Fuller's ESB, Hook Norton Best Bitter, Brains SA Best Bitter (nicknamed 'skull attack'), Theakston Best Bitter - and a lively atmosphere, whereas the beamed Lounge Bar with its fine brick fireplace offers a convivial atmosphere for meals. The bar menu is good value with dishes like chunky vegetable broth (£1.85), Irish stew (£5.15), bean and vegetable casserole (£4.95). A more imaginative menu is served in the attractive restaurant (booking advisable). Beyond the skittle alley is a small sheltered garden.

Brewery: Free house
Licensees: David and Chrissie Butler and John Jenner
Opening hours: 11am-2.30pm, 6-11pm; Sun12-3pm, 7-10.30pm
Bar food: 12-2pm, 6-9.30pm; Sun 12-2.30pm, 7-9pm
Restaurant: 7-9.30pm (except Sun evening and all day Mon)
Children: In Public Bar only
Credit cards: Access, Visa

⊜ KINGS HEAD
South Street, Cuckfield RH17 5JY. Tel 0444 454006

Cuckfield

Once host to royalty in the heyday of the coaching era, the 18th-century King's Head is now first and foremost a popular village meeting place catering for all. In the lively atmosphere of the panelled Public Bar and games room you can enjoy darts, pool, a juke box, electronic games, and live entertainment on winter Saturday nights to accompany simple bar snacks and well conditioned, Sussex-brewed ales from Harveys and King & Barnes. In contrast, the beamed restaurant, with its oak tables, leather-covered chairs, and fresh flowers offers a more relaxed atmosphere in which to enjoy imaginative food. Changing twice daily, the menu may start with rich satisfying soups such as cream of cauliflower, or smoked-duck salad (£2.20), both accompanied by home-baked bread, followed by lemon chicken (£3.95), beef and venison pie (£4.25), or medallions of lamb with almonds (£8.50) with, perhaps, a chocolate tart for dessert. Nine comfortable bedrooms have all the usual facilities.

Brewery: Free house
Licensee: Peter Tolhurst
Opening hours: 12-11pm (Mon 12-2.30pm, 5.30-11pm); Sun 12-3pm, 7-10.30pm
Bar food: As opening hours
Restaurant: 12-2.30pm, 5.30-9pm (closed Sun and Mon evening)
Accommodation: (Price per room) single £32-£42, double £42-£55
Children: In games room and main dining area only; own menu available
Credit cards: AMERICAN EXPRESS®, Access, Visa

🍺 GEORGE AND DRAGON
Dragons Green, Shipley, near Horsham RH13 7JE. Tel 0403 741320

Dragons Green

Best found by following the signs from the A272, this splendid old brick cottage dates from the 17th century, and the low ceiling and even lower beams add to the atmosphere and a little to the possibility of a headache. A log fire burns in the inglenook fireplace and warms the small Lounge Bar; the adjacent dining area is attractively furnished with dark oak tables and wheelback chairs, while the tiny Public Bar houses the darts board and bar billiards table. In summer the scene transfers to the peaceful well kept garden and orchard - the perfect spot to appreciate those fine King & Barnes ales, Sussex Bitter and malty Festive Ale.

Brewery: King & Barnes
Licensees: R Nash and M Saint
Opening hours: 11am-2.30pm, 6-11pm; Sun12-3pm, 7-10.30pm
Bar food: 12-2.30pm, 6-10pm; Sun 12-2.30pm, 7-9.30pm
Children: Welcome anywhere

🍺 THREE HORSESHOES
Elsted, near Midhurst GU29 0JX. Tel 0730 825746

Elsted

Built as a drovers' ale house in the 16th century, this pretty tiled house in the village centre takes you back a few centuries as you step through the latched doors into four cosy, connecting rooms, full of rural charm. Chairs, oak benches, antique settles and sturdy tables crowd the brick, tile and wood floors. In winter there are log fires, and beneath the heavy beams, ochre walls are hung with engravings, old photographs and a large blackboard menu displaying a hearty range of home-cooked dishes, served in the bars and the candlelit dining room overlooking the South Downs. Start with a choice of thick soups or pâté, followed by chicken and leek pie (£5.25), dressed crab (£5.50), rabbit pie in cider (£5.25) or fresh fish, with treacle tart or fruit crumble for pudding. Up to six regularly changing real ales are tapped straight from the barrel - among them may be Mitchell's Best Bitter, Wadworth 6X, Hook Norton Best Bitter, Adnams Best, or Ballard's Wassail. There are two farmhouse ciders, a list of about 30 wines and some country fruit wines. The vast garden, with its views of the South Downs, has resident chickens, a goat, pigs and other pets, and is a popular place on fine summer days.

Brewery: Free house
Licensees: Andrew and Sue Beavis
Opening hours: 11am-3pm, 6-11pm; Sun 12-3pm, 7-10.30pm
Bar food: 12-2pm, 7-10pm; Sun lunch 12-2pm only in winter
Children: Not permitted under 14 years inside

🍺 ELSTED INN
Elsted Marsh, near Midhurst GU29 0JT. Tel 0730 813662

Elsted Marsh

Good quality fresh produce from local suppliers is used in the cooking of the imaginative dishes served at this unassuming Victorian railway pub, which stands on a country lane about a mile away from the village and was

Brewery: Free House
Licensees: Tweazle Jones and Barry Horton
Opening hours: 11am-3pm,

once the home of Ballard's Brewery. The sausages for the hearty sausage and bacon pudding (£6.50) are made by a local pensioner, vegetables and lamb come from a nearby organic farm, fish comes from Selsey and game is provided by the Elsted shoot. The varied, daily changing menu may include mushroom soup (£2.75) and smoked salmon pâté for starters, followed by cassoulet (£5.75), courgette and spicy bean casserole (£5.95), or grilled Alresford trout (£6.50) with plum crumble, treacle tart or a selection of Sussex cheeses to finish. Country furniture, tables covered with gingham cloths, open fires and fresh flowers set the scene in the two bars and dining room. All three Ballard's beers - Trotton, Best and Wassail - are stocked as well as four other regularly changing ones and there is a good choice of wines. Honey and free range eggs are sold over the bar. Traditional games include shove halfpenny and garden boules; on the first Sunday of each month there is a craft fair; at midsummer there are Revels and a vintage sports car club holds its regular meetings here.

5.30-11pm; Sun 12-3pm, 7-10.30pm
Bar food: 12-2.30pm, 7-10pm
Children: Welcome, but not in Public Bar

⊜ DUKE OF CUMBERLAND

Henley Village, Fernhurst, near Haslemere GU27 3HG. Tel 0428 652280

Fernhurst

Tricky to locate, but worth finding in a tiny wooded lane off the A286, is this splendid 15th-century country inn, its brick and stone walls covered with roses and wisteria. The bar reverberates with atmosphere, created by the painted, panelled walls, low wood-beamed ceiling, quarry-tiled floor, scrubbed pine tables and benches and open log fires, with gas lamps (working in winter), old indentures and stuffed animals and birds decorating the walls. Sup a pint of King & Barnes Sussex Bitter or Festive, drawn straight from the cask, or a glass of local farmhouse cider while you take in the unspoilt charm. An extensive list of lunchtime bar snacks includes soup (£2.20) and an interesting range of sandwiches - such as toasted Stilton and ham (£2) - with a full lunch and evening menu offering mixed grills, steaks, fish and, with 24 hours' notice, game dishes such as venison, pheasant and duck. Outdoor seating can be enjoyed on the old cobbled front patio, in the colourful shrub and tree-filled terraced gardens and around the small trout pond, which is fed by the stream that runs through the garden. Jacob sheep and chickens roam in the three and a half acres of land.

Brewery: Free house
Licensee: David Allen
Opening hours: 11am-3pm, 5-11pm; Sun 12-3pm, 7-10.30pm
Bar food: 11am-2pm (snacks 2.30pm), 7.30-9.30pm; Sun 12-2.30pm, 7-9pm
Children: At lunchtime only

SHEPHERD AND DOG
High Street, Fulking, near Bramber BN5 9LU. Tel 0273 857382

Fulking

Deservedly popular for its glorious setting at the base of the South Downs - a footpath from the terraced garden leads to the South Downs Way - this long, low, cream-painted pub has a high reputation for its food and if you are eating you need to arrive early to avoid the long queues at the servery. At lunchtime there are about nine variations on the ploughman's theme (£3.30 - £4.75), several fish dishes (£3.95 to £4.95), plus daily fresh fish specials, a range of hot meat dishes, a vegetarian dish, huge salads, and triple-decker sandwiches. In the evenings there is even more choice, with starters at about £2.95 and main dishes (at busy times you must order a main dish, not just a starter), such as beef and Guinness pie or trout stuffed with spinach and crab at around £5.95. All this good food is served in the partly panelled, low-beamed bar, which is decorated with shepherds' memorabilia and furnished in country style with flowers on the tables and candles in the evenings. Ruddles County, Courage Directors, Webster's Yorkshire Bitter and Harveys Sussex Best are the beers and there are 15 wines. Morning coffee is another option.

Brewery: Courage
Licensee: Laurie McConochie
Opening hours: 10am-2.30pm, 5.30-11pm; summer 10am-11pm; Sun 12-3pm, 7-10.30pm
Bar food: 12-2pm, 6.30-9.30pm; Sun 12-2pm, 7-9.30pm
Children: Not permitted under 14 years inside; outdoor play area
Credit cards: AMERICAN EXPRESS®, Access, Visa, Diners

✆ ROYAL OAK
Hooksway, near Chilgrove PO18 9JZ. Tel 0243 59257

Hooksway

Set in a secluded hollow at the base of the South Downs off the B2141, this 'off the beaten track' 15th-century cottage is a real challenge to find. It has been an ale house for over 300 years and in its time has served no fewer than three kings - Edward VII, George V and King Alfonso of Spain - all of whom were on a shooting trip on the nearby estate. Today it is popular with walkers, because of the network of footpaths around the pub. At least five cask-conditioned ales - Gibbs Mew Bishop's Tipple, Courage Directors, Ruddles County and Best Bitter, Webster's Yorkshire Bitter - and Guinness are on tap. A range of country fruit wines and hearty snacks are served in the two simply furnished bars, which are warmed by open fires in winter. Every Friday evening there is live jazz or folk music, or at other times you can play dominoes, crib or shove halfpenny. Wooden picnic benches are scattered around the sunny front lawn.

Brewery: Free house
Licensee: David Jeffrey
Opening hours: 11am-3pm, 6-11pm (closed Mon Oct-Mar); Sun 12-3pm, 7-10.30pm
Bar food: 12-2pm, 6.30-10pm; Sun 12-2pm; 7-9.30pm
Children: In children's room only; outdoor play area
Credit cards: Access, Visa

⊜ LICKFOLD INN
Lickfold, near Petworth GU28 9EY. Tel 07985 285

Lickfold

The outstanding attraction of this timber-framed Elizabethan coaching inn on the edge of the village is the splendid shrub-filled garden with its 11 separate sitting areas on six different levels - definitely the place to be in summer. Another interesting feature are the old shoes, dating back to the time when the pub was built and now displayed in a glass case by the entrance. On cooler days a roaring log fire in the huge central chimney brightens the wood-panelled main bar with its rug-strewn brick floor, heavy oak tables and chairs and Georgian settles. A wide-ranging blackboard menu includes such dishes as Thai beef (£5.75), pheasant and red wine pie (£6.25), steak and kidney pie (£5.25), plus a range of filled jacket potatoes and ploughman's; puddings might included ginger and pear dumpling and lemon fudge cake (£2.50), all of which can be enjoyed in the heavily beamed dining area. Up to nine real ales are always available.

Brewery: Free house
Licensees: Ron and Kath Chambers
Opening hours: 11am-2.30pm, 6-11pm (Nov-Mar 10.30pm); closed Mon evening; Sun 12-3pm, 7-10.30pm
Bar food: 12-2pm, 7-9.30pm (except Sun evening in winter, occasionally in summer)
Children: Not permitted under 14 years inside
Credit cards: Access, Visa

⊜ HALFWAY BRIDGE INN
Lodsworth, near Petworth GU28 9VP. Tel 07985 281

Lodsworth

Set midway between Midhurst and Petworth, this is a rambling, upmarket 18th-century coaching inn. Inside, a number of stylishly decorated rooms radiate out from the central bar, furnished with a pleasing mix of old and new. Old dressers, long-case clocks, cushioned pews, paintings, prints and open log fires help preserve a traditional atmosphere. The two dining rooms, one with an inglenook fireplace, one with an old range, and the separate restaurant, housed in the old stables, make this a popular place for eating out. Freshly prepared dishes from the daily changing menu might include crab pâté (£2.95), courgette gratinée (£1.50), or Parma ham and melon (£3.25), as starters. Main courses range from lamb in red wine and rosemary (£5.50), Stilton and celery pasta bake (£4.25), to Dover sole (£12.95), with chocolate nut crunch or gooseberry and apple crumble (£2.25), for pudding. There is a good selection of wines by the glass and bottle and three real ales on handpump - Brakspear, Marston's Pedigree and Flowers Original.

Brewery: Free house
Licensees: Sheila and Edric Hawkins
Opening hours: 11am-2.30pm, 6-11pm; Sun 12-3pm, 7-10.30pm (closed Sun evening in winter)
Bar food: 12-2pm, 7-10pm; Sun 12-2.30pm, 7-10pm (summer only)
Children: In dining rooms only; not permitted under ten years
Credit cards: Access, Visa

⊜ BLACK HORSE
Nuthurst Street, Nuthurst, near Horsham RH13 6LH. Tel 0403 891272

Nuthurst

Relax on the sunny front terrace or in the delightfully secluded rear garden of this 17th-century coaching inn, which occupies part of a row of cottages on the old Brighton to Horsham road. The heavily beamed and timbered bars, with flagged and wooden floors, an assortment of country furniture and old photographs of local scenes help preserve a traditional atmosphere. On tap you will find King & Barnes Sussex Bitter, Tetley Bitter, Adnams Bitter, Greene King Abbot Ale, and Wadworth 6X. Bar food consists of good hearty dishes - for example daily specials such as lamb and rosemary pie (£5.25), or tuna, sweetcorn and pasta bake (£4.95). The regular menu offers a large choice including basket meals (also available as children's portions), jacket potatoes, 'hot' dishes like curry and Mexican chilli, and a variety of ploughman's from £2.95. Summer Sunday barbecues are proving very popular. Morning coffee is always available.

Brewery: Free house
Licensees: Trevor and Karen Jones
Opening hours: 11am-3pm, 6-11pm; Sun 12-3pm, 7-10.30pm
Bar food: 11am-2.30pm, 6-10.15pm; Sun 12-3pm, 7-10.30pm
Children: In dining area only
Credit cards: Access, Visa

THE GRIBBLE INN Oving *see page 140*

⊜ ANGEL HOTEL
Angel Street, Petworth GU28 0BG. Tel 0798 42153

Petworth

First and foremost an inn, this smart and well run town-centre hostelry has welcomed guests since the 13th century. A wealth of oak beams and inglenook fireplaces characterises its comfortably furnished bars and restaurant and there is a range of home-cooked bar meals for the casual passer-by. Dishes include whitebait, tuna Provençale, a salad bar selection or chicken curry, all at £3.50, or venison pie (£3.95), and omelettes (£2.95). In the evening there is a more elaborate bar menu supplemented by four specials of the day - for example, rack of lamb, escalope of veal, fresh fish and chicken with a tomato, pepper ham and garlic sauce, all at £8.50, with an excellent cheese board and sweet-trolley selection to finish. On Sunday lunchtimes a carvery roast is popular. Ballard's, Gale's, Adnams or Badger beers are available from the well stocked bar and a choice of 40 wines is on offer. There are eight pleasantly furnished, well equipped bedrooms. The secluded walled garden and paved courtyard are often the setting for jazz evenings and the like in summer.

Brewery: Free house
Licensee Mervyn Church
Opening hours: 11am-3pm, 5.30-11pm; Sun 12-3pm, 7-10.30pm
Bar food: 12-2pm, 6.45-9.30pm; Sun 12-2pm, 7-9.30pm
Restaurant: 6.45-9.30pm; Sun 12-3.30pm
Accommodation: (Price per room) single £40-£60, double £50-£75
Children: Very welcome; half portions available
Credit cards: AMERICAN EXPRESS®, Access, Visa

⊕ GRIBBLE INN
Oving, near Chichester PO20 6BP. Tel 0243 786893

Oving

A good reason for finding this most attractive 16th-century thatched cottage in the centre of the village is to sample the excellent range of ales brewed on the premises - Gribble Ale, Blackadder, Reg's Tipple, Harvest Gold and Pigs Ear - as well as Hall & Woodhouse Badger Best and Tanglefoot, all served in the low, heavily beamed bar which boasts a big, raised log fire, brick and timber walls, old pews, country furniture and a bustling atmosphere. Beyond this is an open-plan dining area and food servery with a menu ranging from substantial snacks to generous home-made pies, salads and steaks; next door there is a charming no-smoking family room. Traditional pub games include shove halfpenny, cribbage, dominoes and a popular skittles alley. A delightful cottage garden with apple trees and climbing roses is ideal for summer drinking.

Brewery: Free house
Licensees: James and Connie Wells
Opening hours: 11am - 2.30pm, 6 - 11pm; Sun 12-2.30pm, 7-10.30pm
Bar food: 12- 2pm, 6.30 - 9.30pm; Sun 12-2pm
Children: In family room only
Credit cards: Access, Visa

The Making of Beer

The traditional ingredients of beer are water, barley malt, hops, yeast and ripe judgement. One traditional brewery's products will taste different from another's because of variations in the blending of the ingredients and the timing of processes. It all starts with barley, malted in a kiln at the maltings: the higher the temperature, the darker the beer. The powdered malt is mixed with hot water to make a mash. How hot the mash is and how long it is allowed to stand will affect the taste and in the old days local spring water gave beer a distinctive local flavour. Burton upon Trent's eminent reputation for bitter rested on the gypsum in the town's water.

The liquid from the mash is boiled up with hops - the more hops, the bitterer - and sugar is often added. Next the liquid is cooled and yeast is stirred in to make it ferment. The 'green beer' is eventually run into casks to mature. Or it used to be, but nowadays most beer is filtered, sterilised and carbonated. This is keg beer, which is stored in sealed containers and tastes more like bottled beers, which are put through the same processes.

⊜ WELLDIGGERS ARMS
Pulborough Road, near Petworth GU28 0HZ. Tel 0798 42287

Petworth

As its name suggests, welldiggers once occupied this 300-year-old roadside pub, situated on the A283 just east of Petworth. It is very much a food-oriented pub - the comfortable beamed bar and Snug are always busy with diners, all seated on long settles and benches at huge oak tables, tucking into the hearty range of good value restaurant-style meals. Starters like oysters, fish soup (£3.50) or sardines (£3.95); main courses such as Dover sole (£12.50), grilled halibut (£9.50 and fresh salmon (£8.50) typify the excellent seafood choice which dominates the daily changing menu. Casseroles, game and steaks are also featured as well as salads and a vegetarian dish - for example courgette and cheese bake at £4.50. Well kept, hand-pulled beers include Young's Best and Special and Ruddles Bitter. At the side and back of the pub are an attractive garden with raised flowerbeds and a paved patio.

Brewery: Free house
Licensee: E H Whitcomb
Opening hours: 11am-3pm, 6-11pm; Sun 12-3pm, 7-10.30pm (closed Sun evening in winter)
Bar food: 12-2.30, 6-10pm; Sun 12-2pm, 7-10pm (summer only)
Children: Welcome anywhere; half portions available
Credit cards: AMERICAN EXPRESS®, Access, Visa, Diners

⊜ WHITE HART
High Street, South Harting GU31 5QB. Tel 0730 825355

South Harting

Pride of place in the village centre goes to this attractive 16th-century coaching inn, headquarters of one of the oldest men's clubs in the country - established in 1800 - and reputedly haunted by the ghost of a groom who roams the ancient, heavily beamed bars. Antique furniture, open fireplaces, a collection of old keys, plates and pictures of the village in bygone times all add to the atmosphere. Well priced bar food includes good daily specials, for example, stuffed marrow (£4.50), fresh sardines (£4.50), paella

Brewery: Free house
Licensees: Allan and Angie Hayter
Opening hours: 11am-2.30pm, 6-11pm; Sun12-3pm, 7-10.30pm
Bar food: 11am-2pm, 7-10pm; Sun 12-2pm, 7-10pm
Restaurant: 7-10pm (Thu, Fri and Sat only)
Children: In games room and

(£5.50), and mousaka (£4.50) as well as vegetarian dishes, the usual snacks, an excellent value Sunday roast and a separate restaurant menu served in the small cosy dining room. On summer days take your drink out into the beautifully kept and secluded flower-filled walled garden. Pool, darts, dominoes and charity quiz nights are all played in the Public Bar/games area and a large box of toys keeps children amused.

restaurant only; own menu available; outdoor play area

⊜ WHITE HART
Stopham Bridge, near Pulborough RH20 1DS. Tel 0798 873321

Stopham Bridge

The White Hart is a Sussex stone pub set picturesquely by the old and graceful Stopham Bridge which spans the River Arun just off the A283 west of Pulborough. Inside, it is a delightful jumble of nooks and crannies, with beams, brasses and cottage-style furniture, evoking a convincing feel of Old England. Decent wines and two real ales - Flowers Original and Harveys Best - are served, while the bar menu offers the usual snacks and bar meals plus hot specials such as celery soup (£1.50), pork chop 'Ardentaise' (£4.25), local trout (£4.95), various platters and a separate vegetarian menu. The adjacent candlelit restaurant - once the old forge - is renowned for its fresh fish with over 15 seafood starters; the main 'catch' featuring tuna, shark, swordfish, red snapper and Scottish salmon among others. Darts, crib, dominoes and bar billiards can be played in the Village Bar and in the summer music nights are held in a marquee on the big lawn laid out with benches beneath the willow-edged river bank.

Brewery: Whitbread
Licensee: John Palmer
Opening hours: 11am-3pm, 6.30-11pm; Sun 12-3pm, 7-10.30pm
Bar food: 12-2pm, 6.30-9.30pm; Sun 12-2.15pm, 7-9.30pm (Sun evening summer only)
Restaurant: Times as bar food
Children: Welcome anywhere; own menu available; outdoor play area
Credit cards: Access, Visa

HORSEGUARDS
Tillington, near Petworth GU28 9AF. Tel 0798 42332

Tillington

Originally three cottages, this charming, part-16th-century village pub offers high-quality food that draws a clientele from miles around. There are three attractive dining areas with exposed brick and timber walls, open fires, a variety of antique furniture, and fresh flowers on each table. Lighter - lunchtime snacks include home-made soups - carrot and coriander, freshly prepared terrines - avocado and chicken - and a range of imaginative ploughman's. The blackboard menu changes in the evening, displaying more elaborate dishes - for example, fillet of pork in plum sauce (£8.95), breast of chicken with a French mustard sauce (£8.20), halibut steak with yellow pepper sauce (£8.75), all accompanied by vegetables and a home-baked roll. Desserts

Brewery: Free house
Licensees: Rex Colman
Opening hours: 11am-3pm, 6-11pm; Sun 12-3pm, 7-10.30pm
Bar food: 12-2pm, 7-10pm
Accommodation: £45 per room; children not permitted overnight
Children: In main dining area only
Credit cards: Access, Visa

at £2.95 might include gooseberry fool and chocolate roulade. Good wines are available by the bottle and glass with Hall & Woodhouse Badger Best, Wadworth 6X and Horseguards Bitter on draught. There are two comfortable cottage-style bedrooms.

⊜ KEEPERS ARMS
Trotton, near Midhurst GU31 5ER. Tel 0730 813724

Trotton

T his rambling tile-hung inn, positioned on a rise above the A272 was originally a blacksmith's shop and dwellings, which doubled up as the village alehouse. Known as the Blue Anchor for many years, it became the Keeper's Arms in the 1950s and is now a popular pub for good food, with most of the tables in the comfortable, carpeted, open-plan bar being reserved for diners. The lunch menu features standard favourites plus good home-cooked hot dishes - steak and kidney pie, Alabama chilli and oriental chicken with rice, all at £4.90, with more ambitious evening fare on a blackboard menu. Starters at £2.85 may include pâté or Sussex salad to be followed by lamb medallions (£9.50), chicken cardinale (£8.25), and salmon fillet (£9.95), with vegetables included in the price. A well stocked bar has three real ales - Ballard's, Hall & Woodhouse Badger Best and a guest beer - and a list of 30 wines as well as a good selection of malt whiskies.

Brewery: Free house
Licensees: Colin and Pauline Machin
Opening hours: 11am-2.30pm, 6-11pm; closed Mon; Sun 12-3pm, 7-10pm
Bar food: 12-2pm, 6-10pm; Sun 12-2pm, 7-9.30pm
Restaurant: 7-10.30pm (except all day Mon and Sun evening)
Children: In restaurant only; half portions available
Credit cards: Access, Visa

GREETS INN
Friday Street, Warnham RH12 3QY. Tel 0403 265407

Warnham

D ating from 1450, this unspoilt tile-hung and timbered farmhouse, on the western edge of the village, retains its original layout of small rooms leading off a central room with stone-flagged floor, whose main feature is a vast inglenook fireplace complete with seating and heavy oak overmantel supporting a collection of brass and copper. Old beams, exposed timbers, sturdy oak tables, and high-backed settles all help to maintain a traditional atmosphere. Hearty lunchtime snacks and substantial main dishes live up to the promise of the menu and may include shoulder of lamb (£7.95), chicken teriyaki (£7.65), salmon fillet (£7.95) and a daily special, followed perhaps by banoffii pie and summer fruit soufflé (£2.25) for dessert. Set Sunday lunch at around £9.95 is good value. Flowers Original, Boddingtons Bitter and Strongs Country are on handpump. In summer, the sheltered beer garden, with its flower beds, shrubs and apple trees, makes an inviting setting.

Brewery: Whitbread
Licensee: Trevor Chaplin
Opening hours: 11am-2.30pm, 6-11pm; Sun12-2pm, 7-10.30pm
Bar food: 12-2pm, 7-10pm
Children: In eating areas only
Credit cards:
AMERICAN EXPRESS®, Access, Visa, Diners

ROYAL OAK
Wineham, near Haywards Heath BN5 9A. Tel 0444 881252

Wineham

This delightful, 14th-century, black-and-white timbered cottage has been supplying the local inhabitants with refreshment for over 200 years and maintains a traditional character that many village pubs lost long ago. Beyond the half-stable door lies the low-beamed, simply furnished main bar, which is warmed by a log fire in an enormous fireplace darkened by the smoke stains of centuries. Horse-brasses, various bits of pottery and wrought iron and a collection of ancient corkscrews decorate the two bars where darts and shove halfpenny can be played. Marston's Pedigree, Boddingtons Bitter or Whitbread Pompey Royal - tapped straight from the cask in the still room - are ideal lunchtime tipples to wash down the freshly cut, value-for-money sandwiches that make up the menu. Wooden benches line the spacious front lawns and Morris dancers make regular appearances here.

Brewery: Whitbread
Licensee: Tim Peacock
Opening hours: 11am-2.30pm, 5.30-10.30pm (Fri and Sat 11pm); Sun 12-2.30pm, 7-10.30pm
Bar food: As opening hours
Children: In family room only

WILTSHIRE

⊜ RED LION INN
Axford, near Marlborough SN8 2HA. Tel 0672 20271

Axford

This friendly, brick-and-flint built village pub, dating back in parts to the 17th century, is popular as much for its peaceful Kennet valley setting as for its good food. The main bar is pine-panelled and comfortably furnished and draught beers include Wadworth 6X, Archers Village Bitter and Flowers Original. For entertainment, there are darts and shove halfpenny and a quiz night on Mondays. The attractive dining area and restaurant, overlooking the Kennet valley, displays local paintings on the walls and tables set with linen cloths and fresh flowers. On the varied menu are the usual bar snacks, plus daily specials, very game-oriented in season, often featuring local pheasant, hare, partridge and venison. A separate fresh fish menu may offer scallops pan fried with tarragon (£4.95), fresh sardines ((£3.75), Dover sole (£12.50), or skate wing (£7.50). Meat and game dishes on the à la carte menu range from around £9 to £11. There are lovely country views from the lawns at the side of the pub and there is a garden. Four well equipped bedrooms are available in a separate building.

Brewery: Free house
Licensee: Mel Evans
Opening hours: 11am-3pm, 6-11pm; Sun 12-3pm, 7-10.30pm
Bar food: 12-2.30pm, 6.30-10.30pm; Sun 12-2pm, 7-9.30pm
Restaurant: Times as bar food
Accommodation: (Price per room) single £25, double £40
Children: Welcome anwhere; outdoor play area
Credit cards: Access, Visa

⊜ WAGGON AND HORSES
Beckhampton, near Marlborough SN8 1QJ. Tel 06723 418

Beckhampton

Built of massive stone, this thatched, 16th-century inn near the junction of the A4 and A361 Devizes road, has been popular with travellers journeying between London and Bath for centuries. As its name suggests, waggoners would stop here to refresh themselves and their horses, or get them re-shoed at the inn's smithy, and in the 19th century Charles Dickens featured it in 'The Bagman's Story' in *Pickwick Papers*. The open-plan bar (with a non-smoking area) retains great charm and atmosphere, with comfortable old chairs grouped round the log fire, and an array of settles and sturdy tables at which to sample satisfying bar food and perhaps one of the well kept Wadworth draught beers - 6X, IPA, and Farmer's Glory - or a guest ale such as Hall & Woodhouse Tanglefoot. Sheltered from the noise of traffic, fractious car-bound children can expend some energy in the rear garden and play area; there is also a family room.

Brewery: Wadworth
Licensees: Tereza Pulay and Ian Thackray
Opening hours: 11.30am-3pm, 6-11pm; Sun 12-3pm, 7-10.30pm
Bar food: 12-2pm, 7-9.30pm (Thu-Sat 10pm)
Children: In family room only
Credit cards: Access, Visa

⊜ RISING SUN
Bowden Hill, near Lacock SN15 2PP. Tel 0249 730363

Bowden Hill

Clear, warm summer evenings draw customers to this splendid, isolated country pub, situated high above the village of Lacock, for the magnificent views across the Avon valley from its gravelled terrace. Inside are three simply furnished, inter-connecting rooms with stone-flagged floors, decorated with a grandfather clock and a collection of country pictures, stuffed birds and animals. The bar menu (lunchtimes only) promises - and delivers - wholesome country cooking in keeping with the surroundings and might include a substantial leek and potato soup served with a bacon scone (£2.80), steak and kidney pie or chicken curry (£4.95) and excellent giant sandwiches and ploughman's. The real-ale range is dominated by the local Mole's Brewery - which the landlord also owns - serving Mole's IPA, Brew 97 and Landlord's Choice with the addition of two guest ales. As you drink, you can pass the time with dominoes, shove halfpenny and a variety of card games.

Brewery: Free house
Licensees: Roger and Laura Catte
Opening hours: 12-2.30pm (3.30 Sat), 7-11pm; closed Mon; Sun 12-3pm, 7-10.30pm
Bar food: 12-2pm (except Sun and Mon)
Children: Welcome anywhere; outdoor play area

THREE CROWNS
Brinkworth, near Chippenham SN15 5AF. Tel 0666 510366

Brinkworth

Restaurant-quality food is balanced by generous lunchtime snacks - ploughman's, jacket potatoes and double-decker rolls - at this smart and generally busy stone-built pub set beside the village green and church on the B4042. The attractive, airy conservatory is a pleasant place to sit and to enjoy well prepared dishes such as venison medallions (£11.25), fresh Dover sole (£13.50), pheasant, (£10.95), tuna en croûte (£11.95), and beef and venison or seafood pie (£7.95), all served with fresh vegetables. Home-made desserts at £2.95 include banana pancake, chocolate mint mousse and a range of ice creams. The chatty and more pubby main bar features an open log fire, and an assortment of old pine pews and tables, including one made out of an enormous forge bellows. The five real ales are Wadworth 6X, Boddingtons Bitter, Brains Bitter, Bass and Whitbread Best. There are a good range of malt whiskies and wines. Darts, shove halfpenny, cards and cribbage can be played and there is a sheltered garden with a climbing frame for children.

Brewery: Whitbread
Licensees: Anthony and Allyson Windle
Opening times: 10am-2.30pm (Sat 11am-3pm), 6-11pm; Sun 12-3pm, 7-10.30pm
Bar food: 12-2pm, 6.30-9.30pm (Sun from 7pm)
Children: In dining area only; outdoor play area
Credit cards: Access, Visa

THREE HORSESHOES
Stibb Green, Burbage, near Marlborough SN8 3AE. Tel 0672 810324

Burbage

Reputedly 250 years old, this little cream-painted village local is situated on the old road out of Burbage. Its cosy, simply furnished bar, with a huge inglenook fireplace and large station clock occupying one wall, and a long painting of a hunting scene covering the length of another, warmly welcomes visitors. The food, served on long tables in front of the fire or in the adjacent small lounge is value for money and a great attraction. Tempting daily specials might include chicken and bacon pie (£3.99), shepherd's pie (£3.80), and Cumberland plait (£3.50), and there is also a printed menu which offers standard lunchtime favourites. Wadworth ales - 6X and IPA - and a guest beer are drawn on handpump.

Brewery: Wadworth
Licensees: Phil and Sheila Prew
Opening hours: 12-3pm, 6-11pm; Sun 12-3pm, 7-10.30pm
Bar food: 12-1.45pm, 7-8.45pm; Sun 12-1.45pm only
Children: In lounge area if eating

The Birds of the Air
Pride of place among bird signs is taken by the Swan, often adopted by inns close to a river. The eccentric Swan with Two Necks probably began as a swan with two nicks in its beak. The Cock may be related to cock-fighting or to St Peter. Geese and chickens appear alone or keeping dangerous company with the Fox. The Bird in Hand comes from falconry and the Dog and Duck either from fowling or from the amusement of setting a dog on a pinioned duck. The Eagle is from Heraldry and the Magpie and Stump from the countryside, while rarities include the Parrot and the Peahen.

🍺 WHITE HART
The Hill, Castle Combe, near Chippenham SN14 7HF. Tel 0249 782295

Castle Combe

A pub of great antiquity, with a history even more ancient than that of the 14th-century market cross it faces, the White Hart claims ancestry as an ale house dating back to 1250. Although popular with the crowds of tourists who flock to this picture postcard village in summer, it has retained its traditional character. Its main bar, half-panelled and beamed, has an elegant stone fireplace and a traditional black wall bench built into the mullioned window; adjoining it is a much smaller Lounge Bar, agleam with polished brass. There is always a choice of five real ales, for example Ruddles County, Ushers Founders Ale, Butcombe Bitter, Wadworth 6X and Bass, and a good selection of popular bar food. Beyond the family room and quarry-tiled games room is an attractive and peaceful courtyard. Afternoon tea is served in summer.

Brewery: Free house
Licensee: Gerrard Ashall
Opening hours: Summer 11am-11pm; winter 11am-3pm, 6-11pm (Sat 11am-11pm); Sun 12-3pm, 7-10.30pm
Bar food: 12-2.30pm, 7-9.30pm
Children: In family room only
Credit cards: Access, Visa

HORSE AND GROOM
Charlton, near Malmesbury SN16 9DL. Tel 0666 823904

Charlton

This 300-year-old pub, built of mellow Cotswold stone, is set back from the B4040 on the edge of the village. Its two attractive bars, the Lounge (leading to the dining room) and the Charlton have a welcoming atmosphere, especially in winter when there are roaring log fires in the stone fireplaces. A fixed-price menu, offering plenty of choice including a vegetarian dish, is chalked up on the blackboard daily, with the option of two courses at £6.95 or three courses at £8.95, including coffee. The four starters may include farmhouse pâté and garlic mushrooms, and be followed by trout with almonds or chicken casserole, with chocolate and brandy mousse and lemon cheesecake for pudding. However, if all you want is a snack, there are ploughman's, salads, filled baps and baked potatoes. Four real ales - Wadworth 6X, Archers Village, Mole's Bitter and Tetley Bitter - are on draught; 19 well priced bottles of wine and house wine by the glass are available from the well stocked bar.

Brewery: Free house
Licensee: Martin Hall
Opening hours: 12-2.30pm, 7-11pm; Sun 12-3pm, 7-10.30pm
Bar food: 12-2.15pm, 7-9.30pm (with some flexibility); Sun 12-2.15pm
Children: In the Charlton Bar only; outdoor play area
Credit cards: Access, Visa

HORSESHOE
Ebbesbourne Wake, near Salisbury SP5 5JF. Tel 0722 780474

Ebbesbourne Wake

This delightful village pub enjoys an enviable location in the peaceful Ebble valley, and the countryside can be fully appreciated from its pretty flower- filled garden. Inside, a central serving bar dispenses drinks to two rooms; the tiny Snug and the main bar which is crammed with a vast collection of farm tools, lanterns and other objects. A separate room houses the small, neat restaurant. Apart from the traditional atmosphere and beers - Adnams Broadside, Wadworth 6X, Ringwood Best Bitter and Old Thumper - hearty portions of reliable bar food are the attraction. As well as a good snack menu, extra choices in the evening may include steak and kidney pie (£5.25), pork with Stilton (£6.95), and chicken with prawn and lobster (£5.95), all presented with a choice of several vegetables. The set Sunday lunch served in the restaurant - three courses at £7.95 - is excellent value, and you must book. There are three comfortable, well equipped bedrooms.

Brewery: Free house
Licensee: Tony Booth
Opening hours: 11.30am-2.30pm, 6.30-11pm; Sun 12-3pm, 7-10.30pm
Bar food: 12-2pm, 7-9.30pm (except Mon evening); Sun 7-9pm only
Restaurant: 7-9.30pm (except Mon); Sun lunch 12-2pm
Accommodation: (Price per room) double £33-£35
Children: In Snug Bar and restaurant if eating

WHITE HART
Ford, near Chippenham SN14 8RP. Tel 0249 782213

Ford

Nestling in the Bybrook valley, this fine riverside inn, with a terrace, dating back to the 16th century, is in easy reach of the M4 (junctions 17 and 18), just off the A420. Its main bar, with old beams and dark wood panelling, is the 'local' where up to eight guest beers are stocked - Hook Norton Best Bitter and Old Hooky, Marston's Pedigree, Boddingtons Bitter, Wadworth 6X, Hall & Woodhouse Tanglefoot, Smiles Exhibition and Draught Bass - though the selection may change from time to time. The White Hart has a high reputation for its food, served in the Lounge Bar or dining room overlooking the river. There is both a bar menu, with simple hot dishes and a range of ploughman's and sandwiches, and a weekly changing restaurant menu with dishes like warmed pigeon breast wrapped in bacon on fresh basil sauce (£4.75) or lamb and vegetable broth (£1.95) for starters, and sauté of lamb in cumin, lemon and Marsala sauce with saffron rice (£5.95), and escalope of pork with Dijon mustard, brandy and cream sauce (£6.95), as main courses. A good choice of wines and around ten malt whiskies are stocked. Eleven attractively furnished bedrooms are available, some in a separate building, some with four-poster beds. Residents enjoy the use of an outdoor swimming pool.

Brewery: Free house
Licensees: Chris and Jenny Phillips
Opening hours: 11am-2.30pm, 5.30-11pm; Sun 12-2.30pm, 7-10.30pm
Bar food: 12-2pm, 7-9.30pm (Sun 9.15pm)
Restaurant: Times as bar food
Accommodation: (Price per room) single £43, double £59
Children: In dining area only
Credit cards: AMERICAN EXPRESS®, Access, Visa

⊕ LAMB INN
Hindon, near Salisbury SP3 6DP. Tel 074789 573.

Hindon

The present weathered stone building dates back to the 17th century, but there had been a Lamb Inn on this site for at least two centuries before that. A well-known posting stage on the route from London to the West Country (the village is a mile off the A303), it was also, at one time, the headquarters of a notorious band of smugglers - the Wiltshire Moonrakers - and now enjoys a high reputation both for its food and as a place to stay. At the heart of the inn is a traditionally furnished long bar, split into three separate areas, one of which, the top bar, serves as a dining area, and there is also a separate restaurant. The bar menu might offer chicken in garlic (£5.25), lamb steak (£5.25) or sweet and sour pork (£4.95) and a range of tempting puddings at £2.10. In the restaurant, the three-course menu at £18.95 gives five or six choices at each course and is excellent value, as is the three-course Sunday lunch at around £12. The bar serves Wadworth 6X and Young's Bitter, there are wines to match the standard of the food and, as the owners have another hotel at Bridgend on Islay, a selection of Islay malt whiskies. Fifteen attractively furnished bedrooms offer all modern comforts.

Brewery: Free house
Licensees: John and Paul Croft
Opening hours: 11am-11pm;
Sun 12-3pm, 7-10.30pm
Bar food: 12-2pm, 7-10pm
Restaurant: 12-2pm, 7-9.30pm
Accommodation: (Price per room) single £30-£38, double £55-£65
Children: In top bar only
Credit cards:
AMERICAN EXPRESS®, Access, Visa

⊕ BATH ARMS
Horningsham, Longleat, near Warminster BA12 7LY. Tel 0985 844308.

Horningsham

Occupying a prime, village centre site, this three-storey, family-run hotel is a pleasant place to visit. Game in season comes from the estate and features on the bar and restaurant menu with such choices as wild duck (£6.50), pigeon breast in pepper sauce (£5.25), rabbit casserole (£4.95) and other favourites including beef Wellington, rack of lamb and fish pie, followed by raspberry pudding or apple and blackcurrant pie at £2.25. If you are only calling in for a drink you can relax in one of the two welcoming bars with a pint of Butcombe Bitter, Wadworth 6X, Draught Bass, Eldridge Pope Thomas Hardy Country Bitter or Dorchester Bitter or sit outside in the large garden or under one of the 12 apostles - a group of famous 200-year-old pollarded lime trees that flank the inn. For those wanting a longer stay, there are six comfortable bedrooms and this is an excellent base for tourists.

Brewery: Free house
Licensee: Joseph Lovatt
Opening hours: 11am-11pm;
Sun 12-2pm, 7-10.30pm
Bar food: 12-2pm, 7-10pm (Sun 9.30pm)
Restaurant: 7-9.30pm; Sun, residents only
Accommodation: (Price per room) single £28, double £48
Children: Not permitted under 14 years in the bars
Credit cards: Access, Visa, Diners

⊕ RED LION
High Street, Lacock, near Chippenham SN15 2LQ. Tel 0249 730456

Lacock

Located at the centre of the famous National Trust village, close to the Abbey, this tall, red-brick Georgian coaching inn, has managed to retain a traditional character despite the crowds of tourists. Inside, in the three connecting bars, there is plenty to catch the eye, from the old beams to the collections of farming implements, corn dollies, dried flowers, oil paintings and stuffed birds. Hearty dishes characterise the popular menu, and the blackboard specials are especially recommended, for example, steak and kidney and beef and ale pies (£5.50) and casseroles like beef in red wine and spiced lamb (£5.50), or pork in cider (£6.20), all served with fresh vegetables. Puddings may include walnut and treacle flan and Bakewell tart, both at £2.25. Wadworth beers - 6X and IPA - and a guest beer like Hall & Woodhouse Tanglefoot are served in the bar from midday, and in summer, afternoon teas, best enjoyed in the garden, are served from 3pm. There are three double bedrooms.

Brewery: Wadworth
Licensee: Kevin and Debbie Keeling
Opening hours: Summer 11am-11pm; winter 11am-3pm (coffee only from 11am-noon), 6-11pm; Sun 12-3pm, 7-10.30pm
Bar food: 12-2pm, 7-9.30pm
Accommodation: (Price per room) £40-£50; no facilities for babies
Children: Welcome in areas away from the bar
Credit cards: Access. Visa

CUCKOO INN
Hamptworth, Landford, near Salisbury SP5 2DU. Tel 0794 390302

Landford

Tucked away down a series of country lanes, off the B3079, this isolated 300-year-old thatched cottage, formerly the village shop, draws lovers of real ale into three simply furnished but pleasant bars, where 12 admirably kept beers are drawn from casks in the back room, including Hall & Woodhouse Badger Bitter and Tanglefoot, Wadworth 6X, Bunces Best Bitter, and Hampshire King Alfred's. Guest beers may change periodically. There is a pleasant, box-hedged garden where you can play pétanque; on winter evenings, the quiz night and impromptu Friday evening folk nights are popular, or there are always darts and dominoes. Food is limited to rolls, ploughman's and pasties.

Brewery: Free house
Licensees: Derek and Jean Proudley
Opening hours: 11.30am-2.30pm, 6-11pm (Sat 11am-11pm); Sun 12-3pm, 7-10.30pm
Bar food: As opening times
Children: In family room and garden bar only; outdoor play area

---

Heraldic Devices
The animals on inn signs are frequently drawn from heraldry. The most common of all, the Red Lion, was the badge of the kings of Scots from time immemorial and had a prominent place in the British royal arms after the accession of James I in 1603. So did the Unicorn, which is also a pub name, while the Greyhound was a Tudor badge. The White Horse was the Hanoverian emblem (and an ancient badge of Kent). Other devices include the Eagle and Child of the Stanleys, Earls of Derby, the Blue Boar of the De Veres, Earls of Oxford, and the Bear - with or without Ragged Staff - of the Earls of Warwick. Other well-known heraldic signs are the Chequers, the Spread Eagle and the Stag's Head, and many pubs display the coat of arms of the local landowning family, which might own the pub or with whom it was desirable to be on good terms.

⊛ HARROW INN
Little Bedwyn, near Marlborough SN8 3JP. Tel 0672 870871

Little Bedwyn

Resurrected from closure over a year ago by an enterprising village co-operative, who now owns it, this friendly Victorian village pub, situated close to the Kennet and Avon canal, is rapidly re-establishing its popularity and has a reputation for good home cooking. Lunchtime snacks include celery, apple and tomato soup at £1.95, houmous and hot bread at £2.50, marinaded veal kebabs at £3.95 and pasta with chicken and bacon at £3.95. In the evening, dishes are more elaborate - for example, chicken breast in black bean sauce, baked skate with a herb crust, or fillet steak stuffed with blue cheese - and are served in the candlelit dining room. Draught beers include Hook Norton Best Bitter and Mole's Landlord's Choice; guest beers change periodically. Three freshly decorated bedrooms are ideal for people wanting to explore the pretty Kennet valley.

Brewery: Free house
Licensees: Sean and Louize Juniper
Opening hours: 11am-2.30pm, 5.30-11pm (Sat 6.30pm); Sun 12-2.30pm, 7-10.30pm
Bar food: 12-2pm, 7-9pm (except Mon); Sun 12-2pm only
Restaurant: 7.30-9pm (except Mon)
Accommodation: (Price per room) single £20, double £35-£40
Children: Welcome anywhere
Credit cards: Access, Visa

⊛ HATCHET
Lower Chute, near Andover SP11 9DX. Tel 0264 70229

Lower Chute

This 16th-century thatched pub has an idyllic setting in a peaceful village well off the beaten track among a web of tiny downland lanes north of Andover. Settle in front of the enormous inglenook fireplace in the cosy low-beamed bar and enjoy a pint of Gale's HSB, Wadworth 6X or Charrington IPA and a good country dish such as venison pie, venison sausage casserole, jugged hare, steak and kidney pie, cauliflower and courgette bake (all £4.95) from the bar menu. There is a separate restaurant for more formal meals (booking advisable at weekends), with 10 to 12 choices at each course and including, for example, grilled red snapper (£8.75), magret of duck (£9.85), steaks from (£9.85) and lambs' kidneys in Dijon mustard sauce (£8.95). You can play dominoes, cards, chess and darts in the bar without any distraction from electronic games, music etc. Picnic benches line two front terraces and a side lawn has a children's play area.

Brewery: Free house
Licensees: Jeremy and Christina McKay
Opening hours: 11am-3pm, 6-11pm; Sun 12-3pm, 7-10.30pm
Bar food: 12-2pm, 7-10pm (Sun 9.30pm)
Restaurant: Times as bar food
Children: Not permitted under 14 years inside; outdoor play area
Credit cards: Access, Visa

⊛ SILVER PLOUGH
Pitton, near Salisbury SP5 1DU. Tel 0722 72266

Pitton

Tucked away in a downland village off the A30, this neat and welcoming 250-year-old farmhouse is a low, white-painted building with a restaurant extension. Customers come from miles around to sample the excellent food either

Brewery: Free house
Licensees: Charles Manktelow, Paul Parnell and Michael Beckett
Opening hours: 11am-3pm,

in the bar or in the restaurant. There are two bars - Lounge and Snug - both comfortably furnished in traditional style and decorated with jugs, mugs, brasses, old prints and paintings. Dominoes and board games can be played, but nothing electronic; there is also a skittle alley. Draught beers include Wadworth 6X, Courage Best Bitter and Draught Bass and about ten wines are served by the glass. The good bar-snack menu ranges from avocado, bacon and feta cheese salad (£3.95), to Indonesian fish hot pot (£4.65) and lamb and lentil curry (£4.95) plus, at lunchtimes, a selection of ploughman's. There is also a fixed-price menu, with two courses at £11.50, and three courses at £13.95, offering main dishes such as sauté of lambs' liver and red onions Venetian style, or whole grilled plaice with caper butter. White linen and fresh flowers grace the restaurant, where the menu offers you two courses at £12.95 or three at £15.95.

6-11pm; Sun 12-3pm, 7-10.30pm
Bar food: 12-2pm, 7-9.30pm;
Sun 12-2pm only
Restaurant: 12-2pm, 7-10pm
(except Sun and Mon evenings)
Children: In Snug Bar and skittle
alley which is used as a family
room when no game is booked
Credit cards:
AMERICAN EXPRESS®, Access,
Visa, Diners

⊛ BELL INN
The Square, Ramsbury, near Marlborough SN8 2PE. Tel 0672 20230

Ramsbury

This fine old coaching inn stands in the square and has been a focal point in the village since the 17th century. Its exterior is unassuming, but inside, the large bar, with its two fine bay windows, has a pleasantly convivial atmosphere. There is also a very comfortable dining area consisting of two interconnecting rooms. The good and reasonably priced bar menu starts with a selection of ploughman's and filled jacket potatoes, working up to a wide choice of hot dishes plus a number of daily specials. First courses (or snacks) range from moules marinière (£3.95) to deep fried Brie with cranberry sauce (£3.50); main dishes from leek, Stilton and bacon pie (£4.95) to steaks and grills (£5.20-£7.95), with apricot crumble and apple strudel (£2.50) for dessert. On draught there are Wadworth 6X and Henry's Original IPA, Hook Norton Best Bitter and Fuller's London Pride. With at least 25 to choose from, lovers of malt whisky will not feel neglected. A delightful terrace leads to a sheltered garden.

Brewery: Free house
Licensees: Graham and Julia
Dawes
Opening hours: 11.45am-
2.30pm, 6-11pm; Sun 12-
3.30pm, 7-10.30pm
Bar food: 12-2.30pm, 7-9.30pm
(Fri and Sat 10pm); Sun 12-3pm,
7-9pm (Sun evening in summer
only)
Children: In main dining area or
family room only
Credit cards:
AMERICAN EXPRESS®, Access,
Visa

⊛ GEORGE AND DRAGON
High Street, Rowde, near Devizes SN10 2PN. Tel 0380 723053

Rowde

The George and Dragon stands in the village centre, set well above the A432, and its rather plain, pebble-dash exterior hides two attractive, welcoming bars dating back to the 17th century. Newspapers are set out for customers to read, and old kitchen tables, farmhouse chairs and solid benches help maintain a traditional atmosphere. However, it

Brewery: Wadworth
Licensee: Tim and Helen Withers
Opening hours: 12-3pm, 6-
11pm; Sun 12-3pm, 7-10.30pm
Bar food: 12-2pm, 7-10pm
(except Sun evening and all day

is not only its character that makes the inn such a popular place, but the excellent quality of the food, in particular the fresh fish listed on a daily menu that usually includes about eight varieties - for example, fillet of turbot with crab sauce (£11.50), grey mullet baked with cider and cheese (£6.50), or baracuda with mussel sauce (£10.50). Soup, ploughman's, meat and vegetarian dishes are on a separate menu and range from leek and mustard tart (£3.25) to lobster and chicken sausage with spring onion purée (£4). Puddings (£3) such as hot chocolate soufflé and plum crumble round off a meal that is excellent value for money, and there is a £10 set lunch. Wadworth 6X and Henry's Original IPA are on draught.

Mon)
Children: Welcome anywhere
Credit cards: Access, Visa

⊜ HAUNCH OF VENISON
14 Minster Street, Salisbury SP1 1TB. Tel 0722 322024

Salisbury

Parts of this ancient, city-centre pub date back to 1320 when it was the church house for the nearby Church of St Thomas. The pub is tiny, and its three bars are often crowded with locals and tourists soaking up the atmosphere while sampling well kept Ringwood Best Bitter, Courage Best and Directors, or one of the 100 malt whiskies displayed behind the pewter-topped bar with its rare set of antique taps for gravity-fed spirits. The tiny Snug called the Horsebox opens off the entrance lobby; the House of Commons, as the main bar is called, has a chequered stone floor, oak-panelled walls, and massive beams; the House of Lords is a cosy upper room boasting an ancient fireplace and a smoke-preserved, mummified hand holding some 18th-century playing cards, which was found by workmen in 1903 and is now displayed behind glass. Bar snacks are excellent value, but space is very limited.

Brewery: Courage
Licensees: Anthony and Victoria Leroy
Opening hours: 11am- 11pm; Sun 12-3pm. 7-10.30pm
Bar food: 12-2.30pm, 7-9.30pm (except Sun evening)
Children: In upper room only

SPREAD EAGLE
Stourton, near Warminster BA12 6QE. Tel 0747 840587

Stourton

Only a stone's throw from Stourhead House and its magnificent gardens, this delightful inn, also owned by the National Trust, dates back to the 18th century and stands in a picturesque courtyard that also houses a National Trust shop. After admiring the splendours of Stourhead, the inn is a convenient place to stop for a drink or a meal in comfortable bars that have been completely restored and refurbished by the Trust. Ash Vine Bitter, brewed at nearby Frome, features among the real ales, others include Draught Bass and a guest beer such as Adnams Broadside. Good,

Brewery: Free house
Licensees: Keith Lawrence and David Murray
Opening hours: 10am-2.30pm, 6-11pm; Sun 12-3pm, 7-10.30pm
Bar food: 11.45am-2pm, 6-9.30pm; Sun 12-2pm, 7-9.30 (afternoon tea 3-5.30pm)
Accommodation: (Price per room) single £35, double £56

home-cooked bar meals include a range of hot dishes such as Huntingdon pie (£4.75), steak and ale pie (£5.25) and vegetable crumble (£4), with a hearty treacle or steamed chocolate pudding (£2.15), to follow. For a simpler meal, there are five different ploughman's, priced from £2.85. Morning coffee is always available, and afternoon tea on Sundays. There are five attractively furnished bedrooms.

Children: In dining areas only; high chairs available
Credit cards: AMERICAN EXPRESS® , Access, Visa, Diners

ROYAL OAK
Wootton Rivers, near Marlborough SN8 4NQ. Tel 0672 810322

Wootton Rivers

Pride of place in the centre of this village near the Kennet and Avon canal goes to the Royal Oak, looking like the very model of an old English inn with its thatched roof, old beams and exposed timbers. The Public Bar has a lively atmosphere, being popular for pool, darts, crib, and dominoes; a juke box can add to the noise and makes an interesting contrast with the more peaceful atmosphere of the Lounge Bar and restaurant. Food here is very popular, so booking is advisable. The menu is extensive, beginning with 15 or so starters (from £1.75), going on to basket meals (from £2.25), then sandwiches and snacks (lunchtime only), salads (from £3 to £14.50), fish (from £4.50) meat and poultry (from £6.95). As if this were not enough, there are also daily specials - for example, game and port pie (£8), or country rabbit and vegetable pie (£7). Beers include Wadworth 6X from the barrel and a guest beer. The pub has four double and two single bedrooms in a separate house.

Brewery: Free house
Licensees: John and Rosa Jones
Opening hours: 11am- 3pm, 6-11pm; Sun 12-2pm, 7-9pm
Bar food: 12-2.30pm, 7-9.30pm; Sun 12-2pm only
Accommodation: (Price per room) single from £20, double from £30
Children: In family area only
Credit cards: Access, Visa

LONDON

LONDON

FOX AND ANCHOR
115 Charterhouse Street, EC1M 6AA. Tel 071 253 4838

EC1

Visit this friendly pub for breakfast to experience the atmosphere at its best, for it is then that the doctors and nurses from the nearby hospital, and the other early risers in the area, come in to start the day with a hearty meal. So famous is the food, the barman confides, that a group of businessmen flew over from New York especially to have breakfast here, and they kept a taxi waiting outside to whisk them back to the airport when they had finished. The English breakfast costs £6.50, and there are steaks and mixed grills from £8 to £13. Smaller appetites are also catered for, with dishes ranging upward from £1, and beers on draught include Burton Ale, Tetley, Young's and John Bull. Built in 1898, the pub has been recently refurbished but retains its Victorian atmosphere, highly polished and ornamented with numerous mirrors, pictures, photographs and prints.

Brewery: Taylor Walker
Licensee: John Hale
Opening hours: 6am-11pm (Sat 8am-1pm); closed Sun
Bar food: 7-10.30am, 12-2.30pm, 4-11pm (snacks only)
Children: Welcome if eating
Credit cards: Access, Visa

YE OLDE MITRE TAVERN
1 Ely Court, Ely Place, EC1N 6SJ. Tel 071 405 4751

EC1

This small 17th-century pub is not easy to find but it is well worth making the effort to seek it out. The impressive iron gates which separate Ely Place from Holborn Circus mark the boundary of what was, for several centuries, the town residence of the Bishops of Ely and thus a small part of Cambridgeshire in the centre of London. To find the pub go through the gates and turn left down a narrow passageway – if you reach the church, you've missed the turning. Inside there are two fairly small, wood-panelled bars, with the bar-less Bishop's Room at the top of the narrow stairs. The furniture is largely 17th-century and an old table in the centre of one bar is too big to have come through any of the doors; perhaps the pub was built around it. There is also a preserved chunk of a cherry tree around which Queen Elizabeth I is said to have danced. For present-day cutomers draught beers consist of Burton, Friary Meux, Tetley and Guinness, but toasted sandwiches at £1 are all that is on offer in the way of food. There is a courtyard with a few tables outside.

Brewery: Taylor Walker
Licensee: Don O'Sullivan
Opening hours: 11am-11pm; closed weekends
Bar food: 11am-10.30pm
Children: Not permitted inside

BLACK FRIAR
174 Queen Victoria Street, EC4V 4DB. Tel 071 236 5650

EC4

Situated on the corner of the street opposite Blackfriars station, this attractive stone-built pub has large leaded windows and a mosaic-tiled fascia. It is so popular with local office workers that suited figures frequently spill out to crowd the wide pavement. Built in 1885 on the site of a 13th-century Dominican priory, the bar is decorated with huge copper panels depicting the life of the Brothers. Through the marble columns at the back there is a plush seating area whose large mirrors give an impression of space, but this is only an illusion and the pub is often tightly packed so come early in the week to admire the ornate decor. On draught are Tetley, Wadworth 6X, Marston's Pedigree, and a guest beer, such as Charles Wells IPA, which changes every fortnight. A selection of imported bottled lagers includes one from an all-women brewery in Lapland! A short menu changes daily, and includes such favourites as lasagne and beef and ale stew, both at £4.25.

Brewery: Allied Breweries/Nicholson's
Licensee: Tom Eales
Opening hours: 11.30am-10pm; closed Sat and Sun
Bar food: 11.30am-2pm
Children: Not permitted inside
Credit cards: Access, Visa

⊕ YE OLDE CHESHIRE CHEESE
Wine Office Court, 145 Fleet Street EC4A 2BU. Tel 071 353 6170

EC4

There has been a pub on this site since 1538 but when the original building burnt down in the Great Fire of 1666 it was rebuilt the following year. The few beams that were not destroyed can still be seen in the ceiling of the Cellar Bar. The small, discreet entrance in Wine Office Court gives no clue as to the size and warren-like style of the building. There are six bars in all, a restaurant, and three rooms used for private parties, ranging from the large Cellar Bar with walls of whitewashed stone, to the tiny Courtyard Bar with only two tables, to Johnson's Bar with its elegant drawing-room style. Most rooms have sawdust-covered floorboards, dark wood-panelled walls and high-backed church pews. The pub has associations with many famous literary figures, such as Dr Samuel Johnson, Charles Dickens and Oliver Goldsmith, and there is a visitors' book dating from 1909 full of comments from the famous and the lesser-known characters of that century. Bar food is available in the Cheshire and the Cellar bars, and the Chop Room serves such dishes as steak, kidney and mushroom pie for £5.95, sirloin steak for £10.95, and grilled trout for £7.50. On draught are Samuel Smith Old Brewery, Museum Ale and Extra Stout. There is also a selection of bottled beers in pints and half pints, and wines served by the glass and the bottle.

Brewery: Samuel Smith
Licensees: Mr and Mrs Garrity
Opening hours: 11.30am-11pm (Sat 11.30am-3pm, 5.30-11pm); Sun 12- 3pm, 7-10.30pm
Bar food: 12-2.30pm, 5.30-9pm
Restaurant: 12-2.30pm, 6-9.30pm (last orders)
Children: Welcome in the Chop Room, Courtyard and Cheshire bars, away from serving area
Credit cards: AMERICAN EXPRESS®, Access, Visa, Diners (accepted only if eating)

PAXTON'S HEAD
153 Knightsbridge SW1X 7PA. Tel 071 589 6627

SW1

Situated just around the corner from Harrods and a few minutes' walk from the Albert Hall, this attractive Victorian pub is a convenient stop for shoppers, tourists, business people and concert-goers. It is named after Sir Joseph Paxton who designed Crystal Palace for the Great Exhibition of 1851; he was also the first man in Europe to make the colossal lily 'Victoria Regis' - a plant so huge a child could walk across its leaves - to flower. Inside and out, the pub looks very fresh and smart. The main bar is of polished wood, etched glass and mirrors, and there is also a Cellar Bar where children are permitted, plus a function room upstairs. In addition to its draught ales, which include Tetley, Greene King IPA, Wadworth 6X and a guest beer, such as Adnams Broadside, the pub serves a large selection of imported bottled beers, some of which are quite unusual. Sandwiches are available throughout the day until 8.30pm, but for a more hearty meal at lunchtime customers can choose from a daily changing menu, with dishes such as steak and mushroom pie for £4.30, lasagne for £4.10 and shepherd's pie for £3.95.

Brewery: Nicholson's
Licensee: S Wheatman
Opening hours: 11am-11pm
(Sat 11am-8.30pm); closed Sun
Bar food: 12-2.30pm;
sandwiches until 8.30pm
Children: Welcome at lunchtime
in the Cellar Bar only
Credit cards: Access, Visa

GROUSE AND CLARET
14 Little Chester Street, Belgravia SW1X 7AP. Tel 071 235 3438

SW1

The very prosperous area of Belgravia is the home of this attractive corner pub. Beyond the stone frontage are two bars and an upstairs restaurant, all with the discreet atmosphere redolent of a gentleman's club. The bars have wood panelling and plush seating, and one has a slightly higher level of booth areas with leatherette benches and ornamented tables. Thai food is served in the evening, while at lunchtime wholesome dishes include vegetarian lasagne, Somerset pork chops, and shepherd's pie, all at £3.80. Beers on draught are Brakspear Special, Wards Mild, Young's, Wadworth 6X, Marston's Pedigree and Boddingtons, and there are also five lagers and a cider on draught.

Brewery: Free house
Licensee: Regent Inns Plc
(manager Mrs R J Cox)
Opening hours: 11am-11pm
(Sat 11.30am-3pm, 6-11pm); Sun
12-3pm
Bar food: 12-2.30pm, 6.30-9pm;
Sun 12-2.30pm only
Restaurant: Times as bar food
Children: Welcome anywhere
away from the bar
Credit cards:
AMERICAN EXPRESS®, Access,
Visa, Diners

A Pride of Rams
Known for its Shire horses and determined adherence to real ale, the family firm of Young has run the Ram Brewery in Wandsworth, south-west London, since Charles Allen Young bought it in 1831. There had been a brewery on this site on the bank of the dilatory River Wandle, close to the point where it enters the Thames, as far back as 1675. An 18th-century house is the oldest building here today, having survived Second World War bombing.

☙ GRENADIER
18 Wilton Row SW1X 7NR. Tel 071 235 3074

SW1

Approach from the top of Wilton Row rather than from Barrack Yard for the best view of this bright and pretty pub, with its red sentry box, bright window boxes and its walls covered in ivy and a grape vine. Built in the 1820s, the Grenadier is proud of its connection with the Duke of Wellington who stabled his horse in the cobbled yard, and whose soldiers used the pub as their mess. Little has changed since then, for, excepting the military paintings and prints, the bar is very bare, and the restaurant only slightly more decorative. It is very popular though and, in summer, drinks are enjoyed out in the quiet mews while an open fire creates a more cosy atmosphere in winter. Beers on draught include Ruddles Best and County, Courage Directors, and Webster's Yorkshire, and the pub is also famous for its Bloody Marys. The restaurant offers an à la carte menu for about £25 a head, while more modest bar meals include soup for £2.30, scampi for £4.90, and salsa with tortilla chips for £4.40.

Brewery: Chef & Brewer
Licensee: Peter Donald Martin
Opening hours: 12-3pm, 5-11pm; Sun 12-3pm, 7-10.30pm
Bar food: 12-2.30pm, 6-10pm; Sun 12-3pm, 7-10.30pm
Restaurant: Times as bar food
Children: Welcome in the restaurant only
Credit cards:
AMERICAN EXPRESS®, Access, Visa, Diners

⊜ COOPERS ARMS
87 Flood Street SW3 5TB. Tel 071 376 3120

SW3

This super corner pub is to be found in a residential area just off the Kings Road. Built in 1784, its cream-painted exterior, brightened with window boxes, is unassuming. Inside there is one bar, with a room upstairs which is used as a restaurant at lunchtime and a function room in the evening. The bar is spacious and light, featuring a central serving area surrounded by a mixture of kitchen tables, desks and benches, odd chairs and stools, the floorboards covered with large rugs and the walls decorated with paintings and prints of many styles and sizes. Other items of interest include a grandfather clock and a large buffalo head on one wall. This is a lively conversation pub - there are no games or music - and the bar staff are young and friendly; the clientele ranges from young local workers and business people to old Chelsea characters. The bar food is excellent, but it's wise to order early as some dishes can run out quite quickly. Typical dishes include deep-fried Gorgonzola at £4.75, smoked chicken and avocado salad at £4.95, and macaroni, bacon and leek bake at £4.75. Young's Bitter, Special and Porter are on draught, along with four lagers and a cider, and the pub also offers a selection of about seven wines by the glass.

Brewery: Young's
Licensee: Charles Gotto
Opening hours: 11am-11pm; Sun 12-3pm, 7-10.30pm
Bar food: 12-2.30pm, 6.30-9.30pm; lunchtime only at weekends
Children: Welcome away from the bar
Credit cards: AMERICAN EXPRESS®, Access, Visa

⊜ RED LION
1 Waverton Street, Mayfair W1X 7FJ. Tel 071 499 1307

W1

Built in 1752, this charming small pub, with its leaded windows and pretty hanging baskets, sits in a quiet corner of Mayfair. The small dimly-lit and cosy bar has wooden floorboards and panelled walls decorated with old black-and-white photographs and prints of London scenes; it is furnished with comfortable old sofas, stools and tables. Courage Directors and Best, Webster's Yorkshire, and Greene King IPA are on draught, and typical bar meals include Cumberland sausage and mash, and chicken Italiana, both at £4.75. There is also a separate restaurant.

Brewery: Chef & Brewer
Licensee: Ray Dodgson
Opening hours: 11am-11pm (Sat 11.30am-3pm, 6-11pm); Sun 12-3pm, 7-10.30pm
Bar food: 12-2.30pm, 6-10pm (Sun from 7pm)
Restaurant: 12-2.30pm, 7-10pm
Children: Welcome away from the bar
Credit cards: AMERICAN EXPRESS®, Access, Visa, Diners

ARGYLL ARMS
18 Argyll Street W1V 1AA. Tel 071 734 6117

W1

Situated close to Oxford Circus Tube station, the Argyll Arms is a popular meeting place and as a result tends to be busy with people wandering in, looking around, and waiting for friends. In good weather, many take their drinks back outside where barriers prove useful for support, as well as keeping pub customers from spreading over the whole street. There has been a tavern here since 1716, but the Argyll Arms itself dates from 1868. It has a welcoming aspect; the frontage is covered in ivy, and tubs with flowers and shrubs ornament the entrance. Inside, a long entrance hall has large mirrors along one wall reflecting the wood and etched glass walls and doors opposite. Two doors lead to small bars, little more than booths, at the front, but the hall carries on to reach a large open bar area with a high moulded ceiling, ornate mirrors, carved pillars and staircase, and comfortable plush seating. Beers on draught include Tetley, Wadworth 6X, Marston's Pedigree, Greene King IPA, and Nicholson's Best, with four lagers and a cider also available. Bar food is served all day, and dishes include steak and kidney pie for £4.50, roast beef and Yorkshire pudding for £4.95, and specials such as mushroom, leek and potato pie for £4.25. Morning coffee and afternoon tea are served.

Brewery: Free house
Licensee: Mike Tayara
Opening hours: 11am-11pm; closed Sun
Bar food: Hot food 11am-7.30pm; cold buffet 11am-9.30pm
Children: Welcome if well behaved; usually accommodated upstairs

☺ GUINEA
30 Bruton Place, Mayfair W1X 7AA. Tel 071 409 1728

W1

Sitting in the centre of an attractive and prosperous mews, the etched windows of this smart pub give its date as 1423. Inside, the bar is small, busy and rather luxurious, with friendly and efficient service. Caricature prints and sketches share wall space with certificates awarded to the pub for excellent food - 1991 Pub Sandwich of the Year, and current champion of the Great Steak and Kidney Pie award. This great pie is £3.95, and other dishes include steak Mirabeau at £3.95 and chicken Siciliano at £4.25; vegetarians are limited to sandwiches here. There is also a beautifully decorated restaurant offering an à la carte menu at about £35 a head. Beers on draught are Young's Special, Ordinary and Porter, and a dozen wines are available by the glass.

Brewery: Young's
Licensee: Carl Smith
Opening hours: 11am-11pm; closed Sun
Bar food: 12-2.30pm, 6.30-10.30pm (except Sat)
Restaurant: 12.30-2.30pm (except Sat and Sun), 6.30-11pm (except Sun)
Children: Welcome in restaurant only
Credit cards: AMERICAN EXPRESS®, Access, Visa, Diners

OLD COFFEE HOUSE
49 Beak Street W1R 3LE. Tel 071 437 2197

W1

Just a few minutes' away from Liberty and Carnaby Street, this Victorian pub on the edge of Soho sits comfortably alongside designer clothes shops, trendy restaurants and offices. Originally an 18th-century coffee house, it is now the only surviving establishment of that type that still bears the name. The one bar has plenty of tables and leatherette settles from which to study the extraordinary collection of prints, paintings, sketches and mirrors, battered copper pots, Toby jugs and chamber pots. Squeezed in amongst all this are an antelope head and a violincello. A comprehensive menu in the bar and the upstairs restaurant includes such dishes as chicken, ham and leek pie, salmon and broccoli shantie and steak and kidney pudding, all at £3.95. Puddings are £1.60 and include Spotted Dick and apple, toffee and pecan pie. Beers on draught are Courage Best, Ruddles Best, Young's Special and John Smith's, with five lagers and a cider also available.

Brewery: Courage
Licensee: B Hawkins
Opening hours: 11am-11pm; Sun 12-3pm, 7-10.30pm
Bar food: 12-3.30pm (except Sun)
Restaurant: Times as bar food
Children: Welcome at lunchtime in restaurant

MUSEUM TAVERN
49 Great Russell Street WC1B 3BA. Tel 071 242 8987

WC1

This is an attractive 18th-century pub with large windows, old-style street lamps and pretty hanging baskets decorating the exterior. The large, ornate bar which dominates the narrow room allows space for only one row of tables along the opposite wall - an arrangement which seems to encourage everyone to talk to each other, rather than keep to themselves. This is probably also due to the friendly, jocular staff and the range of different types of people who come here. Being opposite the British Museum and surrounded by stamp and antique-book shops, the pub attracts tourists, local workers, students - all sorts of all ages, and all happy to share tables and conversation. A good range of real ales consists of Greene King IPA and Abbot Ale, Brakspear Old, Special and Bitter, Ruddles Best and County, and Webster's Yorkshire. Bar food is very fresh and very tasty, and served in almost daunting portions. The cold buffet offers salads with, for example, Gala pie, quiche, and Scotch egg, all for £3.95. This is available all day, supplemented with a few hot specials such as braised steak, roast chicken and shepherd's pie, all at £4.95. Morning coffee and afternoon tea are served.

Brewery: Grand Metropolitan
Licensee: John Keating
Opening hours: 11am-11pm; Sun 12-2.30pm, 7-10.30pm
Bar food: 11am-10pm (except Sun)
Children: Welcome before 5pm
Credit cards:
AMERICAN EXPRESS®, Access, Visa, Diners

CITTIE OF YORK
22-23 High Holborn WC1V 6BS. Tel 071 242 7670

WC1

This superb pub is easily identified from a distance by the large black-and-gold clock that hangs outside. The fairly narrow exterior suggests a small, cosy pub, but this is deceptive as the smaller of the two ground floor bars (there is also one in the cellar) is quite spacious, with a high ceiling and wood-panelled walls decorated with prints of old London scenes. The main bar stands on the site of the original pub dating from 1430. It was rebuilt in 1695 to form Gray's Inn Coffee House, which in turn was partially demolished and reconstructed in the 1890s. This huge bar has a surprisingly high, beamed ceiling, old vats above the dark wood bar, and some booth seating. Outside seating consists of a few tables at the front. Well managed, with cheerful, friendly staff, this is a popular and busy pub that gives the feeling of being at the very heart of London life. On draught are Samuel Smith Old Brewery and Museum Ale. The bar menu includes deep-fried Camembert for £3.50, salmon fish cakes for £4.50 and Raj vegetable curry for £4.25, with daily changing blackboard specials.

Brewery: Samuel Smith
Licensee: Stuart Browning
Opening hours: 11am-11pm (Sat 11am-3pm, 5.30-11pm); closed Sun
Bar food: 12-2.30pm, 5.30-9pm
Children: Welcome before 5pm
Credit cards: Access, Visa

☞ LAMB
94 Lamb's Conduit Street WC1N 3LZ. Tel 071 405 0713

WC1

This quiet, unpretentious pub is situated at the north end of Lamb's Conduit Street, a pedestrianised road of shops, offices and houses with the atmosphere of a small village. Built in the late 18th century, the Lamb is a typical Victorian pub, with etched glass, green tiles and window boxes, and is known to have been a regular haunt of the Bloomsbury group. The one bar is spacious and relaxed, with leatherette seating lining the walls decorated with black-and-white photographs and prints. There is a patio at the back. Beers on draught are Young's Special, Ordinary, Porter and Winter Warmer, supplemented with four lagers and a cider also on draught, and a choice of ten whiskies. A regularly changing bar menu might include chicken, cheese and pineapple pie, beef in ale and sweet and sour pork, all priced at £3.95.

Brewery: Young's
Licensee: Richard Whyte
Opening hours: 11am-11pm; Sun 12-3pm, 7-10.30pm
Bar food: 12-2.30pm, snacks till 10pm; Sun Carvery 12-2.30pm (booking necessary)
Children: In dining room for Sun Carvery only
Credit cards: AMERICAN EXPRESS®, Access, Visa, Diners

PRINCESS LOUISE
208 High Holborn WC1V 7BW. Tel 071 405 8816

WC1

Built in 1872 and now a Grade II listed building, this is probably one of the most attractive pubs in London. It has an impressive marbled exterior, with large windows and

Brewery: Free house
Licensee: Ian Phillips
Opening hours: 11am-11pm

a tiled entrance. Inside, the decor dates from 1891 and features colourful, ornate tiles and mirrors on the walls, Portland stone columns, and a splendid ceiling of plasterwork introduced by the prominent architect Arthur Chitty. Light and bright, with friendly staff and a good range of well kept beer (Brakspear IPA and Special, Wards Yorkshire, Sheffield Best, Thorne Best and Princess Louise, Benskins Best, Bass and Burton Ale being on draught), this is a popular meeting place and can get very crowded from quite early evening. Only sandwiches are served in the bar, but there is a wine bar that serves Thai food during the week. Live entertainment is featured on Saturday nights, when the pub is host to jazz, blues and other bands.

(Sat 12-3pm, 6-11pm); Sun 12-2pm, 7- 10.30pm
Bar food: 12-2pm only
Restaurant: Wine bar 12-3pm, 5.30-11pm (except Sat and Sun)
Children: Not permitted inside

⊜ SEVEN STARS
53 Carey Street WC2A 2JB. Tel 071 242 8521

WC2

Situated in a quiet street just off Chancery Lane, this is a haven for those wanting to enjoy a drink without music or games to distract them. Built in 1690, it is a small, narrow pub with bare boards and very few furnishings. Solitary drinkers pop in throughout the day to read, chat or contemplate life, while lunchtimes bring an influx of City workers. Courage Best and Directors are the only beers on draught, and bar food is limited to just a few dishes such as cottage pie for £2.10, beef in Guinness for £2.40, and chilli for £2.20, but these and sandwiches are available all day.

Brewery: Courage
Licensee: J Crawley
Opening hours: 11am-11pm; closed Sat and Sun
Bar food: As opening hours
Children: Not permitted inside

⊜ LAMB AND FLAG
33 Rose Street, Covent Garden WC2 E9EB. Tel 071 497 9504

WC2

Dating from 1627, this claims to be the oldest tavern in Covent Garden. It originally stood across the road from its present site, to which it moved in 1730, and was named The Cooper's Arm. The name changed to the Lamb and Flag in the early 19th century when the pub was known to the locals as the Bucket of Blood because of the bare fist fights held in the room upstairs. This room is now called the Dryden room, named after the poet who was almost beaten to death in 1679 by men hired by the Duchess of Portsmouth because she took offence at Dryden's public comments regarding her relationship with Charles II. Partly wood-panelled and with an open fire and an assortment of prints, the pub is lively and busy, serving Courage Best and Diretors, and John Smith's Yorkshire on draught. Snacks are available all day, while hot lunches include dishes such as steak and kidney pie and hot roast beef, both at £3.50.

Brewery: Courage
Licensee: A Zimmerman
Opening hours: 11am-11pm (Fri and Sat 11am-10.45pm); Sun 12-3pm, 7-10.30pm
Bar food: 12-2.30pm, snacks until 6pm; Sun 12-2.30pm (snacks only)
Children: Not permitted inside

⊛ SHERLOCK HOLMES
10-11 Northumberland Street WC2 5DA. Tel 071 930 2644

WC2

Formerly part of the Northumberland hotel, this attractive building set back from the road, painted black with etched glass windows and colourful hanging baskets, has been a pub for about 100 years. The large central bar divides the richly furnished room into two sections, one of which contains lots of interesting Holmes memorabilia, including photographs of Conan Doyle and of various film and theatre productions of Sherlock Holmes stories, and mounted pages from manuscripts. Upstairs in the handsome restaurant a section of the room behind glass contains an astonishing display of memorabilia collected by Barclays Bank (current occupants of 221 Baker Street) presented to suggest the living room of Sherlock Holmes, complete with a model of the man himself. The restaurant menu also reflects the theme, with dishes such as Doctor Watson's whitebait at £2.95 and Shoscombe Old Place treacle sponge at £2.55. Bar food includes steak, ale and mushroom pie at £4.25 and Boardroom bangers at £2.75. Morning coffee and afternoon tea are also available. On draught are Boddingtons, Flowers Original, Brakspear, Marston's Pedigree, Wadworth 6X and Greene King Abbot Ale. Enthusiastically run, with friendly, welcoming staff this is a lively and, above all, fun pub to visit.

Brewery: Whitbread
Licensee: Catherine Brown-Allen
Opening hours: 11.30am-11pm;
Sun 12-2.30pm, 7-10.30pm
Bar food: 12-5pm; Sun 12-2.30pm
Restaurant: 12-3pm, 6-11pm;
booking necessary
Children: Welcome in the restaurant only
Credit cards:
AMERICAN EXPRESS®, Access,
Visa, Diners

⊛ FREEMASONS ARMS
81 Long Acre, Covent Garden WC2 9NG. Tel 071 836 3115

WC2

This modern, lively pub, conveniently situated near Drury Lane and the centre of Covent Garden, is a popular meeting place for people in their 20s and 30s. The large bar downstairs, with polished floorboards, some booth seating with leatherette settles and plain wooden furniture, has a small, tiled fireplace with an attractive wooden mantle and mirror, and a small skylight with stained glass and a shelf of books and bottles beneath. The walls are covered with pictures, prints and framed theatre bills. Upstairs is the more comfortable Lodge Bar where hot dishes such as Irish stew and Lancashire hot pot at £3.25 are served. Sandwiches and snacks are available downstairs, although hot food can be sent down. The pub tends to get very loud, especially when the video juke-box is playing, so it is recommended for those who enjoy a lively night out rather than a quiet drink. Cask-conditioned Greene King IPA, Abbot Ale and Rayments Special are on draught.

Brewery: Greene King
Licensees: Mr and Mrs M A Dee
Opening hours: 11.30am-11pm;
Sun 12-2.30pm, 7-10.30pm
Bar food: 12-2pm, sandwiches until 8pm (except Sun)
Children: Not permitted inside
Credit cards: Access, Visa

PROSPECT OF WHITBY
57 Wapping Wall, Wapping E1 9SJ. Tel 071 481 1095/1317

E1

Sitting by the Thames, near new developments of flats and working dockyard areas, this large, attractive pub is dwarfed by the adjacent office block. Over 470 years old, the long bar has a flagstone floor, big, solid wooden furniture, a slightly elevated dining area, and a small terrace overlooking the river. Lots of pictures and historically interesting artefacts decorate the walls, and large old barrels stand in various corners. Upstairs, the restaurant is more luxuriously furnished, complementing the age and style of the building. Once a week in winter various jazz and rhythm and blues artists add to the lively, cheerful atmosphere of this friendly pub. Beer on draught includes Webster's Yorkshire, Ruddles County and Best, Courage Directors and Guinness, with four lagers, two ciders and a wide range of bottled beers also available. The bar menu offers steak and kidney pie, beef in ale pie, both at £3.95, and various ploughman's and salads at £3.55. The restaurant serves mainly English food for about £25 a head, and booking is necessary.

Brewery: Chef & Brewer
Licensee: Christopher Reeves
Opening hours: 11.30am-3pm, 5.30-11pm; Sun 12-3pm, 7-10.30pm
Bar food: 12-2.30pm, 6-9.30pm (Sun from 7pm)
Restaurant: Bookings taken for 12-2pm, 7-9.30pm
Children: Welcome in the dining area; not permitted under five years in the restaurant
Credit cards:
AMERICAN EXPRESS®, Access, Visa, Diners

LARKSHALL
Larkshall Road, Chingford E4 9HZ. Tel 081 524 6026

E4

This is a very unusual pub in that it combines two totally different styles under one roof. The original 16th-century building was a farmhouse and one dimly lit bar retains this character, with bare floorboards, lots of beams and exposed brickwork hung with various farming implements, and stairs leading up to a small gallery. Extended in 1890, a few steps lead up to a spacious and luxurious bar resembling an Edwardian drawing room, complete with tall bay windows and wooden shutters, a high ceiling with decorative plaster coving, winged chairs, large round tables, and smart prints on the cream-painted walls. Well presented and tasty home-made dishes include chicken curry and Hungarian goulash, both at £3.50, and cheese and broccoli flan with salad for £2. Beers on draught are Courage Best and Directors and John Smith's Yorkshire, and there is a wide selection of bottled beers.

Brewery: Chef & Brewer
Licensee: Stuart Bentley
Opening hours: 11am-3pm, 5.30-11pm (Sat 12-4pm, 7-11pm); Sun 12- 3pm, 7-10.30pm
Bar food: 12-2.30pm (except Sun)
Children: Welcome in the gallery

GRAPES
76 Narrow Street, Limehouse E14 8BP. Tel 071 987 4396

E14

Built in 1730, this unspoilt pub sits quietly by the Thames in an area of residential and working dockland. Inside, the bar is long and narrow, with a tiny conservatory at the far end which has good views of the river. The partly wood-panelled walls are decorated with old prints of London and sketches of Dickens' characters, and attractive Victorian-style wall lamps light the bar. Beers on draught are Tetley, Burton and Guinness, with Lowenbrau and Castlemaine XXXX lagers and Gaymer's Olde English cider. The fish restaurant upstairs is immensely popular, with an à la carte menu at about £20 a head, but the bar food is also good value and very tasty. Blackboard specials supplement the regular menu which offers such dishes as savoury pancakes for £3.10, vegetable bake for £3.75 and poached cod with shrimp sauce for £3.95, and puddings at £2.25 include profiteroles, bread-and-butter pudding, and apple crumble.

Brewery: Taylor Walker
Licensee: Kerry Chapman
Opening hours: 12-3pm, 5.30-11pm (Sat 7-11pm); Sun 7-10.30pm only
Bar food: 12-2pm (except Sat and Sun), 5.30-10pm (except Sun)
Restaurant: 12-2pm, 7-10pm; booking necessary
Children: Welcome if well behaved
Credit cards: AMERICAN EXPRESS®, Access, Visa, Diners

COLLEGE ARMS
807-809 Forest Road, Walthamstow E17 4JD. Tel 081 501 8001

E17

The attractive wood and glass frontage of this modern, friendly pub sits within a row of shops close to the Waltham Forest college and the town hall. The bright bar has wood-panelled walls decorated with colourful pictures, tiles and mirrors, while a few steps lead down to the eating area where the tables are covered in bright check cloths. Popular for both its real ales and its food, the bar offers blackboard specials such as cauliflower and mushroom bake and lasagne, both at £3.10, and serves draught Courage Best, Flowers Original, Greene King Abbot Ale, Webster's Yorkshire, Marston's Pedigree, and a guest beer such as Wethered Winter Royal. Both morning coffee and afternoon tea are served. Special sporting events captured on satellite television are celebrated with cheap beer and food, and a quiz is held once a week.

Brewery: Free house
Licensee: J A Devenish
Opening hours: 11am-11pm; Sun 12-3pm, 7-10.30pm
Bar food: As opening hours
Children: Welcome in the eating area, if well behaved

Bottoms Up

As a customer in a 17th-century inn or alehouse, you might find yourself with a pint or quart pot made of wood, horn or leather in your hand. They all had the advantage of not breaking if dropped, though the effect on the beer's taste might not suit today's palates. A cut above these utensils were mugs and tankards of pewter, which some pubs still supply and some drinkers still swear by. In 19th-century hostelries, however, pewter gradually gave way to china and glass, with the occasional joky china mug made with a frog crouching at the bottom, to give the unwary toper a nasty shock.

⚓ ANCHOR
34 Park Street, Southwark SE1 4NB. Tel 071 407 1577

SE1

Situated on the corner of Park Street, not far from London Bridge and Clink Prison, this lovely, rambling pub was built in 1603 and has a part-wood, part-brick exterior, with hanging baskets and tubs adding splashes of colour, and a large waterside terrace with tables overlooking the Thames. Inside, there are several different areas with steps leading up and down into the rooms. The older rooms are the most attractive and full of character, with their oak beams, wooden floorboards and exposed brick walls, but the more modern bar, though lacking the character of the others, is sympathetically decorated and draws the customers with its appetising food bar. Another bar upstairs is sometimes used as a family room, and there is also a delightful restaurant, furnished in Elizabethan style with heavy wooden tables and richly cushioned chairs, with sparkling tableware. The à la carte menu costs around £25 a head, and it is usually necessary to book. Bar food includes sausage, beans and jacket potato for £2.95, chicken casserole and chilli con carne, both for £4.30. On draught are John Smith's, Ruddles County, Courage Directors and Best, Anchor Best, Beamish, and Guinness.

Brewery: Free house
Licensee: Brian Redshaw
Opening hours: 11.30am-11pm; Sun 12-3pm, 7-10.30pm
Bar food: 12-2.30pm, 5-9pm; Sun 12-2.30pm, 7-9pm (limited menu)
Restaurant: 12-2.30pm, 6-10pm; Sun 12-2.30pm, 7-9pm
Children: Welcome in areas away from bars
Credit cards: AMERICAN EXPRESS®, Access, Visa, Diners

GEORGE
77 Borough High Street SE1 1NH. Tel 071 407 2056

SE1

An archway on Borough High Street leads to the cobbled courtyard of the long, black-and-white, beamed building of the George. Though a part of it was built in 1542, most of the inn dates from 1676, making it the only 17th-century coaching inn left in London in its original form. Unfortunately, the courtyard is overlooked by new offices, and the traffic noise does invade, but the inside is a treat. Steps lead up and down between each of the four long, narrow bars which are furnished with low tables and chairs and decorated with some memorabilia of Dickens, who is said to have frequented the inn after he achieved success. Bar food includes a wide range of pies such as turkey and leek, steak and beer, and vegetable, all at £3.75, and mini bloomer loaves with meats, cheeses, pâté and salad for £2.25. Beers on draught are Fuller's London Pride, Wadworth 6X, Boddingtons, Flowers Original and Murphy's, with two lagers and a cider also available, supplemented by a vast range of imported strong lagers. Live entertainment is provided in the form of a folk night at the beginning of each month.

Brewery: Whitbread
Licensee: John Hall
Opening hours: 11am-11pm (Sat 11am-3pm, 6-11pm); Sun 12-2.30pm, 7-10.30pm
Bar food: 12.15-2.15pm daily; Wed-Thu 6-9pm, please telephone to check if bar food is available on other evenings
Restaurant: 12-2pm (except Sun); please check if open evenings
Children: Welcome in the wine bar area
Credit cards: AMERICAN EXPRESS®, Access, Visa, Diners

PHOENIX AND FIRKIN
5 Windsor Walk, Denmark Hill SE5 8BB. Tel 071 701 8282

SE5

Built in 1866 for the London, Brighton and South Coast Railway, this super pub straddles the bridge by Denmark Hill station and features cast-iron and brick details associated with Victorian railway architecture. The one bar is furnished with wooden pews and chunky tables and stools, and a cast-iron spiral staircase leads up to a gallery. Station signs and posters decorate the walls, a model train runs back and forth behind the bar, and the huge clock hanging just inside the door originally hung in Euston station. Relaxed and peaceful during the day, the pub is popular with women who want a quiet drink on their own without unwanted attention. In the evening the atmosphere is much more lively, and blues and rock bands play here twice a week. Firkin beers brewed on the premises include Phoenix, Rail, and Dogbolter, and also on draught are Tetley, three lagers and two ciders. The pub also stocks a wide range of imported bottled beers. A few daily changing hot dishes are served, but the pub is best known for its enormous baps, which are very good value at £1.95.

Brewery: Firkin
Licensee: John McKeone
Opening hours: 11am-11pm; Sun 12-3pm, 7-10.30pm
Bar food: 11am-3.30pm, 5-9pm; Sun 12-2.30pm only
Children: Welcome away from the bar

⊜ TRAFALGAR TAVERN
Park Row, Greenwich SE10 9NW. Tel 081 858 2507

SE10

A good location by the Thames and a noteworthy history make this an interesting pub to visit. It was built in 1837 to commemorate the 1805 Battle of Trafalgar, Dick Turpin was known to have frequented the pub, and scenes from Dickens's *Our Mutual Friend* were set here. The attractive white stone building has a bare, dark bar, a cheerful restaurant with green-and-white check tablecloths, and a room upstairs decorated to replicate the fo'c'sle of a 1750s gunner. Here, antique fairs are sometimes held, while entertainment downstairs takes the form of a small swing band on Mondays and Thursdays, and jazz on Sundays. Beers on draught are Ruddles County and Best, Webster's Yorkshire, Courage Directors, and Guinness and there is a 40-item wine list. An à la carte menu at around £15 a head is served in the Whitebait Brasserie, and bar food is also available, with such dishes as steak and kidney pie, chicken chasseur and cottage pie, all for around £4 to £5.

Brewery: Courage
Licensee: Charles Maou
Opening hours: 11am-11pm; Sun 12-2.30pm, 7-10.30pm
Bar food: 12-3pm only
Restaurant: 12-10pm; Sun 12-3pm
Children: Welcome anywhere at lunchtime; evenings only in restaurant
Credit cards: Access, Visa

⊕ YACHT TAVERN
Crane Street, Greenwich SE10 9NP. Tel 081 858 0715

SE10

This low, brick building is decorated with hanging baskets and is attractively lit at night. Over 200 years old, it is situated by the river, just down the lane from the Trafalgar Tavern, and is preferred by locals for its unpretentious, more relaxed atmosphere. There are lovely views from the terrace. The bar is decorated to resemble the interior of a yacht, with round, lipped tables and cushioned seating. A higher level has wood-panelled walls, dark wood furniture and big sash windows draped with heavy curtains on brass rods. Rowing boats, oars and other gear hang from the ceiling, and the walls are decorated with good photographs of boats at sea. Bar food is only available at lunchtime, and consists of unexceptional hot dishes such as cottage pie and lasagne for £4.25, with jacket potatoes, salads and ploughman's also available. Beers on draught are Ruddles Best and County, Webster's Yorkshire and Guinness.

Brewery: Courage
Licensees: Mr and Mrs Moore
Opening hours: 11am-11pm; Sun 12-2.30pm, 7-10.30pm; closed on occasional afternoons and Sun evening in winter
Bar food: 12-2.30pm
Children: Welcome until 8.30pm
Credit cards:
AMERICAN EXPRESS®, Access, Visa, Diners

FOX AND FIRKIN
316 Lewisham High Street, Lewisham SE13 6NL. Tel 081 690 8925

SE13

This lively pub on the edge of Lewisham town centre is popular not only for the Firkin beers brewed on the premises, but for the entertainment provided four nights a week (Thursday to Sunday). This ranges from live bands to sing-alongs with a piano player, to Sumo wrestling! The large bar is furnished with wooden tables, chairs and pews, with a pulpit at one side and a piano at the back. Lots of bottles are ranged along the back of the bar, and the walls are covered with old theatre bills, prints, sketches and cartoons. On the back wall photographs show the brewing process, and you can look through the portholes there to see various tuns of mash. The beers brewed here are Firkin Mild, Ladywell, Dogbolter and Fox, and the bar also sells Tetley and a guest beer such as Theakston Old Peculier. They also stock ten bottled beers and three imported lagers. A changing blackboard menu features good-value dishes such as meat and potato pie for £1.45, chicken tikka for £1.55, burgers for £1.65 and toasties for around £1.30. There is a beer garden at the back where barbecues are held in summer.

Brewery: Firkin
Licensee: Tony Powell
Opening hours: 12-3.30pm, 5.30-11pm; Sun 12-3pm, 7-10.30pm
Bar food: As opening hours
Children: Not permitted inside

⊜ FAMOUS ANGEL

101 Bermondsey Wall East, Rotherhithe SE16 4NB Tel 071 237 3608

SE16

Although there has been a pub on this riverside site since the 17th century, the current building dates from the 1800s. There is just one bar, comfortably furnished and decorated along a sailing theme with the highly polished bar resembling the bows of a ship, and ships' lanterns and boating pictures adorning the walls. Even the doors to the toilets have portholes and are labelled Gulls and Buoys! There is a restaurant upstairs, and a jetty at the back has a few tables and wonderful views of the Thames. Typical bar meals include chilli at £3.95, pork and apple pie at £3.50, and sausage roll salad at £3.50; vegetarians are usually limited to a salad. Beers available on draught are Wadworth 6X, John Smith's Yorkshire, Larkins Traditional and Courage Best and Directors.

Brewery: Free house
Licensee: Trusthouse Forte (manager Sherry Holland)
Opening hours: 11am-3pm, 5.30-11pm; Sun 12-3pm, 7-10.30pm
Bar food: 12-2.30pm, 5.30-10pm; Sun 12-2.30pm, 7-10pm
Restaurant: 12-2pm, 7-9.45pm (except Sat lunchtime and Sun evening)
Children: Welcome on jetty, or speak to the barman; no toddlers
Credit cards: AMERICAN EXPRESS®, Access, Visa, Diners

MAYFLOWER

117 Rotherhithe Street, Rotherhithe SE16 4MF. Tel 071 237 4088

SE16

This pretty 17th-century pub is situated by the Thames, just a minute's walk from Rotherhithe Tube. There is one main bar, with partly wood-panelled walls, original supporting beams, a large brick fireplace and heavy wooden furniture, including old carved settles. On the walls are paintings and sketches, mostly of the *Mayflower* after which the pub is named. An airy upstairs room, furnished with large heavy tables, is used as a dining area and for families and functions. Through the leaded windows are good views of the river, which can also be enjoyed from the jetty. On draught are Bass, Charrington IPA and Guinness, and there is also a vast range of imported beers. A substantial menu features steak and vegetable pie, mushroom and nut fettucini and chicken and bacon stir fry, all at £4.95, with such desserts as toffee, apple and pecan pie for £2.65, apple muffin at £2.25 and lemon brûlée at £2.75. Occasionally, a flautist and harpist entertain customers on the jetty.

Brewery: Bass
Licensee: D Pascoe
Opening hours: 12-3pm daily, 6-11pm (Sat 6.30pm); Sun 7-10.30pm
Bar food: 12.30-2.30pm, 6.30-9pm (inc Sun)
Children: Welcome upstairs and on jetty
Credit cards: Access, Visa

WHITE HORSE
1-3 Parsons Green, Fulham SW6 4UL. Tel 071 736 2115

SW6

This attractive Victorian pub has huge windows, decorative ironwork above the doors, colourful hanging baskets and white cast-iron furniture on a front patio overlooking Parsons Green. The large bar is light and airy, mostly furnished with leather sofas, stools and low tables, with some long settles arranged booth-like near the food bar, which is a non-smoking area. The tasty food is served in generous portions, and typical specials include beef creole for £5.50, chicken Jambalaya for £4.75 and aubergine and potato bake for £3.95. Well known for its Old Ale beer festivals, the pub regularly stocks draught Bass, Charrington IPA, Adnams Extra and Highgate Mild, in addition to a vast selection of bottled beers from around the world, including Anchor Liberty, Brooklyn, Chimay Red and Trafair House Ale. Jazz singers and guitarists entertain regularly through the year, and Morris dancers are a feature of the beer festivals.

Brewery: Bass
Licensee: Sally Cruickshank
Opening hours: 11am-3pm, 5-11pm; Sun 12-2.30pm, 7-10.30pm
Bar food: 12-3pm, 6-10.30pm; booking necessary in the evening; Sat and Sun 'mega' breakfasts from 11am; Sun 1-2.30pm
Children: Welcome, if eating, at lunchtime only
Credit cards: AMERICAN EXPRESS®, Access, Visa, Diners

SUN INN
7 Church Road, Barnes SW13 9HE. Tel 081 876 5256

SW13

This attractive, white-painted, three-storey pub sits in the centre of Barnes opposite the pond. It has a mansard roof, big sash windows and pretty hanging baskets and flower boxes; picnic tables at the front provide outside seating. Originally a wine warehouse, it has been a pub since 1750 and is now a listed building. Inside, there are lots of nooks and crannies created by the interesting shape of the building and some wood and glass partitions. The two bars have mustard coloured walls which are partly wood-panelled and decorated with photographs, prints and mirrors. The dining area has big farmhouse tables and chairs, and a lovely pine dresser. Blackboard specials, for example steak and kidney pie and vegetarian lasagne, both at £4.25, supplement the regular menu. On draught are Marston's Pedigree, Burton Ale, Tetley, Young's, Guinness, five lagers and a cider. Please note: cheques are not accepted here.

Brewery: Allied Breweries
Licensee: Peter Bull
Opening hours: 11am-11pm; Sun 12-3pm, 7-10.30pm
Bar food: 12-3pm; Sun 12-2.15pm
Children: Welcome in dining area if eating

⊜ SHIP INN
41 Jews Row, Wandsworth SW18 1TB. Tel 081 870 9667

SW18

From the road, this 19th-century building has nothing to distinguish it from any other pub apart from the figurehead above an unused doorway. However, should you approach the pub from the river walk, you will pass through the two-level terrace with its barbecue area and lots of seating, summer bar and colourful trellises, flower boxes and hanging baskets, to the attractive conservatory-style Lounge Bar. This light, airy bar has heavy wooden tables and chairs, old desks and even an old butcher's table, ranged on the wooden floor. The small Public Bar is less decorative but seems popular with local workers. Staff are friendly and easy-going, and the atmosphere is relaxed. Food is a big attraction here, and typical dishes include Brie and apricot in filo pastry for £4.50, king prawns in lemon butter for £6.50 and fresh spaghetti with smoked chicken and cream for £5.50. Young's Bitter and Special are on draught, along with Guinness, Beamish, three lagers and cider, and there is also a list of about 30 wines from around the world.

Brewery: Young's
Licensee: Charles Gotto
Opening hours: 11am-11pm; Sun 12-2.30pm, 7-10.30pm
Bar food: 12-3pm, 7-10pm; Sun 12-2.30pm, 7-10pm
Children: Welcome away from the bar
Credit cards: AMERICAN EXPRESS®, Access, Visa, Diners

⊕ ALMA
499 Old York Road, Wandsworth SW18 1TF. Tel 081 870 2537

SW18

This very attractive Victorian pub, with etched-glass windows, green tiles and hanging baskets, stands on the corner of a quiet road near the railway station. The bar's high ceiling, large windows and decorative mirrors combine to create an impression of space, and the absence of music ensures the air is full of lively conversation. There is an informal arrangement of scruffy tables and chairs, a few wood and glass partitions, and a big carved staircase leading up to the function room. In addition to the many prints and posters on the walls, there is an unusual breathalyser by the door, and an old wooden fridge used for wine storage. There is a separate dining area, and the menu follows a 'Franglais' theme which is popular with regulars. The food is superb, and dishes include filo parcels of wild mushrooms, rice and pine nuts at £3.75, and quail with fennel stuffing, Pernod gravy and légumes at £6.50. Particularly good value is the Sunday lunch, and the fixed-price weekday lunch that offers two choices for each of the three courses, all for £12. On draught are Young's Bitter, Special and Porter, Beamish and four lagers, and there is a very good wine list, with many wines offered by the glass.

Brewery: Young's
Licensee: Charles Gotto
Opening hours: 11am-3pm, 5-11pm; Sun 12-2.30pm, 7-10.30pm
Bar food: As opening hours (except Sun evening)
Children: Welcome if well behaved
Credit cards: AMERICAN EXPRESS®, Access, Visa, Diners

FLASK
77 Highgate West Hill, Highgate N6 6BU. Tel 081 340 7260

N6

Built in 1663, this very attractive pub stands just off the high street, close to the Heath (parking near by is a problem). Its sheltered forecourt is full of picnic tables , and window boxes and wisteria brighten the entrance. Although there are only two bars, there are lots of different seating areas on four levels, including the former cellar. A mixture of solid wooden furniture is arranged in cosy sections on floorboards and rug-covered flagstones, while bottles, books and flasks fill the shelves around the walls, which in turn are covered with photographs, paintings, prints and mirrors. On draught are Tetley, Burton Ale, Benskins, Young's Bitter, Special and Winter Warmer. In addition to the printed menu, a daily changing blackboard menu offers dishes such as lasagne for £4.60, chicken chasseur for £4.95 and tagliatelle Niçoise, also for £4.95. Once a week in winter there is a jazz/blues night.

Brewery: Taylor Walker
Licensee: Andrew Barker
Opening hours: 11am-11pm; Sun 12-2.30pm, 7-10.30pm
Bar food: 12-2pm (Sat and Sun 2.30pm), 6-9pm
Children: Welcome if eating
Credit cards: Access, Visa

OLD BULL AND BUSH
North End Way, Hampstead NW3 7HE. Tel 081 455 3685

NW3

This is the pub to which the famous song refers, and the bars are decorated with posters and prints of music hall memorabilia. Built in 1645, it is a large, red-brick building in a salubrious residential area opposite the Heath with picnic tables at the front. The large main bar is partly open plan and partly divided into booth-like areas, with a higher level eating area where children are permitted. The Whitestone lounge resembles a small library, with full bookcases, a couple of armchairs by the fire, and other seating in the bay windows. Standard pub fare is available throughout the day, ranging from pizzas for £1.95 to lasagne for £4.60 and chicken Kiev for £6.35. Tetley, Young's Bitter and Special, and Burton Ale are on draught.

Brewery: Taylor Walker
Licensee: Dave Pitcher
Opening hours: 11am-11pm; Sun 12-2.30pm, 7-10.30pm
Bar food: 12-2.15pm (snacks 3-10pm), 6-8.30pm (except Sat and Sun)
Children: Welcome in eating area or Whitestone lounge if bar not in use

HOLLY BUSH
22 Holly Mount, Hampstead NW3 6SG. Tel 071 435 2892

NW3

Do not drive to this small 18th-century pub, for you will not be able to park anywhere as it is situated in a 'permit holders only' residential area just off the high street. Fortunately, it is very close to Hampstead Tube station, making access easy. Originally the stables of the portrait painter George Romney, the building was converted into a tavern in the early 19th century. There are two bars, of which the back bar is the most cosy and intimate. Etched mirrors, plates, and old prints and photographs of local scenes decorate the walls, and there is a raised area where bands play twice a week - 1960s music on Wednesday, jazz on Thursday. Bar meals are served only at lunchtime, and include jumbo sausage, Cornish pastie and various salads, all at £2.95. On draught are Young's Special, Benskins, Tetley, Burton Ale, three lagers and a cider.

Brewery: Taylor Walker
Licensee: Peter Dures
Opening hours: 11am-3pm (Sat 4pm), 5.30-11pm ; Sun 12-3pm, 7-10.30pm
Bar food: As morning opening hours (except Mon)
Children: Welcome in room away from bar, but preferably not after 9pm

SPANIARDS INN
Spaniards Road, Hampstead NW3 7JJ. Tel 081 455 3276

NW3

Built in 1585, this is a long, three-storey building, part brick, part weatherboard, painted white with large, black, sash windows. It has a lovely garden with plenty of seating between the rose beds, an aviary at the end, and a willow tree by the gate in the white picket fence. Inside, the nicest rooms are off the bar area; a small Snug and a dining area which have wood panelling and cushioned settles and are decorated with old prints and various antiques and other

Brewery: Bass
Licensee: Philippa Rendall
Opening hours: 11am-11pm; Sun 12-3pm, 7.30-10.30pm
Bar food: 12-3pm, 6-9.30pm (Sat 12-9.30 pm, cold buffet only 3-6pm); Sun 12-3pm, 7-9.30pm
Children: Welcome in dining area

ornaments. There is also an attractive function room upstairs. Imaginative dishes are fresh and tasty, although the size of your helping may depend on who serves you. Typical dishes include cauliflower and Stilton soup for £2.50, beef in Guinness pie for £5.25, and courgette and mushroom crumble for £4.75. A good range of beer includes Greene King IPA, Highgate Mild, Fuller's London Pride, Young's Special, Bass and Charrington IPA.

if eating, in Snug and upstairs if function not booked
Credit cards: Access, Visa

ADAM AND EVE
The Ridgeway, Mill Hill NW7 1RL. Tel 081 959 1036

NW7

Set back a little from the road in this surprisingly rural part of London, this old coaching inn was updated in the 1930s. The large bar has cushioned settles, open fires, books on shelves, and old prints of rural and urban scenes. The raised area known as the balcony has dining tables and chairs, and outside there is an enclosed garden and patio where barbecues are held in fine weather. On draught are Burton Ale, Tetley, John Bull, Wadworth 6X and a guest beer such as Adnams. Popular at lunchtime with a cosmopolitan clientele from the nearby National Medical Research Council, the pub offers a good range of regular meals and snacks supplemented by daily blackboard specials such as cottage pie at £2.90 and liver and onions at £2.60. Wednesday night is quiz night, and once a month there is either a disco or a singer of 1960s and '70s songs.

Brewery: Taylor Walker
Licensee: Ken Jones
Opening hours: 11.30am-3pm, 5.30-11pm (Sat 11.30-4pm, 7-11pm); Sun 12-3pm, 7-10.30pm
Bar food: 12-2.15pm (except Sun)
Children: Welcome if eating on balcony; no prams

CROCKERS
24 Aberdeen Place, St John's Wood NW8 8JR. Tel 071 286 6608

NW8

This beautiful, palatial pub was built as a hotel in 1898 specifically to attract travellers using the new Marylebone railway station. Unfortunately, the location was miscalculated and the station was built over half a mile away so the hotel did not become the thriving success it was hoped to be. There are two bars and a large adjoining lounge with a raised area designated as a non-smoking area, all of which are spacious and luxuriously furnished in Victorian style, complementing the original marble bar, walls and fireplaces, and the moulded, gilt-edged ceilings. Among the real ales are Brakspear Special, Eldridge Pope Royal Oak, Bass, Wards Sheffield Best and Crockers. Good value bar food such as steak and kidney pie, tuna patties, and potato and leek pie is on offer at £3.95 for all dishes. Sunday roast is £4.95. Live music is provided on Wednesday and Saturday nights by a piano player, and light jazz is featured on Sundays.

Brewery: Free house
Licencee: Regent Inns Plc (manager: David Toft)
Opening hours: 11am-11pm; Sun 12-3pm, 7-10.30pm
Bar food: 12-2.30pm, 6.30-9.45pm; Sun 12-2.15pm, 7-9.30pm
Children: Welcome in lounge adjoining bar, if well behaved

⊕ BULLS HEAD
15 Strand on the Green, Chiswick W4 3PQ. Tel 081 994 1204

W4

This attractive, white-painted brick building with black shutters and pretty hanging baskets is best approached from the river terrace. There is seating outside with good views of this busy section of the river. Part of the building dates from 1630 and it is said that Oliver Cromwell was betrayed here, but managed to escape through a tunnel which no longer exists. Although there is only one bar as such, there are lots of different areas on three levels – one of which is a food and non-smoking area. There is also a cheerful, bright conservatory. Ruddles County and Best, Webster's Yorkshire and Guinness are on draught, and rich, mouth-watering aromas will tempt you to try such dishes as curried vegetables for £4.20, steak and mushroom pie for £4.45 and mandarin chicken, also for £4.45.

Brewery: Free house
Licensee: Roger D Smart
Opening hours: 11am-11pm; closed 3-5pm mid-Oct to mid-Mar; Sun 12-2.30pm, 7-10.30pm
Bar food: 12-2.30pm, 6.30-9.30pm; Sun 12-2.30pm
Children: Welcome in conservatory and Snug area
Credit cards: Access, Visa

⊕ CITY BARGE
27 Strand on the Green, Chiswick W4 3PH. TEL 081 994 2148

W4

Built in 1484, and originally known as The Navigator's Arms, this pub was renamed in the 19th century when the state barge of the Lord Mayor of the City of London had its winter moorings here. It is a pretty, white-painted pub with blue steel steps up to the New Bar and conservatory, and a blue steel door to the Old Bar. This door is not just decorative; when the Thames runs high, the front of the pub is cut off and the door keeps the water out. Riveside seating is available outside. Attractively furnished with stripped-pine farmhouse tables and chairs, and cushioned settles, the bar offers Courage Best and Directors, John Smith's Yorkshire, Guinness and Beamish on draught. Standard dishes such as steak and kidney pie at £4.50, scampi at £ 4.65 and ploughman's at £3.65 are available from the printed menu.

Brewery: Chef & Brewer
Licensee: Blair Walls
Opening hours: 12-11pm (Fri and Sat 11am-11pm); Sun 12-2.30pm, 7-10.30pm
Bar food: 12-2.30pm, 7-9pm (except Sat and Sun evenings)
Children: Welcome in conservatory area until 9pm
Credit cards: Access, Visa

London Pride

London ranked second only to Burton upon Trent as an early brewing centre and its famous names include Watney, Meux, Charrington and Truman, but the most durable is Whitbread. The company, now one of the industry's 'big six', was founded by a Bedfordshire man named Samuel Whitbread in 1742. He used to sit up four nights a week at his brewing, reading the Bible at intervals, and he ended up a rich landowner, MP for Bedford and a generous philanthropist, and had his portrait painted by Sir Joshua Reynolds before dying in 1796. His only son, another Samuel, who had no head for business, was a radical MP and close ally of Charles James Fox, but committed suicide in 1815. The family continued in the brewing trade and the founder's great-great-great-great-grandson became Chairman in 1984.

⊕ DOVE
19 Upper Mall, Hammersmith W6 9TA Tel 081 748 5405

W6

This is a very popular pub, and with good reason. A 17th-century building, it looks tiny from the outside and you enter into a small, cosy bar with low tables, stools and wall benches. Go up the few steps to the food bar with its good-size dining tables, then down a few steps to small paved area with tables for two, before going out on to the terrace to enjoy the river views. Particularly popular in summer, you need to get there early to be sure of a seat. Fuller's ESB and London Pride are on draught, along with Guinness, three lagers, including Grolsch, and a cider. In addition to salads, jacket potatoes and samosas, blackboard specials offer carbonade of beef for £4.65, shepherd's pie for £4.25, and vegetable hot pot, also for £4.25.

Brewery: Fuller's
Licensee: Brian Lovrey
Opening hours: 11am-11pm; Sun 12-3pm, 7-10.30pm
Bar food: 12-3pm, 6-9pm; Sun 12-3pm ,and 7-9pm in summer only
Children: Welcome until 7pm

⊕ OLD SHIP
25 Upper Mall, Hammersmith W6 9TD. Tel 081 748 3970

W6

This large pub dates from 1780 and overlooks the Thames between Hammersmith and Chiswick. In addition to the picnic tables to one side, there are large tables and settles on the front patio, sheltered by a balcony. Ivy climbs up one side, and flower boxes add splashes of colour. In spite of its size, the bar is surprisingly cosy and intimate. The polished bar gleams and the red cushioned stools and settles look very comfortable. Rowing boats, lanterns and copper kettles hang from the beams, and the walls are decorated with prints and old photographs of boats and local scenes. On draught are Ruddles Best and County, Webster's Yorkshire and Fuller's London Pride. The selection of hot bar meals changes daily, and might include mousaka, chicken and ham pie, both at £4.45, and cauliflower and broccoli bake at £3.50.

Brewery: Courage
Licensee: Sean McCormack
Opening hours: 11am-3pm, 5.30-11pm; Sun 12-2.30pm, 7-10.30pm
Bar food: 12-2.30pm, 7-9pm
Children: Welcome until 7pm

⊕ RUTLAND ALE HOUSE
15 Lower Mall, Hammersmith W6 9DJ Tel 081 748 5586

W6

This 18th-century pub sits next to the Thames near Hammersmith Bridge. In summer, the doors along the front of the building are opened and customers move out to the picnic tables and benches on the mall. Inside, there is just one bar with an adjoining panelled dining area, with rowing boats hanging from the ceiling, prints on the walls, and small collections of old telephones and wirelesses. Jazz and rock and roll bands play on Wednesday nights in winter. Good-value bar food is available throughout the day; typical

Brewery: Chef & Brewer
Licensee: Tony Quinn
Opening hours: 11am-11pm; Sun 12-3pm, 7-10.30pm
Bar food: 12-7pm; Sun 12-2.30pm
Children: Welcome away from the bar
Credit cards: Access, Visa

dishes might include leek and potato soup for £1.75, cheese and vegetable pie for £4.25, and chicken and mushroom pie for £4.25. Beers on draught are Ruddles Best and County, Webster's Yorkshire, and Courage Best, with four lagers, two ciders and a wide selection of imported bottled beers.

FOX
Green Lane, Hanwell W7 2PJ. Tel 081 567 3912

W7

Situated in a residential area near the Grand Union Canal, this 19th-century pub attracts local residents, workers and passers-by enjoying a canal walk. There is just one large bar, part of which is set out as a dining area. The wood-panelled walls are decorated with plates and wildlife pictures, and there are farm implements hanging from the high, beamed ceiling. There is also a small garden, mostly laid to grass, with plastic furniture. Popular locally for its food, the pub holds a restaurant licence and offers separate lunch and dinner menus which include such dishes as roast lamb, spaghetti Bolognese and steak and mushroom pie, all at £4, with desserts at £1.50 such as apple crumble, sherry trifle and strawberry cheesecake. On draught are Courage Best and Directors, a guest beer such as Marston's Pedigree, Guinness, Beamish, three lagers and a cider.

Brewery: Free house
Licensee: B Shacklady
Opening hours: Summer 11am-11pm; winter11am-3pm, 5.30-11pm; Sun 12-3pm, 7-10.30pm
Bar food: 12-2pm, Sun 12-3pm
Children: Welcome if eating

☻ BRITANNIA
1 Allen Street, Kensington W8 6UX. Tel 071 937 1864

W8

Situated in the middle of a residential street off Kensington High Street, this attractive 200-year-old pub was formerly a stables; it has a wooden frontage with white shutters and pretty window boxes. The Saloon Bar is narrow, but long, with plenty of comfortable seating on two levels. There is also a lovely pine-furnished conservatory which is a non-smoking area, suitable for families. Though rather brightly lit, this is a very relaxed pub with friendly staff. Hot bar food is only available at lunchtime, but represents very good value; typical dishes are chicken tikka, lamb casserole and steak and kidney pie, all at £2.70. Young's Bitter, Special and Porter are on draught, along with Guinness, Beamish, four lagers and a cider, and there is also a 30-item wine list and a selection of 15 malt whiskies.

Brewery: Young's
Licensee: John Eaglestone
Opening hours: 11am-11pm; Sun 12-3pm, 7-10.30pm
Bar food: 12-2.30pm, snacks 5.30-9.30pm
Children: Welcome in conservatory

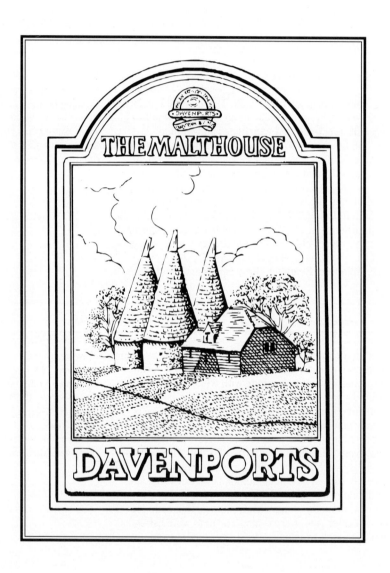

EAST ANGLIA &
EAST MIDLANDS

Bedfordshire

❖

Cambridgeshire

❖

Essex

❖

Leicestershire

❖

Lincolnshire

❖

Norfolk

❖

Northamptonshire

❖

Nottinghamshire

❖

Suffolk

❖

BEDFORDSHIRE

⊕ COCK
Broom, near Biggleswade SG18 9NA. Tel 0767 314411

Broom

Brewery: Greene King
Licensee: Mr Little
Opening hours: 12-3pm,
6-11pm; Sun 12-3pm, 7-10.30pm
Bar food: 12-3pm, 7-9.30pm
(except Sun and Mon evening)
Restaurant: Times as bar food,
with coffee and tea served
throughout opening hours;
booking advisable at weekends
Children: Welcome except in
bar (which includes cellar
entrance); children's menu
available; outdoor play area

Unspoilt and unusual, this 270-year-old yellow and grey brick pub occupies a quiet village-centre position, backed by fields; what appears to be a row of country cottages - complete with hollyhocks - flanking the entrance to the car park is in fact the restaurant, and the rest of the building is compatible in style. A series of small, individual, wood-panelled rooms is centred on the bar itself (actually the cellar), and though the dining room is larger it maintains the same intimate atmosphere. Six whiskies and a malt are available as well as a good range of bottled beers with IPA, Abbot Ale and Rayments Special Bitter (all from Greene King) on draught. Pub games (restricted to one bar) include darts, skittles, dominoes and shove halfpenny, and it is hoped to make folk music a regular Sunday event. Bar food (which includes both a separate children's menu and vegetarian options) is well cooked and sensibly priced, with a variety of ploughman's platters from £3.25 to £3.95 and dishes like steak and kidney pie (£4.50) or lasagne and salad (£4.75) followed by a choice of puddings at £1.95. In summer, additional seating is provided in the secluded garden.

⊕ KNIFE AND CLEAVER
The Grove, Houghton Conquest MK45 3LA. Tel 0234 740387

Houghton Conquest

Brewery: Free house
Licensees: David and Pauline
Loom
Opening hours: 12-3pm,
6-11pm; Sun 12-2.30pm
Bar food: 12-2.30pm, 7-9.30pm
(except Sun evening)
Restaurant: 12-2.30pm,
7-9.30pm; Sun 12-2.30pm;
booking necessary
Accommodation: (Price per
room) single £35-£51, double
£41-£66
Children: Welcome except in
bar; half portions available
Credit Cards:

The bar and restaurant of this particularly pleasant establishment occupy a 16th-century building set back from the road opposite the medieval church. A low, modern hotel block is divided from this by a terrace with fountain, and there are also nine orchard bedrooms, all accommodation being both tastefully decorated and well equipped. Up-market diners and business people mingle in the relaxed, dark-panelled bar with its open log fires and wood-burner, undisturbed by any entertainment except the jazz band that accompanies themed dinners some Friday evenings, and the part-conservatory restaurant with its hanging plants promotes an almost French atmosphere. A typical bar meal might be hors d'oeuvre at £3.75 followed by chicken casserole with white wine and herbs (£4.95), then one of a selection of home-made desserts (£1.50) or a choice of farmhouse cheeses (£2.20) and a good cup of coffee. Both bar and restaurant menus change monthly, and both offer vegetarian options(though food may be too sophisticated for the average child's taste). A choice of 20 malt whiskies and a list of some 90 wines are featured alongside draught beers by Banks and Taylor of nearby Shefford, and Bateman XB.

AMERICAN EXPRESS®, Access, Visa

⊕ WHITE HORSE
Kimbolton Road, Keysoe MK44 2JA. Tel 0234 376363

Keysoe

The frontage of this whitewashed pub on the outskirts of the village - a 16th-century building with a partly thatched roof - is made attractive by hanging baskets of flowers, and its interior is both comfortable and welcoming. Brass and copper trays and old tiles add visual interest to the bar where an across-the-board clientele gathers, and traditional games are supplemented by a fruit machine and occasional live music. Draught beers include Wells Eagle IPA and Bombardier, Noggin and Mansfield Riding Dark Mild, while generously served portions of savoury bar dishes like chilli con carne (£3.50), chicken Kiev or steak, kidney and brown ale pie (both at £5) can be followed by a home-made dessert (from £1.80 to £2). In summer you can enjoy your meal in a large peaceful garden, surrounded by open countryside, while children are kept amused by the pub's collection of animals and an Old Mother Hubbard play house.

Brewery: Charles Wells
Licensee: John Crummey
Opening hours: 11am-11pm
(Sat 11am-2.30pm, 6.30-11pm in winter); Sun 12-2.30pm (3pm in summer), 7.30-10.30pm
Bar food: 12-2pm, 7-9.45pm; Sun 12-2pm only
Restaurant: 7-9.45pm; Sun set lunch 12-2pm; booking advisable
Children: In restaurant only

⊕ MAD DOG
Odell, near Olney MK43 7AR. Tel 0234 720221

Odell

Farm implements adorn the car park walls at this thatched stone pub, a building dating from 1605, set right on the main road at the edge of the village. An L-shaped bar with low beams and wood-block floor is both spacious and homely, enlivened by piped music and electronic games; pleasant and unpretentious, its mixed clientele includes a good proportion of elderly folk attracted by special pensioner rates from Monday to Wednesday. A range of bottled beers (Newcastle Brown, Budweiser and Holsten Pils being noteworthy) is sold alongside draught Greene King Abbot, IPA and Rayments Special Bitter and Guinness. Generously served bar meals include five or six vegetarian options, dishes like duck in orange sauce (£6.25) and beef and mushroom pie (£4.25), sandwiches and a selection of jacket potatoes. Children will certainly approve of the garden, which, in addition to swings, has a fairground roundabout.

Brewery: Greene King
Licensees: Ken and Jean Parry
Opening hours: 11am-2.30pm, 6-11pm; Sun 12-2.30pm, 7-10.30pm
Bar food: 12-1.45pm, 7-9.30pm; Sun 12-1.30pm, 7-9.30pm
Children: Not permitted in bar; outdoor play area
Credit Cards: Access, Visa

HARE AND HOUNDS
Old Warden, near Biggleswade SG18 9HQ. Tel 0767 627225

Old Warden

This 200-year-old cream-washed and tiled pub on the edge of the village, attractively fronted by brick flower beds and backed by a steeply sloping garden surrounded by woods, features unusual rounded arches over its windows - a characteristic it shares with other village buildings. Two pleasant, uncluttered bars are cosy in winter - one warmed by an open fire, the other by a wood-burner - and here a clientele drawn from all walks of life (USAF personnel, students from the agricultural college, walkers and members of the local Round Table, for example) gather to partake of a range of beers that includes Wells Bombardier, Eagle and Noggin, and Guinness, on draught. A quiz machine and juke box in the Public Bar supplement the traditional pastime of darts, and a pianist sometimes provides live music. Restaurant and bar menus are the same, only one main meal a day (steak pie, for example, at £4.75) being made on the premises and the rest bought in prepacked; the best buys are the range of filled jacket potatoes - 13 in all - for which the pub is famed. In summer, afternoon tea can be arranged for coach parties.

Brewery: Charles Wells
Licensee: Ian Rodney
Opening hours: 11am-2.30pm, 6-11pm; Sun 12-3pm, 7-11pm
Bar food: 12-2pm, 7-9pm (Sat 9.30), except Mon evening
Children: Welcome except in Public Bar; children's portions available; outdoor play area
Credit Cards: Access, Visa

SWAN
Radwell, near Felmersham MK43 7HS. Tel 0234 781351

Radwell

Food is the raison d'être of this pub set in rolling countryside on the edge of a village six miles from Bedford, and it is most frequented by the middle-aged and middle-class, either individually or for business entertainment purposes. Originally two cottages and probably dating back to the 17th century, the part-thatched, part-tiled stone building is surrounded by an expensive garden with large willow trees - ideal for children and provided with play equipment. Two very small but pleasant, low-beamed bars displaying collections of horse-brasses, barrel taps and lace-spinning shuttles offer a guest beer on draught as well as Wells Eagle IPA, Guinness and Red Stripe and Kellerbrau lagers; lack of space precludes the sale of draught cider. The same good, imaginative menu is served both here and in a separate restaurant. A starter like grilled sardines or tuna and kiwi mayonnaise (both at £1.75), might be followed by, for example, home-made steak and kidney pie (£4.95), sautéd kidneys (£5.25), lemon sole (£8.75) or the vegetarian dish of the day, while a range of desserts includes profiteroles, rum baba or Caribbean bananas at £2.30.

Brewery: Charles Wells
Licensee: Mr Naysmith
Opening hours: 12-2.30pm, 7-11pm; Sun 12-3pm, 7-10.30pm
Bar food: As opening hours (except Tue evening and Sun)
Restaurant: Times as bar food; booking preferable
Children: Not permitted in bar; outdoor play area
Credit Cards: AMERICAN EXPRESS®, Access, Visa

✦ MUSGRAVE ARMS
Aspley End, Shillington, near Hitchin SG5 3LX. Tel 0462 711286

Shillington

This creeper-clad, mellow brick pub occupies a position just outside the village backing on to open countryside; in summer, seating dotted about the large garden allows visitors to appreciate the tranquillity of this setting. During the winter months the two low-ceilinged bars are warmed by open fires in inglenook fireplaces, and in their relaxed atmosphere a largely business and professional clientele enjoys a selection of drinks which includes three malts (one a 23-year-old McCallan) as well as a wide choice of bottled beers and Greene King IPA, Abbot and Rayments Special, and Guinness, on draught. A short but well thought out wine list with named wines by the glass accompanies the extensive menu served in both restaurant and bar; main dishes like jugged hare (£7.50), venison (£11.50) and steak Chartreuse (£14) are all accompanied by three fresh vegetables, starters range from beautifully crisp garlic bread at £1.45 to garlic mushrooms at £4.50, and desserts feature such traditional favourites as rhubarb and apple crumble or treacle tart (both £1.95) alongside more exotic sweets like orange liqueur dessert (£2.50). A published diary of forthcoming entertainment details, for example, classical music recitals, Morris dancing and the annual pig roast; folk music has a regular slot on Wednesday evenings.

Brewery: Greene King
Licensee: Cliff Stuckey
Opening hours: 11am-11pm; Sun 12-3pm, 7-10.30pm
Bar food: As opening hours
Restaurant: 12-2.30pm, 7-10.30pm
Children: Welcome in dining room in early evenings; outdoor play area
Credit Cards: Access, Visa

✦ FRENCH HORN
Steppingley, near Flitwick LU7 7YJ. Tel 0525 712051

Steppingley

A family-run pub/restaurant at the centre of the village near the church, its small beer garden adjoining the churchyard, the French Horn offers a relaxed and informal atmosphere. A predominantly young clientele frequents its two pleasant bars - the beamed, timbered Lounge and the Public with its open fire, bar games and piped music - where an extensive wine list is available as well as a varying selection of draught beers from Tetley, Hook Norton, Bass, and sometimes Fuller's London Pride. Here and in the comfortably elegant restaurant is served a range of delicious home-made dishes, attractively presented and reasonably priced, with French onion soup at £1.85, smoked salmon pâté at £2.10, prawns with mushrooms and rice at £4.95 and beef and mushroom pie at £5.95; vegetarian meals must be ordered in advance.

Brewery: Free house
Licensee: Eric Gilliland
Opening hours: 12-3pm, 6-11pm; closed Mon; Sun 12-3pm, 7-10.30pm
Bar food: As opening hours (except Sun evening)
Restaurant: 12-3pm, 7-10pm; Sun 12-4pm; booking advisable
Children: Welcome in bars and restaurant if eating; half portions available
Credit Cards: AMERICAN EXPRESS®, Access, Visa

⊜ JACKAL
Thurleigh, near Bedford MK44 2DB. Tel 0234 771293

Thurleigh

For families with children, the restaurant of this pub is an ideal place to eat, providing an unsophisticated meal at a reasonable price - sausage or ham and chips, for example, at £2.25, mousaka or lasagne at £3 and salads from £1.50; all items on the bar meals list are normally available here, but it is necessary to book if you require the à la carte menu, and vegetarian dishes should be ordered in advance. Two cheerful, fairly modern bars (one displaying a copy of the original deeds of the pub) offer about a dozen malts as well as a selection of beers which includes Wells Eagle IPA, Mansfield Ridings, Murphy's and Guinness on draught and bottled Grolsch. Traditional pastimes like darts, pool and dominoes are supplemented by electronic games, piped music and karaoke music in the Public Bar, but the Lounge remains a quiet haven for the many elderly customers. The pub itself, an attractive whitewashed building at the centre of the very small village, was created by the conversion of 17th-century cottages and boasts a large rear garden which, though rough, features a row of ancient willows and cages of parrots and other exotic birds.

Brewery: Charles Wells
Licensees: Mr and Mrs Dossett
Opening hours: 12-3pm,
7-11pm; Sun 12-2.30pm,
7-10.30pm
Bar food: 12-3pm, 7-9.30pm;
Sun 12-2.30pm, 7-9.30pm
Restaurant: Times as bar food
Children: Permitted in
restaurant only

YE THREE FYSHES
Bridge Street, Turvey MK43 8ER. Tel 0234 881264

Turvey

Both farmhouse scrumpy and its own Nix Wincott beer, brewed on the premises, are served in this old stone pub, a 17th-century building set beside the A428 in a fairly rural position with its pleasant little garden running down to the river. The full range of draught beers includes Nix Wincott Two Henrys Bitter, Old Nix and THAT, together with guest bitters and Murphy's Stout. The carpet in the bar is worn through to the backing in places, but a large fire burns there on colder days, there is a quiz machine as well as the traditional bar games, and food ranges from a sandwich well filled with chunky, home-cooked ham for £1.50 to an 8oz sirloin steak with mushrooms at £7.50. Vegetarian dishes such as vegetable lasagne or korma (both £4.75) are available.

Brewery: Free house
Licensee: Mr Charles Wincott
Opening hours: 11.30am-3pm,
5.30-11pm; Sun 12-3pm,
7-10.30pm
Bar food: 12-2pm, 7-9pm
Children: Welcome anywhere;
half portions available
Credit Cards:
AMERICAN EXPRESS®, Access,
Visa

⊜ THREE COMPASSES

Wellingborough Row, Upper Dean, near Rushden PE18 0NE. Tel 0234 708346

Upper Dean

One of Dick Turpin's Bedfordshire hideaways, this 350-year-old pub - an attractive, white, thatched building surrounded by fields - stands on a bend in the road just outside the village. A welcoming landlord and the pleasant atmosphere of a typical 'local' draw a complete cross-section of customers from a 15-mile radius to drink in a homely beamed bar warmed by an open fire and enlivened by skittles matches, games of darts and - rather loud - background music. Draught beverages include Scrumpy Jack, Strongbow and Woodpecker ciders as well as Wells IPA and Bombardier Best Bitter, and Murphy's Stout; Kellerbrau and Red Stripe lagers are also on draught. Bar food, though unsophisticated, provides very good value for money, following huge helpings of filling dishes like sausage, mash and gravy (£2.80), Yorkshire pudding and savoury mince with vegetables (£3.70), lasagne (£2.60) or various 'with chips' options (steak, gammon or plaice, for example) by such puddings as strawberry cheesecake or apple pie with cream at £1.50. Both vegetarians and children are well catered for, and Sunday lunch is so popular that it is essential to book. There is no separate restaurant, but a small dining room is available for hire to private parties.

Brewery: Charles Wells
Licensee: Ronald Peat
Opening hours: 12-2.30pm, 7-11pm; closed Mon lunchtime, except BHs;Sun 12-2.30pm, 7-10.30pm
Bar food: 12-1.45pm, 7-9.30pm; Sun lunch by appointment only, bar snacks 7.30-8.30pm
Children: Not permitted under 14 years except in Snug; outdoor play area

⊜ BELL INN

21 Bedford Street, Woburn MK17 9QD. Tel 0525 290280

Woburn

Built between 1630 and 1640 and located on the main street towards the outskirts of the village, this cream-washed brick and timber inn offers accommodation in a building on the opposite side of the road. The comfortable bar, tastefully furnished in muted colours and displaying only copper and brass, maintains a tranquil atmosphere undisturbed by games or loud music; here a clientele from all walks of life can choose from a good range of malts and an extensive wine list as well as Greene King IPA and Abbot on draught and bottled beers like Budweiser, Becks and Grolsch. Food - served both in the bar and a very attractive beamed restaurant - has an Egon Ronay recommendation and is reasonably priced, with fisherman's crumble at £4.80, lasagne or cold poached salmon at £4.95, and a range of desserts that includes summer pudding and rhubarb and pear crumble at £1.95. A vegetarian dish is always provided.

Brewery: Greene King
Licensee: Tim Chilton
Opening hours: 11am-3pm, 6-11pm; Sun 12-3pm, 7-10.30pm
Bar food: As opening hours
Restaurant: Times as bar food (except Sat lunchtime and Sun evening)
Accommodation: AA-listed 2-star hotel on opposite side of road
Children: Welcome anywhere
Credit Cards:
AMERICAN EXPRESS®, Access, Visa, Diners

CAMBRIDGESHIRE

⊜ JOLLY ABBOT
High Green, Abbotsley PE19 4UL. Tel 0767 677243

Abbotsley

A mixed but mainly professional clientele create a relaxed atmosphere in this pleasant, 18th-century village pub. Comfort is provided by a carpeted floor, padded leather settles and a coal-effect fire at each end of the L-shaped bar. Although shielded from the main road by a grassy bank, the pub enjoys a raised position giving views over open countryside. Old-fashioned lanterns adorn the front of the long, low, cream-coloured building, while on the patio at the back picnic tables take advantage of the pleasant outlook. Webster's Yorkshire Bitter, Ruddles County and Marston's Pedigree are on sale, and the food includes ploughman's lunch at £2.75 and mushroom dip at £2.25 and main courses like mousaka at £5.65 and grilled halibut at £7.50. Four vegetarian dishes are on offer, and a two-course Sunday lunch at £7 with a choice of ten main courses and six sweets. Cheesecake and Belgian apple flan are among the sweets, all at £2.25.

Brewery: Free house
Licensee: Mr A B Grant
Opening hours: 12-3pm,
6-11pm; Sun 12-3pm, 7-10.30pm
Bar food: 12-2pm, 7-9.30pm
Restaurant: 12 2pm, 7 9.30pm
(Sat 9.45pm)
Children: Welcome if eating with adults
Credit Cards:
AMERICAN EXPRESS®, Access, Visa

⊜ THREE HILLS
Ashdon Road, Bartlow CB1 6PW. Tel 0223 891259

Bartlow

With its peaceful village setting and generous portions of well cooked food, this pub attracts a clientele consisting mainly of business and older people. Starters such as mushrooms in garlic butter at £2.75 and seafood cocktail at £3.20 are on offer, and the main courses include home-made steak and mushroom pie at £4.90. Several home-cooked vegetarian dishes are served daily, and the sweets include home-made apple pie at £1.95 and toffee and pecan pie at £2.40. The low-ceilinged bar is carpeted and comfortably furnished with dark tables and cushioned settles, but diners will enjoy their meal more if they sit at the restaurant end, out of range of fumes from the kitchen. Greene King Abbot Ale and IPA are on sale, along with three good malt whiskies and a fair selection of wines. The front of the long, low, cream-washed building, which dates back some 500 years, is fetchingly decorated in summer with flowers in tubs and hanging baskets. At the back a covered terrace draped with vines and more baskets of flowers overlooks a secluded, tree-fringed garden furnished with picnic tables.

Brewery: Greene King
Licensees: Sue and Steve Dixon
Opening hours: 11.30am-2.30pm, 6.30-11pm; Sun 12-3pm, 7-10.30pm
Bar food: As opening hours (except Mon evenings in Jan)
Restaurant: Times as bar food
Children: In restaurant only, although not encouraged
Credit Cards: Access, Visa

⊜ FREE PRESS
Prospect Row, Cambridge CB1 1DU. Tel 0223 68337

Cambridge

Engagingly old-fashioned in its decor, this town pub is used mainly by a young but peaceable crowd and, at lunchtime during the week, by older customers. The staff offer a friendly welcome in the two bars, where cricketing and rowing memorabilia decorate the part-cream-painted, part-dark-panelled walls. The beers on sale are Greene King Abbot Ale and IPA, while the food includes home-made soup at £1.75, dishes like game pie and springtime pie, both at £4.25, and vegetarian quiche and nutloaf, both at £3.75. All the cold dishes come with salad and granary bread, and also on offer is a hot dish of the day. Among the sweets served are carrot cake at £1.65 and chocolate cake and cream at £1.75. Ten minutes' walk from the city centre, the pub is a converted early Victorian terraced house with a sunny patio and a small, tree-shaded garden which both offer outdoor seating. Parking is prohibited outside the pub and in the surrounding streets, but there is a fee-paying car park 300 yards away.

Brewery: Greene King
Licensee: Chris Lloyd
Opening hours: 12-3pm, 6-11pm; Sun 12-3pm, 7-10.30pm
Bar food: 12-2pm, 6-8.30pm; Sun 12-2pm, 7-8.30pm
Children: Welcome anywhere

Which is the Oldest Pub?

The question has no sure answer. Records are fragmentary and a building, or part of it, may be far older than its use as a drinking house. The Olde Ferry Boat Inn at Holywell in the Cambridgeshire fens is claimed to go back to the 6th century as a monastic ferry station and the Olde Fighting Cocks in St Albans to the 8th century as an abbey fishing lodge by the River Ver. A more believable contender is the Bingley Arms at Bardsey, West Yorkshire, recorded as 'the priest's inn' in 905, but it was completely rebuilt in 1738. The Ostrich at Colnbrook, Buckinghamshire, is apparently on the site of a monastic hospice recorded in 1106 (and its odd name is a pun on 'hospice'). Others claiming a 12th-century origin include the wonderfully named Olde Trip to Jerusalem in Nottingham, the Cromwell-linked Royal Oak at Whatcote in Warwickshire, the venerable Oxenham Arms at South Zeal in Devon, the half-timbered Pandy Inn at Dorstone, Hereford and Worcester, the Olde House Inn at Llangynwyd in South Wales and the Olde Boar's Head at Middleton, Greater Manchester. All of them, of course, have been repeatedly rebuilt and altered over the centuries.

⊜ CHEQUERS
Fowlmere, near Royston SG8 7SR. Tel 0763 208369

Fowlmere

During both World Wars this town-centre pub was popular with airmen from nearby Fowlmere Airfield, and its sign honours pilots of the RAF with its blue-and-white chequers on one side and their American counterparts with red-and-white chequers on the other. Inside, photographs of Fowlmere-based planes from both conflicts decorate the bar. Food is a priority here, with customers invited to help

Brewery: Pubmaster (Allied)
Licensees: Norman and Pauline Rushton
Opening hours: 12-2.30pm 6-11pm; Sun 12-2.30pm, 7-10.30pm
Bar food: 12-2pm, 7-10pm; Sun

themselves from a wide selection of starters which includes Stilton and walnut pâté at £2.90 and Paris mushrooms and garlic bread at £3.60. The imaginative menu also offers main courses like Vietnamese chicken at £6.85, pork escalope at £6.20 and creamed courgettes and almonds at £5.95. Tolly Cobbold Original and Tetley Bitter are on sale, along with a choice of malt whiskies from the Scottish islands and a wide range of wines, including some unusual items from Spain. Dating from the 16th century, the white-painted, part-timbered pub has a hotel-like feel, with efficient staff attired in black and white. At lunchtime in particular, business people use the single bar, which has a timbered serving area and comfortable upholstered seats. At the back of the pub a patio leads into a good-sized garden, flanked by trees and supplied with picnic benches.

12-2.30pm, 7-9.30pm
Restaurant: Times as bar food
Children: Welcome anywhere if well behaved; children's snack menu and half portions available
Credit Cards:
AMERICAN EXPRESS®, Access, Visa, Diners

⊛ QUEENS HEAD
Fowlmere, near Royston SG8 7SZ. Tel 0763 208288

Fowlmere

The speciality of this village pub is its cheeses, of which there is usually a choice of 24, such as fruitcake Cheddar and basil and apricot Wensleydale. At £2.80 to £3.60, each portion is accompanied by a choice of nine different loaves and a selection of pickles and relishes. Also on offer are cold meats at £2.80 to £3.75 and home-made soup at £1.50. Real ale partners most cheeses perfectly, and here the choice is between IPA, Abbot Ale and XX Mild, all from Greene King. Of the four pubs in the village, this is the one most used by local people, and the clientele is well assorted although lacking in youngsters. Dating back some 350 years, the thatched white building looks down the village high street and comprises two pleasantly decorated bars. Darts, dominoes and Shut the Box can be played, while alongside the garden, which is furnished with tree-shaded tables, is the unusual attraction of a piste for pétanque, the southern French version of bowls.

Brewery: Greene King
Licensee: Gascoyne
Opening hours: Mon-Tue 12-2.30pm, 7-11pm; Wed-Fri 12-2.30pm, 6-11pm; Sat 12-2.30pm, 7-11pm; Sun 12-3pm, 7-10.30pm. NB: Open all day Mon-Sat if busy
Bar food: Mon-Tue 12-2pm; Wed-Fri 12-2pm, 6-9.30; Sat 12-2.30pm, 7-9.30pm; Sun 12-2.30pm, 6-9.30pm
Children: In Lounge Bar only; outdoor play area

⊕ PEAR TREE
Hildersham, near Linton CB1 6BU. Tel 0223 891680

Hildersham

Facing the green and with local people of all ages providing most of its custom, this friendly turn of the century pub is very much a part of the village. Reinforcing this role, it hosts special evening events such as cider and Eastern European wine tasting, fundraising drives and, on 23 April, a St George's Day sausage and mash supper. Among the wide variety of food on offer the rest of the time are liver pâté and mackerel pâté, both home-made, and chicken satay, all at £2.45, grilled trout at £5.95 and chicken Kiev at £5.75. The sweets, each at £1.75, include treacle tart, chocolate fudge cake and blackcurrant sorbet. Greene King Abbot Ale and IPA are served in the bar, which is furnished with padded settles and benches and has a floor partly covered with sisal matting and partly crazy-paved. At the front of the white-painted pub a couple of picnic benches look on to the pretty green, while much of the small garden at the back is given over to a children's play area with a bouncy castle.

Brewery: Greene King
Licensee: Diane and DavidJamieson
Opening hours: 12-2.30pm, 6-11pm; Sun 12-2.30pm, 7-10.30pm
Bar food: As opening hours
Children: Not permitted inside; children's menu available; outdoor play area

OLD FERRY BOAT INN
Holywell, near St Ives PE17 3TG. Tel 0480 63227

Holywell

This low-built, whitewashed and thatched pub is said to be the oldest in Britain. Documents show that liquor was sold here as long ago as AD560, although experts date the foundations to the previous century. Situated at the end of a long country lane, the pub overlooks the sinuous River Ouse, and nearby short-term mooring allows waterborne visitors to drop in. The clientele is mixed, with a fair number of business people visiting for lunch during the week and the attractive setting guaranteeing a full house in good weather. A beamed ceiling, copper-topped tables and a large open fire lend a warm, traditional character to the carpeted, L-shaped bar, which is divided by timbers into separate areas. Stones IPA, Greene King Abbot Ale, Adnams Broadside, Fuller's London Pride and a weekly guest beer are on offer, along with a selection of malt whiskies. The varied menu offers unusual starters such as squid stir fry at £3.50 and turkey tzatziki at £2.95, while the main courses include trout 'n' fennel at £7.25, chicken Italienne at £6.75 and pasta à la Holywella (pasta bows with fresh vegetables, cream and cheese) at £5.95. There is a choice of home-made sweets, all at £2. Seven double rooms are available, all pleasantly furnished - two with four-poster beds - and two with a view of the river.

Brewery: Free house
Licensee: R G Jeffrey
Opening hours: 11am-3pm, 6-11pm; Sun 12-3pm, 7-10.30pm
Bar food: 12-2pm, 6.30-9.30pm; Sun (from 7pm)
Accommodation: (Price per room) single £39.99-£49.50, double £49.50-£68
Children: Welcome anywhere; children's menu available
Credit Cards: Access, Visa

⊕ PLOUGH AND FLEECE
High Road, Horningsea CB5 9JC. Tel 0223 860795

Horningsea

Fortunately the recent addition of a dining room has not spoilt this 300-year-old pub, blessed with a quiet situation on the outskirts of the village. Locals, students and business people alike find the beamed, quarry-tiled main bar, with its old wooden furniture, Georgian fireplace, farm implements and stuffed fox, a pleasant place to enjoy the Greene King IPA or Abbot Ale. Food is served in the bar and in the dining room next to the small back bar, and the excellent home-made fare includes Stilton and broccoli flan and devilled crab with hot, buttered toast, both at £2.90. Also on offer are Welsh fish pie at £5.40, Ramsey rabbit at £7 and beef Wellington at £10, while among the sweets, all at £2.10, are Norfolk treacle tart and toffee apple pie. Snacks are not available in the dining room, although in the evening some of the bar snacks are served in larger portions and at correspondingly higher prices. Behind the low-built, cream-washed pub there is a flowery patio with white tables and a pleasant garden with trees and picnic benches.

Brewery: Greene King
Licensee: Mr Grimes
Opening hours: 11am-2.30pm, 7-11pm; Sun 12-2pm, 7-10.30pm
Bar food: 12-2pm; Sun 12-1.30pm
Restaurant: 12-2pm, 7-9.30pm (except Mon evening); Sun 12-1.30pm
Children: In restaurant only and if over ten years
Credit Cards: Access, Visa

⊕ ACRE
9 Acre Road, March PE15 9JD. Tel 0354 57116

March

Probably part of the old mill, this handsome, square, grey-brick pub stands on the banks of the River Nene near the town bridge. An adjacent park with trees leads down to the water's edge and picnic benches are set out by the pub's clematis-covered veranda. Inside, a cosy bar furnished with wooden settles adjoins a country-style kitchen where prospective diners can take a look at the food on offer. Local people, including pensioners at lunchtime during the week, form the majority of the friendly clientele in both the small and the larger bar, which is also carpeted and has an assortment of chairs and tables, some with copper tops. Greene King IPA and Rayments Special Bitter from the keg are on sale, and the plain, home-cooked food is good value for money. Among the dishes are roast pork, steak and kidney pie and rosemary and redcurrant lamb cutlets (three), all at £3.50, while the sweets include bread-and-butter pudding and apple and blackcurrant crumble, each at £1.25.

Brewery: Greene King
Licensees: Don and Ros Lang
Opening hours: 11am-3pm, 7-11pm; Sun 12-3pm, 7-10.30pm
Bar food: 12.30pm until sold out; no food in evening; booking necessary on Sun
Children: Only if eating; half portions available

THREE PICKERELLS
The Bridge, Mepal, near Ely CB6 2AR. Tel 0353 777777

Mepal

Most likely Edwardian, this yellow-brick pub enjoys a quiet riverside setting at the end of a cul-de-sac. The bar, half-panelled in pine and furnished with scrubbed deal farmhouse tables and chairs, has large windows overlooking the water and the garden which leads down to it. The assorted clientele enjoys a selection of beers from Tetley, Ansons and Ind Coope Burton Ale which is changed each month. In addition to bottled beers from many parts of the world, including the Netherlands, Africa and Mexico, there is a choice of malt whiskies. The menu offers starters such as deep-fried Camembert at £3.50 and garlic mushrooms at £2.95, while typical main courses are duck in black cherries and Drambuie at £10.25, salmon en croûte at £6.75 and, at £3.25 for three, baked potato skins with various fillings, such as beef Stroganoff. Among the sweets are hot pecan pie and crêpes with maple syrup and ice cream, both at £1.50. Three twin rooms are available, one of which takes a third bed. Attractively furnished, all still have their original windows and cast-iron fireplaces.

Brewery: Free house
Licensee: Mr Hammond
Opening hours: 11.30am-3pm, 6.30-11pm; Sun 12-3pm, 7-10.30pm
Bar food: As opening hours
Restaurant: Times as bar food
Accommodation: (Price per person) single £22.50, double £30
Children: Welcome if eating
Credit Cards: Visa

☻ QUEENS HEAD
Newton, near Sawston CB2 5PQ. Tel 0223 870436

Newton

This friendly village pub has the slightly worn but reassuring look, increasingly rare nowadays, of the traditional country inn. CAMRA paid testimony to its appeal by making it the Cambridgeshire Pub of the Year in 1988. Plain wooden tables, benches and settles furnish the Public Bar, while the beamed lounge has polished log tables, a tiled floor and the luxury of large open fire at each end. Talking points are provided by Belinda, a white goose, and other stuffed birds, and drawings and cartoons, including one on the ceiling of the comic character Chad peering quizzically over a wall. Adnams Bitter and Broadside are the ideal accompaniment to a choice of snacks which includes wholesome home-made soup in a cup at £1.70, sandwiches - for example, beef, ham, smoked salmon and various cheeses - at £1.30 to £1.90. Festooned with vines, hops, tomatoes, marigolds and a fig tree, the L-shaped, brick building in part dates back 300 years. Those who prefer to enjoy their drink outside can sit at the tables in front of the pub or on the two grass islands opposite.

Brewery: Free house
Licensee: David Short
Opening hours: 11.30am-2.30pm, 6-11pm; Sun 12-2pm, 7-10.30pm
Bar food: 11.30am-2.30pm, 6-9.30/10pm; Sun 12-2pm, 7-9.30/10pm
Children: In games room only

BELL INN
Great North Road, Stilton, near Peterborough PE7 3RA. Tel 0733 241066

Stilton

Numbering among its historic guests Dick Turpin and Lord Byron, this restored and extended former coaching inn dates from around 1500. It offers 19 bedrooms - two of which have four-poster beds - all differently furnished and provided with colour television, direct dialling and tea and coffee-making facilities. During the week the clientele is mostly business people, while at the weekends it is largely families. Two separate bars cater for non-residents and residents, there is a theatre-style conference centre which can seat 80 and behind the inn a large, attractive courtyard is set out with plastic tables and chairs. The bar menu offers starters such as coronation chicken at £4.50, garlic mushrooms or prawns at £4.75 and Stilton and hazelnut pâté at £3.25. Among the main dishes are Bell beef pie at £6.75, Stilton chicken at £7.25 and kleftico at £6.50, and also served are vegetarian dishes such as pasta bake. Typical sweets are bread-and-butter pudding and rich chocolate gâteau. The restaurant offers set menus at £14.50 and £19.50 plus an à la carte menu. Boddingtons Bitter, Tetley Bitter and Marston's Pedigree are on sale, and a wine list complements the restaurant menus.

Brewery: Free house

Licensee: Leon McGivern

Opening hours: 12-2.30pm, 6-11pm (Sat 11am-3pm, 6-11pm); Sun 12-3pm, 7-10.30pm

Bar food: 12-2pm, 6.30-9.30pm; Sun 12-2pm, 7-9pm

Restaurant: 7-9.30pm (by arrangement during day); Sun 12-2.30pm, 7-9.30pm

Accommodation: (Price per room) single £57-£67, double £62-£82

Children: Welcome anywhere if well behaved; children's menu available

Credit Cards: AMERICAN EXPRESS®, Access, Visa, Diners

CROSS KEYS
Upwood, near Ramsey PE17 19QE. Tel 0487 813384

Upwood

Situated in a quiet hamlet, this white-painted, 17th-century pub relies for most of its trade on country regulars, winning their loyalty with generous helpings of well prepared food and a relaxed atmosphere. At lunchtime the bar menu offers dishes such as vegetable curry at £3.95 and, both at £4.50, chicken and asparagus pie and seafood platter, while in the evening starters are served, including garlic mushrooms at £2.75 and avocado and crab at £3.25, followed by main courses like venison in red wine at £7.50 or a 16oz rumpsteak at £9.50. Half a dozen vegetarian dishes are on offer every day. An extensive menu is available in the attractively decorated restaurant, which specialises in steaks with various salads and serves a traditional Sunday lunch at £5.75. Meals from the restaurant menu can also be eaten in the comfortable, beamed Lounge Bar, with its Persian-style rugs on quarry tiles, dark-oak furniture and large, ornamental, brick fireplace with, sadly, an electric rather than a real fire. Plainer but pleasant, the Public Bar offers darts, dominoes, cards and electronic games. Courage Directors, John Smith's Bitter and Chestnut Mild are on sale, along with a locally produced brew known as Nelson's Blood and Guinness and Beamish. Picnic benches are set out in front of the pub and in the garden at the back.

Brewery: Courage
Licensees: Bob and Helga Martin
Opening hours: 12-2.30pm, 6.30-11pm; closed Mon lunchtime; Sun 12-2.30pm, 7-10.30pm
Bar food: 12-2pm, 7-9pm (Fri and Sat 10pm); Sun 12-2pm only
Restaurant: Times as bar food
Children: In restaurant only; own menu available; outdoor play area

TICKELL ARMS
Whittlesford, near Sawston CB2 4NZ. Tel 0223 833128

Whittlesford

The landlord's policy of turning away men with long hair or earrings, and anyone he considers improperly dressed, may well help to preserve the air of genteel decay of this village pub. It looks like the country house it once was, and preserves this illusion by being set back from the road behind a hedge which likewise obscures the sign. Built around 1700, the unusual, blue-washed building is overrun with hollyhocks, honeysuckle and roses and has an established conservatory opening on to a terrace and a garden with seating. Its pleasantly neglected character echoing the faded charm of the two high-ceilinged, traditional brown bars, the garden has a large, overgrown lily pond with fountains. Customers are offered the choice of Adnams Bitter or Greene King Abbot Ale , and an imaginative menu. The starters include seafood gratinée at £3.75 and avocado in nutmeg sauce at £1.75, while typical main courses are pheasant pie at £7.35, devilled kidneys at £6.35 and aubergine dolmas at £5.95. Sweets are about £2.75.

Brewery: Free house
Licensee: Mr Fischer
Opening hours: 11am-2.30pm, 7-11pm but flexible; closed Mon; Sun 12-2.30pm, 7-10.30pm
Bar food: As opening hours
Children: In conservatory only

ESSEX

⊜ WIG AND FIDGET
Straight Road, Boxted CO4 5QX. Tel 0206 272227

Boxted

Some 200 years old according to the records, but seemingly earlier, this village pub owes its name to the fact that it was at one time used as a circuit courthouse. Those caught smuggling goods through Harwich were sentenced here and put in the stocks at the nearby crossroads. Decorated with cartwheels and a plough perched on the roof of the extension, the pebble-dashed cottage has a sizeable lawned garden at the back with swings and a climbing frame. The small, beamed bar serves three rooms cosily furnished with red-velvet bench seats, matching cushioned chairs and no more than a dozen tables in all. A pair of carthorse shafts forms an inside porch and a fascinating array of farm implements, cigarette cards, pictures, plates, musical instruments, horse-brasses and other ornaments lines the walls and ceiling. The selection of beers changes frequently and includes ales from brewers like Adnams and Ruddles, although the food is no less of a draw. The menu, which pokes gentle fun at the legal process by referring to the 'Jury's Decision' and the 'Hangman's Noose', includes starters such as Camembert at £1.75 and home-made soup at £1.35. Typical main courses are barbecue pork chop at £4.25, mushroom and nut fettuccini at £4.50 and fillet steak at £9.25, and the sweets include pineapple sorbet and hot chocolate fudge cake.

Brewery: Courage
Licensee: M Wilson
Opening hours: 11am-2.30pm, 6-11pm; Sun 12-3pm, 7-10.30pm
Bar food: As opening hours
Children: Permitted in side room only; outdoor play area

⊜ KINGS ARMS
295 Main Road, Broomfield CM1 5AU. Tel 0245 440258

Broomfield

Standing beside the green in a village which is effectively a suburb of Chelmsford, this friendly pub attracts a well-assorted trade. The 16th-century building, its imposing, timbered frontage punctuated by three bay lattice windows, has an oak bar which serves two spacious rooms. These offer comfort with their carpeted floor, tapestry-covered chairs and brick fireplaces, and pool, darts, dominoes and cards can be played in one of the rooms. Outdoor seating is available at the handful of tables in front of the pub. On sale are Greene King IPA, Tetley Bitter and, occasionally, Tolly Cobbold Original, while a further attraction is the food, which is well cooked and very good value for money. Options might be fresh salmon at £6.55, beef Wellington at £6.95 and steaks from £7.95.

Brewery: Pubmaster
Licensee: Innings Ltd (manager John Beard)
Opening hours: 11.30am-2.30pm, 6.30-11pm; Sun 12-3pm, 7-10.30pm
Bar food: 12-2pm, 7-9.30pm; Sun 12-3pm, 7-9.30pm
Children: Not permitted inside

⊜ BELL INN
Castle Hedingham, near Halstead CO9 3EJ. Tel 0787 60350

Castle Hedingham

Blessed with its original features, this rambling pub echoes the unspoilt character of the fine old village in whose high street it stands. Formerly a coaching inn dating back to the 15th or 16th century, the tall, unusually shaped building has always been a pub, although the barrel-ceilinged function room upstairs has served as a theatre, a magistrates' court and a Conservative Party headquarters. Its name, the Disraeli Room, recalls the fact that the 19th-century Prime Minister used to speak here. In all the pub consists of four beamed rooms, all intact, of which two have bars: the split-level Lounge and the small Public Bar. At the rear is a spacious walled orchard garden with a croquet lawn and, to keep children occupied, a suspended tyre, a rope ladder and the allure of undergrowth. Served straight from the barrel, the beer is Greene King IPA and Abbot Ale, and the mixed clientele is also offered a menu of well presented, sensibly priced food. Soup with wine and cream is on sale at £1.90, and smoked prawns with garlic dip at £3.30. The main courses are served with at least three vegetables and warm bread. Typical of the interesting choice are Thai chicken curry and haddock and prawn gratinée, both at £4.50, while rainbow trout at £5.50 and shepherd's pie at £3.90 are among the more traditional fare. The treacle tart deservedly enjoys a reputation all of its own.

Brewery: Greene King
Licensee: Sandra Ferguson
Opening hours: 11.30am-3pm, 6-11pm; Sun 12-3pm, 7-10.30pm
Bar food: 12-2pm (Sat 2.30pm), 7-10pm (except Mon); Sun 12-2.30pm, 7-9.30pm
Children: Welcome anywhere except Public Bar; outdoor play area

⊜ CRICKETERS
Clavering, near Saffron Walden CB11 4QT. Tel 0799 550442

Clavering

Fine food, attractively presented, is the hallmark of this large yet cottage-like pub, which was built in the 16th century and stands imposingly in a corner of the village. Regulars provide most of the trade, although others likewise value the varied and imaginative menu. The food is complemented by a comprehensive wine list, while beer drinkers' needs are answered by Wethered's Traditional Bitter, Boddingtons and Flowers IPA. Among the main courses are sliced, home-cured gravlax at £3.75, pan-fried pigeon breast with tarragon at £7.75, and, both at £8.75, steamed mélange of seafood and baked filo-pastry parcels of lamb with curry sauce. Vegetarian dishes on offer include vegetable lasagne at £6.95 and Cheddar cheese salad at £6, and the desserts - among them a selection at £2.75 and a cocktail of summer fruits at £3.60 - are excellent. The bar, featuring a cricketing theme, and the restaurant both benefit from restful colour schemes, and there is additional seating at tables in the courtyard in front of the pub.

Brewery: Free house
Licensee: T K Oliver
Opening hours: 11am-2.30pm, 6-11pm; Sun 12-3pm, 7-10.30pm
Bar food: 12-2pm, 7-10pm
Restaurant: 7-9.30pm (except Mon); Sun 12-1.45pm
Children: In children's room only
Credit Cards: Access, Visa

⊕ PELDON ROSE
Mersea Road, Colchester CO5 7QJ. Tel 0206 735248

Colchester

Enormous old beams and ancient furniture, leaded windows, an uneven flagstone floor and open fires speak of this building's 600-year history, for a third of which it has served as an inn. There is one bar and at the rear a large conservatory leads on to a terrace which in turn overlooks the ample garden. Running along one side of the garden is a pond fringed by overhanging willows, where geese and ducks complete the delightful rural scene. Regulars, business people and families supply most of the trade, drawn by a constantly changing bar menu and a choice of Flowers Original and IPA, Bentley's Yorkshire Bitter and five alternating guest beers. An extensive wine list accompanies the food, which, if a little more expensive than average, is well prepared and served in generous portions. The choice ranges from sandwiches at £1.80 to £3.60, through soups such as goulash at £3, to dishes like sweet and sour chicken at £5.15, cod in batter at £4.95 and lasagne at £5.45. Dutch apple pie and chocolate mint cheesecake, both at £2.45, are among the sweets served. An indoor barbecue operates on a Friday and Saturday evening for which it is necessary to book. Three cottagey rooms are available, each provided with colour television and tea- and coffee-making facilities.

Brewery: Free house
Licensee: Alan Everett
Opening hours: 11am-2.30pm, 5.30-11pm; Sun 12-2.30pm, 7-10.30pm
Bar food: 12-2pm, 7-9.30pm
Accommodation: (Price per room) single £25, double £35
Children: Welcome except in bar; half portions available
Credit Cards: AMERICAN EXPRESS®, Access, Visa, Diners

⊕ MARLBOROUGH HEAD HOTEL
Mill Lane, Dedham, near Colchester CO7 6DH. Tel 0206 323124

Dedham

Built in 1465, this substantial, half-timbered pub stands in a pretty village in the heart of Constable country, the area around the Essex-Suffolk border which inspired many of the artist's best-known paintings. But although tourists flock to this tranquil landscape, the pub's clientele is mainly regulars, families and business people. Two bars serve a number of rooms, including a lounge area furnished with armchairs and low tables, while to the side of the pub is a small, secluded garden and one of the bars gives on to a patio. Meals can be eaten at mellow wooden tables in a choice of rooms. The varied menu includes egg mayonnaise at £1.40, a whole avocado pear with prawns and garnish at £4.95, lasagne at £4.85 and duck with black cherry sauce at £5.25. Among the sweets are cheesecake at £2.25 and sherry trifle at £2.95. The wines range from £6.25 to £24.50, while for beer drinkers there is the choice of Adnams Bitter, Benskins Best Bitter or Tetley Bitter. The bedrooms are traditional in style, with their beams and flowery decor, and each has a television and tea-making facilities.

Brewery: Ind Coope (Allied)
Licensees: Brian and Jackie Mills and Linda Mower
Opening hours: 11.30am-3pm, 6.30-11pm; Sun 12-2.30pm, 7-10.30pm
Bar food: 12-2pm, 7-9.30pm
Accommodation: (Price per person) single £32.50, double £25
Children: In one room only; outdoor play area
Credit Cards: Access, Visa

CROWN
High Street, Elsenham CM22 6DG. Tel 0279 812827

Elsenham

L ong, low-built and decorated with the relief plasterwork known as pargetting, this former coaching inn retains much character inside and out. It dates from between 300 and 350 years ago, and its flower-decked frontage has bay windows which provide window seats in the two bars. Both rooms are decorated in a traditional brownish beige, and furnished with dark ladderback chairs and tables. In front a few tables are set out, while at the back there is a garden with seating and a swing and climbing frame. The pub is frequented by an assortment of customers, although as the home of the local club it plays host to a good number of cricketers. Indoor-sports enthusiasts are catered for by pool, darts, skittles, bar skittles, dominoes, shove halfpenny, cards and electronic games. Crouch Vale Woodham IPA and Ind Coope Burton Ale are on tap, along with three lagers, and food is served by uniformed staff. The menu relies heavily on local produce - for example the well-known Braughing sausages - and offers starters such as home-made soup at £2 and grilled grapefruit with sherry at £2.25. Among the main courses are mixed seafood pancake at £3.95 and shepherd's pie at £3.75, and customers can help themselves at the salad bar. A range of unusual home-made ice creams is served, among them one with a whisky relish at £1.25.

Brewery: Allied Breweries
Licensee: Mrs B A Good
Opening hours: 11am-3pm, 6-11pm; Sun 12-2.30pm, 7-10.30pm
Bar food: 12-2pm, 7.30-9.30pm (except all day Sun and Mon evening)
Children: Welcome anywhere; outdoor play area
Credit Cards: Visa

⊜ PHEASANT
Gestingthorpe, near Halstead CO9 3AX. Tel 0787 61196

Gestingthorpe

P eople travel a long way to eat at this pub, whose food, all home-cooked, is both adventurous and appetising. The menu changes regularly, but starters might include mushrooms in garlic butter at £1.75 and salade tiède (warm salad) at £2.25, while typical main courses are swordfish steak at £5.95, barbecued pork steaks at £5.25 and leek croustade at £4.95. Chocolate chestnut russe at £2.25 and gooseberry cheesecake at £1.95 are among the sweets.

Brewery: Free house
Licensees: A P and P A McGrillen
Opening hours: 11am-3pm, 6-11pm; Sun 12-3pm, 7-10.30pm
Bar food: As opening hours
Children: Welcome anywhere; outdoor play area

The Essex Brewer
The Ridley family still runs the brewery by the River Chelmer at Hartford End, near Great Dunmow, which the founder, Thomas Dixon Ridley, built in 1842. He started brewing as a sideline from his business of flour milling and malting. The brewery is scarcely changed outwardly and its oldest wooden fermenting vessel is said to have been made by no less a person than the great Thomas Chippendale. Like the other independent brewers, Ridley's has drawn strength from the real ale revival since the 1970s.

Adnams Bitter, Greene King IPA and Abbot Ale, and Nethergate Bitter and Old Growler are the regular beers, and guest ales are served. There is a good choice of bottled beers, ten malt whiskies and a wide selection of wines, including varieties from Australia and California. Its plainness relieved somewhat by a large bay window, the twin-roofed pub, built in 1725, stands at one end of the village. At the back there is a small garden with just three tables and three swings, while the three bars are unspoilt and simply furnished without being austere. Welcome in winter are the open wood fires, raised up so as to warm the parts other fires cannot reach, and the bay-window seat is a particularly pleasant place to sit. With a well assorted and relaxed clientele, women on their own feel comfortable here, as do families, particularly since there is a selection of children's games to hand.

⊜ WHITE HART
Great Saling, near Braintree CM7 5DX. Tel 0371 850341

Great Saling

A galleried interior and a situation opposite what was the largest and oldest tree in England and is now the largest stump, are just two of the features which make this pub a delight for its mixed clientele, who range in age from 18 to 80. The cream-painted building, some 400 years old, stands at the heart of a remote village, backed by a good-sized, secluded garden with generous seating. Furnished with half a dozen tables and settles, the gallery overlooks the Lounge Bar through ceiling beams, while the Public Bar has a giant log serving as a table, an open fire, a flagstone floor and exposed wall timbers. Guinness, Ridleys IPA and Adnams Extra are on sale, along with a good selection of bottled beers. It was in the former bakery at the back of this pub that the local snack known as the huffer originated, and the place is now renowned for this feather-light, three-cornered bap. On offer at £1.75 is soup and a huffer with a choice of filling - for example cheese and salad. Darts, chess, dominoes, shove halfpenny and a fruit machine are available, while occasional live entertainment is provided by folk bands.

Brewery: T D Ridley & Sons Ltd
Licensee: Kenneth Laver
Opening hours: 11am-3pm, 6-11pm; Sun 12-3pm, 7-10.30pm
Bar food: 11am-2.30pm, 6-10.30pm; Sun 12-2.30pm, 7-10pm
Children: Not permitted inside

⊜ RAINBOW AND DOVE
Hastingwood Common, near Harlow CM17 9JX. Tel 0279 415419

Hastingwood Common

The rural aspect of this 16th-century pub belies the fact that it is only half a mile from the M11, and despite the drone of traffic outdoors, inside it is very cosy. Served by a central bar, the three rooms are lovingly cared for and lent a

Brewery: Free house
Licensee: A R Bird
Opening hours: 11.30am-2.30pm, 7-11pm; Sun 12-

warm look by masses of shiny brass, while golf clubs provide additional decoration. The clientele, mainly regulars and business people, is offered the choice of Tetley Bitter or Ansells Bitter, two draught lagers and several bottled lagers, including Molson and Becks. Also on sale is a wide selection of malt whiskies. The straightforward menu includes soup at £1.80, pâté at £2.20 and whitebait at £2.40, with main courses such as rainbow grill at £3.90, pizza at £3.50 and T-bone steak at £10.25. Each at £1.90, apple flan, Spotted Dick and pancakes are among the sweets. Set back from the road, the pub has a few tables with umbrellas near the front entrance and many more in the adjacent eight-acre paddock, where children are welcome to play.

2.30pm, 7-10.30pm
Bar food: 12-2pm, 7-9.45pm (except Sun, Mon and Tue evenings)
Children: Welcome anywhere if eating

⊛ BLACK LION
The Street, High Roding CM6 1NT. Tel 0279 872847

High Roding

This long, white pub, still unspoilt after five centuries, lies on the main road through the village and is used mostly by locals and families. Beams, settles, horse-brasses and brewery memorabilia lend a traditional stamp to the bars, one of which serves as a restaurant, and additional seating is available in the small garden. Ridleys IPA and Adnams Extra are on sale, along with two draught lagers, one cider and Old Bob bottled beer. Most customers rate the food highly, and on offer are starters such as Burgundy snails at £3.50 and main courses like fried seafood platter at £4.60, vegetarian pancake at £5.50 and home-made cannelloni at £4.80. Apple pie and apricot pancake, both at £1.40, are among the sweets served.

Brewery: T D Ridley & Sons Ltd
Licensee: Osvaldo Ricci
Opening hours: 11am-3pm, 6-11pm (Sat 11.30pm); Sun 12-3pm, 7-10.30pm
Bar food: 12-2.30pm, 7-10pm
Restaurant: Times as bar food
Children: Welcome anywhere
Credit Cards: Access, Visa

⊛ BELL
High Road, Horndon-on-the-Hill SS17 8LD. Tel 0375 673154

Horndon-on-the-Hill

There is something of the country house about this mellow, 500-year-old village pub, with its oak panels, flowery frontage and courtyard and friendly landlord and staff. Beams, cushioned oak settles, and stone flags in one bar and a wooden floor with rugs in the other, all impart a traditional flavour to the pub, whose clientele is mainly regulars and families. In a ceremony which dates back to 1901, hot cross buns are hung from one of the beams. French windows open on to the courtyard, where a set of stocks and some old mangles are on show and flowers abound, and a barbecue is held on summer weekends. The interesting menu offers starters such as home-made game terrine at £4.20, poached eggs with smoked chicken sauce at

Brewery: Freehouse
Licensee: J S B Vereker
Opening hours: 11am-2.30pm, 6-11pm; Sun 12-3pm, 7-10.30pm
Bar food: 12-2pm, 6.30-10pm (Sun from 7pm)
Children: Welcome anywhere
Credit Cards: AMERICAN EXPRESS®, Access, Visa

£3.95 and salmon and herb potato cakes at £3.30. Typical main courses are beef with ale and leeks at £4.70, rump steak, lentils and peppercorns at £11.20 and breast of duck in blackcurrant sauce at £12.20. The beers are Bass Charrington IPA and a guest ale which changes fortnightly, and some 100 wines are on offer, including a wide selection dispensed by the glass by a machine. Accommodation, including two honeymoon suites, each with a jacuzzi, and a self-contained flat with a spiral staircase, is available in the separate hotel building. Dogs are not permitted in any of the accommodation.

CROSS INN
Horsley Cross, near Manningtree CO11 2NX. Tel 0206 396391

Horsley Cross

Although its small rooms have been opened up to make one long bar, this pink-washed, 16th-century pub remains cottage-like inside. At one end of the pub, spick and span throughout, an open fire and padded seats recreate the comfort of a sitting room, while the other end is given over to a pool table. Sited centrally along one side of the room, the bar serves regulars, families and business people with Abbot Ale, IPA, Rayments Special Bitter and XX Mild, all Greene King beers. Also on draught are Murphy's Stout, three lagers and one cider, and there is a good choice of malt whiskies. The simple, home-made fare includes soup at £1.60, whitebait at £2.75 and pâté at £1.95, and, as main courses, chilli con carne and mushroom pancakes, both at £3.50, and pie of the day at £3.95. Alongside the low-built pub there is a lawned and fenced garden incorporating a children's play area. Three double rooms and one single are available - all smallish but comfortable, and equipped with colour television and tea- and coffee-making facilities.

Brewery: Free house
Licensee: R N Eaton
Opening hours: Summer 11am-11pm; winter 11am-3pm, 6-11pm; Sun 12-3pm, 7-10.30pm
Bar food: Summer 11am-9.30pm; winter 11-2.30pm, 6.30-9.30pm; Sun 12-3pm, 7-9.30pm
Restaurant: 12-2.30pm, 7-9pm
Accommodation: (Price per room) single £18, double £35
Children: In restaurant only; outdoor play area
Credit Cards: Access, Visa

⊕ GREEN MAN
Kelvedon Road, Little Braxted, near Witham CM8 3LB. Tel 0621 891659

Little Braxted

Run by an elderly former Marine with an enduring passion for collecting, this village pub is a treasure house crammed with odds and ends: Royal Marines memorabilia, historic model cars, sporting prints, horse-brasses, tools, pictures and much besides. The earliest surviving record of the brick and tile-hung building dates from 1620, when it was listed as a farmhouse. Some distance behind the pub is a garden equipped with wooden benches and fringed by attractive borders and trees. Customers, most of whom are regulars, have the choice of a simply furnished quarry-tiled Public Bar, where darts, dominoes, cards, shove halfpenny, crib and electronic games can be played, and the cosier Lounge with its mellow wooden furniture and 2lb shell cases adapted to serve as pump handles. Ridleys IPA is on sale, along with three draught lagers and a cider, and a wide selection of bottled beers. In addition to haggis sent down from Scotland, home-made food is served, including rollmops at £2.15, lasagne verde at £3.05, smoked trout at £4.75 and apple crumble at £1.55.

Brewery: T D Ridley & Sons Ltd
Licensee: Eion McGregor
Opening hours: 11am-3pm, 6-11pm; Sun 12-3pm, 6.30-10.30pm
Bar food: 12-2.15pm, 7.30-10.15pm, but flexible
Children: At the landlord's discretion

FOX
Mashbury, near Great Waltham CM1 7TJ. Tel 0245 31573

Mashbury

Tucked away deep in the countryside, and quite hard to find, this pub, dating from 1647, remains untouched almost to the point of neglect. The low, pink, pebble-dashed building has a single bar, frequented by an assortment of customers. Simply furnished and decorated with antiques, old photographs and plates, the low-beamed bar enjoys in winter the combined comforts of an open fire and a wood-burning stove. Bagatelle, skittles, bar skittles, dominoes, shove halfpenny and dominoes are to hand, and live folk music can be heard at lunchtime on the first Sunday of the month. Sheltered tables are set out in the garden behind the pub, and there is a field where children can play. Ridleys IPA Bitter and Adnams Extra complement the regularly changed bar-food menu, which offers whitebait as a starter at £2.95, with main courses like Scotch salmon at £6.95, vegetable pie at £5.45 and peppered steak at £10.75. The sweets include apple pie, pecan pie and sorbet, each at £1.50. At lunchtime on Mondays (summer only) and Saturdays the only fare is a well-known local snack : the huffer, a triangular bap with a variety of fillings.

Brewery: T D Ridley & Sons Ltd
Licensee: M Balshaw
Opening hours: 12-2.30pm, 6.30-11pm; closed Mon lunchtime in winter and Tue lunchtime all year; Sun 12-3pm, 7-10.30pm
Bar food: 2-2.30pm, 6.30-11pm; Sun 12-1.45pm (bookings only); 7-8.45pm
Children: Welcome anywhere if well behaved

⊛ VIPER
Mill Green, near Ingatestone CM4 0PS. Tel 0277 352010

Mill Green

Reputedly the only inn in the country to pay tribute to the viper, this fascinating pub stands on the edge of secluded woodland, scarcely disturbed by passing traffic. The building dates back 400 years, and at the beginning of this century was three cottages, although it is still tiny. Covered with flowers outside, it has four rooms, which remain quite unspoilt, and in the case of the taproom, with its wooden benches and yellow-ochre, half-timbered walls, stark. Carpeted and provided with cushioned seats, the 'private' bar is more comfortable, although still basic. The pub's plainness clearly does not deter trade - in fact its rejection of gimmickry probably encourages it - for its clientele embraces all types. To accompany simple fare like toasted sandwiches at £1.30, soup and French bread at £1.15 and hot fruit pancakes at £1.50, there is a regularly changing selection of beers from Adnams, Fuller's, Ruddles and Webster's, amongst others. Darts, dominoes, cards and shove halfpenny can be played, but for those who prefer a quiet drink in the fresh air there is additional seating on the grass beside the pub.

Brewery: Free house
Licensee: F Beard
Opening hours: 11am-2.30pm (Sat 3pm), 6-11pm; Sun 12-3pm, 7-10.30pm
Bar food: 11am-2.30pm (Sat 3pm), 6-9pm; Sun12-3pm, 7-9pm
Children: Not permitted inside

⊛ FERRYBOAT INN
Ferry Road, North Fambridge, near Woodam Ferrers CM3 6LR. Tel 0621 740208

North Fambridge

With a secluded, riverside setting, this crowded, friendly pub is popular with sailing types, as well as with local regulars, families and business people. The long, low building, some 500 years old, forms an L shape at the end of a road which stops at the water. Low stools at tables, and bench seats, furnish the three, low-ceilinged rooms, which are served by a long bar decked out with masses of banknotes. On tap are Boddingtons Bitter and Flowers IPA, Copperhead cider and two lagers. Straightforward fare is served, including home-cured pork, egg and chips at £2.30, rump steak at £5 and grilled lemon sole at £5.50. A more exotic touch is provided by deep-fried chicken stuffed with prawns and lobster at £5.50, or with cheese at £5. The sweets include champagne-flavoured ice cream at £2 and roly-poly at £1.50. Outside the pub there is a grassed area with tables and a children's swing.

Brewery: Free house
Licensees: R Maltwood and B Noyce
Opening hours: 11am-3pm, 6-11pm; Sun 12-3pm, 7-10.30pm
Bar food: 12-2pm, 7-10pm (Sun 9pm)
Restaurant: 7-10pm; Sun 12-1.30pm
Children: In restaurant and children's room only; half portions available; outdoor play area
Credit Cards: Access, Visa

🍺 PLOUGH AND SAIL
East End, Paglesham Eastend, near Rochford SS4 2EQ. Tel 0702 258242

Paglesham Eastend

A peaceful location five minutes from a river, a 400-year-old building full of character both inside and out, and food courtesy of a landlady who has won several catering awards, together make this coastal pub well worth a journey. Not that the locals overlook it, for they provide much of its trade, along with retired folk and families. Dimpled-glass windows punctuate the white weatherboarding, while flowers in baskets and tubs adorn the double-fronted building and trees surround it. There are two gardens: one, with an aviary to one side, for adults only; the other, with a tree house and a swing, for families. Three comfortable, carpeted rooms lead off the bar, which has above its exposed beams a small room displaying a wealth of horse-brasses and a central cartwheel suspended parallel to the ceiling. A room next to the bar is for games and committed drinkers, and there are two dining rooms. Decoration is provided by old photographs of local subjects, 400 miniatures, gleaming brassware and arrangements of local dried flowers. Courage, Ruddles and Flowers beers are on sale, and the pub specialises in low-alcohol beers and wines. The traditional, home-cooked dishes, at £7 to £8, are all accompanied by fresh, seasonal vegetables, and include liver and bacon, steak and kidney pie and ham, chicken and leek pie.

Brewery: Courage
Licensee: K Oliver
Opening hours: 12-3pm, 7-11pm
(Sun 10.30pm)
Bar food: As opening hours
Children: In family garden only; half portions available; outdoor play area
Credit Cards: Access, Visa

🍺CRICKETERS ARMS
Rickling Green, near Saffron Walden CB11 3YG. Tel 079988 322 /595

Rickling Green

Standing on the large village green, overlooking the pitch, this pub inevitably displays a collection of cricketing memorabilia. With its origins in the 15th century, the building has been modified at various times, including the Victorian era and as recently as four years ago, when seven spacious, light and comfortable double rooms were added. The two bars are friendly but often crowded, and in fine weather some visitors may prefer to sit on the patio or the green itself. A complete mixture of people use the pub, the food receiving high praise from those who eat here regularly. The interesting menu offers starters such as deep-fried Brie in greengage sauce at £1.95 and soup of the day at £1.45. Mussels are a speciality, and also served are half a duck in orange sauce at £6.25 and spare ribs at £4.75. The beer, gravity-fed and very well kept, is Tetley Bitter, Bateman Dark Mild and a guest ale, while the bottled beers include Jenlain and Bière de Garde, both from France. Jazz can be heard on the last Thursday of the month.

Brewery: Free house
Licensees: Timothy and Joan Proctor
Opening hours: 11am-3pm, 6-11pm; Sun 12-3pm, 7-10.30pm
Bar food: 11am-3pm, 6-9.30pm; Sun 12-3pm, 7-9.30pm
Restaurant: Times as bar food
Accommodation: (Price per person) single £40-£50, double £25-£30
Children: In family room and restaurant only
Credit Cards: AMERICAN EXPRESS®, Access, Visa

EIGHT BELLS
18 Bridge Street, Saffron Walden CB10 1BU. Tel 0799 522790

Saffron Walden

Located in one of the oldest parts of the picture postcard town, this pub inevitably numbers tourists among its well mixed clientele.The long, black-and-white building dates from the 16th century, when it was home to a merchant, has an overhanging upper storey with leaded lights, and is decorated with pargetting - relief plasterwork. Exposed wall timbers partition the two bars which are furnished with high settles between tables. An interesting feature in an otherwise unornamented pub is the woodcarvings, depicting dolphins. Teley Bitter, Burton Ale, Wadworth 6X and Adnams Bitter are on tap, and there is an international selection of bottled beers. Qualified chefs provide excellent, efficiently served food, including starters such as salmon pâté at £3.45 and, both at £4.35, mushrooms au gratin and Cromer crab. Typically inventive main courses are gilded chicken in saffron sauce at £6.10, calves' liver with smoked ham, mushrooms and cream sauce at £7.15 and mushrooms Thermidor at £5.40. Converted from an adjacent barn of the same period, the Tudor Barn restaurant features a minstrels' gallery. Jazz bands provide occasional live music.

Brewery: Ind Coope
Licensee: David Gregory
Opening hours: 11am-3pm, 6-11pm; Sun 12-3pm, 7-10.30pm
Bar food: 12-2.30pm, 6-9.30pm (Sat 10pm); Sun 12-2.30pm, 7-9.30pm
Restaurant: Fri and Sat evenings 7-9.30pm; other times by arrangement
Credit Cards: AMERICAN EXPRESS®, Access, Visa

CAP AND FEATHERS
Tillingham, near Southminster CMO 7TH. TEL 0621 779212

Tillingham

A large, rambling building situated on the main street of a village near the coast, this 15th-century pub attracts a complete mix of customers. Serving the full range of Crouch Vale beers, it is the brewery's only tied house, although as an alternative to beer. Thatcher's farmhouse cider and a selection of fruit wines are on offer. Plain inside, and furnished with wheelback chairs, wall seats, a floor-to-ceiling settle and large tables, the pub has a single bar. With character supplied by low, wayward beams and warmth in winter by an imposing wood-burning stove, the bar serves two rooms, one of which is set aside for families. Bar billiards, darts, cards, shove halfpenny and dominoes are available, as well as various board games and a set of bar skittles in each room. Four tables are set out on the small lawn behind the pub. No starters are served, the meals being restricted to simple meals like vegetable burger, chips and salad at £3.95 and casseroles and home-made pies at £4. A speciality is the beef and fish smoked on the premises. Three large double rooms are available, all plain but comfortable.

Brewery: Crouch Vale Brewery Ltd
Licensee: Brian Warrens
Opening hours: 11am-11pm; Sun 12-2pm, 7-9pm
Bar food: 12-2pm, 7-9pm
Accommodation: (Price per person) single or double £15
Children: In family room only

LEICESTERSHIRE

⊜ WHITE HORSE
Main Street, Empingham, near Oakham LE15 8PR. Tel 078086 221

Empingham

This attractive 300-year-old stone village inn is located close to Europe's largest man-made lake - Rutland Water - which is one of the most popular recreation venues in the area. Watersports enthusiasts and walkers are among the visitors swelling the numbers in the large comfortable open-plan bar, who call in for morning coffee or afternoon tea, sample a quality dish or two from the varied bar and restaurant menus or stay overnight in one of the clean, well-appointed bedrooms the inn has to offer. Good home-made bar food, using local produce, may include a tasty soup for £1.95, garlic hoagies with various fillings from £2, a hearty ploughman's lunch for £4.75 and hot dishes such as Rutland trout at £7.20, vegetarian lasagne for £5.25 and steak and kidney in Guinness at £5.45, with sticky toffee meringue, seasonal fruit fool and blackberry and apple pancakes featuring on the pudding list. Three real ales - John Smith's Bitter, Courage Best and Directors, a range of unusual bottled beers and ciders and a good choice of wines are available. Fine weather imbibing can be enjoyed in the side garden or at the benches and tables to the front of the pub.

Brewery: Courage
Licensee: Roger Bourne
Opening hours: 11am-11pm; Sun 12-3pm, 7-10.30pm
Bar food: 12-2pm, 6.30-10pm; Sun 12-2.15pm, 7-10pm
Restaurant: 7.15-10pm (except Sun)
Accommodation: (Price per room) single £28-£38, double £38-£60
Children: Welcome anywhere; own menu available
Credit Cards: AMERICAN EXPRESS®, Access, Visa, Diners

⊜ OLD BARN
Main Street, Glooston, near Market Harborough LE16 7ST. Tel 085884 215

Glooston

Dating from the 16th century and occupying an attractive and peaceful position in a tiny hamlet, the Old Barn is a popular destination for those seeking a relaxed, civilised atmosphere and good home-cooked food. The main beamed and carpeted bar features country pine tables and chairs fronting an open fire, with various plates and prints adorning the walls. This provides a comfortable setting in which to sample one of the regularly changing real ales, such as Hook Norton Old Hookey, Theakston Best and XB, Adnams Broadside or possibly Wadworth 6X, and to savour one of the dishes from the varied menu. Starters range from Old Barn broth at £1.85, to home-made pâté and toast from £3.45; well presented main dishes range from turkey and pheasant pie for £6.25, or goujons of plaice at £5.50 to lamb cutlets for £5.75, and puddings at around £2. Vegetarians are catered for and a set-price menus are offered in the restaurant. Three neat, tastefully decorated bedrooms, all with good facilities, are available and there is a small rear garden.

Brewery: Free house
Licensee: Charles Edmondson-Jones
Opening hours: 12-2.30pm, 7-11pm; Sun 12-3pm, 7-10.30pm
Bar food: 12-1.30pm, 7-9.30pm; Sun 12-1.45pm
Restaurant: Times as bar food
Accommodation: (Price per room) single £37.50, double £42.50
Children: Welcome anywhere
Credit Cards: Access, Visa

BEWICKE ARMS

1 Eastgate, Hallaton, near Market Harborough LE16 8UB. Tel 085889 217

Hallaton

An attractive unspoilt village in the heart of fine countryside is the setting for this pretty 400-year-old thatched inn, which stands opposite the green and its conical-shaped butter cross. A charming flower-decked terrace with seating leads to a lawned area complete with a pen for sheep and chickens. Inside, two beamed bars furnished with old-fashioned cushioned settles and oak tables are serve Marston's Pedigree, Ruddles County and Best Bitter - or a bottle of wine from the superior list - to accompany the reliable home-cooked bar food and restaurant fare. The printed bar menu is enhanced by a daily specials board which may feature smoked salmon salad at £3.95 for starters, followed by lamb steak with Stilton butter for £7.60, Cromer crab salad for £5.80, beery beef cassorole at £6.20 or an imaginative vegetarian dish. Home-made desserts include trifle, hot butterscotch and walnut fudge cake and Pavlova, all at £2.25. Piped music is played regularly and once a month the sound of a local band fills the bars. Bed and breakfast is available in the pub's three bedrooms.

Brewery: Free house
Licensee: Neil Spiers
Opening hours: 12-2.30pm, 6-11pm; Sun 12-3pm, 7-10.30pm
Bar food: 12-2pm, 7.30-9.45pm; Sun 12-1.30pm. 7-9.30pm
Accommodation: (Price per room) single £32.50, double £39.50. Self-catering flat for up to eight people also available
Children: Welcome anywhere; own menu available; outdoor play area
Credit Cards: Access, Visa

FOX AND GOOSE

Main Street, Illston-on-the-Hill LE7 9EG. Tel 053755 340

Illston-on-the-Hill

This traditional and unspoilt 16th-century village pub is a real gem, its two cosy and welcoming bars being a favourite destination for a real mix of customers, from country regulars to cyclists and walkers. As well as the relaxed 'sitting-room' atmosphere found in the front bar and the simply furnished back room complete with old brick floor, settles and various hunting memorabilia, the popular attraction is the range of real ales on offer - Everards Tiger, Beacon Bitter and Old Original, plus a guest beer such as Morland Old Speckled Hen. Bar food is limited to filled cobs and sandwiches. The chatty, music-free ambience is conducive to playing some of the interesting board games that are at hand. Tubs of flowers around a picnic bench brighten up the small courtyard.

Brewery: Everards
Licensee: Mike Boar
Opening hours: 12-2pm (Sat 2.30pm), 7-11pm; Sun 12-2pm, 7-10.30pm
Bar food: As opening hours (except Sun)
Children: Welcome at landlord's discretion

The Wool Business

The trade in wool and cloth, which was the backbone of England's economy all through the Middle Ages and on into modern times, has left its mark behind it in such inn names as the Woolpack, the Ram, the Lamb (sometimes religious), the Shears, the Weavers Arms and the Fleece, often with sign of a dangling ram or sheep. The Golden Fleece is a neat reference to both the wealth derived from the wool business and the classical legend of Jason and the Argonauts.

⊜ CAP AND STOCKING
20 Borough Street, Kegworth, near Derby DE7 2FF. Tel 0509 674814

Kegworth

Hidden down one of the back streets in this large village is the Cap and Stocking, a lively old-fashioned Victorian brick local where time seems to have been frozen in the 1950s. Excellent real ales - Bass and a guest beer - are served in jugs straight from the cellar to a mixed bag of locals, ranging from businessmen to students, who fill the three friendly and atmospheric bars. Coal fires, an old range, cast-iron framed tables, stripped pine, etched glass and a Wurlitzer playing a 1950s selection maintain the dated ambience. Bar food, however, is well up to date in style and good value-for-money. Home-made snacks and main dishes range from soup at 95p, salad Niçoise for £1.55, filled cobs from 65p, chilli at £3.15 and speciality curries - beef for £3.45 and chick pea for £2.95 - plus at least four vegetarian choices. The large sheltered garden and terrace are floodlight, as is the pétanque pitch.

Brewery: Bass
Licensees: Chris and Dominique Poulter
Opening hours: 11.30am-3pm, 6-11pm; Sun 12-3pm, 7-10.30pm
Bar food: 12-2.30pm, 6-9pm
Children: Welcome in the Smoke Room

⊜ BLACK BOY
35 Albion Street, Leicester LE1 6LB. Tel 0533 540422

Leicester

Situated close to the main shopping centre and the Grand Hotel, this 19th-century brick-built city pub is notable for its classic interior, in particular the beautiful old wood-panelled Lounge Bar which has an open fire, carved wooden benches, various sporting prints and a magnificently decorated Victorian plaster ceiling. At weekday lunchtimes the music-free bars are favoured by local businessmen who drop in for one of the basic but good-value bar snacks - chicken curry at £2.95, steak, kidney and mushroom pie at £3.75 or crusty bread sandwiches from £1.50 - and a decent pint of the Guinness, Bass, Boddingtons or Worthington Best draught beers that are dispensed on handpump. A large gravelled courtyard with timber tables is ideal for summer drinking. Morning coffee is always available.

Brewery: Bass
Licensee: P A Jessop
Opening hours: 11am-11pm (Sat 11-3pm, 7-11pm); Sun 12-3pm, 7-10.30pm
Bar food: 11.30am-2.30pm (except Sun)
Children: Welcome in dining room only; half portions available

⊜ BLACK BULL
Market Overton, near Oakham LE15 7PW. Tel 0572 767

Market Overton

The attractive thatched exterior, its peaceful village setting and the good quality food draw customers to this 15th-century cottage. The interior is relaxed and traditional, filled with beams, a part flagstone floor, open fires, polished tables and an assortment of comfortable chairs and banquettes. A well priced menu displays the choice of home-

Brewery: Free house
Licensee: Valerie Owen
Opening hours: 11am-2.30pm, 6-11pm; Sun 12-3pm, 7-10.30pm
Bar food: 12-2pm, 7-10pm
Accommodation: (Price per

cooked dishes available, which may include garlic breaded mushrooms or smoked salmon leaves, both at £2.50 for starters, followed by barbary duck for £7.95, sweet and sour chicken at £5.25, lasagne for £4.95 and a mixed grill for £6.25, all of which are served in generous portions. Vegetarians are catered for too. For those just popping in to play darts, crib or a quiz game the well stocked bar has two real ales on draught - Ruddles County and Bass. A pretty front terrace by the roadside is popular on fine days. Overnight accommodation is available in the form of one traditionally furnished twin room and one double, and a self-catering cottage can be rented on a weekly basis.

person) single £20, double £18
Children: Welcome in dining room only; half portions available
Credit Cards: Access, Visa

⊕ CROWN INN
Debdale Hill, Old Dalby, near Melton Mowbray LE14 3LF. Tel 0664 823134

Old Dalby

It is well worth tracking down this rambling 300-year-old converted farmhouse tucked away along a gated road in the village centre. The original layout of a series of tiny rooms remains unspoilt; each has an open fire, low beamed ceilings, various antique furnishings - oak settles and Windsor chairs - good fabrics, hunting and rural prints and fresh flowers. Imaginative, freshly prepared and well presented dishes grace the varied menu which may include starters such as blue Stilton dip and crudités for £4.95; main courses like pasta with spicy chicken at £7.50, black pudding with fried apple in cream of mustard sauce for £7.50, with Sicilian trifle or chocolate fudge cake, both £2.95, and an unusual selection of cheeses for dessert. Booking is necessary in the separate restaurant. Real ale enthusiasts are spoilt for choice with the range of at least eight regularly changing beers tapped straight from the cask, with Marston's Pedigree, Hardy & Hansons Kimberley Classic and Mansfield always available on draught. These, together with a good selection of wines and malt whiskies, are dispensed from a hatchway bar. Outdoor seating can be found on the large rear lawn and terrace and customers are welcome to play croquet and use the pétanque pitch.

Brewery: Free house
Licensees: Lynne Bryan and Salvatore Inguanta
Opening hours: 12-3pm, 6-11pm; Sun 12-2.30pm, 7-10.30pm
Bar food: 12-2pm, 6.30-10pm (except Sun evening)
Restaurant: 12-1.30pm, 6.30-9.30pm; Sun 12-2pm
Children: Welcome except in the front bar
Credit Cards: Access, Visa

FOX AND HOUNDS
Cross Lane, Preston, near Uppingham LE15 9NQ. Tel 057285 492

Preston

Dating from the 16th century, this unassuming mellow stone local enjoys a central position within a most delightful village and makes a handy refreshment stop for those visiting nearby Rutland Water. A warm welcome awaits customers in either the simple Public Bar which is home to a

Brewery: Free house
Licensees: Phil and Maureen Parker
Opening hours: 11.30am-3pm, 6.30-11pm (Fri and Sat from

juke box, dart board, sets of dominoes and an electronic game, or in the pleasantly furnished Lounge Bar where a beady-eyed stuffed fox presides over the serving of the good home-made food that can be selected from a varied menu. Dishes may include seafood lasagne for £4.95, steak and kidney pie at £4.25, steak au poivre for £7.75 or a vegetarian meal such as broccoli and cheese pie at £4.50. Desserts are priced from £1.95. Draught beers include Guinness, Flowers, Marston's Pedigree, Boddingtons and Murphy's Stout. For sunny days there are picnic tables under the trees in the attractive garden, complete with barbeque.

6pm); Sun 12-3pm, 7-10.30pm
Bar food: 12-2pm, 7-9.30pm; Sun 12-2.30pm, 7-9.30pm
Children: Welcome anywhere

✆ PEACOCK
Main Street, Redmile NG13 0GF. Tel 0949 42554

Redmile

Located close to Belvoir Castle, this stone-built 18th-century village pub draws a discerning clientele into its three beamed and comfortably furnished rooms (two of which are no-smoking areas). Tiled floors, exposed stone walls, open fires, plenty of stripped pine furniture and chintzy fabrics help create the relaxing and convivial atmosphere in which to savour the beautifully presented food on offer here. Main dishes might include medallions of pork in apple and Calvados for £6.50 or escalope of turkey in green peppercorn sauce at £6.30; the puddings are excellent, lemon pancake terrine at £2.25, for example. Good ale is also an attraction - Tetley Bitter, Bass, Greene King Abbot Ale, Marston's Pedigree plus a weekly guest ale such as Timothy Taylors Landlord - and a choice selection of wines is available for diners. Those wishing to sit outside can do so on the gravelled terrace at the front of the pub.

Brewery: Free house
Licensee: Colin Crawford
Opening hours: 12-3pm, 6-11pm; Sun 12-2.30pm, 7-10.30pm
Bar food: 12-3pm, 6.10pm (Sun from 7pm)
Restaurant: Times as bar food (except Sun and Mon evenings)
Children: Welcome in two rooms
Credit Cards: Access, Visa, Diners

✆ CHANDLERS ARMS
Shearsby, LE17 6PL. Tel 0533 478384

Shearsby

Enjoying a peaceful village setting beside the green, this recently renovated 200-year-old brick-built pub is well known locally for its good value bar food, especially the unusual spicy Indian curries that are served in the two relaxing and unpretentious bars. The simple chip-free menu features such dishes as smoked haddock pot for £3.95, beany casserole at £3.95 and a selection of home-made curries, with bread-and-butter pudding and chocolate trufito for dessert. Hearty food combined with a good choice of real ales - Marston's Pedigree, Adnams Best and Broadside and Boddingtons Bitter - encourages regulars to come back time and again. Tables and chairs are laid out on the lawn.

Brewery: Free house
Licensees: Ray and Louise Ward
Opening hours: 12-2pm, 7-11pm; Sun 12-3pm, 7-10.30pm
Bar food: As opening hours (Sun to 9.45pm)
Accommodation: Offered near by; enquire for details
Children: Welcome in one bar

COCK INN
Sibson, near Nuneaton CU13 6LB. Tel 0827 880357

Sibson

Low heavy beams, exposed wattle and daub walls, lattice windows and plenty of quiet nooks and crannies to relax in testify to the age of this attractive thatched and half-timbered rural inn, which was built in 1250 on the edge of the village. A cosy atmosphere pervades throughout the various comfortably furnished small rooms where families and regulars come to enjoy the good value bar food, restaurant fare and the two real ales - Draught Bass and Mitchells and Butlers Brew XI.The bar menu features vegetarian dishes, steaks from £6.75, beef curry at £4.35, chicken Kiev for £4.50 and a traditional set Sunday lunch for £8.50. Bar billiards and an electronic game are conveniently placed out of the way in one of the passageways. Picnic tables are laid out on the rear lawn.

Brewery: Mitchells and Butler
Licensees: Graham and Stephanie Lindsay
Opening hours: 12-2.30pm, 6.30-11pm; Sun 12-2.30pm, 7-10.30pm
Bar food: 12-2pm, 6.30-9.45pm; Sun sandwiches only at lunchtime, 7-9.30pm
Restaurant: 12-2pm, 6.30-9.45pm; Sun set lunch 12-2pm only
Children: Welcome in no-smoking room; own menu available
Credit Cards: AMERICAN EXPRESS®, Access, Visa

⊜ WHITE SWAN
Swan Street, Sileby LE12 7NN. Tel 0509 814832

Sileby

The key to success here is the ever-changing hand-written menu offering freshly prepared and imaginative home-cooked dishes in the two tastefully furnished and welcoming bars and dining room that hide behind the unprepossessing 1930s façade to this village-centre local. A broad cross-section of customers settle among the collections of frogs and bottled beers to tuck into such delicious starters as fish soup with fresh mussels at £1.75, Northumbrian smoked salmon at £4.25 and Stilton and apple pastry slice for £2.75; main courses might include fresh seafood tagliatelle at £6.25, baked salmon in pastry with prawns in a cream sauce for £7.75 or casserole of chicken at £5.50, all of which are served with fresh vegetables. Fresh puddings may include apricot cheesecake at £2.75. Good ales - Marston's Pedigree, Shipstones Bitter and Ansells Bitter - and a fine range of whiskies can be ordered from the well stocked bar. Traditional games exist in the form of darts, cards and a skittle alley, which also houses the children's playroom, and occasional theme nights are held. Outside seating is provided in the garden and covered patio.

Brewery: Free house
Licensee: Theresa Miller
Opening hours: 11.30-3pm, 7-11pm, Sun 12-3pm, 7-10.30pm
Bar food: 12-2pm, 7.30-10pm (except Mon); Sun 12-1.30pm only
Children: Welcome in children's room and family room; own menu and half portions available
Credit Cards: AMERICAN EXPRESS®, Access, Visa

⊕ BAKERS ARMS
Main Street, Thorpe Langton LE16 7TS. Tel 085884 201

Thorpe Langton

In the village centre, this 16th-century thatched pub oozes atmosphere and charm within its ancient walls and low beamed ceilings. Several small and intimate areas are tastefully furnished with large pine tables, antique pews, settles and country chairs, creating a relaxing ambience in which to savour a pint of Webster's Yorkshire Bitter, Ruddles Best or County. Alternatively, a bottle of wine can be ordered from the comprehensive list to accompany one of the freshly prepared dishes from the varied menu. Vegetarian dishes vie with home-made steak and kidney pie at £5 and halibut and prawns in a champagne sauce for £8.10, followed by raspberry crowdie, treacle tart and sponge, all at £2.25. Fish is a speciality, especially on Thursday evenings when it is advisable to book a table. Darts is the only game played in the peaceful, music-free bar. The small rear garden has a lawned area with picnic benches and rosebeds.

Brewery: Grand Met
Licensee: Richard Dore
Opening hours: 6.30-11pm (Sat 12-3pm, 6.30-11pm); Sun 12-3pm. 7-10.30pm
Bar food: 6.30-9.30pm (except Mon); Sat 12-1.45, 6.30-9.30pm; Sun 12-1.45pm
Children: Occasionally allowed in with landlord's permission

⊕ ROYAL HORSESHOES
Melton Road, Waltham-on-the-Wolds, near Melton Mowbray LE14 4AJ. Tel 066478 289

Waltham-on-the-Wolds

Behind the thatched and creeper-clad mellow stone façade of this 17th-century village inn lies one large well furnished bar and four neat and comfortable bedrooms, all with good facilities. A good mix of locals, families and weekday businessmen frequent the friendly bar for the well kept real ales - Marston's Pedigree, John Smith's Bitter and Courage Directors, the good range of chilled bottled lagers and the choice of bar food listed on the short printed menu and the daily specials board. Starters range from butterfly prawns in garlic butter for £3.50 to melon and summer fruits cocktail at £2.25; main dishes from Rutland trout at £6.90, or vegetable au gratin for £5.25 to a filled giant Yorkshire pudding for £3.95. A selection of salads and sandwiches is also available. Flower tubs adorn the newly built, bench-filled patio.

Brewery: Free house
Licensee: Michelle Doyle
Opening hours: 12-2.30pm, 7-11pm; Sun 12-3pm, 7-10.30pm
Bar food: 12-2.30-pm, 6.30-9.30pm; Sun 12-2.30
Restaurant: 12-1.30pm, 7-9.30pm; Sun 12-2pm only
Accommodation: (Price per room) single £27, double £49
Children: Welcome inside if eating; half portions available

Everard's of Leicester

Most of the Everard's pubs are in the Leicester area. The company has been run by successive generations of the family since two brothers, William and Thomas Everard of Narborough, acquired a brewery in Leicester in 1849. The firm brewed its Tiger Bitter in Burton upon Trent, at the Tiger Brewery (now home to the Heritage Brewery Museum) for close on 100 years, until in 1979 it returned to the Everards' original home town and built a new brewery in Narborough, which opened in 1985.

LINCOLNSHIRE

⊜ TALLY HO! INN
Aswarby, near Sleaford NG34 8SA. Tel 05295 205

Aswarby

Set in the depths of the country but right on the A15 for easy access, the Tally Ho! Inn offers some quite fashionable dishes on its menu, for example, kromeskies at £3.60, and Mexican chicken bits for £3.95 come with salad or some particularly tasty chips, and Lisa's chocky mousse and sticky date cake are delicious at under £3. Bateman XB, Flowers Original and Guinness are on draught, and the pub has a good wine list. In the summer drinks are served outside, but indoors it's all cushioned settles, exposed stone, brick and beams, and a wood-burning stove and open fire to keep it cosy in winter. There are six motel-style bedrooms.

Brewery: Free house
Licensee: John Andrews
Opening hours: 12-3pm, 6-11pm; Sun 12-3pm, 7-10.30pm
Bar food: 12-2.30pm, 6.30-10pm; Sun 12-2.30pm, 7.30-9.30pm
Restaurant: Times as bar food
Accommodation: (Price per person) double £21
Children: Welcome anywhere at lunchtime and early evening; outdoor play area
Credit Cards: Access, Visa

LEAGATE INN
Coningsby, near Lincoln LN4 4RS. Tel 0526 342370

Coningsby

There is plenty of atmosphere at this charming old country inn which stands on the B1192 a mile north-east of the village. Its one large bar is divided into three sections, each warmed by an open fire when the weather is cold. Cushioned oak settles and old oak beams are in keeping with the period and exactly suit the mixed but quiet clientele, many of them real-ale lovers who come to enjoy Eldridge Pope Dorchester Bitter, Whitbread Castle Eden Ale and Timothy Taylor Landlord. The food is all home-baked, and there is a separate vegetarian menu which might include lentil crumble or nut cutlet, both at £4. Outside the white-painted brick building is a very large garden where koi carp swim around a pool and waterfall. A 340-year-old yew tree keeps a quiet watch over the seating area.

Brewery: Free house
Licensee: R B Dennison
Opening hours: 11.30am-2.30pm, 7-11pm; Sun 12-2.30pm, 7-10.30pm
Bar food: 11.30am-2pm, 7-10pm; Sun 12-2pm, 7-10pm
Restaurant: Times as bar food
Children: Welcome until 9pm if eating; outdoor play area

⊜ BLACK HORSE
Donington-on-Bain, near Louth LN11 9TJ. Tel 0507 343640

Donington-on-Bain

Walkers on the long-distance path, The Viking Way, often call into this friendly country pub as they pass by, but are requested to leave their muddy boots in the entrance hall. The beers on tap are enough to tempt most thirsty

Brewery: Free house
Licensee: A D Pacey
Opening hours: 11.30am-3pm, 7-12pm; Sun 12-3pm, 7-10.30pm

drinkers inside, and include Ruddles Best Bitter, Ansells Mild, Adnams Bitter, Courage Directors, Guinness and a real ale from Websters. The superbly cooked and very generous home-cooked meals can also be thoroughly recommended, and offer good value for money. On the menu might be a half roast duck and orange sauce for £7.95, West Country ham cooked in cider at £4.75, and vegetarian grill, all served with a choice of potatoes. The two low-beamed bars have furnishings that recall the pub's 18th-century origins and are decorated with brasses, attractive murals and cartoons. Outside there is a small patio and a large garden with plenty of seating. Eight very attractive motel-style rooms (i.e. separate from the pub) are available for overnight stays.

Bar food: 12-2pm, 7-10pm; Sun 12-2pm, 7-9.30pm
Accommodation: (Price per person) single £25, double £20; family room available
Children: In family room only; outdoor play area

⊕ BLACK HORSE INN
Grimsthorpe, near Bourne PE10 0LY. Tel 077832 247

Grimsthorpe

The emphasis is on superb food at this idyllic Georgian coaching inn, where fresh local ingredients including herbs from the garden are combined to produce mouth-watering dishes. Everything is cooked to order - although a hasty open sandwich can be rustled up for those in a hurry - and the house speciality is old English food. The two separate attractive restaurants, the larger one for non-smokers, offer a set four-course dinner at £15.95, as well as lunches, and the bar menu might include Lincolnshire lamb baskets and Mrs Beeton's steak, kidney and mushroom pie both at £4.95, or Grimsthorpe Gastronomy for vegetarians at £4.75; slimmers' and vegetarian meals are clearly marked on the menu. Wine is taken as seriously as the food, with a very wide choice on offer, and Tetley Bitter is on draught in the two bars which have different country themes. The Saddle Bar, decorated in keeping with its name, has alcoves and cushioned settles, while armchairs and settees make the thatched Pheasantry Bar very comfortable. Grimsthorpe Castle and grounds are just across the road, and the hotel's own garden is currently being improved. Upstairs, four bedrooms, decorated in country-house style, are available, among them the Royalty Room which has had many famous guests.

Brewery: Free house
Licensees: Kenneth and Joyce Fisher
Opening hours: 10am-2pm, 7-11pm; closed Sunday
Bar food: 11am-2pm, 7-11pm
Restaurant: 12-2pm, 7-11pm
Accommodation: (Price per room) single £42, double £55-£65
Children: Children under eight years old not permitted in the restaurant in the evenings
Credit Cards:
AMERICAN EXPRESS®, Access, Visa

⊛ NAGS HEAD

High Street, Heckington, near Sleaford NG34 9QZ. Tel 0529 60218

Heckington

The Nags Head is said to have been a favourite haunt of Dick Turpin, and this friendly country inn still attracts its fair share of regulars. Original horse-racing paintings by a local artist line the walls of the two bars, where cushioned settles and carpeted floors provide comfort and occasional entertainment in the form of jazz evenings and quizzes. Food on the extensive menu is superbly cooked and presented, and dishes like Lincolnshire sausage, bacon and cauliflower cheese, and fresh salmon and broccoli quiche at around £3.60 come in large portions. Vaux Samson and real ales from Wards and Bass are on tap. Three well equipped double rooms are available for overnight accommodation.

Brewery: Vaux
Licensees: Bruce and Gina Pickworth
Opening hours: 11am-3pm, 7-11pm; Sun 12-3pm, 7-10.30pm
Bar food:12-2.30pm, 7.30-9.30pm; Sun 12-2pm, 7.30-9.39pm
Accommodation: (Price per room) single £22, double £32
Children: Welcome anywhere if well behaved
Credit Cards: Access, Visa

⊛ WIG AND MITRE

29 Steep Hill, Lincoln LN2 1LU. Tel 0522 535190

Lincoln

Once the dining room of a manor house, this quiet 14th-century pub, close to Lincoln cathedral in a pedestrianised part of the old city, with vehicle access at the rear for disabled visitors, is much frequented by the 'cloth'. Its two bars have stone-tiled floors, exposed beams and cushioned settees, with the upstairs bar/restaurant being the more interesting. The walls are adorned with cigarette cards, currency notes, prints and cartoons which add to the atmosphere, while outside a small sheltered courtyard provides some seating. Samuel Smith Old Brewery Bitter and Museum Ale are on tap, and there is a large selection of malted whiskies. The imaginative menu ranges from tasty dishes like tuna, pasta and sweetcorn salad, and a bowl of chilli with bread, both at £4.50, to veal escalope with wholegrain mustard sauce for £11.50. Soup is £1.90, and sweets cost £2.75; portions are generous and quality is high. Afternoon tea and morning coffee are also available.

Brewery: Free house
Licensees: Michael Ashworth and Valerie Hope
Opening hours: 8am-11pm
Bar food: As opening hours
Restaurant: Times as bar food
Children: Welcome anywhere if well behaved
Credit Cards: AMERICAN EXPRESS®, Access, Visa, Diners

Bar Billiards

This ingenious blend of billiards and skittles is a relative newcomer to the pub scene. It was introduced here from Belgium in the 1930s, with support from billiard table manufacturers. The game caught on rapidly, especially in the South and Midlands, and leagues had been organised by the time the Second World War began. Its much more recent rival is pool, which came here from America in the 1960s in the wake of the Paul Newman film The Hustler.

⊜ RED LION
Newton, near Sleaford NG34 0EE. Tel 05297 256

Newton

Friendly personal attention is in constant supply at this pub in spite of the mixed lunchtime and evening crowd which keeps staff busy. One large bar has several serving rooms leading off it, and an old world atmosphere is much in evidence. Cushioned settles, exposed stone in places, and quarry-tiled floors with carpeting reflect the pub's 17th-century origins, and the walls are lined with sporting cartoons, wheels and farm artefacts. Superbly cooked food offers good value for money with dishes like carbonnade of beef at £5.75, or meat from the Carvery costing £6.50 to £8.50 depending on size of portion. On tap are Bateman XXXB, John Smith's Bitter, and Draught Bass. Outside, a large wisteria drapes itself along the walls, and cast-iron furniture in the garden and patio make for pleasant al fresco eating and drinking in summer. The pub has its own squash club with two courts.

Brewery: Free house
Licensee: Graham Watkin
Opening hours: 11.30am-3pm, 6-11pm; Sun 11.30am-3pm, 7-10.30pm
Bar food: 12-2pm, 7-10pm
Children: Welcome anywhere if well behaved; outdoor play area

⊜ RED LION INN
Raithby by Spilsby PE23 4DS. Tel 0790 53727

Raithby by Spilsby

Nobody who eats at this pleasant old 16th-century pub leaves hungry, as the portions are extra large and the cooking excellent. Only fresh ingredients are used in the kitchen, and the results speak for themselves. Starters like garlic mushrooms, smoked ham with melon and salmon mousse cost £1.95, and main courses might include breast of duckling and venison pie at £8, or mushroom and celery korma for £6.75, four or five vegetables being included in the price. All meals, including bar snacks, are eaten in the 16th-century alcoved restaurant, with its exposed brickwork and beams. The quiet, pleasant bar has a collection of coins decorating the ceiling and an open fire. Home Bitter and Theakston XB are on tap; Old Peculier is sold in bottles. The pub appeals to a wide range of quiet customers, and there is a small terrace outside as well as plenty of parking space. Four well furnished bedrooms, two of them planned to be ready in1993, are available.

Brewery: Free house
Licensee: Roger Smith
Opening hours: 7-11pm (Sat and BHs 12-3pm, 7-11pm); Sun 12-3pm, 7-10.30pm
Bar food: As opening times
Restaurant: Wed-Fri 7-11pm; Sat 12-3pm, 7-11pm; Sun 12-3pm
Accommodation: (Price per person) single £15, double £12
Children: Not permitted under 14 years in the bar; family room
Credit Cards: Access, Visa

⊕ HORSESHOES
London Road, Silk Willoughby, near Sleaford NG34 8NZ. Tel 0529 303153

Silk Willoughby

Speciality evenings are occasionally held at this large imposing pub on the A15: on 'Lobster Night', for example, the crustacean is cooked in five different ways, each costing only £6.50. At other times dishes like home-made fisherman's pie and chilli con carne, served with chips and salad or new potatoes and fresh vegetables, are £3.95. Open sandwiches cost around £2.60. The food is carefully cooked, imaginatively presented, and backed up by a well-stocked wine cellar. On tap in the attractively decorated and spacious bar are Mansfield Riding Dark Mild, Riding Traditional Bitter, and Old Baily; an open fire makes the place cosy in winter. The restaurant has a wide-ranging menu and booking is advisable at weekends.

Brewery: Mansfield
Licensee: David Williams
Opening hours: 12-2.30pm, 7-11pm; closed Mon lunchtime; Sun 12-3pm, 7-10.30pm
Bar food: As opening hours
Restaurant: 7-11pm; Sun 12-3pm, 7-10pm
Children: Welcome anywhere if well behaved

⊕ BLACKSMITHS ARMS
Main Road, Skendleby, near Spilsby PE23 4QE. Tel 0754 85662

Skendleby

A pear tree in the main eating area and an illuminated glass-covered well provide novel interest at this welcoming country pub. The pear tree was successfully left in place when an extension was built on to the outside wall where it was growing. Booking for meals is essential as the food is locally very popular, and prices for dishes like cashew nut and celery risotto, beef curry and various omelettes are not high at around the £4 mark. Bateman Dark Mild, XB and XXXB are on tap, as well as Murphy's and Guinness. Blacksmiths' tools and brass ornaments adorn the friendly bar, and through a large window behind, the cellar can be viewed. Chairs and settles provide the seating on quarry-tiled floors, and in winter a cheerful open fire burns. Outside, seating is arranged in the several sections of the large garden. A separate cottage offers holiday accommodation but the gallery bedroom makes it unsafe for young children.

Brewery: Free house
Licensee: Robert Rose
Opening hours: 11am-3pm, 6.30-12pm; Sun 12-3pm, 7-10.30pm
Bar food: As opening times
Restaurant: Times as bar food
Accommodation: £80 per week
Children: Welcome anywhere if well behaved

⊕ GEORGE OF STAMFORD
High Street, St Martins, Stamford PE9 2LB. Tel 0780 55171

Stamford

Parts of this lovely old building date back to the 10th century, but most of it is 16th-century, and there is much exposed stonework and old panelling inside to prove it. One 18th-century regular, Daniel Lambert, was reputedly Britain's heaviest man at 52 stone, but nowadays most of the up-market tourists, business and local customers who frequent this luxurious hotel are considerably lighter weight.

Brewery: Free house
Licensees: Christopher Pitman and Ivo Vannocci
Opening hours: 11am-2.30pm, 6-11pm
Bar food: 12-2.30pm, 6.30-10pm
Children: Welcome anywhere if

Ruddles Best Bitter and Adnams beers are on draught in the bar and there are 30 different bottled beers to choose from. Superbly cooked bar meals served by charming staff come in large portions, and customers can enjoy dishes like plaice and salmon mousse with chive sauce and new potatoes for £7.95, and sardines with herbs, tomatoes and peppers for £5.95. A delightful courtyard garden with seating and lights makes for even more easy-going eating and drinking. Accommodation here is, not surprisingly, more expensive than the normal range of pub or inn prices, as is the very formal hotel restaurant.

well behaved; family room
Credit Cards:
AMERICAN EXPRESS®, Access, Visa, Diners

Swinhope

CLICKEM INN
Swinhope, near Binbrook LN5 6BS. Tel 0472 398253

A real-ale drinker's paradise can be found in the bar of this quiet 19th-century pub one mile outside the village of Swinhope, buried in the heart of the Lincolnshire countryside. Five beers are on tap here; Timothy Taylor Best Bitter, Theakston Old Peculier and XB, Ruddles Best Bitter, and Bateman XB. Occasional jazz nights and traditional pub games liven up the bar. The reasonably priced food includes king-size Yorkshire pudding with beef goulash (£3), gammon and eggs (£3.90), and mushroom omelette (£2.60), all served with chips. Puddings cost from 50p to £1.30. A small patio and gardens lie alongside the road.

Brewery: Free house
Licensee: T Winfield
Opening hours: 11am-3pm, 7-11pm ; closed Mon lunchtime; Sun 12-3pm, 7-10.30pm
Bar food: 12-2pm, 7-10pm; Sun 12-2pm, 7-9.30pm
Children: Not permitted in bar area

Tetford

⊜ WHITE HART
East Road, Tetford, near Horncastle LN9 6QQ. Tel 0507 533255

This outstandingly friendly pub is well worth a visit even though it's a bit off the beaten track. Dating from 1520, it has associations with Tennyson and locals are enthusiastically in favour of the rapid improvements taking place under fairly new management, and also rate the food very highly. Typical choices from the bar menu are seafood platter at £3.75, chicken tikka masala for £5.50, and steak and mushroom for £4.95, all served with chips or jacket potatoes and salad. A four-course Sunday lunch costs £5.95. Wards Sheffield Best Bitter and Kirby Strong Bitter, and Vaux Samson are on tap in the two bars, where quarry tiles, exposed beams and an inglenook fire add to the old-world atmosphere. The walls are decked with brasses. Six bedrooms are decorated in modern style, and there is some seating in the garden.

Brewery: Free house
Licensee: Rowena Ridgeway
Opening hours 12-3.30pm, 7-11pm; closed Mon lunchtime; Sun 12-3.30pm, 7-10.30pm
Bar food: 12-2pm, 7-9.30pm (except Mon)
Restaurant: 7-9.30 pm (except Mon); Sun 12-2pm
Accommodation: (Price per room) single £16, double £32
Children: Welcome if well behaved; family room; outdoor play area

⊕ PLOUGH INN
Main Street, Wilsford, near Grantham NG32 3NS. Tel 0400 30304

Wilsford

A large black dog is a friendly presence at this pleasant country pub, but as it doesn't take kindly to competition; no other dogs can be allowed inside. Two-legged visitors are more than welcome, however, and the quiet bars are conducive to relaxing for an hour or two at least. Exposed stonework and beams and open fires are the background for some excellent beer on tap, including Stones Best Bitter, Worthington Best Bitter, Draught Bass and Murphy's. The first-class chips are well worth trying with the bar food, served with dishes like chicken Kiev and lasagne at £3.50, and sirloin steak for £8.50. Starters such as breaded mushrooms and scampi offer good value for money at £2. The stone-built pub is set close to the church in the centre of this quiet village, and in the small patio and garden there is some seating for summer visitors.

Brewery: Free house
Licensee: R J W German
Opening hours: 7-11pm (Sat 12-11pm); Sun 12-3pm, 7-10.30pm
Bar food: 7-11pm (except Mon); Sat 12-2pm, 7-11pm; Sun 12-2pm
Children: Welcome if well behaved

NORFOLK

⊕ BUCKINGHAMSHIRE ARMS
Blickling, near Norwich NR11 6NF. Tel 0263 732133

Blickling

Widely known as 'the inn at Blickling Hall' (the village being made up of that famous National Trust property and a few houses), this beautiful 16th-century pub boasts a well kept, pretty garden and courtyard where outside service is provided in summer. The two unspoiled bars offer a choice of six malts and a superior wine list as well as a range of draught beers (Adnams, Woodforde's, Beamish and weekly guest beers). Competently prepared and attractively presented bar meals include roast lamb (£5.75), cottage pie (£5.95) and cauliflower cheese (£4.75), but prices in the separate restaurant might be considered high. Accommodation is olde worlde and features bedrooms with four-poster beds.

Brewery: Free house
Licensee: Robert Dean
Opening hours: 10am-2.30pm, 6-11pm; Sun 12-2.30pm, 7-10.30pm
Bar food: 12-2pm daily, 7-9pm (except Sun)
Restaurant: 7-9pm (except Sun and Mon)
Accommodation: (Price per room) single from £40, double from £50
Children: Welcome in restaurant and family room; outdoor play area
Credit Cards: Access, Visa

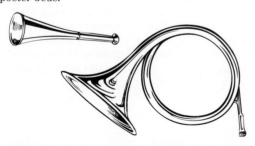

⚓ JOLLY SAILORS
Brancaster Staithe, near King's Lynn PE31 8BJ. Tel 0485 210314

Brancaster Staithe

An across-the-board clientele is attracted to this well run 200-year-old pub which stands in a village on the main coast road, but a tennis court and large gardens with a children's play area make it particularly popular, especially during the summer weekends. The traditional bar area, with its open fires, flagged floors, cushioned settles offers Greene King IPA and Abbot Ale and a choice of lagers on draught as well as an award-winning wine list prepared by the landlord. Food is reasonably priced, with home-made soup at £1.30, jacket potatoes from £1.75, and lasagne and chips or mussels (March to October)in white wine and cream at £5.20; the separate restaurant has its own menu.

Brewery: Free house
Licensee: Alister Borthwick
Opening hours: 11am-3pm, 7-11pm; (Jul and Aug and BH weekends 11am-11pm); Sun 12-2.30pm, 7-10.30pm
Bar food: 12-2pm, 7-9pm (Jul and Aug and BH weekends 11am-11pm)
Restaurant: 12-2pm, 7-9pm
Children: Not permitted near bar but welcome in family room; outdoor play area
Credit Cards: Access, Visa

⚓ HOSTE ARMS
The Green, Burnham Market, near King's Lynn PE31 8HD Tel 0328 738257

Burnham Market

An inn since 1650, this large white-painted pub at the centre of a particularly pretty village is extremely comfortable, offering magnificent accommodation and the use of a wonderful walled garden. The bar - which comprises three well furnished, beamed rooms with open fires - has a relaxed but bustling atmosphere, the only entertainment being piano music on Wednesday evenings and jazz on Monday evenings and the last Friday of each month; a good range of both beers (Woodforde's Wherry, Ruddles County, Guinness and Yorkshire Bitter on draught) and malts is available, and the superior wine list offers a low mark-up on the more expensive bottles. Bar food is of a high standard and, compared with other local establishments, not overpriced, with oysters or mussels in season at £3.95 and main courses like beef in beer (£5.25) or mackerel (£4.95). Vegetarian options are always available, and a 'house special' of rich Austrian truffle cake (£2.50) might bring your meal to a triumphant close.

Brewery: Free house
Licensee: Pauline Osler; owner Paul Whittome
Opening hours: 11am-3pm, 5-11pm; Sun 12-3pm, 7-10.30pm
Bar food: 12-9.15pm (Fri 10pm); Sun 12-3pm, 7-9.15pm
Restaurant: 7-9pm (or later if specially booked)
Accommodation: (Price per person) £31 to £38
Children: Welcome if well behaved; family room; outdoor play area
Credit Cards: Access, Visa

Naval and Military
Britain's seafaring tradition has influenced inn signs on the coast and far inland. The ship is sometimes Noah's Ark, but more often the sign depicts a famous vessel such as the Victory or the Royal George. Names like the Anchor, the Channel Packet, the Jolly Tar and the Drum and Monkey (meaning a naval powder monkey) are in the same tradition and Lord Nelson leads the famous admirals loyally honoured on inn signs. Plenty of pubs celebrate British military history, too, with names like the Artilleryman, the Rifleman, the Volunteer, the Gurkha and the Bugle. Battles from the Alma to Waterloo are remembered, Wellington is pre-eminent among generals and the Marquis of Granby, an 18th-century war hero, still has many pubs to his name.

⊕ RATCATCHERS
Eastgate, Cawston, near Aylsham NR10 4HA Tel 0603 871430

Cawston

A good choice of select malts, an extensive wine list and a range of draught beers that includes Adnams, Worthington, Toby, M&B mild and Guinness, are among the attractions of this well run and efficient 19th-century pub which stands at a remote crossroads outside Cawston, with a small garden at its side. A comprehensive menu of high quality snacks and meals is served in the comfortable bar - with its open fires, old photos and ratcatchers' cages - and in a separate restaurant. Snacks (£1.25 to £4.85) include jacket potatoes, toasted sandwiches and a ploughman's; sandwiches (£1.45 to £3.45) are freshly made to order and salads (with huntsman's pâté, for example, at £4.35, or Greenland prawns, at £6.75) are served with warm home-made bread rolls. Grills, pies, seafood specialities, Continental and eastern dishes (like Caesar's spaghetti or Jaffri Madras curry) add up to an almost bewildering choice. There are also vegetarian dishes and plenty of choice for children, as well as a list of 12 or more puddings, mostly named after Dickensian characters, offering temptations like Mr Micawber's cake (rum baba) at £2.35 and Bill Sikes' pudding (Spotted Dick), or Fagin's Fancy (treacle sponge) at £2.15. A traditional roast lunch (£6.95 for pork or £7.55 for beef) is seved on Sundays, but must be booked in advance.

Brewery: Free house
Licensee: Eugene Charlier
Opening hours: 11.45am-3pm, 6-11pm; Sun 12-3pm, 7-10.30pm
Bar food: As opening times till 2pm and 10pm
Restaurant: Times as bar food
Children: At the discretion of the landlord; children's menu available

THREE HORSESHOES
North Walsham Road, Scottow, near Coltishall NR10 5BZ. Tel 0692 69243

Coltishall

Pool, electronic games and piped music impart a lively atmosphere to the bars of this thatched 17th-century pub on the edge of the village, though the paintings of Norfolk scenes and collection of old bottles are in keeping with the original character of the beamed rooms; discos held in the adjacent Scottow Barn four evenings a week prove an additional attraction to an across-the-board clientele. Dry Blackthorn and Red Rock ciders and a choice of lagers are available on draught, together with Flowers, Tolly, Tetley, Whitbread, John Bull, Murphy's and Guinness. The reasonably priced bar food has many popular dishes, and a vegetarian selection, all of a high quality. Soup (£1.40) or prawn cocktail (£2.85), for example, might be followed by chicken Kiev (£5.65), scampi (4.25) or wheat and walnut casserole (£4.50), the meal ending with passion cake or Death by Chocolate (both at £1.85).

Brewery: Brent Walker
Licensee: Keith Blackwell
Opening hours: 11am-3pm, 6-11pm; Sun 12-3pm, 7-10.30pm
Bar food: 12-2.30pm, 6-10pm; Sun 12-2.30pm, 7-10pm
Children: Welcome anywhere if well behaved; family room

⊕ WHITE HORSE INN
East Barsham, near Fakenham NR21 0LH. Tel 0328 820645

East Barsham

All tastes are catered for by this very friendly, well run establishment, a rambling whitewashed brick and flint inn dating from the 17th century with an enclosed patio behind it and set at the centre of the village. A fantastic range of liqueurs from all over the world is available, as well as a choice of draught beers that includes Woodforde's, Boddingtons, Tolly Cobbold and Greene King Abbot. The extensive menu offers some unusual main courses - sole with whisky sauce at £13.50, for example - as well as the simpler grilled trout (£5.50), steak and kidney pie (£4.05), lasagne (£3.85) or curry (£4.05). Overnight accommodation is traditional in style.

Brewery: Free house
Licensees: Lilian and Chris Baines
Opening hours: Summer 11am-11pm; winter 11am-3pm, 7-11pm; Sun 12-3pm, 7-10.30pm
Bar food: 12-2pm, 7-10pm
Restaurant: Times as bar food
Accommodation: (Price per person) single £30, double £22.50; family suite available
Children: Welcome if well behaved; family room
Credit Cards: Access, Visa

⊕ CHERRY TREE
Harleston, near Diss IP20 9BZ. Tel 0379 852345

Harleston

A good choice of malts and whiskies, together with straightforward but wonderfully cheap and well presented lunchtime bar snacks - soup at 90p, toasties from 65p, rolls and bocklanders (German sausage in hot French bread) - at £1.30 (only the latter being available in the evenings and on Sundays) - are inducements to visit this substantial 18th-century pub on the edge of town; draught beers include the whole Adnams range. Unspoiled and well run, it is 'home' to many local societies and sports teams as well as having a staunch following of regulars and attracting a fair amount of business trade. Two simply furnished bars hung with old advertisements, photos, prints and plates are reliably cosy (the Public warmed by a wood-burner, while the Lounge boasts a beautiful open fire), and electronic games supplement the more traditional amusements of darts, dominoes, cards and pétanque. A sheltered garden set with tables and benches is attractive in summer.

Brewery: Adnams
Licensee: Frank Long
Opening hours: 11am-2.30pm, 6-11pm; Sun 12-3pm, 7-10.30pm
Bar food: 12-2.30pm; only bocklanders in evenings and on Sundays
Children: Not permitted inside; outdoor play area

⊕ HARE AND HOUNDS
Hempstead, near Holt NR25 6LD. Tel 0263 713285

Hempstead

This attractive, unspoiled, Norfolk flint-and-brick pub, dating from the 17th century, enjoys a delightful setting in the depths of the country between two villages, and serves as a popular local meeting place as well as catering well for visitors. A traditional bar with tiled floor and wood-burning

Brewery: Free house
Licensee: James Hobson
Opening hours: 11am-3pm, 6-11pm; Sun 12-3pm, 7-10.30pm
Bar food: 12-2pm, 7-9pm

stove displays a man-trap alongside the more predictable pewter mugs and watercolours. Here, in a relaxing atmosphere undisturbed by piped music or games - the only entertainment being provided by the landlord, who occasionally sings to the accompaniment of his own guitar - customers have a choice of Adnams, Bass or Woodforde's draught beers. Bar food is excellent, a range of main courses at £5.50 including pork marengo, poached fillet of salmon and braised venison, being followed, perhaps, by fresh fruit flan or apple strudel (both at £1.50). The large garden is popular in summer.

Children: Welcome in room linked to bar

🍺 EARLE ARMS
The Street, Heydon, near Saxthorpe NR11 6AD. Tel 026387 376

Heydon

The range of draught beers served here from the cask (real ale being a speciality) includes Worthington, Adnams, Fuller's London Pride, Greene King Abbot Ale and Bass; there is also a good choice of bottled beers (Becks, Newcastle Brown, Sam Smiths Pale Ale and Budweiser), Tennent Pilsner and Extra Strong lagers and Red Rock cider. Bar snacks represent excellent value for money, with rolls at 50p and a ploughman's at £2, but the selection is limited and will not necessarily include a vegetarian option. The picturesque 16th-century pub, with a secluded garden to the rear, overlooks the green of a village which, despite its fame as a beauty spot, is unspoiled. A delightful, traditional Public Bar with open fire and serving hatch offers piped music and electronic games as well as more old-fashioned amusements like darts, pool or dominoes, and there are occasional folk evenings. The Lounge provides a more peaceful environment for patrons wanting simply to enjoy a good drink.

Brewery: Free house
Licensees: Derek and Molly Williams
Opening hours: 11am-3pm, 6.30-11pm; Sun 12-3pm, 7-10.30pm
Bar food: As opening hours
Children: Welcome anywhere; outdoor play area

SWAN
Ingham, near Stalham NR12 9AB. Tel -692 581099

Ingham

A good choice of bottled beers supplements those on draught (Woodforde's Wherry, Adnams Bitter and Mild, Murphy's, Felinfoel Double Dragon and guest beers) at this lovely 14th-century thatched inn, and there is a decent wine list too. Set next to the church at the centre of the village, with a sunny patio behind it, the Swan attracts an across-the-board clientele - its excellent, reasonably priced, home-cooked food being a popular feature. Whitebait (£2.95) or duck and orange pâté (£3.15), for example, might be followed by beef Stroganoff with rice (£5.95) or medallions of beef in Marsala and orange sauce (£6.75), while puddings include lemon lush pie and pancakes with fruit and cream (both at £2.70); there is always a vegetarian dish and children will find things they like on the menu. Two bars with ancient beams and exposed brickwork provide traditional amusements like cribbage, draughts and chess. An old stable block has been converted to provide overnight accommodation. Rooms have four-poster beds and there is a family room.

Brewery: Free house
Licensees: Iain and Michaela Kemp
Opening hours: 11am-3pm, 6-11pm; Sun 12-3pm, 7-10.30pm
Bar food: 12-2pm, 6.30-9pm (except Mon); Sun 12-2.30pm only
Accommodation: (Price per room) double £52-£62
Children: Welcome anywhere; family room; outdoor play area
Credit Cards: AMERICAN EXPRESS®, Access, Visa

☺ REEDHAM FERRY INN
Reedham, near Norwich NR13 3HA. Tel 0493 700429

Reedham

A marvellous place to moor - or, if you are land-based, to sit and watch the ferry and other river traffic on the Yare - this white-painted, grey-roofed inn dating from the late 17th century stands right on the waterfront, the tables on its jetty attracting all comers. A lively atmosphere permeates the bar, with its quarry-tiled floor, thick horizontal beams and Broads' memorabilia, and amusements like dominoes, cards and piped music are occasionally superseded by an outburst of spontaneous live entertainment! The modern sun room, running across the front of the bar and restaurant, has elecronic games and padded seats, so providing a suitable area for children. Beverages range from Scrumpy Jack to Continental lagers and local wines, with Adnams and Woodforde's beer being available on draught. Good value bar food (also served in the restaurant) includes dishes like stuffed vine leaves at £5.50 alongside the more predictable roast Norfolk duckling (£8.30); there is always a vegetarian dish.

Brewery: Free house
Licensee: David N Archer
Opening hours: 11am-3pm, 6.30-11pm (7-11pm in winter); Sun 12- 3pm, 7-10.30pm
Bar food: 12-2pm, 7-10pm
Restaurant: Times as bar food; booking preferred
Children: Welcome in family room and in restaurant until 9pm
Credit Cards: Access, Visa

✑ GIN TRAP INN
Ringstead, near Hunstanton PE36 5JU. Tel 0485 25264

Ringstead

The visitor to this well run, friendly and popular village pub - a beautiful 17th-century coaching inn with a large garden to the rear - can sample Gin Trap Bitter as well as a range of draught beers including Adnams, Greene King Abbot Ale, Guinness, Woodforde's Norfolk Nog, Bass and M&B mild; and a choice of seven malts. An across-the-board clientele - with the exception of rowdy youngsters - is welcomed into the comfortable carpeted bar with its extensive collection of memorabilia; neither piped music nor games is in evidence here, though occasional live entertainment is provided by Morris dancers or a ballad singer. Reasonably priced, popular bar food items, like lasagne and salad and steak and kidney pie at £4.60, or scampi with peas and chips at £5, are supplemented by daily specials, with a vegetarian option always available.

Brewery: Free house
Licensees: Brian and Margaret Harmes
Opening hours: 11.30am-3pm, 6.30-11pm; Sun 12-3pm, 7-10.30pm; closed Sun evening in winter
Bar food: 12-2pm, 7-9pm, 9.30 Fri and Sat); Sun 12-1.30pm, /-9pm
Children: Welcome at landlord's discretion, but not in main bar

✑ LODGE
Vicarage Road, Salhouse, near Norwich NR13 6HD. Tel 0603 782828

Salhouse

Originally a Georgian rectory, this large and comfortable red-brick pub is set in its own extensive grounds on the edge of the village, parasol-shaded tables dotting pleasant lawns where live music is performed on summer evenings. Carpeted bars furnished with green velvet chairs and banquettes serve a range of beverages which includes over 80 malt whiskies, as well as a good choice of draught beers (Woodforde's, Stones, Greene King IPA and Murphy's Stout), lagers and ciders. By comparison, the selection of bar meals is quite limited - roast beef (£4.75) or gammon salad (4.15), for example, with gâteau or raspberries and cream (both at £2.20) to follow; it is nevertheless advisable to book a table in the Carvery at popular times.

Brewery: Free house
Licensee: Tom Farrell
Opening hours: 10.30am-3pm, 5.30-11pm; Sun 12-3pm, 7-10.30pm
Bar food: 12-2pm, 7.30-9.30pm (except Sun evening in winter)
Children: Welcome if eating; outdoor play area
Credit Cards: Visa

✑ SCOLE INN
Scole, near Diss IP22 4DR. Tel 0379 740481

Scole

A good range of drinks - including 85 wines, a wide choice of malts and several notable bottled beers (Rolling Rock, Red Stripe, San Miguel, Lowenbrau, Elephant, Becks and Budweiser), as well as Adnams Best and Broadside and Fuller's London Pride on draught - is served at this large, remarkably attractive and well run 17th-century inn which, strategically located at the junction of the A140 and A143, attracts business trade during the week and families at

Brewery: Free house
Licensee: Phil Hills
Opening hours: 11am-11pm
Bar food: 12-2.30pm, 6-10pm; Sun 12-2pm, 7-10pm
Restaurant: Times as bar food; booking advisable
Accommodation: (Price per

weekends. Accommodation is luxurious in style, some rooms having four-poster beds, but the two bars retain a more intimate atmosphere, with open fires in the old fireplaces and well worn wooden tables. Here and in the restaurant, bar food represents reasonable value for money, with popular dishes like Cumberland sausage, chips and salad at £4.95 and Dover sole at £10.95, for example. For the summer months the small fenced garden offers the possiblity of a barbecue.

room) single from £49.50, double £62.00- £69.50
Children: Welcome anywhere
Credit Cards:
AMERICAN EXPRESS®, Access, Visa, Diners

Scottow see Coltishall

⊜ ROSE AND CROWN
Old Church Road, Snettisham, near King's Lynn PE36 7LX. Tel 0485 541382

Snettisham

A history dating back to the 14th century and a delightful exterior may be the things that first attract visitors to this village inn, but a friendly atmosphere, excellent service, real ales and value-for-money food are the things that bring them back time and time again. The Rose and Crown provides ideal conditions for children, having both a spacious walled garden (complete with rabbits and a well equipped play area) and a large family room. The three bars - one sporting barrel seats - have been redecorated in keeping with the original character of the building and both have open fires. Beers on draught include Adnams, Greene King Abbot Ale and Bass, and there is also a good choice of lagers and ciders. Bar meals, generously served, offer a selection of dishes ranging from Stilton or Cheddar ploughman's at £3.25 to fillet steak at £10.50.

Brewery: Free house
Licensee: Margaret Trafford
Opening hours: 11am-3pm, 5.30-11pm (Sat11am-11pm); Sun 12-3pm, 7-10.30pm
Bar food: 12-2pm, 6.30-10pm
Accommodation: (Price per person) single £25, double £15-£25
Children: In large family room; children's menu available; outdoor play area
Credit Cards: Access, Visa

⊜ RED LION
Stiffkey, near Wells-next-the-Sea NR25 1AJ. Tel 0328 830552

Stiffkey

Shut for 17 years, but now reopened after tasteful restoration, this very pleasant, well run pub at the end of the village originally dates back to the 16th century. Two well furnished bars with open fires offer Greene King IPA and Abbot Ale and Woodforde's Wherry and Nelson's Revenge on draught and the wide-ranging bar menu is reasonably priced with steak and kidney pie at £5.50 or duckling and apricot sauce at £7.25 (the choice always including a vegetarian option). Electronic games are provided in addition to the more traditional pursuits of pool and darts, and live entertainment is a regular feature. Both garden and patio command fine views of the Stiffkey valley

Brewery: Free house
Licensee: Adrienne Cooke
Opening hours: 11am-3pm, 6-11pm; Sun 12-3pm, 7-10.30pm
Bar food: 12-2.30pm, 7-9.30pm
Children: Welcome except in main bar; family room

☻ HARE ARMS
Stow Bardolph, near King's Lynn PE34 3HT. Tel 0366 382229

Stow Bardolph

Large gardens surround this welcoming, well run and attractive 19th-century village-centre inn, which also has a paved patio and yard. Its one bar, warmed by open fires, is crammed with all kinds of memorabilia and is a popular meeting place for a wide cross-section of the local community. On draught are Greene King beers - IPA, Abbot and Rayments; Harp and Kronenbourg lagers, and Blackthorn Dry and Red Rock ciders. A good wine list accompanies an imaginative range of bar meals, and the separate restaurant offers a table d'hôte menu from Monday to Thursday as well as the à la carte selection. Typical dishes might be Stilton and bacon soup (£1.75) or local samphire (£1.95), followed by either pork steak with mustard sauce or sea bream au poivre at £5.20, while puddings include such favourites as summer pudding and banoffii pie. Neither vegetarians nor children should have any difficulty in finding suitable dishes.

Brewery: Greene King
Licensee: David McManus
Opening hours: 11am-2.30pm, 6-11.30pm; Sun 12-2.30pm, 7-10.30pm
Bar food: 12-2pm, 7-10pm
Restaurant: 7.30-9.30pm (except Sun)
Children: Welcome in conservatory and coach house

☻ SUTTON STAITHE HOTEL
Sutton Staithe, near Stalham NR12 9QS. Tel 0692 580244

Sutton Staithe

This 18th-century, red-brick inn, halfway between a pub and an hotel, has a lovely rural setting right beside Sutton Broad and a patio that gives its patrons a fine view of the many boats. Much of its business is obviously holiday trade, but its decent overnight accommodation also attracts a business clientele during the week. Two pleasant rooms - one with an old tiled floor and a wood-burner, the other carpeted and warmed by an open fire - make up the bar, and here patrons can sample a range of bottled beers as well as a good choice of draught beers including Norwich Mild, Adnams, Ruddles, and Webster's Bitters, with Adnams on cask. Bar food is fairly priced and offers a choice of standard favourites such as meat salads at around £4.15 or lasagne at £4.60; meals can be eaten either in the bar or in the separate Garden Restaurant. Occasional discos offer lively entertainment (the proceeds often going to charity).

Brewery: Free house
Licensees: Cath and Danny Taylor
Opening hours: Summer 11am-11pm; winter 11am-2.30pm, 6-11pm; Sun 12-3pm, 7-10.30pm
Bar food: 12-2pm, 7-9pm
Restaurant: 7-9.30pm; booking necessary
Accommodation: (Price per room) double £49
Children: Welcome in eating area
Credit Cards: AMERICAN EXPRESS®, Access, Visa, Diners

☻ DARBYS
Elsing Road, Swanton Morley, near Dereham NR24 4NY. Tel 0362 637647

Swanton Morley

Originally a 19th-century farmhouse, this attractive red-brick village pub - one of the best in Norfolk - makes families especially welcome; as well as its pleasant garden, it

Brewery: Free house
Licensee: J Carrick
Opening hours: 11am-2.30pm,

boasts not only an adventure playground but also a field where children can let off steam. Farm implements are displayed in a beamed bar with open fire and a background of good quality taped (or, on occasion, live) folk music . A decent wine list and wide selection of draught beers including Adnams Broadside, Woodforde's Wherry and three guest beers are available, as well as a choice of lagers and Stowford Press cider. Meals are imaginative and sensibly priced - dishes including, for example, mushrooms with Stilton and garlic at £ 3.25, beef and Guinness pie at £5.25 or chicken chasseur at £4.95; vegetarian options are always available. For anyone looking for holiday accommodation, the landlord has several self-catering cottages in the village and also offers bed and breakfast at nearby Castle Farm.

6-11pm; Sun 12-3pm, 7-10.30pm
Bar food: 12-2pm, 7-10pm; Sun 12-2pm, 7.30-9.30pm
Restaurant: Times as bar food
Children: Welcome anywhere; children's menu available; adventure playground
Credit Cards: Access, Visa

CHEQUERS
Griston Road, Thompson, near Watton IP24 1PX Tel 0953 83360

Thompson

Run by an enterprising husband and wife team and set on the edge of the village, this long, low, thatched pub, dating from 1500, is a beautiful old building with an attractive garden at the back. Its three beamed bars - where old farm implements find a natural place among a wealth of original features - serve a range of draught beers that includes Fuller's London Pride, Adnams, Bass and one or two guest beers, as well as a fair choice of lagers (some imported), Kingfisher Farm Cider and a good wine list. An extensive and reasonably priced bar food menu caters for all comers and offers a meal in which hot soup (£1.50) might be followed by lasagne (£3.95), steak and kidney pie (£3.75) or sirloin steak (£7.00) and then fruit pie (£1.75). Popular with businessmen and tourists at lunchtime, the Chequers also attracts a good local trade in the evenings.

Brewery: Free house
Licensee: Bob Rourke
Opening hours: 11am-3pm, 6-11pm; Sun 12-3pm, 7-10.30pm
Bar food: 12-2pm, 6.30-10pm; Sun 12-1.30pm, 7-10pm
Children: Welcome anywhere; family room; outdoor play area
Credit Cards: Access, Visa

☺ LIFEBOAT INN
Thornham, near Hunstanton PE36 6LT. Tel 0485 26236

Thornham

A well known, classic pub - though recent enlargements have not altogether added to its charm - this rambling 16th-century inn stands beside a lane running from the village to the sea; as well as a garden, it boasts a quiet courtyard area and a patio with a 100-year-old vine. In the pleasantly old-fashioned bars with their open fires and oil lamps, a large range of imported beers and an extensive wine list, as well as a choice of draught bitters including Adnams, Greene King IPA and Abbot and regular guest

Brewery: Free house
Licensees: Lynn and Nick Handley
Opening hours: 11am-11pm; Sun 12-3pm, 7-10.30pm
Bar food: 12-2pm, 7-10pm (last orders)
Restaurant: 7-10pm (last orders)
Accommodation: (Price per

beers, offer ideal accompaniments to a good, original (deep-fried mushrooms with crab meat at £3.75, fresh salmon at £7.25 and ragout of vegetables at £5.50 are typical examples) and fairly priced selection of dishes which is also served in the restaurant. Overnight accommodation is provided in pine-furnished rooms.

person) single £37.50, double £35
Children: Welcome anywhere; outdoor play area
Credit Cards: Access, Visa, Diners

⚜ THREE HORSESHOES
Warham, near Wells-next-the-Sea NR23 1NL Tel 0328 710547

Warham

No one should miss this classic, 18th-century flint-and-brick Norfolk pub, tranquilly set at the centre of the village with its charming tree-shaded garden. A wonderfully unspoiled interior still retains its stone floors, scrubbed tables, open fires and gas lighting, there are old fruit machines, and the walls are decked with prints and local beer advertisements from bygone days; traditional amusements like pool, darts, dominoes and shove halfpenny are occasionally augmented by an old-fashioned sing-song to the strains of a pianola.Greene King, and Woodforde's beers are offered on draught, togethr with Guinness, and both bar and restaurant serve unpretentious English food at sensible prices - chicken and vegetable pie or lamb casserole at £4.80, and cauliflower cheese at £2.90, for example, perhaps being followed by a rhubarb and apple crumble at £2.20. There is always a vegetarian choice and children's tastes are considered, though there are positively no chips! Overnight accommodation is provided in one single and three double rooms.

Brewery: Free house
Licensee: Iain Salmon
Opening hours: 11am-2.30pm, 6-11pm; Sun 12-3pm, 7-10.30pm
Bar food: 12-2pm, 7-8.30pm
Restaurant: Times as bar food
Accommodation: (Price per person) £17-£21
Children: Welcome except in bar; family room; outdoor play area

---

Fishermans Return, Winterton-on-Sea, *see page 231*

⚜ SARACENS HEAD
Wolterton, near Norwich NR11 7LX. Tel 0263 768909

Wolterton

Housed in a fine, late Georgian building on a lonely road near Wolterton Park, surrounded by open country and boasting both a secluded walled garden and a lovely old courtyard, this well run and sophisticated operation offers relaxed, efficient service. Two bars, comfortably furnished with banquettes and wicker chairs, warmed by open fires and undisturbed by any form of entertainment, feature a range of beers which includes Adnams Bitter and Broadside and Murphy's on draught as well as several bottled varieties - notably Becks, Elephant, Liefmans Raspberry Beer, Grolsch and White Shield - in addition to a choice of ten malts and a superior wine list. Bar meals, though not cheap, represent

Brewery: Free house
Licensee: Robert Dawson-Smith
Opening hours: 11am-3pm, 6-11pm; Sun 12-3pm, 7-10.30pm
Bar food: 12.15-2.15pm, 7.15-9.15pm (approx); Sun 12.15-2pm, 7.15-8.45pm
Restaurant: Times as bar food
Accommodation: (Price per room) double from £45; winter breaks: £65 for double room for two nights

excellent value for money. Imaginative dishes include pigeon with nuts and raisons or lambs' kidneys and rice, both at £4.95. Two pretty bedrooms are provided for overnight guests.

Children: Welcome if well behaved
Credit Cards:
AMERICAN EXPRESS®, Access, Visa

⊕ FISHERMANS RETURN
The Lane, Winterton-on-Sea, near Great Yarmouth NR29 4BN. Tel 0493 393305

Winterton-on-Sea

Home to the local cricket team, this attractive pub - a 300-year-old brick-and-flint Norfolk inn - also welcomes a complete cross-section of customers; families, in particular, are drawn by its position only ten minutes' walk from the beach and the fact that the garden is filled with play equipment in summer. As well as the wood-panelled main bar with its church pew seating and a cosily peaceful smaller bar, a garden room with pool table is open during the summer months (and may be hired for functions). Very good, sensibly priced meals include seasonal daily specials in addition to dishes like a seafood platter with prawns and smoked salmon at £5.25 and a Stilton-topped burger with chips or jacket potato and salad at £4.50. Twenty or more malt whiskies are served, a guest wine is always featured, and draught beers include Adnams Best Bitter and Courage Directors. Surprisingly roomy accommodation is provided in pretty, chintzy bedrooms.

Brewery: Free house
Licensee: John Findlay
Opening hours: 11am-2.30pm, 6-11pm (winter 7-11pm); Sun 12-3pm, 7-10.30pm
Bar food: 11am-2pm, 6-9.30pm (winter 7-9.30pm)
Accommodation: (Price per person) single up to £28, double up to £20
Children: Not permitted inside under 14 years; welcome in garden room in summer

NORTHAMPTONSHIRE

OLDE COACH HOUSE
Ashby St Ledgers, near Rugby CV23 8UN. Tel 0788 890349

Ashby St Ledgers

Behind the creeper-clad, Victorian stone façade of this fine village-centre inn lies a comfortable and atmospheric interior, consisting of several rambling little rooms with standing timbers, oak beams, tiled and stone floors, huge log fires and high-backed winged settles. A well stocked bar boasts Guinness and a good range of ales such as Flowers Original and IPA, Everards Beacon and Old Original, Mitchell's ESB, Jennings Cumberland and Boddingtons Bitter, plus an interesting choice of wines, which may accompany the straightforward selection of bar food on offer - for example, vegetable and Stilton soup for £1.50, venison sausage at £4.50 and chilli for £3.95. Candles and piped classical music make a cosy dining ambience in the main bars while the lively front bar houses the pool table, dart board and table skittles. The large, well tended garden is a popular summer attraction. For those looking for a relaxing overnight stay the inn has six neatly refurbished bedrooms, all with good facilities.

Brewery: Free house
Licensees: Brian and Phillipa McCabe
Opening hours: 12-2.30pm, 7-11pm; Sun 12-2pm, 7-10.30pm
Bar food: 12-2pm, 7-10pm
Accommodation: (Price per person) single from £22.50, double from £38.
Children: Welcome anywhere; own menu available; family room; outdoor play area
Credit Cards: AMERICAN EXPRESS®, Visa

BARTHOLOMEW ARMS
High Street, Blakesley NN12 8RE. Tel 0327 860292

Blakesley

The two cosy beamed bars of this welcoming 18th-century village pub ooze charm and originality. The lively and friendly Public Bar has a nautical theme with a notable model ship collection and various seafaring instruments, while the comfortable Lounge Bar exhibits guns, cricketing memorabilia and numerous rural nick-nacks. Country regulars and locals fill the bars to enjoy the homely pub fare served at lunchtimes which may include broccoli and cheese pie at £3.10, tuna and pasta bake for £3.50 and sausage, egg and chips for £2.60, with a more limited menu on offer in the evenings. Three well kept real ales - Webster's Yorkshire Bitter, Ruddles County and Marston's Pedigree - and Murphy's Stout, plus an excellent range of 70 malt whiskies add an extra appeal as does the large secluded garden, filled with tables and chairs for fine-weather imbibing. For overnight stays there are three well maintained bedrooms. Morning coffee always available.

Brewery: Free house
Licensee: C A Hackett
Opening hours: 11am-2.30pm, 5.30-11pm; Sun 12-3pm, 7-10.30pm
Bar food: 12-2pm, 6-9.30pm; Sun 12-2pm,7-9.30pm
Accommodation: (Price per room) single £18-£20, double £36-£40.
Children: Welcome in back room only; half portions available

🍺 GEORGE AND DRAGON
Silver Street, Chacombe, near Banbury OX17 2JW. Tel 0295 710602

Chacombe

In summer months, colourful flower-filled hanging baskets decorate this fine 17th-century village pub, its mellow sandstone frontage hiding a truly traditional rustic interior. Three rooms with flagstone floors and open fireplaces are adorned with agricultural and domestic implements and furnished with cushioned settles and farmhouse chairs. A music- and electronic-game-free atmosphere lends itself to relaxed dining in both the bars and adjoining restaurant. Bar food is well presented with a good range of fish dishes, including swordfish steak at £5.25 or fish pie for £3.25 and real ale enthusiasts will find Marston's beers - Burton Best, Pedigree and Border Exhibition - and Wadworth 6X on draught. Traditional pub games feature well here with darts, dominoes, shove halfpenny and cards all available for customers to play. Outdoor seating is limited to a secluded small lawned area to the rear of the pub.

Brewery: Free house
Licensee: David Loomes
Opening hours: 12-2.30pm,
5.30-11pm (Fri and Sat 12-11pm);
Sun 12-3pm, 7-10.30pm
Bar food: 12.30-2pm, 6.30-
9.30pm; Sun, to order
Restaurant: Times as bar food
Children: Welcome in side room
and restaurant

🍺 WOOLPACK
St Andrews Lane, Cranford St Andrew, near Kettering NN14 4AQ.
Tel 0536 78256

Cranford St Andrew

The Birds have been at the helm of this 18th-century whitewashed village local for 36 years now, maintaining the traditional and timeless atmosphere that exists beyond its thatched porch. The two simple and peaceful bars, ornamented with various pieces of brass and copper, have wooden beams and open fires, and are thankfully devoid of modern intrusions such as electronic games and piped music. Pub games survive in time-honoured fashion in the form of darts, skittles, dominoes and cards and are housed in a separate bar for all to play. Flowers Original, Whitbread Trophy, Guinness and Tetley Bitter are the real ales dispensed by handpump. Outdoor seating can be found in the very small garden. No food is served.

Brewery: Pubmaster
Licensee: Frank Bird
Opening hours: 10.30am-3pm,
6-11pm, Sun 12-3pm, 7-10.30pm
Children: Welcome in games
room

🍺 RED LION
Main Street, East Haddon, near Northampton NN6 8BU. Tel 0604 770223

East Haddon

Enjoying a peaceful country village location, yet handy for the M1, this neat 17th-century inn of golden stone and thatch draws a mixed clientele into its stylish and comfortable bars and restaurant. A mix of furniture - from old panelled settles to easy chairs - an assortment of antiques, including china, pewter and old prints plus

Brewery: Charles Wells
Licensee: I Kennedy
Opening hours: 11am-2.30pm, 6-
11pm; Sun 12-2.30pm,
7-10.30pm
Bar food: 12.30-2pm, 7-9pm

classical music create a convivial atmosphere in which to appreciate the imaginative home-cooked dishes available from the daily changing menus. Bar snack choices range from stock pot soup at £2.20 and hot croissant with prawns at £4.50 to steak and kidney pie for £6.50 and pasta tossed with prawns and bacon at £5.95, whereas more elaborate restaurant fare may include salmon, bacon and herbs en papillote for £14.25 and chicken Wellington at £12.75. Lemon soufflé pudding at £2.75 and chocolate and banana trifle for £3 feature on the dessert list. Good wines from a comprehensive list and well kept Charles Wells Eagle Bitter, Bombardier, Noggin Keg Bitter and Guinness can be sampled with your meal. Large flower-filled gardens are ideal for fine-weather drinking. Accommodation consists of five comfortable bedrooms.

(except Sun)
Restaurant: 12.30-1.30pm (except Mon), 7-9.30pm (except Sun)
Accommodation: (Price per room) single £29, double £39.
Children: Welcome if eating; half portions available
Credit Cards: AMERICAN EXPRESS®, Access, Visa, Diners

☺ FALCON INN
Fotheringhay, near Peterborough PE8 5HZ. Tel 08326 254

Fotheringhay

B ooking is advisable if you wish to appreciate the quality of the pub food served at this pretty 18th-century stone building, located in front of the village church and near the site of Fotheringhay Castle where Mary Queen of Scots was beheaded. Both the comfortable, traditionally furnished bars, the airy conservatory and, in summer months, the colourful and well tended garden and patio, bustle at mealtimes with customers ordering and tucking into good, imaginative, home-cooked food. Fresh produce is used in creating such main courses as African bobotti for £4.20, carbonnade of beef at £7.90, or rabbit in cider with apples and walnuts for £5.40, with quails' eggs and salmon at £4 and pear with Stilton and walnut dressing for £1.90 as unusual starters. Top marks are also given for the interesting list of 50 wines and the fine range of beers dispensed on handpump - for example, Guinness, Adnams Bitter, Elgood's Cambridge Bitter, Greene King IPA and Abbot Ale, Ruddles County and Best, John Smith's Bitter. Traditional games include darts and dominoes.

Brewery: Free house
Licensee: Alan Stewart
Opening times: 10am-3pm, 6-11pm; Sun 12-3pm, 7-10.30pm
Bar food: 12.30-2pm, 6.45-9.30pm (except Mon); Sun 12.30-2pm, 7-9.30pm
Children: Welcome anywhere
Credit Cards: Access, Visa

Irish Elixir

'Guinness is Good For You' was the slogan of one of the most successful campaigns in advertising history. Launched in 1928, with pictures and words by Rex Whistler and Dorothy L Sayers among others, it made a brew of black stout from Ireland into a household name. The firm originated with Arthur Guinness, who started brewing in Dublin in 1759. Besides fathering some 21 children, he sired Ireland's most famous commercial product and one of the great dynasties of the annals of brewing.

LAMPORT SWAN

Harborough Road, Lamport, near Market Harborough NN6 9EZ.
Tel 060128 555

Lamport

A warm, enthusiastic welcome awaits those who patronise this very popular old coaching inn situated on the edge of the village opposite Lamport Hall. A relaxed atmosphere fills the large main bar which is comfortably furnished, warmed by an open fire and justifiably busy with a diverse clientele seeking out the reliable bar food on offer here. A varied menu features the usual pub favourites as well as reliable dishes such as pea and ham soup for £1.50, carrot and mange tout stir fry at £5.95, cod and prawn Mornay for £4.25, an imaginative range of vegetarian meals and for dessert, treacle sponge or charlotte russe both at £1.95. Booking is advisable if dining in the restaurant. There is a choice of 38 wines, and beers include Bentley's Yorkshire Bitter, Flowers Best Bitter, Whitbread Trophy Bitter and Guinness. A games area is home to a pool table, electronic games and a juke box, while piped music fills the main bar. There is a small garden.

Brewery: Free house
Licensee: F E Jolliffe
Opening hours: 11am-2.30pm, 5.30-11pm; Sun 12-3pm, 7-10.30pm
Bar food: 12-2pm, 7-10pm
Restaurant: 12-2.30pm, 7-9.30pm
Children: Welcome anywhere; family room; half portions available
Credit Cards: Access, Visa

SUN INN

Main Street, Marston Trussell, near Market Harborough LE16 9TY.
Tel 0858 465531

Marston Trussell

An 18th-century whitewashed front hides a newly built pub with 21 modern, hotel-style bedrooms that are popular with businessmen during the week. Good food is the other attraction here. Well presented and value-for-money dishes are served in the comfortably furnished bars or in the separate restaurant. Bar food may include such starters as pea and ham soup for £1.75 and pâté at £2.75, followed by good hearty snacks like red dragon hot pot at £3.85, chicken and ham pie for £4.25, or tagliatelle Bertrano at £3.75. Puddings range from brandy cream roulade and lemon soufflé to fresh fruit Pavlova and at £1.15 they are excellent value. Vegetarians are well catered for. To accompany your meal there is a choice of 60 wines and four real ales - Ansells Best Bitter, Bass, Ind Coope Burton Ale and Tetley Bitter. Games such as darts, pool and various electronic machines are confined to a separate bar. Tables and chairs for summer drinking can be found on the patio.

Brewery: Free house
Licensee: Simon Smith
Opening hours: 11am-3.30pm, 6.30-11pm; Sun 12-3pm, 7-10.30pm
Bar food: 11am-2pm, 7-10pm; Sun 12-2pm, 7-10pm
Restaurant: 12-2pm, 7-9.30pm
Accommodation: (Price per room) single £35, double £40-£45. Children welcome
Children: Welcome anywhere; half portions available
Credit Cards: AMERICAN EXPRESS®, Access, Visa, Diners

BLACK HORSE

Fotheringhay Road, Nassington, near Peterborough PE8 6QB. Tel 0780 782324

Nassington

Summer flowers brighten up the whitewashed façade of this well maintained 17th-century, village-centre inn which enjoys a growing reputation for good home-cooking. Three real ales - Benskins Bitter, Tetley Bitter and Burton Ale - and a list of 35 wines by the bottle are available to accompany the well presented dishes that can be ordered from a varied menu in both the bar and restaurant. Starters may include Arbroath smokies for £2.85 or crespelle at £2.95, followed by pork Marsala at £8.95, poached lemon sole for £8.55, steak and kidney pie for £8.55 and a good range of vegetarian dishes, with apple and sultana pie and chocolate cream cheese pie, both £2.60, for dessert. Two comfortable and smartly decorated dining rooms complete with a stone fireplace and a mix of easy chairs are linked by the bar servery and provide a relaxed atmosphere in which to enjoy the good food. Live music - jazz, rhythmn and blues or rock music - is a regular Sunday evening feature. Outside are both a garden and a patio.

Brewery: Free house
Licensees: Ronald Orchard and Roland Cooke
Opening hours: 12-3pm, 7-11pm; Sun 12-3pm, 7-10.30pm
Bar food: 12-1.45pm, 7-9.45pm; Sun 12-1.45pm only
Children: Welcome anywhere; half portions available
Credit Cards: Access, Visa

☺ SHUCKBURGH ARMS

Main Street, Southwick PE8 5BL. Tel 0832 274007

Southwick

Once the village bakehouse, this unspoilt stone-built and thatched village local has two simply furnished bars with open fires, various horse-brasses and topographical prints. Popular with country regulars who come here to relax in the chatty, music-free atmosphere and drink some of the fine regularly changing real ales - Hook Norton Best Bitter, Timothy Taylor Landlord and Morrells Varsity and Graduate - that are dispensed straight from the cask, or one of the unusual and strong bottled Belgian beers available. Entertainment is provided in the form of traditional pub games, namely darts, dominoes, shove halfpenny, cards, bar billiards and on occasions live folk music, all of which are found in the small bar. On summer weekends you can settle in the large rear garden with a drink and watch the cricket on the adjacent green. No food is served.

Brewery: Free house
Licensee: A Parsons
Opening hours: 11am-2.30pm, 7-11pm; Sun 12-3pm, 7-10.30pm
Children: Not permitted inside

⊜ FOX INN
Carlton Road, Wilbarston, near Corby LE16 8QC. Tel 0536 771270

Wilbarston

Dating in parts from the 14th century, this friendly, unpretentious, village-centre local is popular for the good value pub food served in the relaxed and comfortably furnished split-level Lounge Bar. Standard bar fare includes pâté and toast for £1.50, bean and vegetable pie for £2.75, scampi and chips at £2.60, followed by blackberry and apple pie at £1.10. A more elaborate choice of food and a special Sunday lunch menu are available in the separate dining room. Two real ales are on offer - Marston's Pedigree and Burton Best Bitter - as well as a selection of 12 malt whiskies and more than 20 bottles of wine. A lively games room offers a darts board, skittles, dominoes, cards and some electronic games, while on fine days a game of boules can be played on one of the two outdoor patios. For those looking for a place to stay there are four modern bedrooms, all with good facilities.

Brewery: Marston's
Licensee: A McHarg
Opening hours: 12-2.30pm, 6.30-11pm; Sun 12-3pm, 7-10.30pm
Bar food: 12-2pm, 7-10pm; Sun 1-3pm, advance booking essential
Children: Welcome in the dining room; half portions available
Credit Cards: Access, Visa

NOTTINGHAMSHIRE

⊜ WAGGON AND HORSES
Gypsy Lane, Bleasby, near Southwell NG4 7GC. Tel 0636 830283

Bleasby

Good value pub fare draws customers into this attractive and peacefully located 18th-century village local, where homely dishes may include a range of filled jacket potatoes from £1.75, shepherd's pie and steak and onion pie at £3.50 and chicken curry for £3.25, all served in the two friendly and simply furnished bars, along with four real ales - Theakston XB and Old Peculier, Home Bitter and Mild. A popular feature here are traditional pub games, namely darts, pool, dominoes and cards. Outdoor drinking can be enjoyed on the quiet front patio.

Brewery: Scottish & Newcastle
Licensees: D J Samples and G J Howes
Opening hours: 11am-3pm, 6-11pm; Sun 12-3pm, 7-10.30pm
Bar food: 12-2pm only (except Mon)
Children: Welcome anywhere; outdoor play area

BIRD IN HAND
Main Street, Blidworth, near Nottingham NG21 0QH. Tel 0623 792356

Blidworth

Lovely views across Sherwood Forest can be admired from the one comfortable bar at this unpretentious Victorian village local, which does a brisk trade and offers a friendly welcome to all. Imaginative vegetarian dishes, such as vegetable tikka masala and leek and mushroom crumble, both at £3.75, highlight a short and simple value-for-money

Brewery: Mansfield
Licensee: Ivan Colls
Opening hours: 11am-11pm; Sun 12-3pm, 7-10.30pm
Bar food: 12-2pm, 5.30-8.30pm (except Sun)

menu, where 'early bird' diners can order two meals for the price of one. Mansfield Riding and the stronger Old Baily ales are dispensed by handpump. Other entertainment is catered for in the form of darts, dominoes and cards and occasional musical evenings. In the summer months visitors enjoy the well kept garden with its field and woodland views

Children: Welcome if eating; children's menu available; outdoor play area

ANGEL INN
Bawtry Road, Blyth, near Worksop S81 8HU. Tel 0909 591213

Blyth

This large, medieval, town-centre coaching inn is popular with locals and especially with travellers on the A1 who seek relaxation or a bar snack from the straightforward menu, served in the welcoming and comfortably furnished open-plan Lounge Bar and cosy Snug area, which both have open fires. Six well maintained bedrooms are reasonably priced and make an ideal stopover for those on business or longer journeys. A lively Public Bar with piped music dispenses Hardys & Hansons Kimberley Best Mild and Best Bitter as well as Guinness and houses a dart board, pool table, other games such as dominoes and cards. Morning coffee is always available, on fine days in the spacious rear garden.

Brewery: Hardys & Hansons
Licensee: Peter Wragg
Opening hours: 12-3pm, 6-11pm; Sun 12-3pm, 7-10.30pm
Bar food: 12-2pm, 7-10pm
Accommodation: (Price per person) single £18, double £28.
Children: Welcome anywhere; children's menu available; family room

⊛ BLACK HORSE
Caythorpe, near Lowdham NG14 7ED. Tel 0602 663520

Caythorpe

Unpretentious and unspoilt are words that aptly describe this pretty, white-painted, 17th-century village local, which comprises two old-fashioned bars complete with beams, pictures, plates and a warm and friendly atmosphere, especially in the charming Lounge. The wide-ranging menu offers the usual favourites - mushrooms in garlic, smoked trout with horseradish both for £2.50, mixed grill at £6.50 and fillet steak for £8.50 - plus good home-made daily specials and vegetarian dishes, which can be accompanied by a glass of Shipstone's Bitter or Mild and, on occasions, Tetley Bitter. Darts, dominoes and cards can be played and the secluded garden to one side of the pub is ideal for summer drinking.

Brewery: Shipstone's (Greenalls)
Licensee: Sharon Andrews
Opening hours: 11.45am-2.30pm, 6-11pm; Sun 12-2.30pm, 7-10.30pm
Bar food: 12-2pm, 6-9pm (except Sun)
Children: Not permitted inside

🍺 MARTIN ARMS INN
School Lane, Colston Bassett, near Melton Mowbray NG12 3FD.
Tel 0949 81361

Colston Bassett

Dating from 1700, this fine old village-centre inn not only has a charming interior, beautifully furnished and boasting an excellent collection of pictures, but is rapidly acquiring a reputation for its exceptional cooking. The smoke charcoal grill is a speciality, and the wide range of home-cooked dishes cater for all requirements, from well made sandwiches from £2.50 and beetroot and orange soup at £2.50 to game pie for £7.50 and more imaginative fare such as monkfish in white wine, cream and fennel sauce for £9.95 and unusual vegetarian choices may include tofu with sweet pepper, peanuts and oyster sauce at £5.95. A well stocked bar offers a comprehensive wine list - many served by the glass - and at least five real ales, namely Marston's Pedigree and Border Exhibition, Bass, and Bateman XB and XXXB. There is no piped music, but a pianist occasionally entertains. In the large garden customers are welcome to play croquet.

Brewery: Free house
Licensees: Lynne Bryan and Salvaturi Inguanta
Opening hours: 12-3pm, 6-11pm; Sun 12-3pm, 7-10.30pm
Bar food: 12-2pm, 6.30-9.30pm; Sun 12-2pm only
Restaurant: 12-2pm, 7-9.30pm (except Mon); Sun 12-2pm only
Children: Not permitted inside; outdoor play area
Credit Cards: Access, Visa

🍺 CROSS KEYS
Epperstone, near Southwell NG14 6AD. Tel 0602 663033

Epperstone

A good village 'local' atmosphere is guaranteed at this charming and popular 150-year-old inn, where the three unadorned bars are the scene for lively conversation, a traditional pub game - dominoes, cards or darts, live folk music on Thursday nights and home-cooked meals, especially the pies - cottage, steak and kidney or turkey, all at £3.20 - salads from £3.20 and sirloin steak at £5.50. A lone real ale, Hardys & Hansons Kimberley Classic, is dispensed by handpump, and there are also cask-conditioned Kimberley Best Bitter and Mild, while whisky drinkers have a good range of single malts to choose from. The spacious lawned garden has plenty of seating.

Brewery: Hardys & Hansons
Licensee: Barry Taylor
Opening hours: 11.45am-2.30pm, 6-11pm; Sun 12-2.30, 7-10.30; closed Mon lunchtime
Bar food: 12-2pm, 6.30-9.30pm (except Mon); Sun 12-2pm only
Children: Welcome in family room; children's menu available

🍺 SUN INN
Gainsborough Road, Everton, near Doncaster DN10 5BW. Tel 0777 817260

Everton

Located in the heart of the village, this modest, white-painted 18th-century pub with low beamed ceilings, open fires and various brass and copper artefacts enjoys a friendly country atmosphere within its main bar. Popularity stems from the excellent value of the menu, which may include home-made soups at 90p, steaks from £4.75, good vegetarian

Brewery: Free house
Licensee: Carol Smith
Opening hours: 12-3pm, 6-11pm; Sun 12-3pm, 7-10.30pm
Bar food: 12-2pm, 7-10pm
Children: Not permitted inside

choices such as aubergine lasagne or mushroom stir-fry, home-made apple pie for dessert and a three-course Sunday lunch for only £4.75. Winter evening games include darts, dominoes and cards and piped music fills the bar. Regular ales on draught are John Smith's, Stones Best Bitter, Guinness, and Tetley Bitter. For fine weather there is a choice of either a large garden or a patio for outdoor refreshment.

under 14 years; children's menu available; outdoor play area

⊜ REINDEER INN
Main Street, Hoveringham, near Southwell NG14 7JR. Tel 0602 663629

Hoveringham

Food, wine and beer are taken very seriously at this picturesque 17th-century pub, strategically placed in front of the cricket pitch of a most delightful riverside village. Friendly and entertaining hosts preside over the two beamed bars, furnished with antiques and filled with curios, where discerning evening diners can experience, for starters, cream of parsley, potato and smoked bacon soup at £3.10, or calves liver sautéd in orange juice and Dubonnet for £6.75, followed by duck breast in port and cranberry sauce at £13.90 or baked halibut in lemon cream sauce with prawns for £12.95. Lunchtime snacks are both imaginative and good value for money. Quality wines, unusual whiskies and well kept ales - Marston's Best Bitter, Pedigree and regularly changing guest beers are available to complete your meal. A genuine Public Bar, free of piped music, is home to a variety of traditional games including Shut the Box, Connect 4, cards, and dominoes. There is no garden, but a patio at the front of the pub is popular in summer.

Brewery: Free house
Licensees: Ashley and Lesley Grice
Opening hours: 12-3pm, 5-11pm (Mon 5.30pm); Sun 12-3pm, 7- 10.30pm; closed Mon lunchtime except BHs
Bar food: 12-2pm (except Mon); Sun 12-3pm only
Restaurant: 7-9.30pm (except Mon)
Children: Not permitted in Public Bar
Credit Cards: Access, Visa

⊜ DOVECOTE INN
Moorhouse Road, Laxton, near Newark NG22 0NU. Tel 0777 871586

Laxton

This welcoming 17th-century, red-brick pub is located in England's last remaining open-field village, whose medieval history is explained in the converted stables behind the pub. Two cosy carpeted bars, decorated with local prints and paintings are popular with both tourists and locals alike, who seek out the good honest pub food - beef in Guinness at £5.85, home-made steak and kidney pie for £4.45, chicken curry at £4.75 chilli with fries for £4.95 and hearty open sandwiches from £2.75 - and the well kept Mansfield Riding and Old Baily ales and Guinness and Murphy's stouts that are served here. A lively pool room has electronic games, a juke box and a dartboard. A front terrace near the disused dovecote has tables and chairs for summer days.

Brewery: Free house
Licensees: John and Elizabeth Waters
Opening hours: 11am-3pm, 6.30-11pm; Sun 12-3pm, 7-10.30pm
Bar food: 12-2.30pm, 7-10pm
Children: Welcome in family room; children's menu available; outdoor play area
Credit Cards: AMERICAN EXPRESS®, Visa

⊜ YE OLDE TRIP TO JERUSALEM
Brewhouse Yard, Nottingham NG1 6AA. Tel 0602 473171

Nottingham

Originally a brewhouse for Nottingham Castle and with an 800-year ancestry as a public house, this ancient old inn once accommodated crusaders on their way to the Holy Land. Behind its 16th-century façade, visitors will find a honeycomb of passages, rooms, cellars and a 60-foot chimney, all hewn out of the sandstone rock on which the castle stands. Its long history and olde worlde atmosphere, enhanced by stone-flagged floors, dark wood panelling, open fires and fine old cushioned settles, has made it popular with tourists worldwide, as the vast collection of foreign bank notes on the beams indicates. An interesting range of whiskies and three real ales - Hardys & Hansons Kimberley Best Bitter, Best Mild and Classic, Guinness and Marston's Pedigree - are served. Bar food is limited to a range of popular favourites ranging from filled hot rolls from 80p to giant, filled Yorkshire puds from £2.30. The only pub game in evidence is the unusual and popular Ring the Bull. For fine weather the courtyard and patio have seating.

Brewery: Hardys & Hansons
Licensee: Brian Palethorpe
Opening hours: 11am-3pm (Sat 4pm), 5.30-11pm; Sun 12-3pm, 7-10.30pm
Bar food: 12-2pm only
Children: Not permitted inside

The Church's Sway
Inn signs reflecting the past importance of the Church include the Cross, the Mitre, the Adam and Eve, the Angel. The Salutation commemorates the Annunciation to the Virgin Mary. The Anchor is not always a nautical sign, but can be a Christian symbol of hope. The Star may be the one the three kings followed to Bethlehem and the Seven Stars are the Virgin Mary's crown. The Bell is a church bell and names like the Eight Bells are generally related to a notable local peal. Inns near a church dedicated to St Peter may be called the Cross Keys, which are the saint's keys of heaven and hell, or the Cock, for the one that crowed thrice. The Lamb and Flag was the badge of the crusading Knights Templar (and was later adopted by the Merchant Tailors). The Catherine Wheel is the Emblem of St Catherine of Alexandria, who was much venerated in the crusading period and according to legend was martyred by being broken on a spiked wheel.

⊜ CROSS KEYS
Upton, near Newark NG23 5SY. Tel 0636 813269

Upton

Heavily beamed ceilings, a log fire in winter, and tasteful furnishings, including pews from a local church, characterise this agreeable pub dating back in parts nearly 300 years. Extensive lists of wines by the bottle and glass and a good choice of beers - Marston's Pedigree, Boddingtons Bitter, Bateman XXXB, Brakspear Bitter and Guinness - accompany an interesting selection of home-made dishes from a daily changing blackboard menu. Potted shrimps at £3.25 and egg and prawn mayonnaise for £3.65

Brewery: Free house
Licensee: M Kirrage
Opening hours: 11.30am-2.30pm, 5-11pm; Sun 12-2.30, 7-10.30pm
Bar food: 11.30am-2.30pm, 6-10pm; Sun 12-2pm, 7-10pm
Restaurant: Wed-Sat 7-10pm; Sun 12-2pm

may precede a generous steak and mushroom pie or Normandy pork, both for £4.50, followed by home-made ice-creams and sorbets at £1.50. The old dovecote upstairs serves as the restaurant. Diners are entertained by a piano on Wednesdays and folk is featured on Sundays. The courtyard to the rear makes a pleasant sitting-out area in summer weather.

Children: Welcome in family room and restaurant; half portions available; outdoor play area

---

STAR INN

Melton Lane, West Leake, near Loughborough LE12 5RQ. Tel 0509 852233

West Leake

Also known locally as the Pit House, a name that lingers from the days when cockfights were popular here, this 18th-century, rural village pub has a traditionally furnished and quarry tiled main bar, decorated with various rural implements and a comfortably modernised lounge. As well as the promise of a warm welcome, the Star is noted for well kept Draught Bass and Adnams ales and for the good-value lunchtime cold table that greets customers. An imaginative range of freshly prepared salads accompanies selected meats and fish and a daily home-made hot dish is generally available for £3.25. For the fine weather, there are picnic tables by the lane and in the rear garden.

Brewery: Company Centric
Licensee: Frank Whatnall
Opening hours: 12-2.30pm, 6-11pm; Sun 12-3pm, 7-10.30pm
Bar food: 12.30-2pm (except Sat and Sun)
Children: Welcome in eating area at lunchtime; children's menu available

---

WATERFRONT INN

The Marina, West Stockwith, near Doncaster DN10 4ET. Tel 0427 891223

West Stockwith

A favourite among the boating fraternity, this charming and well refurbished Victorian pub is bustling during the summer months, especially the sunny patio and garden which overlook the picturesque marina on the River Trent. Inside, light and airy rooms with wooden tables, cushioned benches and, in winter, open fires create a relaxed atmosphere in which to appreciate the bar food which is very good value for money - for example, vegetable hot pot for £3.50, lasagne at £3.65, and a Sunday lunchtime Carvery - and a decent range of real ales, such as Adnams Southwold and Extra, Everards Tiger and Old Original and Theakston XB. A separate bar accommodates electronic and traditional games - darts, pool, dominoes, cards and shove halfpenny. The pub can offer camping facilities.

Brewery: Free house
Licensee: Charles Walton
Opening hours: 12-3pm, 7-11pm; Fri and Sat and summer 11am-11pm; Sun 12-3pm, 7-10.30pm
Bar food: 12-3pm, 7-11pm (except Sun and Mon evenings)
Children: Welcome anywhere; family room

SUFFOLK

⊕ SIX BELLS INN
The Green, Bardwell IP31 1AW. Tel 0359 50820

Bardwell

Historic timbers from ships which sank the Spanish Armada were used in the building of this heavily beamed 16th-century coaching inn. Set beside the original highway, the inn is now isolated on the edge of the village of Bardwell, but its rather uninteresting appearance conceals a warm and welcoming interior. The comfortable dining room with its old range and country kitchen atmosphere is the setting, along with the small bar, for some memorable dishes, and the food is a magnet for those who enjoy eating well. Dishes like 18th-century potted shrimps at £3.25 and hot spicy mushrooms at £2.45 make popular starters, with salmon and prawn Thermidor and fondue both offering good value at £9.95. A fabulous selection of wines from all over the world complements the food. Also on sale are Wadworth 6X and Adnams ales. A separate row of motel-style chalets provides eight double rooms, each with a good view, and there is an assault course and a Wendy house behind the inn.

Brewery: Free house
Licensees: Richard and Carol Salmon
Opening hours: 12-2.30pm, 7-11pm, Sun 12-2.30pm, 7-10.30pm
Bar food: As opening hours
Restaurant: Times as bar food
Accommodation: (Price per person) double from £20
Children: Welcome anywhere; outdoor play area
Credit Cards: Access, Visa

⊕ CHEQUERS
23 Bridge Street, Bungay NR35 1JD. Tel 0986 893579

Bungay

The very cosy, cottagey atmosphere in this unassuming 16th-century town-centre pub attracts a mixture of people including a number of regulars. The emphasis is on comfort in the two adjoining rooms which share a bar, and seating comes in dark oak chairs upholstered with tapestry fabric, as well as traditional benches and bar stools. Old wood is much in evidence, with half-panelled walls and a few beams exposed in the centre of the pub. A huge collection of jugs provides great interest, and there are several brasses and coppers on display. Greene King IPA and Guinness are on tap, as well as real ales from Adnams and Bass, and there are four guest ales. The lunchtime-only food is quite simple, and includes dishes like home-made lasagne and curries at £3 to £3.50, and jacket potatoes with fillings at £1.50 to £2.50. On Wednesdays fresh fish also appears on the menu.

Brewery: Free house
Licensee: Victoria Godbold
Opening hours: 12-3pm, 5-11pm (Fri and Sat 11am-11pm); Sun 12-3pm, 7-10.30pm
Bar food: 12-3pm (except Sat and Sun)
Children: Welcome anywhere; outdoor play area

● LINDEN TREE
7 Out Northgate, Bury St Edmunds IP33 1PQ. Tel 0284 754600

Bury St Edmunds

A reputation for well cooked, imaginative food draws people from all over Suffolk to this former railway inn. A conservatory overlooking the glorious shrub-filled garden is the setting for the restaurant, with its twisted cane furniture, pretty pink tablecloths and railed veranda. In the bar you can try starters like tagliatelle verde with prawns and bacon at £2.95 or whitebait for £2.50, followed by choices such as chestnut and vegetable pie for £5.50, and venison haunch steak at £9.95. A separate lunchtime menu is also available. There is a fine wine list, and freshly squeezed orange juice makes an unusual alternative. The two large bars, each with is own quite different character, serve Greene King Rayments Special Bitter and IPA on tap. In the first bar, stripped pine furniture is arranged on a platform skirted by a banister rail, while an eye-catching shelf stretching around the room is crammed with bottles, pictures and ornaments. The second bar provides a relaxing atmosphere with its dark furniture, open fire, books and bay windows. Outside in a paved patio area of the very large landscaped garden tables are spaced well apart for al fresco eating or drinking.

Brewery: Greene King
Licensees: J and L Wise and J Spenser-Ward
Opening hours: 11am- 3pm, 5-11pm; Sun 12-3pm, 7-10.30pm
Bar food: 12-2pm, 6-9.30pm; Sun 12-2pm, 7-9.30pm
Restaurant: Times as bar food
Children: Welcome anywhere; outdoor play area
Credit Cards: Access, Visa

● PEACOCK INN
The Street, Chelsworth, near Hadleigh IP7 7HU. Tel 0449 740758

Chelsworth

In its delightful setting opposite the lovely Chelsworth Bridge, this very old inn - dating back to 1470 - makes a quiet and pleasant haunt to escape to. Real ales from Adnams, Mauldons and Greene King as well as Guinness are on tap in the three rambling bars, and there are plenty of little private places to enjoy a quiet drink or meal. The walls are adorned with pictures and photographs, and highly polished wood, beams and inglenooks complete the comfortable rustic picture. The atmosphere changes on Friday nights when well-known British and visiting American musicians arrive to play modern jazz. The food offers reasonable value, with starters like smoked trout pâté at £3 and seafood pancakes for £4.75, while crab salad comes at £6 and mushroom Stroganoff costs £4.75. There is also a Carvery, and sweets are available at £2.50. Five exceptionally pretty bedrooms are furnished with dusky rose carpets, chintz and pine.

Brewery: Free house
Licensee: Tony Marsh
Opening hours: 11am-3pm, 6-11pm (winter from 7pm); Sun 12-3pm, 7-10.30pm (7-10pm or closed winter)
Bar food: As opening times
Accommodation: (Price per room) single £22-£30, double £40; babies with own sleeping facilities, or children over ten years only
Children: Welcome anywhere, and in back bar when eating

⊜ TROWEL AND HAMMER
Mill Road, Cotton, near Stowmarket IP14 4QL. Tel 0449 781234

Cotton

The Greek owner of this sprawling 14th-century inn in the depths of the countryside relies heavily on his native land for the delicious food he serves. Taramosalata and pitta bread for £2.75, mousaka, £4.75, and kleftika (tender lamb roasted in oregano) at £5.75 are some of the Greek dishes on offer, but less exotic choices such as melon, whitebait and rump steak also feature on the menu. Real ales from Whitbread and Adnams, as well as Greene King Abbot Ale and IPA are on tap, and there is a good selection of malt whiskies. A mixed clientele mingles in the bars, one of which is a large horseshoe-shaped room with inglenook fireplaces and oak panelling. The dining room offers a comfortable, softly lit ambience to relax in over a meal. A very popular feature of this out-of-the-way inn is the swimming pool in the large, grassed garden.

Brewery: Free house
Licensee: George Kattos
Opening hours: 11.30am-2.30pm, 6.30-11pm; Sun 12-3pm, 7-10.30pm
Bar food: 11.30am-2pm, 6-30-10.30pm; Sun 12-2.30pm, 7-10pm
Restaurant: Times as bar food
Children: Welcome anywhere

⊜ CRATFIELD POACHER
Bell Green, Cratfield, near Halesworth IP19 0BL. Tel 0986 798206

Cratfield

There's a very lively atmosphere at this 18th-century country pub where the landlord organises a constant stream of fund-raising activities which pack in the punters. The outside walls of the pub are decorated with murals, while the inside is crammed with thousands of full miniature bottles and stuffed animals which perch on the exposed beams. Greene King IPA and Abbot Ale are on tap in the L-shaped bar, as well as real ales from Adnams, and there are over 50 malt whiskies, ten vodkas and six rums to choose from. Seating is on pine furniture, and an inglenook fireplace adds to the cosiness. Traditional bar food includes seafood platter at £5.60, poacher's pie, £3.85, and various ploughman's from £2.95 to £4.95. The pub is the focus of this pretty village, and the landlord claims to stay open as long as there are people around!

Brewery: Free house
Licensee: Graham Barker
Opening hours: 11am-11pm; Sun 12-3pm, 7-10.30pm
Bar food: As opening hours
Children: Welcome anywhere under parental supervision; outdoor play area
Credit Cards: Visa

⊜ SHIP INN
St James Street, Dunwich, near Saxmundham IP17 3DU. Tel 072873 219

Dunwich

There's a rich seafaring atmosphere in this rambling, low-lying pub due to its position close to the ocean and overlooking the marshes. Set in the heart of what remains of Dunwich - the sea continues to claim the village - the pub goes back to Tudor times with Georgian and Victorian additions. Tourists and country regulars rub shoulders in

Brewery: Free house
Licensee: S J and A Marshlain
Opening hours: 11am-3pm, 6-11pm; Sun 12-3pm, 7-10.30pm
Bar food: 12-2pm, 7.15-9.30pm;

the bar, and enjoy the real ales on tap such as Adnams Bitter and Broadside (Old also served in winter), and Greene King Abbot Ale. Diners can choose from dishes like cauliflower cheese for £3.50 and salad platter with quiche or mackerel at £4.75, and the menu includes various puddings at £1.60. There is a range of malt whiskies, and wines from Adnams. Splendid views across the marshes can be enjoyed from the five comfortable rooms, and an enclosed courtyard and large orchard garden are ideal for those who enjoy sitting outdoors.

Sun 7.15-9pm
Restaurant: Times as bar food
Accommodation: (Price per room) single £19, double £38-£48
Children: Welcome in rooms other than the bar

☻ OLD CHEQUERS
Main Road, Friston, near Leiston IP17 1NP. Tel 072888 270

Friston

L ocally grown vegetables and Aldeburgh fish are used in the creation of first class food at this well known pub/restaurant close to Snape. The large double-fronted corner building has been a pub since 1833, and it offers a spacious country kitchen atmosphere in the single bar where real ales from Adnams at nearby Southwold and two guest beers are on tap. The emphasis is on the food, though, and the very interesting menu includes starters like hot potted shrimps and mushroom and cream cheese pâté for £3.75, and herb crust breast of chicken at £9.95. An extensive wine list and a good range of lagers are also on sale.

Brewery: Free house
Licensee: Old English Pub Co
Opening hours: 11am-3pm, 6.30-11pm; Sun 12-3pm, 7-10.30pm
Bar food: 12-2pm, 7-10pm (except Sun evening in winter)
Children: Welcome lunchtime if eating; half portions available

---

☻ BLACK LION
Lion Road, Glemsford, near Long Melford CO10 7RS. Tel 0787 280684

Glemsford

T hree rooms on different levels with quarry tiled floors and occasional carpets share the same bar at this 15th-century bow-fronted pub with later additions. On tap are Guinness and Greene King IPA and Abbot Ale, and the standard bar food offers good value for money with such favourites as shepherd's pie at £2.25, cheese and onion quiches for £1.75, and lasagne priced at £3.25. This simple, basic pub has a pleasant, welcoming atmosphere, and there is a sheltered beer garden providing a secluded area for those who prefer to sit outside in fine weather.

Brewery: Greene King
Licensees: Anne White and Averil Hemingway
Opening hours: 11am-3pm, 6-11pm; Sun 12-3pm, 7-10.30pm
Bar food: 12-2.30pm, 6.30-9pm; Sun 12-2pm, 7-9pm
Children: Welcome if eating with parents; outdoor play area

Suffolk Heritage
The oldest brewery in Suffolk goes back to the 17th century, when it was the brewhouse of the Swan Inn in the charming seaside town of Southwold. It was taken over in 1872 by George and Ernest Adnams, who built the splendid Victorian brewery on the site. The company is the town's biggest employer and some of the local families go back for several generations in its service, while its handsome Percheron horses convey Adnam's Prize Ales to thirsty Southwold throats.

☻ KINGS ARMS
Old Street, Haughley, near Stowmarket IP14 3NT. Tel: 0449 673298

Haughley

Delicious smells waft down the road from this pretty village pub, tempting in passers by and regulars alike to try the home cooking. Port in wine and cream sauce and Suffolk poacher's pie are well worth sampling, and offer good value at £4.25 and £4.50. For pudding there are choices like spicy apple pie for £1.50 or sorbet at £2. The cream-painted building dates from the early 1500s, and the mossy tiled roof is an absolute mass of flowers at the front. Inside the ceilings are heavily beamed but the three bars are high and light, and furnished with dark upholstered bench seating. The small Public Bar with its row of tables on a linoleum floor is popular with senior drinkers, while the pool room is carpeted and has one or two tables. The walls are decorated with cartoon prints, and there is a collection of lighters. On tap are Greene King IPA, Abbot Ale and Rayments Special Bitter.

Brewery: Greene King
Licensee: M W Wixey
Opening hours: 11am- 3pm,
6.30-11pm; Sun 12-3pm,
7-10.30pm
Bar food: 12-2pm, 7-10pm; Sun
12-2pm, 7-9pm
Children: In Lounge and
restaurant only

☻ BEEHIVE
The Street, Horringer, near Bury St Edmunds IP29 5SM. Tel 0284 735260

Horringer

Smokey, yellowing walls and ceilings, and plenty of nooks and crannies for privacy lend this pub an original, old-fashioned feeling. Wooden seating is quite basic, but the well recommended food is delicious, and the main attraction here. Home-made soup comes at £1.60, and good value main dishes include fresh-dressed Cromer crab for £5.95, vegetable bake at £4.25, and a giant rib steak at £9.95. Draught Guinness, and Greene King IPA and Abbot Ale are served in the bar, as well as six malt whiskies. Outside, the red-brick and flint walls are covered in several different types of creeper, and there is a small secluded courtyard in a neat grassed garden.

Brewery: Greene King
Licensee: G R Kingshott
Opening hours: 11am-3pm,
7-11.30pm; Sun 12-3pm,
7-10.30pm
Bar food: 12-2pm, 7-10pm; Sun
12-3pm
Children: Welcome anywhere;
half portions available
Credit Cards: Access, Visa

SWAN
Low Street, Hoxne, near Eye IP23 5AS. Tel 037975 275

Hoxne

Local characters love this mellow pub - including one nonagenarian who is featured weekly in the local paper - and their friendliness is extended to visitors. Another attraction is the delicious food, which comes well presented and without delay. The bar menu changes daily, and starters can include carrot and orange soup at £1.50, avocado with raspberry and avocado vinaigrette, £2.25, and courgettes in tomato and mozzarella for £2.75. Main meals might be duck

Brewery: Free house
Licensees: Tony and Francis
Thornton-Jones
Opening hours: 12-2.30pm (Sat
12-3pm) 5.30-11pm; Sun 12-
2pm, 7-10.30pm
Bar food: 12-2pm, 7-9pm; Sun
12.30-2pm only

breast in blackberry port, £11.95, or cod and prawn gratin for £5.25; Jamaican bananas, sticky toffee pudding and chocolate terrine can appear on the pudding menu. On tap are real ales from Adnams and Tetley, as well as draught Guinness and Greene King Abbot Ale. This very old, unspoilt pub boasts three inglenook fireplaces which are kept blazing in winter, and large wood-panelled doors with latches. The furniture is pine, and interesting ornaments include lots of copper and china. Outside, the beautiful garden was once a bowling green, and its well kept smoothness is still suitable for croquet. It is in an idyllic setting surrounded by lovely trees and shrubs backed by a river, and the landlord is currently developing the borders to competition standards. The timbered building fronts directly on to the road, but there is a large car park at the rear.

Restaurant: Sat 7-9pm only
Children: In eating areas only; half portions available

⊕ HALF MOON
4 High Street, Lakenheath IP27 9JX. Tel 0842 861484

Lakenheath

A collection of coins and notes adds interest to the two bars at this small 200-year-old pub. Set towards the end of the village, the chunky flint building with a grey-tiled roof has been recently decorated, and its bright, fresh interior is matched by the warmth of the welcome. Greene King XX Mild and IPA, and Guinness King Keg are on tap in the bars, one large with padded carvers and a smaller one with unmatching tables and plain floor. Bar food is of the good plain steak variety at around £6.50, served with chips, mushrooms and peas, but other tastes are also catered for. There is a small garden.

Brewery: Greene King
Licensee: B J Reeve
Opening hours: 11am-3pm, 6-11pm; Sun 12-3pm, 7-10.30pm
Bar food: 12-2pm, 7-9pm (Sat 7-10pm)
Children: Only if eating and only in Lounge Bar

⊕ ANGEL
Market Place, Lavenham CO10 9QZ. Tel 0787 247388

Lavenham

First licensed in 1420, the Angel is still a magnet for the many tourists who explore medieval Lavenham and its environs. Visit this lovely old pub on a Friday - evening or lunchtime - and you are likely to be greeted by live classical music on the piano. The pianist is sometimes there on a Monday too, and when he stops playing piped classical music takes over. The bars are cosy and relaxed, with bookshelves, an enormous double inglenook fireplace that burns a wood fire on colder days, and a mixture of scrubbed pine and dark oak tapestry furniture. China, paintings and teapots are on display. On tap are Ruddles County, Courage Directors, Webster's Yorkshire Bitter and Nethergate Bitter. There are 17 malt whiskies and a good selection of clarets, as

Brewery: Free house
Licensees: Roy Whitworth and John Barry
Opening hours: 11am-3pm, 6-11pm; Sun 12-3pm, 7-10.30pm
Bar food: 12-2pm, 7-9pm
Restaurant: 7-9.15pm
Accommodation: (Price per room) £45-£55
Children: Welcome anywhere
Credit Cards: Access, Visa

well as an extensive range of cooled bottled beers. The delicious bar food offers very good value, and is often praised. Starters like pea and mint soup at £2.25 and garlic mushrooms at £2.75 might be followed by rabbit braised in cider and mustard for £6.25, marinaded lamb chops, or steak and ale pie for £5.50. Tables and chairs are spread outside on the market square frontage, and there is a garden and courtyard at the back. Seven comfortable double rooms with plenty of space are available.

☺ KINGS HEAD
Gorams Mill Lane, Laxfield, near Halesworth IP13 8DW. Tel 0986 798395

Laxfield

Artists and musicians frequent this 15th-century pub-with-no-bar where beer is served straight from kegs in the beer cellar. The pub is steeped in character, with narrow passageways, low ceilings and old wooden seats, but any first impressions of Spartan discomfort are quickly dispelled. The four rooms include one with just three settles and a table around an open wood fire, and two others with old pine furniture and tiled floors. The family room is very comfortable with light furniture and its own separate entrance. Little has changed in well over 100 years, and there is a feeling of having gone back in time. Music often starts up spontaneously in this pub, with someone grabbing the old squeeze box and breaking into song. All Adnams beers are served straight from the barrel, making this a must for real ale lovers. Bar food is strictly home-made, even down to the soup stock, and most dishes are good value at under £5. Choices can include apple, celery and tomato soup at £1.50, and both fresh mussels and hot avocado and Stilton with salad cost £3. Behind the pub a large grassed area is divided into one section for bowls and croquet, and another for seating and eating. Horse-and-carriage rides around the countryside with a stop off for lunch can be arranged at the pub.

Brewery: Free house
Licensees: I C and S L Macehiter
Opening hours: 11am-3pm, 6-11pm; Sun 12-3pm, 7-10.30pm
Bar food: As opening times, with less choice after 9pm
Children: Not permitted inside under 18 years except in family room

---

Paradise Restored

The historic Tolly Cobbold brewery in Ipswich, where Thomas Cobbold began brewing in 1746, was opened to the public in 1992, with a new pub called the Brewery Tap established in the former Cobbold family house. The Cobbolds merged with another Suffolk brewing dynasty, the Tollemaches, in 1957, but 20 years later Tolly Cobbold vanished into the maw of a giant multinational. It re-emerged like Jonah from the whale in 1990 and an independent management has set about reviving old beer recipes, such as Cobnut, and contemplates making Beano Stout again.

⊜ BULL
Hall Street, Long Melford CO10 9JG. Tel 0787 378494

Long Melford

Not surprisingly there are local rumours of a ghost haunting this beautifully maintained 15th-century inn at the end of Long Melford village. No bad vibrations disturb the restful atmosphere, however, and the place positively groans with exposed ceiling and wall beams and period antiques. Greene King IPA and real ales from Adnams are on tap, and there is a small range of malt whiskies. Bar food is basic, with Cumberland sausage and mash and varieties of jacket potatoes at £2.95, and various ploughman's at £3.50. A large attractive courtyard contains wrought-iron furniture, and there are several comfortable double and single rooms.

Brewery: Free house
Licensee: Peter Watt
Opening hours: 11.30am-3pm, 6-11pm; Sun 12-3pm, 7-10.30pm
Bar food: 12.15-2.15pm, 7-9pm
Restaurant: 7-9.30pm
Accommodation: (Price per person) double £40-£100, single £70
Children: In Lounge only after 7pm
Credit Cards: AMERICAN EXPRESS®, Access, Visa, Diners

⊜ JOLLY SAILOR
Quay Street, Orford IP12 2MU. Tel: 0394 450243

Orford

Fish is a speciality at this busy and popular 16th-century pub where it is easy to imagine a past connection with smugglers. Little has been done to alter its comfortably old-fashioned image, and the dining room resembles a cosy 1950s fish café. Only the local catch is used in the kitchen when it is available, and goujons of plaice at £3.40 is a favourite. Cheese, onion and tomato flan costs £2.75, and apple pie and treacle tart at £1.10 are usually on the menu. Guinness and real ales from Adnams are on draught. Three fairly Spartan but spacious rooms are available, and outside there is a superb assault course for children.

Brewery: Adnams
Licensee: Patrick J Buckner
Opening hours: 11am-2.30pm, 6-11pm; Sun 12-2.30pm, 7-10.30pm
Bar food: 12-1.30pm, 6.30-8.30pm; Sun 7-8.30pm
Accommodation: (Price per person) single £16, double £15
Children: Not permitted inside under 12 years and then only in dining room and if eating; outdoor play area

EAST ANGLIA & EAST MIDLANDS Suffolk 251

⊛ THREE TUNS
Main Road, Pettistree, near Woodbridge IP13 0HW. Tel: 0728 746244

Pettistree

Brewery: Free house

Licensees: T J and M C Foubister

Opening hours: 11am-3pm, 7-11pm; Sun 12-2pm, 7-10.30pm

Bar food: 12-2pm, 7-9pm

Restaurant: Sat and Sun 12-2pm, Sun 7-9pm

Children: In conservatory or restaurant when open

Credit Cards: Access, Visa

None of the creature comforts have been stinted on in this rebuilt former coaching inn with its generous deep armchairs and settees, open fires and even home-baked bread straight from the kitchen. Retired and elderly people in particular enjoy these pleasures, but the pub is popular too with families and business people. On tap are brews from Webster's, and Adnams Bitter and Broadside, and there are four low-alcohol bottled beers. Delicious home-cooked bar meals come with obliging service, and include starters like salad Niçoise and smoked salmon pâté at £2.95, and pan-fried shark steak or lemon sole bonne femme at £8.50.

⊛ BUTT AND OYSTER
Pin Mill, near Chelmondiston IP9 1JW. Tel 0473 780764

Pin Mill

Brewery: Tolly Cobbold

Licensee: Dick Mainwaring

Opening hours: May-Sep 11am-11pm; Oct- Apr 11am-3pm, 7-11pm; Sun 12-3pm, 7-10.30pm

Bar food: 12-2pm, 7-10pm; Sun 12-2pm, 7-9.30pm

Children: Welcome in rooms other than bar; family room

Perched right on the edge of the River Orwell, this pub attracts sailors and boat-watchers alike, and wellies are practically *de rigueur*. There's plenty to look at on the river, from the terrace or indoors depending on the weather. This is a real 'spit and sawdust' pub with smoky ceilings and an easy going atmosphere, and sailors can go directly from their boats without worrying about messing the quarry-tiled floors. Real ale from Tetley, plus Tolly Cobbold Mild and Original are on tap, and there is a wide selection of excellent bottled beers. Home-made bar food includes smoked chicken and mushroom pie at £4.50.

⊛ BREWERS ARMS
Rattlesden, near Stowmarket IP30 0RJ. Tel 0449 736377

Rattlesden

Brewery: Greene King

Licensee: Ron Cole

Opening hours: 12-2.30pm (Sat 3pm), 7-11pm; closed Mon; Sun 12-3pm, 7-10.30pm

Bar food: 12-2pm, 7-9pm (except Sun and Mon)

Children: Welcome anywhere; outdoor play area

Bread used to be baked here for the community at the turn of the century when the pub combined both functions, and the old baker's oven is still there, lit from the inside and displaying the old utensils. However, this is just one of several attractions, as the landlord and his wife are inveterate collectors and the shelves and walls are crammed with interesting artefacts and memorabilia. There's a lovely country kitchen atmosphere, enhanced by the well behaved families who frequent it. Food is taken seriously here, and instead of steak and chips meals the menu is health conscious with an imaginative vegetarian choice. Other dishes on the daily changing menu include smoked halibut and trout parcels at £3.50, mousaka and Greek salad at £5.50, and walnut and mushroom chilli for £4.50. Greene King IPA, Abbot Ale and XX Mild are on tap, and there's an excellent wine list including English bottles from a Norfolk vineyard.

⊜ PLOUGH
Rede, near Bury St Edmunds IP29 4BE. Tel 0284 89208

Rede

With its rambling early 17th-century buildings, thatched roof and picturesque setting beside a pond on the village green and surrounded by trees, this is a real picture-book pub. Buried in the depths of the country, it isn't easy to find but well worth the effort when you get there. The two bars are comfortable and warm with red-patterned carpets and red upholstery, hanging pewter and glass mugs adorn the walls, and there are collections of teapots, china and copper to hold the eye. Greene King Abbot Ale and IPA are on tap, and there are six different malt whiskies. The pub is famous locally for its steaks, and other dishes on the bar menu include rabbit in prunes and port at £5.50, and minty lamb for £4.95. Puddings like toffee apple tart, treacle and nut tart and Lovable Lemon all cost £2.25. Tables and chairs outside offer a chance to gaze around admiringly when the weather permits.

Brewery: Greene King
Licensee: B J Desborough
Opening hours: 11am-3pm, 6.30-11pm;Sun 12-3pm, 7-10.30pm
Bar food: As opening hours
Restaurant: Times as bar food
Children: Only if eating
Credit Cards: Access, Visa

⊜ FOX INN
London Road, Shadingfield, near Beccles NR34 8DD. Tel 0502 79610

Shadingfield

A treasure trove of fascinating objects and artefacts blends in well with carved foxes' heads on the mantle shelf and a bright red piano at this one-time slaughter house and butcher's shop. The former turnpike coaching inn, dating back from 1600 and having picked up a ghost or two through the ages, is a collector's dream. Irons, hand tools, agricultural gadgets, bottles and horse memorabilia all vie for shelf and wall space, and the result is extremely colourful and entertaining. Serious drinkers will also enjoy draught Guinness, Adnams Bitter and Broadside, and Old Ale is on tap in winter. The home-made bar food comes in generous portions, and the pub is well known for its mixed grills at £7 and Sunday roasts for £4. Vegetable curry and lasagne and chilli all cost £4, and there are puddings like apple pie, pineapple upside-down pudding and blackberry and apple pancake rolls all at £2. The two bars have natural red-brick walls and very old and solid captain's chairs, and a wood stove in each makes for a cosy effect in winter. Cottage accommodation for six is attached to the pub, and a field at the rear has space for 30 touring caravans and tents. There is also a beer garden in a lovely natural setting.

Brewery: Free house
Licensee: Bidwell Walters
Opening hours: 12-12.30pm, 7-11pm; Sun 12-3pm, 7-10.30pm
Bar food: 12-2pm, 7-11pm (except Wed and Sun evenings)
Restaurant: Times as opening hours
Accommodation: Cottage for six persons £100-£200
Children: Welcome anywhere; half portions available; outdoor play area

BRISTOL ARMS
Bristol Hill, Shotley, near Ipswich IP9 1PU. Tel 0473 787200

Shotley

From its imposing position on a quayside at the end of a peninsula, the Bristol offers splendid views of the River Stour, as well as of the ships going between Harwich and the Continent. The pub is renowned locally for its fresh fish dishes, which come in large well cooked portions. Admiral fish pie at £4.95 and wing of skate served with peas and chips are just two of the fishy choices. An unusually large selection of wines - many from the New World - is stocked, and there is a wide range of foreign beers. On tap are Greene King IPA and Flowers Original, as well as real ales from Tetley and Tolly Cobbold. The atmosphere inside the 16th-century building is warm but busy, and groups often come here for their outings. One long fender-shaped bar serves the surrounding tables, and there is a separate restaurant for the popular food. Tables are ranged on the forecourt overlooking the quay for outdoor eating.

Brewery: Free house
Licensee: M Chaplin
Opening hours: Summer 11am-11pm; winter 11am- 2.30pm, 5.30-11pm; Sun 12-2.30pm, 7-10.30pm
Bar food: As opening hours
Restaurant: 7-10pm only
Children: Permitted in restaurant only and must be over seven years
Credit Cards: AMERICAN EXPRESS®, Access, Visa, Diners

⊜ GOLDEN KEY
Priory Road, Snape, near Saxmundham IP17 1SG. Tel 0728 88510

Snape

The emphasis is on game at this comfortable old pub close to Snape Maltings, but the menu is by no means limited to pheasant and hare. Everything is home-made, and choices might include smoked haddock quiche, spinach and mushroom quiche, or sausage, egg and onion pie all at £4.95, or one of the ham or fish speciality dishes. Adnams Bitter, Old and Tally Ho! are on tap in the beamed bars, where a young county set mixes with retired people and visitors. Outside this white 16th-century pub the garden is alive with flowers in the summer, and there are tables and chairs in an alcove to sit and enjoy the scene.

Brewery: Adnams
Licensee: Max Kissich-Jones
Opening hours: 11am-3pm, 6-11pm; Sun 11am-3pm, 7-10.30pm
Bar food: 12-2.30pm, 6-9.30pm; Sun 12-12.30pm, 7-9.30pm
Children: Not permitted under 14 years inside

CROWN
High Street, Southwold IP18 6DP. Tel 0502 722275

Southwold

Over 300 wines are on sale at this former coaching inn, many of them by the glass, and an extensive range of malt whiskies changes monthly. Adnams Bitter and Broadside are on tap throughout the year, with a seasonal swap between Mild in summer and Old in winter. An adventurous bar menu offers choices like baked avocado in filo pastry filled with nuts and cheese for £3.75, pan-fried pigeon breast flamed in brandy for £4.50, and local cod with Basquaise sauce at £6.95. Puddings like Bakewell tart and

Brewery: Adnams
Licensee: Anne Simpson
Opening hours: 10.30am- 3pm, 6-11pm; Sun 12-3pm, 7-10.30pm
Bar food: 12.15-1.45pm, 7.15-9.45pm; Sun 12.15-1.45pm, 7.15-9.30pm
Restaurant: 12.30-1.30pm,

poached peaches with cream cost £2.75. Two rambling bars with comfortable settles are a meeting place for regulars and town visitors alike, and there are seven simple bedrooms.

7.30-9.30pm
Accommodation: (Price per room) single £35, double £55
Children: Welcome except in Public Bar; family room
Credit Cards: AMERICAN EXPRESS®, Access, Visa

☻ ANGEL HOTEL
Stoke-by-Nayland, near Colchester, CO6 4SA. Tel 0206 263245

Stoke-by-Nayland

There is a mellow, country atmosphere at this 16th-century pub in a very pretty part of Suffolk which attracts many tourists. Comfortable armchairs and tallish wooden tables fill the bars, where Greene King IPA and Abbot Ale are on tap along with real ales from Adnams and Nethergate. Game dishes like guinea fowl with lime sauce at £7.50 feature heavily on the menu, but there are plenty of other choices like smoked salmon and cottage cheese roulade for £5.25, and honey baked bacon at £7.50. Blackberry Pavlova and banana and Baileys brûlée both cost £2.65. An attractive gallery overlooking the dining room leads to six double bedrooms.

Brewery: Free house
Licensee: Peter Smith
Opening hours: 11am-2.30pm, 6-11pm; Sun 12-3pm, 7-10.30pm
Bar food: 12-2pm, 6-9pm; Sun 12-2pm, 7-9pm
Accommodation: (Price per room) double £55
Children: Not permitted under 14 years inside
Credit Cards: AMERICAN EXPRESS®, Access, Visa, Diners

☻ FOUR HORSESHOES
Wickham Road, Thornham Magna, Eye IP23 8HD. Tel 0379 71777

Thornham Magna

The food is the attraction here and people travel for miles to sample its delights. This ancient pub - dating back to 1150 and with the wonderful atmosphere that comes from such a great age - is decorated with hundreds of farm implements and artefacts. Outside a thatched roof over the wide white building looks inviting, while indoors are inglenook fireplaces, dark furniture, exposed beams and a long panelled bar. The majority of people come to eat the good value food, and to try dishes like Provençale Wellington, country grill and lasagne, all for under £5. Profiteroles and hot fudge sundae cost £2.25. Real ale drinkers enjoy beers from Adnams and weekly changing guests, as well as Ruddles County and Webster's Yorkshire. Several malts, brandies, liqueurs and wines are also on sale, with a good choice of bottle beers. There are country views from the pretty bedrooms, and a very well cared for garden.

Brewery: Free house
Licensee: Malcolm Saunders
Opening hours: 10.30am- 3pm, 6.30-11pm; Sun 12-3pm, 7-10.30pm
Bar food: 12-2pm, 6.45-10pm; Sun 12-2pm, 7-10pm
Restaurant: 7-10pm
Accommodation: (Price per room) single £37, double £55; family room available.
Children: Welcome if well behaved; own menu available
Credit cards: AMERICAN EXPRESS®, Access, Visa, Diners

⊜ SWAN
Main Road, Westerfield, near Ipswich IP6 9HA. Tel 0473 251447

Westerfield

Smart and stylish furniture and fittings lend the Swan an unmistakably classy air, and in case anyone forgot its name there are many artistic reminders throughout this pub. Copper jelly moulds, bottles and farm implements blend in well with photos and pictures of swans, and the result is very tasteful and interesting. Wood panels and stained glass discreetly divide the five rooms on different levels which are served by long dark oak bars. A large bay window makes an attractive feature both inside and out, and seating is on comfortable low padded settles and large wooden carvers. Welsh dressers with plates and ornaments are part of the decor, and wall lighting casts a subtle glow over the whole area. Tetley Bitter and Tolly Cobbold Bitter are on tap, as well as Guinness and a real ale from Ind Coope, and there is a good wine list. This is also a popular eating place, and the reasonable prices make for good value. Excellent starters include soup for £1.15 and turkey bites with cheese and garlic filling for £1.65, with main dishes like steak and kidney pie for £4.50, chilli con carne at £3.95. Puddings cost under £2, with choices like toffee, apple and pecan pie, and strawberry cream gâteau.

Brewery: Pubmaster
Licensee: Jean Cobb
Opening hours: 11am-2.30pm, 5.30-11pm; Sun 12-3pm, 7-10.30pm
Bar food: 12-1.45pm, 7-9.45pm
Restaurant: Times as bar food
Children: In restaurant only; own menu available; outdoor play area
Credit cards: AMERICAN EXPRESS®, Access, Visa

⊜ CHERRY TREE
73 Cumberland, Woodbridge IP12 1BJ. Tel 0394 382513

Woodbridge

Food at the Cherry Tree is attractively presented and tasty, but portions are enormous so matching appetites are essential when eating here. Starters like giant mussels and garlic butter for £4.75 and Chinese dim sum at £3.85 set the pace for main courses which might include liver and onions at £5.99 and mixed grill for £8.50, or a giant T-bone steak for £12.99. The central 'island' bar with inglenook fireplace is surrounded by seating, and above it a galleried shelf is crammed with memorabilia. Elsewhere in the comfortable, welcoming bar churns, barrels, books, kitchen utensils and plates make a fascinating display. On tap are Tolly Cobbold Bitter, Tetley Bitter and Flowers Original, and a very broad mix of people come to enjoy them. A large garden seats about 120, and opposite the pub an attractively landscaped garden centre lends beauty to the setting.

Brewery: Pubmaster
Licensee: Mike Gurney
Opening hours: 11am- 3pm, 6-11pm; Sun 12-3pm, 7-10.30pm
Bar food: 12-2pm, 6.30-9pm; Sun 12-2pm, 7-9pm
Children: Welcome anywhere, outdoor play area
Credit cards: Access, Visa

CENTRAL ENGLAND

Buckinghamshire

❖

Derbyshire

❖

Gloucestershire

❖

Hereford & Worcester

❖

Hertfordshire

❖

Oxfordshire

❖

Shropshire

❖

Staffordshire

❖

Warwickshire

❖

West Midlands

❖

BUCKINGHAMSHIRE

⊜ OLD THATCHED
Main Street, Adstock MK18 2JN. Tel 0296 712584

Adstock

Vines grow up the whitewashed walls of this pretty 17th-century, thatched pub set in the centre of the village. The garden is nothing special, but inside chunky oak beams, an inglenook fireplace, thick cushions, carpets and flagstones give the three adjoining rooms a warm and cosy feel. There is a pianola for old-fashioned live entertainment in the evenings and regulars play dominoes or cards while enjoying a beer from a list that includes Ruddles County and Best Bitter, Morrells Best, Hook Norton Best Bitter Webster's and Guinness. There are 24 wines on offer. Typical dishes on the menu are diced chicken, pork and bacon braised with button onions and herbs in red wine (£6.50), chunks of salmon and fillets of sole poached in white wine, tomato and cream (£7.50) or a medley of vegetables bound together in a cheese and tomato sauce (£5.00). Booking is advisable for the restaurant.

Brewery: Free house
Licensee: Ian Tring
Opening hours: 12-2.30pm (Sat 3pm), 6-11pm; Sun 12-3pm, 7-10.30pm
Bar food: 12-2pm, 6-10pm; Sun 12-2.30pm, 7-9.30pm
Restaurant: 7-9.30pm; Sun 12-2pm; Mon-Fri business luncheons 12-1.45pm
Children: In family room only

⊜ OLD SHIP
Cadmore End, near High Wycombe HP13 3PN. Tel 0494 881404

Cadmore End

Dating from the mid-1600s, this unpretentious pub has an attractive setting at the centre of the village. What draws the local regulars and the young, however, is the complete absence of any hint of sophistication. Quite unmodernised and totally unspoilt, this is a pub with no frills attached. Both the bars are basic; in the tap room is a plain table, unprepared and unpolished. The beer comes straight from the barrel, and there is none on draught. If you ask at the bar, they will make a sandwich. As for pub games, there is crib and darts, but no electronic games or juke box. There is no piped musak or live entertainment. For those who wish to enjoy their drink outside, there are benches in the pleasant garden. This is a rarity among pubs today, a place for dedicated drinkers.

Brewery: Brakspear
Licensee: P Plumbridge
Opening hours: 11am- 3pm, 6-11pm; Sun 12-3pm, 7-10pm
Bar food: As opening hours
Children: Not permitted inside

⊕ WALNUT TREE
Fawley, near Henley-on-Thames RG9 6JE. Tel 0491 638360

Fawley

Set in the depths of the countryside a few miles north of Henley, the Walnut Tree draws the crowds during Regatta Week. For the rest of the year it is a delightful, quiet inn on the edge of a peaceful village, with tasteful furnishings in the bars, the restaurant and the two pretty bedrooms. There is a large patio and a spacious garden, in which tea is served on summer afternoons. At the bar there is Brakspear Special and Bitter and Guinness on draught, or bottled Sol from Mexico. Tempting dishes on offer in the bar may include baked stuffed mushrooms and salad at £4.25, steak and kidney pudding at £4.95 or cheese, leek and wine pancake at £4.50. And then there might be a sticky toffee pudding to follow, at £2.40. There is always something for the vegetarian. A good wine list accompanies the extensive menu in the restaurant.

Brewery: Brakspear
Licensees: Ben and Diana Godbolt
Opening hours: 11am-3pm (Sat 11am-11pm); Sun 12-3pm, 7-10pm
Bar food: 12-2.30pm, 7-10pm; Sun 12-3pm, 7-10pm
Restaurant: 12-2.30pm, 7-9.30pm
Accommodation: (Price per room) single £40, double £50.
Children: Welcome in the conservatory
Credit cards: Access, Visa

⊕ CHEQUERS INN
Fingest, near Henley-on-Thames RG9 6QD. Tel 0491 638335

Fingest

The Chequers is an ancient pub deep in the countryside. It may look rather ordinary at first sight but it has a large and lovely garden at the back, and everywhere, both inside and out, there is a feeling of spaciousness. The two bars are comfortable and attractive, with cushioned settles and chairs arranged around tables in front of the open fires and brass blow-lamps, pistols and guns to decorate the walls. Vegetarians are well catered for, with a separate menu in the restaurant (both menus £15, booking necessary), while at the bar there is a wide selection of both cold and hot dishes, including cottage pie at £4.25 or spaghetti Bolognese at £4.95, as well as an extensive range of salads and cheeses (but no sandwiches). Everything is well cooked and beautifully prepared (and the pub holds the Buckinghamshire County Council Hygiene Award). For liquid sustenance there is Scrumpy Jack on offer, while beers include Brakspear Pale Ale Special and Old Ale and Guinness.

Brewery: Brakspear
Licensee: B J Hemmet
Opening hours: 11am-3pm, 6-11pm; Sun 12-3pm, 7-10.30pm
Bar food: 11am-2.45pm, 6-9.00pm; Sun 12-3pm only
Restaurant: 12-2.30pm, 7-9.30pm; Sun 12-2.30pm only
Children: Not permitted inside
Credit cards:
AMERICAN EXPRESS®, Access, Visa

⊜ ROYAL STANDARD OF ENGLAND
Forty Green, near Beaconsfield HP9 1XS. Tel 0494 673382

Forty Green

Hidden as it is behind trees up a narrow country lane, this delightful old pub can easily be missed by those visiting it for the first time. Nevertheless, it is well worth seeking out, not only for its attractive garden and patio, and its opulently furnished bars, but for its outstanding bar food. The salad bar has some 25 home-made salads to choose from each day, and a minimum of 40 cheeses. Cooked dishes might include avocado with crab meat and prawns at £2.50, haddock platter (£5.50), beef and smoked oyster pie (£5.95) or venison pie at £6.50. And strawberries are served all year round. There is Marston's Pedigree Bitter and Owd Rodger, Morland Bitter, Eldridge Pope Royal Oak and Thomas Hardy Country Bitter, and Webster's on draught, as well as bottled beer from Germany, Holland, Mexico and USA. Lagers include Holstein, Kronenbourg, Foster and Carlsberg. There are plenty of comfortable little corners in the four bars and, for summer, an attractive tree-shaded patio in which to sit and enjoy the food and drink on offer.

Brewery: Free house
Licensee: Alan Wainwright
Opening hours: 11am-3.30pm, 5-11pm (Fri and Sat 6pm); Sun 12-3pm, 7-10.30pm
Bar food: 12-2.30pm, 6-10pm; Sun 12-2pm, 7-10pm
Children: In family room only; outdoor play area

⊜ YEW TREE
Frieth, near Henley-on-Thames RG9 6RJ. Tel 0494 882330

Frieth

A huge yew spirals majestically outside this 400-year-old building at the heart of an attractive village. Twice a year, in February and October, the landlord holds a special Austrian festival. It is popular and booking is necessary. All year round Austrian Gosser bottled beer is on offer, as well as Laxton Real Ale, Ringwood Old Thumper, Webster's Yorkshire Bitter and Guinness on draught. Lagers include Carlsberg Tiger and Foster. The bar and the restaurant, part of which is in the conservatory at the back, are most attractively and comfortably furnished in traditional style, with pictures of country scenes hanging on the walls. In winter guests can enjoy their refreshment in front of open fires, in summer out on the patio or in the pretty garden. Dishes range from pork curry, rice and a vegetable for £5.95 to tagliatelle verde at £3.95, with home-made sorbet or hot plum crumble at £2.30, and there is always a vegetarian dish on offer.

Brewery: Free house
Licensee: Franz Müller
Opening hours: 10.30am-3.30pm, 5.30-11pm; Sun 12-3pm, 7-10.30pm
Bar food: As opening hours
Restaurant: 12-3pm, 7-10.30pm; booking necessary
Children: Welcome anywhere; outdoor play area
Credit cards: AMERICAN EXPRESS®, Access, Visa

STAG AND HUNTSMAN
Hambleden, near Henley-on-Thames RG9 6RP. Tel 0491 571227

Hambleden

Colourful hanging baskets and tubs of flowers give a welcoming air to this attractive pub on the main street of a very pretty village. Locals and visitors alike come to imbibe both the friendly atmosphere and the Scrumpy Jack or the Old Luxters Barn Ale, Wadworth Farmer's Glory and 6X, Brakspear Special or Bitter that are on tap in the three bars. Bar meals might include vegetable pâté (£2.30), huntsman's pie (£3.75) or salmon in wine and dill sauce (£8.00), followed by brown sugar meringue or treacle tart. There is a separate restaurant open on Friday and Saturday evenings, for which booking is advisable. Both the bar and the restaurant always have a vegetarian dish on offer without prior notice. There are three plain but clean and adequate bedrooms for overnight stays (but children are not accommodated).

Brewery: Free house
Licensees: Mike and Jane Matthews
Opening hours: 11am-2.30pm, 6-11pm; Sun 12-3pm, 7-10.30pm
Bar food: 12-2pm, 7-9.30pm; Sun 12-2pm only
Restaurant: Fri and Sat 7-9.30pm
Accommodation: (Price per room) single £42.50, double £48.50; children not permitted
Children: Not permitted inside
Credit cards: Access, Visa

SWAN
Ley Hill, near Chesham HP5 1UT. Tel 0494 783075

Ley Hill

The Swan is an old highwaymen's haunt, believed to date from the 1550s. Many a villain met his death on the hangman's gibbet on nearby Jason's Hill after taking a last glass of ale here, and some, so it is said, are still making their presence felt at the bar. Hear the chilling cry of the highwayman on his white charger, says the landlord, and you will know that the spirits here are not all of the alcoholic kind. There is also Young's Special, Marston's Burton Best Bitter and Benskins Best Bitter, as well as Addlestone's cider on tap. The menu includes starters such as tuna and lemon mayonnaise choux puffs (£2.80), vegetarian dishes such as wholemeal noodle and tomato bake (£3.90), favourites like steak and kidney pudding (£4.20) or rump steak (£7.25), and a selection of home-made puddings. It is best to book for the restaurant - the food is good and local regulars, families and business people alike enjoy the friendly atmosphere created by the comfortable furnishings, soft lighting, open fireplaces and old prints of Chesham. Come on Boxing Day and you can watch the game of cricket that traditionally takes place on the green in front of the pub.

Brewery: Ind Coope Retail
Licensee: Matthew Lock
Opening hours: 11am-2.30pm (Sat 3pm), 5.30-11pm; Sun 12-3pm, 7.30-10.30pm
Bar food: As opening hours
Restaurant: 12-2pm, 7-9pm; Sun 12-2pm only
Children: In the restaurant and the Snug only; outdoor play area; own menu available

⊕ RISING SUN
Little Hampden, near Great Missenden HP16 9PS. Tel 0494 488393

Little Hampden

It is not easy to find the Rising Sun, but its setting is just reward for the effort. It is up a country lane, a cul-de-sac, in fact, that ends in a wood and visitors can sit on benches on the grass in front of the pub looking into the trees. Indoors, this 18th-century pub has one large bar and a separate dining room, both of which are patronised by a broad clientele, including retired people from neighbouring villages. On draught there is Adnams, Marston's Pedigree, King & Barnes Broadwood, Wychwood Best Bitter and Addlestone's cider, and there is bottled Murphy's Stout. The menu is imaginative and the food well prepared, if a little pricey. There might be pan-fried calves' liver with sweet and sour blackcurrant sauce, for instance, at £9.25, or trout coulibiac at £8.95. There are also sandwiches and ploughman's lunches, however.

Brewery: Free house
Licensee: Rory Dawson
Opening hours: 11.30am-3pm, 6.30-11pm; Sun 12-3pm; closed Sun evening and all day Mon (except BH lunchtimes)
Bar food: 12.30-2pm, 7-9pm
Children: Welcome anywhere
Credit cards: Access, Visa

⊕ CROWN
Little Missenden, Chesham HP7 0RD. Tel 02406 2571

Little Missenden

This is a traditional, old village pub, quiet and unpretentious but comfortable. The one bar is furnished with cushioned benches and chairs and has a collection of farm implements and horse-brasses displayed along with pictures of bygone village scenes. At the back of the pub there is a pretty, tree-shaded garden, with benches on the lawn and a children's play area. Local regulars and business people come for the Morrells Varsity, Marston's Pedigree and Hook Norton Best Bitter, as well as the Old English cider, that is on tap. The bar food is simple and wholesome, with ploughman's ranging from £2.50 to £3 , depending on the cheese, various sandwiches and salads, and perhaps steak and kidney pie or pasty and salad at £2.50.

Brewery: Free house
Licensee: R How
Opening hours: 11am-2.30pm, 6-11pm; Sun 12-2.30pm, 7-10.30pm
Bar food: 12-2pm (except Sun)
Children: Not permitted inside

⊕ OLD HAT
Preston Bissett, near Buckingham MK18 4LN. Tel 0280 848335

Preston Bissett

A fine old English pub, this one, with a delightfully eccentric landlady. She is a churchwarden and whenever there is a wedding in the church opposite she takes a glass of wine across the road for the bride and groom as they leave. She also organises a harvest festival service each year in the pub, auctioning the produce to raise enough money to buy 5cwt of coal for the all the village pensioners so they can enjoy Christmas. Originally a cottage, the building dates

Brewery: Free house
Licensee: Joan Barlow
Opening hours: 11am-11pm; Sun 12-3pm, 7-10.30pm
Children: At the discretion of the landlady only
Credit cards: Access

back to the 14th century. There is no garden. The bar is one of the two rooms (the other is the landlady's office) and has a pleasantly decrepit feel to it. There are some amusing old photographs of village characters and events that have taken place in the pub, and the games are just the traditional ones like shove halfpenny and dominoes. There is no food, but there is Hook Norton Best Bitter, Courage Best Bitter and Watneys Triple Crown on draught.

⊜ OLD CROWN
Skirmett, near Henley-on-Thames RG9 6TD. Tel 0491 638435

Skirmett

It looks unpromising from the outside, right on a main road, and there is no car park, but you need to book well ahead to get a table here on a Friday or Saturday night. For Mrs Mumby's reputation as a first-class cook has spread far and wide; her menu is unusual and her cooking delectable. Try the deep-fried Camembert and gooseberry conserve (£3.85), the medallions of pork with apricots in cream sauce (£8.95) or the lamb cutlets in rosemary and redcurrant jelly (£9.25). There is always a vegetarian dish on the menu too. This is a place for eating rather than serious drinking, although on tap there is Brakspear Old Ale and Special. The one bar is simply, almost sparsely, furnished, but the garden of this 17th-century house is a quite delightful example of a perfect old English country garden.

Brewery: Brakspear
Licensee: Peter Mumby
Opening hours: 11am-2.30pm, 6-11pm; Sun 12-2.30pm, 7-10.30pm
Bar food: 12-2pm, 7-9.30pm (except Mon)
Restaurant: 7-10.30pm
Children: Not permitted inside

⊜ BULL AND BUTCHER
Turville, near Henley-on-Thames RG9 6QU. Tel 0491 638283

Turville

This attractive pub, next to the village cricket ground, has been trading since 1617, but the building is even older than that. In 1942 an unpleasant episode, remembered by newspaper cuttings on the walls, took place here: the landlord killed his wife, then shot himself. Nowadays it is a hostelry popular with walkers, and its reputation for good food also attracts locals, as well as business trade at lunchtime. The menu features Bull and Butcher pie at £4.95, lasagne at £4.50, and Aunt Nancy's treacle tart or coffee cheesecake at £2.25. No sandwiches, and those concerned for their health will appreciate that none of the food is fried. To wash it down, there is Brakspear Bitter, Special and Old Ale and Guinness on tap, as well as Scrumpy Jack, and bottled Mexican Sol. There are two small bars with tables and chairs, and a pleasant garden with tables and chairs under umbrellas.

Brewery: Brakspear
Licensees: Peter and Anne Hanson
Opening hours: 11am-3pm, 6-11pm; Sun 12-3pm, 7-10.30pm
Bar food: 12-2pm, 6.45-9.45pm
Children: Not permitted under 14 years inside; outdoor play area

⊜ GEORGE AND DRAGON
High Street, West Wycombe, near High Wycombe HP14 3AB. Tel 0494 464414

West Wycombe

West Wycombe village was owned until 1929 by the Dashwood family, most famously the 18th-century eccentric Sir Francis Dashwood, notorious for his connection with the Hell Fire Club. In his day, the George and Falcon was one of eight coaching inns in the village. Now, like the entire village, it is in the care of the National Trust, who are, at the time of writing, refurbishing the whole building. Like most of the buildings in the main street, it faces directly on to the road but has a garden at the back. It is a friendly pub, popular with all sorts. A typical menu at the bar includes seafood platter at £7.25 or lamb cutlets at £5.45 and chocolate roulade (£2.25) or apple tart (£1.95). A good, reasonably priced wine list accompanies the menu, while beers offered on draught are Courage Best and Directors, Guinness and guest ales. Nine bedrooms are furnished in Victorian style.

Brewery: Courage
Licensee: Philip Todd
Opening hours: 11am-2.30pm, 5.30-11pm (Sat 11am-11pm); Sun 12-2.30pm, 7-10.30pm
Bar food: As opening hours (last orders 2pm and 9.30pm, 9.00pm Sun)
Accommodation: (Price per person) single £40, double £50, family £60 plus £7 per child
Children: Welcome in family room; outdoor play area
Credit cards:
AMERICAN EXPRESS®, Access, Visa

WHITE SWAN
High Street, Whitchurch, near Aylesbury HP22 4JT. Tel 0296 641228

Whitchurch

This stone and red-brick building has its origins in the 15th century and once had a thatched roof, although little of this now remains, most of it having been replaced by tiles after a fire. Standing at the edge of the village, the pub has a large garden at the back which is framed by trees and set out with benches and tables. Inside there are two small bar rooms, simply decorated and with oak beams and open coal fires, and an oak-panelled dining room. Paintings, a grandfather clock and a few plates lend character to the rooms, to which a varied clientele adds a lively but friendly atmosphere. Fuller's Chiswick Bitter, London Pride and ESB are on sale, along with a choice of up to 20 malt whiskies. Generous helpings of freshly cooked bar food are served, including vegetable lasagne with salad or chips and chicken tikka with rice and salad, both at £4.75.

Brewery: Fuller's, Smith and Turner
Licensees: Rex and Janet Tucker
Opening hours: 11am-2.30pm, 6-11pm; Sun 12-2pm, 7-10.30pm
Bar food: 12-2pm, 6-9.45pm except BH Mon evenings; Sun 12-1.45pm only
Children: In dining room only

The George and Dragon

As England's patron saint, St George figures frequently on inn signs, often with the dragon whose defeat was his most celebrated exploit. According to the legend, he killed it to save a beautiful princess who would otherwise have been given to the monster. Alternatively, the George is the jewel of the Order of the Garter, England's premier order of knighthood, which was founded by King Edward III in the 14th century. An allied name is the Star and Garter, which also refers to the order's insignia. Or again, the George can mean any of the six kings of that name since the Hanoverian dynasty succeeded to the throne.

⊛ CHEQUERS INN
Kiln Lane, Wooburn Common HP10 0JQ. Tel 06285 29575

Wooburn Common

In the 17th century this was a busy coaching inn. Nowadays it is a high-quality hotel offering weekend breaks and conference facilities as well as a restaurant that boasts excellent food and good value. Its heart is in the bar, the oldest part of the building, which is made up of several rooms, each with numerous private corners among the ancient oak beams and posts. Luxuriously furnished with sofas and armchairs, it is especially snug when the open fire is blazing. Popular with business people and locals alike, the bar serves superb dishes from an enterprising menu. Hot goat's cheese and crispy bacon, for instance (£4.25), or mushroom, onion and Brie soup (£2.25), is followed by pork cutlet with baked apple in cider sauce (£5.25) or poached fillet of salmon with orange and lemon butter (£6.25). In summer you can sit out on the benches on the patio to enjoy a glass of Eldridge Pope Thomas Hardy Country Bitter, Guinness or Hook Norton Best Bitter. The tasteful and high-quality decor is carried throughout the restaurant (palm trees, potted plants and old advertisements) and the 17 bedrooms (pine and patterned wallpapers) to make an establishment of great charm where everything is of the best.

Brewery: Free house
Licensee: Peter Roe
Opening hours: 11am-11pm; Sun 12-3pm, 7-10.30pm
Bar food: 12-3pm, 5-10pm; Sun 12-2.30pm, 7-10pm
Restaurant: 12-2.30pm, 6.30-9.00pm; Sun 12-2pm, 7-9.30pm
Accommodation: (Price per room) single Mon-Thu £72.50, Fri-Sun £62.50; double Mon-Thu £77.50, Fri-Sun £67.50.
Children: Welcome anywhere
Credit cards: AMERICAN EXPRESS®, Access, Visa

DERBYSHIRE

⊕ DRUID INN
Main Street, Birchover, near Matlock DE4 2BL. Tel 0629 650302

Birchover

Behind this pub is a long, high pile of gritstone rocks, including two rocking stones, known as Row Tor Rocks and believed, along with other strange rocks in the area, to have connections with the Druids. Hence the unusual name. It is a rural village inn, dating back to the mid-18th century, where the accent is on food. The one bar is comfortable, well furnished and relaxed, with classical music playing in the background. For warmer days there is a terrace outside set out with tables and benches. A typical bar menu, savoured by a wide-ranging clientele, might include devilled mushrooms at £3.50, honey roast saddle of lamb or Stilton and walnuts with tagliatelle at £7.00, and a Bakewell pudding at £2.30. Prices may seem a little high, but it is all superb. At the bar there are 24 malts on offer and beers on tap are Marston's Pedigree, Ruddles County and Best, Webster's Yorkshire and Murphy's.

Brewery: Free house
Licensee: Brian Bunce and Nigel Telford
Opening hours: 12-3pm, 7-11pm; Sun 12-3pm, 7-10pm
Bar food: As opening hours
Restaurant: 12-2pm, 7-9.30pm (9pm in winter)
Children: Normally only if eating in restaurant, before 8pm; otherwise at landlord's discretion
Credit cards: AMERICAN EXPRESS®, Access, Visa

⊕ YE OLDE GATE INNE
Brassington, near Wirksworth DE4 4HJ. Tel 0269 85448

Brassington

A web of lanes and tracks centres on this limestone village and at its heart is this creeper-clad pub, a building which is believed to date to the early 1600s. Indoors, it is all beautiful old beams, open fires, ancient ranges and scrubbed wooden tables. It is a particularly well run and accommodating establishment, well worth a detour if you are touring in the area, and much patronised by local regulars and business people alike. The bar (it has a good collection of tankards) offers Marston's Pedigree and Merrie Monk, Guinness and, in the winter, Marston's Owd Roger. The home-cooked food is of high quality, and worth every penny. The menu changes regularly but features dishes such as duck pie and Cumberland sauce (£6.25), fidget flan and salad (£5.15) and chocolate brandy roulade and cream (£2.15). There is a delightful beer garden at the back.

Brewery: Marston's
Licensees: Paul and Evie Burlinson
Opening hours: 12-2.30pm (Fri and Sat 3pm); Sun 12-3pm, 7-10.30pm
Bar food: 12-1.45pm (Sat 2pm), 7-9pm (except Mon evening); Sun 12-2pm, 7-8.45pm
Children: Welcome in the dining room if over ten years

YE OLDE NAGS HEAD
Castleton, near Chapel-en-le-Firth S30 2WH. Tel 0433 620248

Castleton

A substantial 17th-century coaching inn, the Olde Nags Head is a weathered limestone building at the centre of this attractive High Peak village, famous for its castle and the nearby caverns. Fresh flowers, log fires and fine antique furniture greet the country regulars and the business people who come to enjoy the bar, the restaurant or the guest rooms. The bar menu is wide-ranging, with one or two surprises featuring between standard pub dishes, and the choice for vegetarians is good. There is a range of open sandwiches from £3.75 to £4.65, while main dishes may include home-made steak and kidney pie and fresh dressed crab Creole at £4.95 or quorn and pasta Provençale at £5.15. The draught beers are Sheffield Cannon Stones Best Bitter and Bass and there is a good range of malt whiskies. The eight bedrooms are neat and comfortable, but there is no garden.

Brewery: Free house
Licensee: Carole Walker
Opening hours: 11am-11pm; Sun 12-3pm, 7-10.30pm
Bar food: 12-2.45pm, 7-10.30pm
Restaurant: 12-2pm, 7-10pm; Sun 12-2.30pm, 7-10pm
Accommodation: (Price per person) single from £39.50, double £26-£42
Children: Not permitted in the bar under 14 years (unless resident)
Credit cards: AMERICAN EXPRESS® Access, Visa, Diners

☻ LAZY LANDLORD
Foolow, near Eyam S30 1QR. Tel 0433 630873

Foolow

The village of Foolow is high up in the Peak District and many of the Lazy Landlord's customers are tourists visiting the National Park. But the pub's highly original menu and superb cooking also draws all sorts of other people in, and from miles around. This is a well run establishment that prides itself on its food. A typical menu might include chicken terrine as a starter (£2.75), then halibut with dill and mushrooms, pork with chives and apricots (both £6.95) or a country lamb casserole at £5.75, followed if you can by sticky toffee pudding (£1.95). There is always something on the menu suitable for vegetarians and for children. The bar has Wards Bitter on tap and an occasional guest beer. It is a late 18th-century building, attractively furnished, with a pleasantly laid-out dining room. There is no garden.

Brewery: Free house
Licensees: D W, M D and K G Holden
Opening hours: 11.30am-2.30pm, 6-11pm; Sun 12-3pm, 7-10.30pm
Bar food: 12-2pm, 6-9.30pm; Sun 12-2pm, 7-9.30pm
Restaurant: Times as bar food
Children: Welcome at lunchtime and in the evening up to 9pm

☻ JUG AND GLASS
Ashbourne Road, Hartington, near Buxton SK17 0BA. Tel 0298 84224

Hartington

In its remote upland setting, the Jug and Glass has breath-taking views over the surrounding Peak District countryside, particularly from the terrace. Inside the old, white-rendered building, at the side of the main Ashbourne-to-Buxton road, the atmosphere is welcoming and cosy,

Brewery: Free house
Licensee: C J Bettaney
Opening hours: 11am-3pm, 7-11pm; Sun 12-3pm, 7-10.30pm
Bar food: 11am-2.30pm,

especially when the open fire is alight in the two carpeted bars. Bass, Marton's Pedigree, Ruddles Best plus a guest beer are on draught. The bar food is fairly standard pub fare with, for instance, smoked mackerel at £1.75, roast chicken at £3.75, sirloin steak at £7.95 and blackcurrant cheesecake at £1.20, but for something special ask for the king-size Yorkshire pudding with a choice of filling.

7-9.30pm; Sun 12-2.30pm, 7-9.30pm
Children: Welcome anywhere

✪ BULL I' TH' THORN
Ashbourne Road, Hurdlow, near Buxton SK17 9QQ. Tel 0298 83348

Hurdlow

In 1472 a solitary farmhouse standing at the side of a Roman road became a hostelry, and for 500 years and more it has given refreshment and shelter to countless travellers in this remote upland area of Derbyshire. It is a fascinating, half-timbered building with a genuine olde worlde atmosphere. Ancient wooden panelling, bearing the dates 1642 and 1742, stone-flagged floors and numerous other features of interest provide a fund of talking points while customers imbibe the draught Robinson's and Guinness. The food is good value, standard pub fare, with prawn cocktail at £1.75, steak and kidney or roast beef at £3.50 and chocolate gâteau at £1.25. There are two separate children's rooms, a large function room for private parties and, for overnight visitors, two double bedrooms. Several games are provided, including pool, and now and then there is a karaoke evening. Outside is a walled beer garden.

Brewery: Robinsons
Licensee: G R Haywood
Opening hours: 11am-3pm, 6.30-11pm; Sun 12-3pm, 7-10.30pm
Bar food: 11.30am-2pm, 6.30-9.30pm; Sun 12-2pm, 7-9.30pm
Accommodation: (Price per room) double £28
Children: In children's rooms only; outdoor play area

✪ BARLEY MOW
Kirk Ireton, near Ashbourne DE6 3JP. Tel 0335 370306

Kirk Ireton

An imposing stone building dated 1683, the Barley Mow is one of those rare, unspoilt old-fashioned village pubs. Its setting is quiet and there is an attractive front garden, with benches and chairs, while inside too the atmosphere is peaceful. The three-roomed bar has old tiled floors and wooden settles. Games are the traditional ones only, including chess, and those wanting live entertainment should go elsewhere. The beer is good: there is Marston's Pedigree, Taylor Landlord and Hook Norton Old Hooky, and there are guest beers too. Also on offer is Thatcher's cider. The bar food is simple but excellent and enjoyed by a clientele that includes local regulars, young people and visitors alike: there are bread rolls and, in winter months, there is a heart-warming soup. For an overnight stay there are five bedrooms, simply furnished in traditional style.

Brewery: Free house
Licensee: Mary Short
Opening hours: 12-2pm, 7-11pm; Sun 12-2pm, 7-10.30pm
Bar food: 12-2pm only
Accommodation: (Price per room) single £20, double £35.75
Children: Permitted at landlady's discretion

🍺 PACKHORSE
Little Longstone, near Bakewell DE45 1MN. Tel 0629 640471

Little Longstone

O nce a local miner's cottage, with origins in the late 16th century, the Packhorse is an especially beautiful pub that has been trading in this tiny and charming village for over 200 years. It has all the atmosphere of an unspoilt, traditional local, with open fires, wooden tables and a collection of old beer taps and postcards, and it is well worth tracking down. The clientele is a broad mix, some coming on alternate Wednesdays for the live blues and folk music, others enjoying the good food. Sensibly priced, the menu is imaginative, including dishes such as Stilton with garlic mushrooms (£2.75), marinated chicken (£6.75) or pasta with Italian vegetable sauce (£4.35) and a steamed pudding (£1.75). There is a good wine list and beers on tap are Marston's Pedigree, Burton Best Bitter and Border Mild. For summer months, there is a delightful, sheltered garden at the back.

Brewery: Marston's
Licensees: Mark and Lynne Lythgoe
Opening hours: 11am-3pm, 5-11pm (Sat from 6pm); Sun 12-3pm, 7-10.30pm
Bar food: 12-2pm, 7-9pm
Restaurant: Thu-Sat 7-9pm
Children: Welcome in one of the bars

🍺 LATHKIL HOTEL
Over Haddon, near Bakewell DE45 1JE. Tel 0629 812501

Over Haddon

S pectacularly situated in the heart of the Derbyshire Peak District, the hotel's main boast is perhaps its glorious and panoramic views over Lathkil Dale from both the bar and the stone-paved terrace outside. But it also offers a good selection of traditional beers and good, home-cooked food in an atmosphere that is relaxed and welcoming. The traditionally furnished Victorian bar sports a series of Rowlandson prints and in winter enjoys open fires. The draught beers include Wards Mild, Thorne Best Bitter and Sheffied Best Bitter. While feasting the eye on the views, you can try the soup at £1.40, steak and kidney pie at £4.50, lasagne at £4.25 or smoked trout at £5.10 and a walnut flan at £1.80, all great value. The four bedrooms are in keeping with the rest of this well run establishment, attractive and comfortable.

Brewery: Free house
Licensee: Robert Grigor-Taylor
Opening times: 11.30am-3pm, 6-11pm; Sun 12-3pm, 7-10.30pm
Bar food: 12-2pm only
Restaurant: 7-9pm (except Sun)
Accommodation: (Price per person) single £32.50-£35, double £30
Children: Welcome at lunchtimes only in the dining room
Credit cards: Access, Visa, Diners

Drays and Horses
A few breweries still engagingly use Shire horses and old-style drays to deliver their beer as in days of yore. The older 18th-century drays were two-wheeled wagons drawn by a pair of horses in tandem, with the driver sitting on one of the barrels. From this developed the more familiar four-wheeled dray, drawn by two horses abreast, with the driver perched up on a high seat. Some of them had open sides, others rails or low boards, while some had iron stanchions supporting chains.
Strong, hardy and weighing in at about a ton, Shire horses trace their ancestry from the vast, tank-like warhorses of the Middle Ages, which rumbled into battle at a ground-shaking trot. Their descendants today rumble through the streets on more peaceful and merciful errands.

⊕ MALT SHOVEL
The Wharf, Shardlow, near Derby DE72 2HC. Tel 0332 799763

Shardlow

Reached down a quiet road on the edge of the village and situated on the banks of a canal, the Malt Shovel, as its name implies, is in an old maltings (making the Marston's Brewery advertisements in the bar particularly apt). It is a popular pub that attracts a broad clientele, including in summer people out and about on the canal. A terrace with tables and chairs overlooks the waterway. Indoors, the bar, central to four carpeted seating areas, serves Marston's Mercian Mild, Guinness and Murphy's on draught and, at lunchtime only, a variety of imaginative and well cooked dishes. Typically, there may be pâté or breaded mushrooms in garlic dip at £1.50, braised liver in sherry and mushroom sauce, lamb in lemon and parsley sauce or beef in red wine with red peppers, all at £4.50, and lemon lush pie at £1.50. There are daily specials and there is always something to suit vegetarians.

Brewery: Marston's
Licensee: Christine Hague
Opening hours: 11.30am-3pm, 5-11pm; Sun 12-3pm, 7-10.30pm
Bar food: 12-2pm
Children: In family room only
Credit cards: Access, Visa

⊕ GEORGE HOTEL
Tideswell, near Buxton SK17 8NU. Tel 0298 871382

Tideswell

This is one of a number of Derbyshire villages where the ancient ceremony of well-dressing is held each summer, in this case towards the end of June. The George is at the village centre, a substantial stone-built inn of 18th-century origin with a small tiled bar that features a rogues' gallery of local regulars, and another larger, carpeted room. There is a pool table, and on Fridays there is live 1960s music. The clientele is a mix of locals, tourists and people who come for the good, unpretentious food served in the dining room. Soup may be on the menu, at £1.20, steak and kidney pie at £4.95, lasagne or lamb with apricots at £4.45, and a toffee, apple and pecan nut pie at £1.25. Draught beers on offer are Hardys & Hansons Kimberley Classic, and Guinness. At the rear of the pub is a walled courtyard for drinking outside and there are four comfortable bedrooms for overnight visitors.

Brewery: Hardys & Hansons
Licensee: E D Norris
Opening hours: 11am-3pm, 7-11pm; Sun 12-3pm, 7-10.30pm
Bar food: 12-2pm, 7-9pm
Accommodation: (Price per room) single £17.50, double £35
Children: Permitted at the landlord's discretion; outdoor play area
Credit cards: AMERICAN EXPRESS® Access, Visa

⊜ WHITE HORSE INN
Woolley Moor, near Ashover DE55 6FG. Tel 0246 590319

Woolley Moor

Panoramic views over the valley of the River Amber, real ale, good food and a dedicated husband-and-wife team make this village local popular with a wide range of people. Some are visitors to nearby Ogston Reservoir and bird sanctuary, others are walking in the hills. The pub's superb setting is well appreciated from the garden, where there are plenty of tables, an excellent children's play area and space for pétanque. Inside, in the tidy, tiled bar, you can enjoy Bass and guest beers, all drawn by handpump, while in the separate dining room you can try the garlic mushrooms (£1.75), followed by the game pie (£3.50), seafood and pasta bake (£4.50), or lamb Isabella (£4.50) and perhaps the lemon and ginger crunch (£1.50), all home-made, well presented and good value for money.

Brewery: Free house.
Licensee: Bill and Jill Taylor
Opening hours: 11.30am-2.30pm; 6.30-11pm; Sun 12-3pm, 7-10.30pm
Bar food: 12-2pm, 6.30-9pm; Sun 12-2.30pm
Restaurant: Times as bar food
Children: Welcome in the restaurant; family room; outdoor play area

GLOUCESTERSHIRE

⊜ KILKENEY INN
Andoversford, near Cheltenham GL54 4LN. Tel 0242 820341

Andoversford

The Kilkeney Inn and Brasserie is a long, low Cotswold stone building that was once a terrace of six cottages. Now it is a place where people come, chiefly, to enjoy a relaxed and informal meal. The imaginative menu, generous portions, good service and attention to detail make it a popular venue for locals and passing trade alike. The menu changes regularly, but typical dishes might include a melon and strawberry cocktail at £2.75, then cheese, sweetcorn and capsicum fritters with a tomato and tarragon sauce at £6.15 (there are always two vegetarian dishes) or roast pigeon at £7.95, followed by a choice of up to ten puddings. There is an extensive wine list and a range of malt whiskies, while draught beers on offer are John Smith's, Ruddles Best, Wadworth 6X and Kilkeney Drovers. Newspapers and magazines are always around for those who feel like a quiet browse. In summer the conservatory makes a very attractive alternative to the spacious bar with its wood-burning stove and there is also a pretty garden with wrought-iron chairs and tables.

Brewery: Free house
Licensee: John Fennell
Opening hours: 11.30am-2.30pm, 6.30-11pm; Sun 12-2.30pm, 7-10.30pm
Bar food: 12-2pm, 7-9.30pm (Sun 9pm)
Brasserie: Times as bar food
Children: Only if taking a meal with adults, and not near bar

FARMERS ARMS
Ledbury Road, Apperley, near Tewkesbury GL19 4DR. Tel 0452 780307

Apperley

The main attraction of this 17th-century pub is probably the fact that it has its own brewhouse, supplying the bar with Mayhem Sundowner and Oddas Light. Customers are welcome to step inside and witness the brewer's art. A guest beer is also usually on sale. However, the pub's popularity with its complete mix of customers is perhaps as much due to the cheerful atmosphere and varied menu. Among the starters are home-made soup at £1.50 and Japanese prawns at £2.50, while the main courses include rack of lamb at £5.50 and chicken and Stilton at £4.95. Ten vegetarian dishes are also served daily, each at £4.50. There are sweets at £1.95, and the pub serves its own blend of Viennese coffee in the morning or with a meal at any time. Situated a mile from the village, the extended, part black-and-white farmhouse is adjoined by a landscaped garden with picnic benches. The bar, amply supplied with beams and oak timbers, is carpeted and offers the choice of armchairs, modern Windsor chairs or cushioned settles. Occasionally, trad jazz musicians perform in the evening.

Brewery: Free house
Licensee: Geoff Adams
Opening hours: 11am-2.30pm, 6-11pm; Sun 12-3pm, 7-10.30pm
Bar food: 12-2pm, 6.30-10pm (Sun from 7pm)
Children: Welcome anywhere; own menu available; outdoor play area
Credit cards: Access, Visa

⊜ BOAT INN
The Quay, Ashleworth, near Gloucester GL19 4HZ. Tel 0452 700272

Ashleworth

Right on the banks of the River Severn, with fields all around, the Boat makes a delightful stopping-off or finishing point for several delightful walks in the area. It is a small, creeper-covered brick building down a tiny lane that ends at the riverside, near the National Trust's 15th-century stone tithe barn, and is an altogether cosy, friendly place, run by the same family for at least 200 years. The one bar is tiny, but comfortable, its flagged floors covered in rush mats, and the original oven still in the fireplace. Outside is a small patio. The Boat is patronised by walkers, families and students, some of whom may play quoits while enjoying Weston's cider, Arkell's 3B, and Smiles Best or Exhibition straight from the tap. There is also Flowers Best, Tetley Bitter and Stowfold Press cider, as well as guest beers. The food is simple and wholesome, just filled rolls for about 75p or ploughman's at about £2.25, made with good bread and home-made chutney. The landlady will lay on special teas for walking parties if requested.

Brewery: Free house
Licensee: Jacquie Nicholls
Opening hours: 11am-2.30pm (Sat 3pm), 6-11pm (winter 7-11pm); Sun 12-3pm, 7-10.30pm
Bar food: As opening hours
Children: Welcome anywhere

⊛ CATHERINE WHEEL
Bibury, near Cirencester GL7 5ND. Tel 0285 740250

Bibury

Bibury is a lovely Cotswold stone village that is popular with visitors. There is a friendly welcome awaiting them in this comfortable, old black-beamed inn, especially cosy when logs are blazing away on the open fire in each of the three rooms. Food is homely and freshly prepared and helpings are generous. There is home-made soup with a roll at £1.75, jumbo sausage and chips at £3.80 or chicken Kiev at £7.25, then treacle sponge or sorbet at £1.50, for example. On tap there is Flowers Original, Marston's Pedigree, Courage Best, Whitbread West Country Pale Ale, Archers Black Jack Porter, plus a guest ale. Alternatively, you can try the sloe gin, or one of a wide range of malt whiskies. Your dog, meanwhile, will be presented with a biscuit.

Brewery: Free house
Licensee: Charles Geoffrey David Palmer
Opening hours: 11am-11pm; Sun 12-3pm, 7-10.30pm
Bar food: As opening hours
Children: Welcome anywhere; own menu available; family room
Credit cards: Access, Visa

⊛ KINGS HEAD
The Green, Bledington, near Stow-on-the-Wold OX7 6HD. Tel 0608 658365

Bledington

This is one of those English idylls: a 16th-century Cotswold stone pub set on a peaceful village green, with ducks pottering about in the stream that gently winds its way across the middle. What is more, Morris dancing takes place here every summer weekend. Indoors, half a dozen times a year, there is jazz and traditional folk music. The food is excellent value for money, all made on the premises and of high quality (booking is advisable). The menu changes regularly but examples are home-made soup (£1.50) or mussels (£3.25), kidneys Bledington (£4.95) or sautéd black pudding (£3.25) and a range of homely puddings. There is an extensive wine list, 24 malt whiskies and on draught Hook Norton, Wadworth 6X, Tetley Yorkshire and a monthly guest beer. The two bars are comfortably arranged with groups of settles and chairs and there is a small quiet garden at the back. The nine bedrooms are bright, airy and well equipped.

Brewery: Free house
Licensees: Michael and Annette Royce
Opening hours: 11am-2.30pm, 6-11pm; Sun 12-2pm, 7-10.30pm
Bar food: Buffet 12-2pm; bar Mon-Sat 7-9.45pm
Restaurant: 7-9.45pm (except Sun)
Accommodation: (Price per room) double £49, single £28
Children: Welcome anywhere; own menu available; at lunchtime restaurant acts as family room

⊛ CROWN INN
High Street, Blockley, near Moreton in Marsh GL56 9EX. Tel 0386 700245

Blockley

Facing on to the main street, the Crown is a long, low building of honeyed Cotswold stone overgrown with creepers. Traffic is not heavy in this steep valleyside town and tables are set out in front for visitors to take their coffee, tea or a drink. This is a beautifully appointed inn and hotel, with comfortable lounges and dining areas and 21

Brewery: Free house
Licensee: John Champion
Opening hours: 11am-3pm, 6-11pm; Sun 12-2.30pm, 7-10.30pm
Bar food: 12-2pm, 7-10.30pm

luxuriously furnished bedrooms. Its appeal lies mainly with the older age group and with business people, rather than the young or families with children. In the brasserie the food is the main attraction, the up-market menu perhaps including Spanish tapas at £4.95 or avocado with Stilton at £3.95, trout with crab sauce or chicken breast at £8.95. In the restaurant the table d'hôte menu is £16.95 for a three-course meal. There are over 70 wines to choose from, while beer offered on draught at the bar includes Bass, Hook Norton and a guest beer.

Restaurant: Times as bar food
Accommodation: (Price per room) single £53-£64, double £36-£70; children not generally welcome
Children: Not encouraged
Credit cards:
AMERICAN EXPRESS®, Access, Visa, Diners

BAKERS ARMS
Broad Campden, near Chipping Campden GL55 6UR. Tel 0386 840515

Broad Campden

A small Cotswold stone building with fields all around, the Bakers Arms is a simple, friendly old pub with just one bar. There are open fires, one at each end, gleaming horse-brasses and a selection of games that includes Tippit, played with an old sixpenny piece. The third Tuesday in the month is Folk Club night. At the bar you can try the wines supplied by a local prize-winning vintner or one of a good selection of whiskies. Beer-drinkers may prefer a bottled German wheat beer or, on draught, a Donnington (brewed near by), Theakston, Hook Norton or one of four guest ales. Bar food is home-made, very tasty and well priced. Dishes include pâté at £1.65, mushroom and nut fettucini at £2.95 or chicken Kiev at £5.50, and perhaps apricot crumble flan. A three-cheese ploughman's costs £3.95. In the summer many local families patronise the large and attractive garden at the back of the pub.

Brewery: Free house
Licensees: Carolyn and Tony Perry
Opening hours: Summer 11.30am-11pm; Sep- Etr 11.30am-3pm, 6-11pm; Sun 12-3pm, 7-10.30pm
Bar food: 12-2.30pm, 6-9.45pm; Sun 12-2.30pm, 7-8.45pm (longer hours in summer and at BHs)
Children: Welcome anywhere except on the bar stools; own menu available; outdoor play area

SEVERN TUNS
Chedworth, near Cheltenham GL54 4AE. Tel 0285 720242

Chedworth

Chedworth is a pretty village in the depths of the Cotswolds, notable for its Roman villa. Visitors to the villa, along with walkers enjoying the beautiful surrounding countryside and local regulars and families, find a warm welcome in this delightful, unpretentious pub that dates back to 1610. There is an attractive beer garden which boasts a stream and waterwheel, while indoors are two bars, cosy and comfortable with open fires in winter, and a games room. Beers on tap are Courage Best and Directors, Beamish, John Smith's and one guest ale. The bar food is down to earth pub fare, but the portions are generous and the service friendly. Ploughman's is £2.85, Cumberland sausage £3.20, fisherman's platter £3.75. A pig roast is held here on August bank holiday.

Brewery: Courage
Licensee: Brian Eacott
Opening hours: 12-3pm (except Mon in winter), 6.30-11pm; Sun 12-3pm, 7-10.30pm
Bar food: 12-3pm (except Mon in winter), 6.30-9pm; Sun 12-3pm, 7-9pm
Children: Welcome in Public Bar and games room; outdoor play area

⊜ WYNDHAM ARMS
Clearwell, near Coleford GL16 8JT. Tel 0594 833666

Clearwells

Eight acres of gardens, woods and lawns surround this 14th-century, white-painted stone building in the centre of the former mining village of Clearwell. All guests, whether staying in the hotel or patronising the restaurant or bar, are free to enjoy the grounds. Plenty of fresh garden produce, especially herbs, is used in the kitchen, as is reflected in the seasonal menu. Ploughman's is offered at £4.95, main dishes such as fillet of lemon sole or pasta dish of the day at £5.95, and home-made sweets at £2.50. There are always several vegetarian dishes. Booking is advised for evening meals. The menu is accompanied by an extensive wine list and at the bar there is a choice of 25 malts for whisky drinkers. Draught beers on offer are Flowers Best Bitter and Bass. The bar is very much a hotel bar, with red and purple carpets, modern wooden furniture and uniformed waitresses. The 17 bedrooms, some old, some modern, are all most attractively decorated and well equipped.

Brewery: Free house
Licensees: John and Rosemary Stanford
Opening hours: 11am-11pm; 7-10.30pm; Sun 11am-3pm, 7-10.30pm
Bar food: 12-2pm, 7-9.30pm
Restaurant: Times as bar food
Accommodation: (Price per person) single from £30, double from £27.50; children welcome
Children: Actively encouraged; own menu available
Credit cards: AMERICAN EXPRESS®, Access, Visa, Diners

⊜ GREEN DRAGON
Cockleford, near Cheltenham GL53 9NW. Tel 0242 870271

Cockleford

A large Cotswold stone building, decorated with hanging baskets, the Green Dragon dates back to the 17th century, when it used to be a cider house. Now it is traditional ales that it specialises in. Usually there are eight racked ales and a guest beer, including Wadworth, Boddingtons, Theakston Old Peculier, Abbot, Smiles, Flowers Bitter and Hook Norton. There are two bars, plain but comfortable with stone walls, wooden floors, rugs, cushioned benches and big open fires. Outside, there are benches on a large paved area in front of the pub. There is also a long room used for parties, conferences, skittles etc, and as a Carvery on Sundays. Sunday is family day, Monday evening jazz night and Wednesday folk night. As for the food, it is first class, and portions are generous (tables should be booked). There is roast beef ploughman's at £4, steak from £10, or pork in cider at £4.75, for instance. It's all delicious.

Brewery: Free house
Licensees: Mr and Mrs Hinton
Opening hours: 11am-3pm, 6-11pm; Sun 12-3pm, 7-10.30pm
Bar food: 11.15am-2pm, 6.15-10pm; Sun 12-3pm, 7-10pm
Restaurant: Times as bar food
Children: In restaurant only, and preferably early evenings only
Credit cards: Access, Visa

NEW INN
Coln St Aldwyns, near Cirencester GL7 5AM. Tel 0285 750651

Coln St Aldwyns

A classic 16th-century coaching inn with a courtyard for the horses and carriages, the New Inn is nowadays popular with walkers, as well as villagers and business people. The whole place is splendidly done up. The bar is smart and spacious, but at the same time homely, with flags and carpets and open wood fires. The 11 delightful bedrooms are imaginatively decorated. Meals at the bar and in the restaurant are exceptional, and a far cry from standard pub fare. It is wise to book. The menu is wide-ranging and unusual, the cooking superb, the quantities generous. There may be soufflé omelette and leaf salad (£4.25), confit of duck and creamed potato (£5.65) or French beans and salmon (£5.45). And there is a good wine list too. Beers on tap include Wadworth 6X, Boddingtons, Hook Norton, Flowers IPA and guest beers. Outside there are tables and chairs on a terrace.

Brewery: Free house
Licensees: Brian and Sandra Evans
Opening hours: 11.30am-11pm; Sun 12-3pm, 7-10.30pm
Bar food: 12-2.30pm, 6.30-9.30pm or 10.30pm; Sun 12-2.30pm, 7- 9.30pm
Restaurant: 7-10pm
Accommodation: (Price per person) single £40, double from £27.50; two family rooms
Children: Welcome in all rooms except the bar; family room
Credit cards: AMERICAN EXPRESS®, Access, Visa

☻ FIVE MILE HOUSE
Gloucester Road, Duntisbourne Abbotts, near Cirencester GL7 7JR. Tel 0285 821432

Duntisbourne Abbotts

A roadside pub in a deeply rural area, this very lovely, overgrown building is some 300 years old and still has the feel of a bygone age about it. Twentieth-century man has been nowhere near it, there are no modern amenities, no piped musak or juke box and certainly no electronic games. The bar and the tap room are enticingly run down, with floors of wood and concrete, furniture basic and ancient. There is a grand old settle in the tap room, where sit the country regulars and the young farmers who make up the pub's clientele, as have the generations before them. There is no bar food, no bottled beer or lager, just Courage Best Bitter on tap. There is a garden, with two bench tables.

Brewery: Courage
Licensee: Ms I M Ruck
Opening hours: 11.30am-2.30pm, 6-11pm; Sun 12-2.30pm, 7-10.30pm
Children: In the tap room only; a family room can be made available

☻ VICTORIA INN
Eastleach Turville, near Cirencester GL7 3NQ. Tel 036785 277

Eastleach Turville

Prints of her majesty keep a watch on things here, though the Victoria has been an inn since the 18th century, long before she came to the throne, and the building itself is about 500 years old. This small, stone-built country pub has a quiet and tranquil setting, with a terrace that overlooks the mellowed Cotswold village. Inside, too, the atmosphere is

Brewery: Arkells
Licensee: Mark Jennings
Opening hours: 11am-3pm, 7-11pm; Sun 12-3pm, 7-10.30pm
Bar food: 12-2pm, 7-9.45pm
Restaurant: 7-9.45pm

relaxed and unassuming, the landlord always ready for a chat. The pub is especially popular at weekends, with day trippers, families and regulars, and meals should be booked. There are two bars, carpeted and roomy, with the restaurant area at one end (it has an extra menu). Bar food is wholesome, standard fare, with home-made soup offered at £1.95, red cabbage casserole at £4.25 or herby sausage and chips at £3.25. The ploughman's is £3.25. Draught beers include Arkell's Kingsdown Ale and 3B.

Children: Welcome anywhere
Credit cards: Access, Visa

➌ WILD DUCK INN
Drakes Island, Ewen, near Cirencester GL7 6BY. Tel 0285 770310 or 770364

Ewen

This is a glorious and imposing range of honeyed Cotswold stone buildings, dated to 1563, in the centre of the village. Glorious, too, inside, for the decor is lavish, yet both warm and welcoming. The salmon pink walls, the old oak beams, the comfy wing chairs, the collection of paintings, prints, plates and ephemera all add up to give the place a rich but cosy feel. The eight bedrooms, four of which have four-posters, are equally elegant, while the garden is secluded and well cared for. At lunchtime the clientele is mainly business, in the evening people who have come to eat. For the Wild Duck specialises in excellent food (and booking is advisable). Fish is a speciality, with between six and ten dishes daily, ranging from £6.95 to £12.95. Similarly, there are eight or so vegetarian dishes on the menu daily, for instance garlic courgettes at £4.95. Or you can opt for shepherd's pie and vegetables at £5.95 or the ploughman's at £3.50. In summer, restaurant meals may be served outside. At the bar, there is the house beer Duck Pond Bitter on tap, plus Wadworth 6X, Guinness, Bass and Theakston Old Peculier. There is a choice of about 30 international bottled beers and a comprehensive wine list.

Brewery: Free house
Licensees: Mr and Mrs H B Mussell
Opening hours: 11am-11pm; Sun 12-3pm, 7-10.30pm
Bar food: 12-2pm, 7.15-10pm; Sun 12-2pm, 7.15-9.45pm
Restaurant: 12-2pm, 7.15-10pm; Sun 12-2pm, 7.15-9.45pm
Accommodation: (Price per room) single £48-£55, double £65-£80
Children: Welcome away from bar area
Credit cards: Access, Visa

➌ PLOUGH
Ford, near Temple Guiting GL54 5RU. Tel 0386 73215

Ford

If you are not already aware that this is the depths of racehorse country when you arrive, you soon will be. The bar is cluttered with all manner of horsey paraphernalia, you may well be drinking next to a group of stable lads and, if there is a race on television, the set in the Public Bar will be showing it. This is a lively, friendly, busy place and there is a good range of traditional games, including the highly skilled jenga, as well as electronic games, in a special games room. The bar serves Donnington bottled and draught (BB and

Brewery: Donnington
Licensee: Andrew Porter
Opening hours: 9am-11pm; Sun 12-3pm, 7-10.30pm
Bar food: 9am-12 (breakfast), 12-2.30pm, 6.30-9.30pm; Sun 9am-12 (breakfast), 12-2.30pm
Accommodation: (Price per person) single £25, double £17.50

SBA) and the menu offers a wide choice of dishes. There may be pan-fried garlic mushrooms at £3.25 and trout at £5.95, while prime steaks range from £7.95 to £11.95 and special salads from £4.50 to £6.50. The flower-decked stone buildings are ranged around a courtyard and there is a large garden in which there is a children's play fort. Three large and pretty bedrooms, one of which has a four-poster bed, are available.

Children: In seating area away from bar only; outdoor play area
Credit cards: Access, Visa

☺ LAMB INN
Great Rissington, near Cheltenham GL54 2LP. Tel 0451 820388

Great Rissington

Tucked down below the road in the middle of the village, this is an attractive, flowery pub with a relaxed and comfortable feel to it. The warm pink walls of the bar show off the collection of old cigarette tins, while 1940s and 50s or classical music plays in the background. There is a memorial to a Second World War plane which crashed in the garden with just one survivor. Hook Norton, Wadworth 6X, Bass Traditional, Theakston, John Smith's and guest beers are on tap, and there is a range of wines from all over the world. The bar food is all home-made with great care, and quantities are good. Starters include soup at £2.25, main courses steak pie at £5.50 or mussels at £3.95. The 12 bedrooms are thoughtfully and attractively fitted out by the landlord himself, even down to the carving of the four-poster beds.

Brewery: Free house
Licensee: Richard Cleverly
Opening hours: 11.30am-2.30pm, 6.30-11pm; Sun 12-2pm, 7-10.30pm. Closed Christmas Day and Boxing Day
Bar food: 12-2pm, 7-9pm or 9.30pm; Sun 12-1.30pm, 7-8.30pm
Restaurant: 7-9pm or 9.30pm; Sun 7-8.30pm
Accommodation: (Price per person) single £30, double £18-£35; children and dogs welcome
Children: Welcome if taking a meal; own menu available
Credit cards: Access, Visa

Early Days

People have been consuming alcohol since far back in prehistoric times and when the Romans invaded Britain they found the inhabitants enjoying ale made without hops, and consequently sweeter than today's beer. Rich Britons also imported wine from the Continent.

Places to drink in the Roman world ranged from the humble wine-shop or taberna (the original 'tavern') to simple inns where you could find a bed for the night, a meal and a change of horse, and on to the grand roadhouses where officials and rich merchants could stay in comfort, enjoy a good meal, stable their horses and find a blacksmith's shop for repairs. In many inns the maids doubled as prostitutes. Guide-lists of inns were available, showing the distance from one inn to the next with little picture-symbols indicating their facilities.

Things were more primitive in Anglo-Saxon England. The English drank ale and mead, made of fermented honey and water. They brewed their own at home and also drank at alehouses. Little is known about these establishments, except that the Church forbade priests to frequent them and the government tried to limit them to one per village. These dingy drinking-dens were the ancestors of the sturdy British pub.

⊜ OLDE INN
Guiting Power, near Stow-on-the-Wold GL54 5OX. Tel 0451 850392

Guiting Power

A long, low building on the edge of the village, warm Cotswold stone walls under a stone-tiled roof, this is a good local with an easy-going, friendly atmosphere. Hangingbaskets brighten the front and there is a garden open to customers. There are flagstones in the Public Bar and the restaurant, carpeting in the Lounge Bar, with cushioned seats and open fires. The restaurant has a collection of Spy cartoons and *Punch* prints. Its menu changes weekly, and many locals come regularly each week to sample it. Scandinavian dishes such as Danish herring (£3.25) and gravlax (£3.50) feature on the bar menu, alongside home-cooked ham at £4.95 or lasagne at £4.50, and a choice of desserts at £1.95. The wine list is good, as is the range of malt whiskies. Beers on tap are Guinness, McEwan Export, Hook Norton, Theakston Best Bitter and a guest.

Brewery: Free house
Licensees: Paula and Ken Thouless-Meyrick
Opening hours: 11.30am-2.30pm, 5.30-11pm; Sun 12-3pm, 7-10.30pm
Bar food: 12-2pm, 7-9pm (Sat 9.30 or 10pm)
Restaurant: Times as bar food
Children: Welcome anywhere; outdoor play area

⊜ DOG AND MUFFLER
Joyford, near Coleford GL16 7AS. Tel 0594 832444

Joyford

N arrow lanes wind their way from Berry Hill to this quiet, rambly Forest of Dean village. The pub is at its centre, a cream-painted building of 15th-century origins, with gardens to back and front. One has an adventure playground, popular with the families that come regularly at weekends (when there are special Sunday roast lunches). A large new extension provides overnight accommodation. There are two bars, comfortably fitted out with new wooden tables and chairs and cushioned window seats. There is also a skittle alley. The bar offers Sheep Dip and Pig Nose whiskies, and has Samuel Smith Old Brewery, Ruddles County and a guest beer on tap. Good, solid helpings of mostly home-made food, typically smoked mackerel at £1.95, scampi at £4.20 or curry at £4.25 and a choice of sweets at £1.85, are available from the bar menu.

Brewery: Free house
Licensees: Dennis and Nadia Brain
Opening hours: Summer 11am-2.30pm, 7-11pm; Sun 12-3pm, 7-10.30pm
Bar food: 12-2pm, 7-10pm
Restaurant: Times as bar food
Accommodation: (Price per person) £15
Children: Welcome anywhere; outdoor play area
Credit cards: Access, Visa

⊜ HUNTERS HALL INN
Kingscote, near Tetbury GL8 8XZ. Tel 0453 860393

Kingscote

T his is a large 16th-century, rural coaching inn at the side of a main road. Locally well-thought of and popular with the young, with families and with older people, as well as the business sector, it does a big trade and is efficiently run, but has all the atmosphere of a good, old-fashioned pub. There are three bars, all with open fires and traditional wooden

Brewery: Free house
Licensee: David Barnett-Roberts
Opening hours: 11am-3pm, 6.30-11pm; Sun 12-3pm, 7-10.30pm
Bar food: 12-2pm, 7-9.45pm

settles and benches, and the draught beers include Old Spot Prize Ale, brewed a mile or two away in the village of Uley, along with Bass, Hook Norton and Wadworth 6X. Meals are served in generous portions from a menu that typically features prawn and Stilton mousse (£3.25), pork and apple casserole (£5.10) or chicken Provençale (£5.5) and a selection of home-made desserts at £2.30. The 11 bedrooms are in a converted stable block, light and airy and modern, and there is a garden for customers' use.

Restaurant: 12-2pm, 7-9.45pm; Sun 12-2pm only
Accommodation: (Price per person) £27-£29
Children: In dining room, Snug and upstairs rooms; outdoor play area
Credit cards:
AMERICAN EXPRESS®, Access Visa, Diners

⏣ OSTRICH INN
Newland, near Coleford GL16 8NP. Tel 0594 833260

Newland

Newland is a small but delectable Forest of Dean village whose vast parish church is known as the Cathedral of the Forest. The village has many fine old buildings, one of them the white-painted, flower-decked Ostrich, a tiny, old-fashioned and unspoilt pub where a friendly welcome is assured. Its one bar is small and cosy, all beams and log fires, carpets and comfortable chairs. Real ales include Marston's Pedigree, Ringwood Old Thumper, Whitbread Boddingtons and two guest beers. There will also be at least 30 malt whiskies in at any one time, and there is a good wine list. Bar food is of excellent quality, with Stilton and walnut pie at £2.50, turbot and monkfish Thermidor at £8.00 or Italian vegetable pie at £6.00 being the sort of dishes people come here to sample again and again. It is wise to book a table ahead. The long, walled garden is charming and there are two comfortable bedrooms, white-walled and beamed.

Brewery: Free house
Licensees: Richard and Veronica Dewe
Opening hours: 12-11pm; Sun 12-3pm, 7-10.30pm
Bar food: 12-2pm, 7-9pm
Restaurant: Times as bar food
Accommodation: (Price per person) single £20, double £15
Children: In the dining room only
Credit cards: Access, Visa

⊜ BATHURST ARMS
North Cerney, near Cirencester GL7 7BZ. Tel 0285 831281

North Cerney

Painted pink like all buildings on the Bathurst Estate, this is an attractive 17th-century stone building on the edge of the village. A little stream flows through the large garden, where visitors can sit at bench tables enjoying either sun or shade. In winter log fires, flagstone floors, traditional pub furniture and a collection of pewter mugs create a warm, comfortable atmosphere in the one large bar. On tap there is Hook Norton, Wadworth 6X, Boddingtons and Archers and the menu includes dishes such as mixed grill at £6.50, mushroom and spinach lasagne with salad at £5.95 or ploughman's at £3.50, all prepared to a high standard. Dressed crab, salmon and fresh fish also regularly feature. This is a well run establishment that is especially busy at weekends. It offers overnight accommodation in six pretty and well equipped bedrooms.

Brewery: Free house
Licensee: BA Trading
Opening hours: 11am-2.30pm (Sat 3pm), 6-11pm; Sun 12-3pm, 7-10.30pm
Bar food: 12-2.15pm; also Sat 6.30-9.15pm and Sun 7-9.15pm
Accommodation: (Price per person) £17.50 to £22.50
Children: Welcome anywhere; outdoor play area; own meals available
Credit cards: Access, Visa

⊜ NEW INN
North Nibley, near Dursley GL11 6EF. Tel 0453 543659

North Nibley

Ruby Sainty has been running this pub for 14 years now and very much her pub it is. It may not look anything special but its setting, down a dead-end lane and surrounded by fields and woodland, is delightful and it has an especially lovely garden that has won several awards. The two bars are welcoming and comfortable, with beams and open fire, and a homely collection of clutter. Quiz competitions are held regularly and there is a good selection of pub games. The Stroud Morris Dancers visit occasionally. Cotleigh WB is brewed specially for the New Inn and also on tap are Cotleigh Tawny, Smiles Best and Exhibition, Theakston Old Peculier, Greene King Abbot Ale, Guinness and occasional guest beers. Alternatively, there is Inch's scrumpy and vintage cider from Winkley in Devon. An extensive range of blended and malt whiskies is also available. The bar food is well prepared and helpings are generous. There is home-made pâté and (in winter) soup at £4.95, for instance, then home-made steak and onion pie at £3.95 and peach and banana crumble at £1.40. There are just two bedrooms, modern and well furnished.

Brewery: Free house
Licensee: Ruby Sainty
Opening hours: 12-2.30pm, 7-11pm; Sun 12-2.30pm, 7-10.30pm
Bar food: 12-2pm, 7.30-9.30pm
Accommodation: (Price per person) £17.50-£20; children not permitted
Children: Not permitted under 14 years inside

⊜ ROYAL OAK
Church Road, North Woodchester, near Stroud GL5 5PQ. Tel 0453 872735

North Woodchester

There is a splendid photomontage in the bar of all the Royal Oak regulars. The building dates back to 1620 and is Listed Grade II but it is a pub that has no pretensions to being anything other than a simple, clean, relaxed and friendly village pub, well-liked by the local people. A quiz evening is held every six weeks and there is a selection of games to play in front of the open fires. For the summer months there is an attractive garden. The food is wholesome and home-cooked, served in ample portions (booking is recommended at weekends). There may be soup at £1.50, for instance, and steak pie or plaice at £4.50 and some hearty puddings at £1.75. The bar serves Wadworth Henry's Original IPA and 6X on draught, along with Bass, Adnams Bitter and Beamish.

Brewery: Free house
Licensees: Mr and Mrs Gale
Opening hours: 12-3pm, 7-11pm; Sun 12-3pm, 7-10.30pm
Bar food: 12-2pm, 7-9.30pm
Children: In the Lounge at lunchtimes only
Credit cards: Access, Visa,

BOAT INN
Lone Lane, Penallt, near Redbrook NP6 4AJ. Tel 0600 712615

Penallt

As its name leads one to expect, the Boat is at the water's edge, on the Welsh bank of the River Wye, which here forms the boundary between Gloucestershire and Gwent. It is situated just east of the village of Penallt, an old low stone building sitting snug against the side of the river valley with a terraced beer garden. It is accessible from the Gloucestershire side of the river, over a footbridge from the pub's car park at the Redbrook football ground. It is a superb location and the beer is excellent, too. There is Theakston Old Peculier and XB, Shepherd Neame Spitfire Ale, Courage Directors Bitter, Wadworth 6X, Thwaites and Wickwar Brand Oak Bitter, all racked. Also on offer are some 25 special country wines, sloe, strawberry, parsnip etc. The plain but delicious fare comes in generous portions: tomato and celery soup (£1.40), perhaps, chilli and rice (£3.50) or turkey and mushroom crumble (£4.00) and a good choice of puddings. All in all, the atmosphere is that of a real, easy-going village pub, with a simple, comfortably furnished bar, and it is popular with young and old, regulars and visitors alike. There is live music, folk, rock, jazz or blues, twice a week.

Brewery: Free house
Licensee: Steffan Rowlands
Opening hours: 11am-3pm, 6-11pm; Sun 12-3pm, 7-10.30pm
Bar food: 12-2.30pm, 6-9.30pm; Sun 12-2.30pm, 7-9.30pm
Children: Welcome anywhere

⊜ DANEWAY INN
Sapperton, near Cirencester GL7 6LN. Tel 0285 760297

Sapperton

Built in 1784 for the men working on the Sapperton Canal tunnel, the Daneway today makes a good base for walks along the banks of the now disused canal. It has a lovely canalside setting and there is a quiet garden, surrounded by trees. Indoors, the dominant feature of the comfortable, carpeted Lounge Bar is a magnificent 16th-century Dutch fireplace, while the Public Bar, with lino floor and wood-burner, is a friendly, traditional-style Snug. The food is standard pub fare and is not made on the premises (steak at £7.95, vegetable lasagne at £3.50, apple pie and ice cream, etc), but the house beer, Daneway Bitter, is excellent. Other draughts include Wadworth 6X (from the wood), Archers Best, Bass, Guinness and a changing guest beer. There is also Blackjack cider from Frampton-on-Severn and fresh lemonade. Games are available in the family room.

Brewery: Free house
Licensee: Mrs J Buggins
Opening hours: 11am-2.30pm (Sat 3pm), 6.30-11pm; Sun 12-3pm, 7-10.30pm
Bar food: 12-2pm, 7-9.30pm; Sun 12-1.30pm, 7-9pm
Children: Welcome in family room

⊜ CROWN
Shuthonger, near Tewkesbury GL20 6EF. Tel 0684 293714

Shuthonger

Flower baskets hang outside this bow-fronted Victorian building at the side of a main road just north of Tewkesbury. Visitors to the town are among those who patronise this friendly, efficiently run establishment, the restaurant of which is leased to a chef who also prepares bar meals of outstanding value. The menu typically includes toasted sandwiches from 90p to £1.25, garlic and herb salmon fillet at £6.95, spinach and mushroom lasagne at £4.25 or (especially recommended) a Crown mega-grill at £7.95. This should set you up for the rest of the day, but for the record, puddings might include home-made sherry trifle at £1.75 or pancakes with maple syrup or black cherry topping at £2. Beers on draught are Bass and Charrington, and there is a good range of malt whiskies. There is a nautical flavour to decor the of the bar, a carpeted room with cushioned seats in the bow windows. There is no garden.

Brewery: Free house
Licensee: Mark Thomas
Opening hours: 11am-3pm, 6-11pm; Sun 12-3pm, 7-10.30pm
Bar food: 12-2.30pm, 7-10pm
Restaurant: Times as bar food
Children: In restaurant only
Credit cards: AMERICAN EXPRESS®, Access, Visa, Diners

⊜ RAM INN
The Street, South Woodchester, near Stroud GL5 5EQ. Tel 0453 873329

South Woodchester

From the patio there is a magnificent view over the valley and in summer months a good chance of spotting a hot air balloon or two floating serenely by. Summer or winter, many people regularly drive miles to this lively and well-liked pub. It is popular with locals, young folk, people out for

Brewery: Free house
Licensees: Mike and Eileen McAsey
Opening hours: 11am-2.30pm, 6-11pm; Sun 12-3pm, 7-10.30pm

a meal and, at weekends, families. Three rooms, with two wood-burners, make up the spacious, L-shaped bar where an excellent range of beers is served. There are often specials on tap, in addition to Boddingtons, Hook Norton, Theakston. Archers, Murphy's, Guinness and Uley. The bar menu is a good mix of such traditional pub fare as cauliflower and haddock (£4.95) and more unusual dishes, like chicken tuna (£5.95). There are always five desserts, and several vegetarian dishes. Everything is excellent value for money.

Bar food: 12-2pm, 7-9pm
Children: Welcome anywhere
Credit cards: Access, Visa
(accepted for bar food only)

HEREFORD & WORCESTER

☻ LITTLE PACK HORSE
High Street, Bewdley DY12 2DH. Tel 0299 403762

Bewdley

Unobtrusive, even uninviting from the outside, this town-centre pub is nevertheless not one to pass by. With its down-to-earth atmosphere and good, filling food, it attracts a cheerful mix of customers. Like all the pubs in the local Little Pub Co chain, it does its own cooking, with the result that its cow pie (Desperate Dan Pie £4.65, for example) will differ slightly from the same dish served in the others. Daily specials are available in addition to the brief but sensibly priced menu, which offers starters such as Pack Horse pâté and vegetable samosa, both at £2.25, and main courses like king-size Cradley Porker sausages and bacon and Stilton pie, both at £3.95. Spotted Dick with custard at £1.75 and liqueur ice cream with cream at £1.95 are among the choice of sweets. Ind Coope Burton and Lumphammer - the latter brewed by Ind Coope for the Little Pub Co chain - and a guest beer are on sale in the single bar, which serves three rooms. Rough white walls and low beams, and pews and settles, preserve the traditional character of this 17th-century pub, which has its own bar game, doubtless even older - Pig's Nose, knocking coins off a porker's snout - and a collection of odds and sods which includes a German bomb.

Brewery: Free house
Licensee: Peter D'Amery
Opening hours: 11am-3pm, 6-11pm (Sat 11am-11pm); Sun 12-3pm, 7-10.30pm
Bar food: 12-2.30pm, 6-10pm; Sun 12-2pm, 7-9.30pm
Children: Welcome anywhere away from bar
Credit cards: AMERICAN EXPRESS® , Access, Visa

☻ FARMERS ARMS
Birts Street, Birtsmorton, near Malvern WR13 6AP. Tel 068481 308

Birtsmorton

A true assortment of customers enjoy the fine ales, dependable home cooking and friendly atmosphere offered by this unpretentious, old-fashioned pub. Tucked away, and by no means easy to find, the 15th-century black-and-white building is an appealing reminder of how country

Brewery: Free house
Licensee: Colin Moore
Opening hours: 11am-2.30pm, 6-11pm; Sun 12-3pm, 7-10.30pm
Bar food: 11am-2.30pm, 6-

pubs used to be. On tap in the two beamed, carpeted bars are Hook Norton Old Hooky and Theakston Old Peculier, along with a selection of malt whiskies. The food includes soup at £1.25 and prawn cocktail at £2.95, steak and kidney pie at £4.60, chicken and vegetable curry at £3.50 and trout and almonds at £5.25, with sweets like fruit crumble at £1.25 and fruit meringue at £1.45 to round off a reasonably priced meal. There is seating and tables on the gravelled area at the front and on the terrace at the back, with its clematis-draped arbour, while the swings in the lawned garden will keep young children happy.

10pm; Sun 12-2.30pm, 7-9.30pm
Children: In dining area only; outdoor play area

FLEECE
Bretforton, near Evesham WR11 5JE. Tel 0386 831173

Bretforton

A living museum of the Victorian era, when it first served as a pub, this striking black-and-white house in fact dates back to the early 14th century. Run by the Taplin family from 1848 until 1977, it was given by Miss Taplin, the last owner, to the National Trust on condition that it remain unchanged. The part-thatched, part-tiled building stands in the heart of an ancient village which was probably a Saxon settlement, and has an orchard-like garden where fruit trees provide shade, as well as a lovingly restored barn. The Taplins' furniture graces the two unspoilt bars, with their Victorian measures, pewter collection and flagstones scored by the symbols of witchcraft. Although usually crowded - tourists and older people provide most of the custom - the whole place remains both evocative of the past and genuinely friendly. On sale are Hook Norton Best Bitter, Uley Pig's Ear and guest beers, including Joe's Fat Bastard, which is specially brewed for the pub. The food embraces a variety of ploughman's lunches at £2.60 to £3, pâté at £3, goujons of chicken at £3.90 and ratatouille lasagne at £3.60. Lemon meringue and apple pie and cream, both at £1.20, are among the sweets on offer.

Brewery: Free house
Licensee: Norman Griffiths
Opening hours: 11am-2.30pm, 6-11pm; Sun 12-2.30pm, 7-10.30pm
Bar food: 12-2pm, 7-9.15pm
Children: Welcome anywhere but prams not permitted; half portions available; outdoor play area

⊛ ROEBUCK
Brimfield, near Leominster SY8 4NE. Tel 0584 711230

Brimfield

The exceptional food - probably among the best offered by any pub in Britain - acounts above all for this well run village pub's enduring popularity. Everything is home-cooked, including the sausages, yoghurt and some of the cheeses, and beautifully presented. As a result, whether a meal is enjoyed in the bar or in the restaurant, where the same or similar dishes are served at a higher price, it is

Brewery: Free house
Licensee: Carole Evans
Opening hours: 12-2pm, 7-11pm; Sun 12-2pm, 7-10.30pm
Bar food: 12-2pm, 7-10pm (except Sun and Mon)
Restaurant: Times as bar food

worth every penny. Among the treats from the blackboard in the bar are soup of the day at £1.70, warm salad of smoked chicken at £6.50, savoury bread and butter pudding with onion and watercress at £5.20 and old-fashioned steak and kidney pie at £6.20. A well mixed clientele frequents the three bars, where panelled walls, classic furniture, Spode china and eye-catching modern canvases confer club-like comfort and style. Ansells Best and Tetley Bitter are served from the keg, and Wood Traditional, a local brew, is on draught. The garden behind the white, 15th-century building has sections given over to herbs and vegetables, and is lit at night. Two double and one twin room are available - all fresh, well furnished and pretty.

Accommodation: (Price per person) single £35, double £30
Children: Welcome anywhere away from bar
Credit cards: AMERICAN EXPRESS®, Access, Visa

☺ COTTAGE OF CONTENT
Carey, near Hoarwithy HR2 6NG. Tel 0432 840242

Carey

A secluded setting in remote countryside has preserved this treasure of a pub more or less intact for over five centuries. Tucked away at the bottom of a plunging sunken lane, the pretty black-and-white building stands amid a handful of other cottages, facing a bridge over a stream. With oak beams overhead and wood underfoot, an assortment of customers relax in the mellow comfort of two bars furnished with ancient settles at farmhouse tables and retaining an open range. On sale are Bass Real Ale and Hook Norton Best and Old Hooky, Stowford Press, Old Rosie and Scrumpy Jack ciders, bottled beers and lagers from Kenya and Mexico and a choice of malt whiskies. Good value for money, the food includes starters like avocado and strawberry vinaigrette at £1.95 and king prawns and ginger butter at £3.75, while typical main courses are lamb, rosemary, redcurrant and apple pie, sweet and sour pork and baked trout with melon and dill, each at £4.50. Orange and lemon cheesecake and passion cake, both at £1.95, are among the sweets on offer. Behind the pub, picnic tables are set out in the sloping garden, while at the front there is a paved area with further seating. Three appropriately cottagey double rooms are available for either one or two people.

Brewery: Free house
Licensee: Mike Wainford
Opening hours: 12-2.30pm, 7-11pm; Sun 12-3pm, 7-10.30pm
Bar food: Generally as opening hours, but times vary according to demand
Accommodation: (Price per room) single £30, double £45
Children: Welcome anywhere but preferably not after 9pm
Credit cards: AMERICAN EXPRESS®, Access, Visa

☺ MUG HOUSE
Claines Lane, Claines, near Worcester WR3 7RN. Tel 0905 56649

Claines

Eight hundred years old and unusual in standing in a churchyard, this handsome brick and timber pub further benefits from a large garden with a view of the Malvern Hills. A magnet for tourists in summer and used by regulars all

Brewery: Banks's
Licensee: John Adkins
Opening hours: 11am-3pm, 5-11pm; Sun 12-3pm, 7-10.30pm

year round, it offers the choice of three bars. There is a quarry-tiled Snug with cushioned church pews, a wooden-floored smoke-room and a bright, carpeted lounge looking on to fields and with a painting of the pub in 1745 along an entire wall. On offer are Banks's Bitter and Mild and a selection of malt whiskies. The basic fare includes a variety of ploughman's lunches at £2.50 to £3, jumbo sausages and ham and eggs, both at £3.25 and lasagne at £3.95, while at 80p a basket of chips makes a cheap but filling snack. A jazz band occasionally plays in the evening, and for families using the garden there is a climbing frame to keep lively youngsters occupied.

Bar food: 11am-3pm (except Sun and Mon)
Children: In Snug only; outdoor play area

⊛ PANDY INN
Dorstone, near Hay-on-Wye HR3 6AN. Tel 0981 550273

Dorstone

Reputedly the oldest pub in the county and perhaps in Britain, this pub was certainly among the first to be licensed. Built in 1185, the pleasant, white-painted house fronts a quiet road in the centre of the village and has a garden with seating. Low, dark beams, a flagstone floor, sturdy furniture and simple decoration of hops and horse-brasses lend a plain but friendly stamp to the single bar. Beer drinkers among the mix of customers are catered for by Bass, Hook Norton Best and a guest ale - either Charles Wells Eagle IPA or Wye Valley Hereford Supreme. There is a good choice of malt and Irish whiskies and the pub sells its own-label wines, supplied by Tanners. Sensibly priced and in most cases prepared on the premises, the food includes fresh sardines at £3.25, home-made hummus at £2.65, wild rabbit pie at £5.25, pan-fried trout at £6.35 and honey-roast duck at £9.25. The sweets, all at £1.95, include lemon brûlée, local sheep's milk ice cream and fruit pie in season. A ceilidh band and Morris dancers provide occasional evening entertainment, quoits are to hand and quizzes are held on a Sunday evening in the winter.

Brewery: Free house
Licensees: Chris and Margaret Burtonwood
Opening hours: 12-3pm, 7-11pm; Sun 12-3pm, 7-10.30pm; closed Mon lunchtime and Tue Nov-Etr
Bar food: 12-2pm, 7-9.45pm
Children: In eating area only; outdoor play area

GREEN MAN INN
Fownhope, near Hereford HR1 4PE. Tel 0432 860243

Fownhope

Well prepared food with no frills, coupled with brisk service, is the key to this village pub's success. Soup of the day at £1.50 and pâté at £2.60 are among the starters, and the main courses include beef and Guinness casserole and courgette and mushroom au gratin, both at £3.95, and Tom Spring's succulent steak sandwich with mushrooms and onion at £5.10. Changed daily, the sweets all cost £1.60,

Brewery: Free house
Licensees: Arthur and Margaret Williams
Opening hours: 11am-2.30pm, 6-11pm; Sun 12-3pm, 7-10.30pm
Bar food: 12-2pm, 6.30-10pm (Sun from 7pm)

while for the same price coffee for two comes in a generous pot yielding at least five cups, accompanied by cream and demerara sugar. Hook Norton Best, Marston's Pedigree and Samuel Smith's Old Brewery Bitter are on offer, along with four ciders. Built in 1485, the impressive black-and-white former coaching inn served as the local Court of Petty Sessions and was at one time owned by Tom Spring, England's boxing champion of the day. Along with the Green Man of folklore, the pugilist appears in a detailed modern tapestry gracing the restaurant. Comfortable, with their carpeted floor, cushioned settles and chairs and open fires, the two oak-beamed bars offer the varied clientele enchanting views across the Wye valley. Roses, shrubs and trees embellish the extensive, well tended lawn, which is set out with picnic tables and has easy access for wheelchairs. The accommodation consists of one single room and 19 double rooms, some with four-poster beds - all timbered and furnished in traditional style. Across the yard, the ground-level Stable Room is available for disabled guests.

Restaurant: Times as bar food
Accommodation: (Price per room) single £31, double £47.50
Children: Welcome anywhere; outdoor play area
Credit cards: AMERICAN EXPRESS®, Access, Visa

The Green Man

The most uncanny and enigmatic of inn signs represents a figure of folk custom from the distant past, the Jack in the Green who appeared at May Day revels. He was a man covered with green leaves and branches, who probably stood for the rebirth of plants, trees and greenery in the spring. Virile and wild, part human and part tree, he is often found carved eerily in churches. A connection grew up between him and Robin Hood, the forest outlaw, and this is perpetuated in some Green Man pub signs, which show an archer or a forester in Lincoln green.

⊛ BLUEBELL

4 Charlford Road, Barnard's Green, Great Malvern WR14 3QP. Tel 0684 575031

Great Malvern

The combination of sensibly priced food and an appealing setting on the edge of town below the Malvern Hills guarantees this pub's popularity. Locals, business people and lively youngsters, but above all families, find the straightforward, well cooked dishes very much to their liking. A basic wine list accompanies the menu, which includes soup at 95p, crudités at £1.85 and smoke trout fillet at £1.95 as starters. The main courses include poached salmon at £4.85, a pair of pork chops at £3.95 and three lamb chops at £4.20. A separate menu of vegetarian dishes is available and a roast Sunday lunch is served at £4.75, or £2.50 for children. Dating from the early 18th century, the handsome, white-painted building, although part of Marston's Tavern Tables chain, has retained its individuality

Brewery: Marston's
Licensee: Simon Parsons
Opening hours: 11.30am-3pm, 6-11.00pm; Sun 12-3pm, 7-10.30pm
Bar food: 12-2pm, 6.30-10pm; Sun 12-2.30pm, 7-9.30pm
Children: In eating areas only
Credit cards: Access, Visa

inside. The carpeted, open-plan bar is divided into several areas, each with its own character, and is lent a solid, traditional feel by beams, panelling and dark furniture. Marston's Pedigree and Bitter and Banks's Mild are on sale, along with half a dozen draught lagers. The patio garden offers outdoor seating in pleasant surroundings.

☞ THREE KINGS
Hanley Castle, near Worcester WR8 0BL. Tel 0684 592686

Hanley Castle

Standing at the centre of a tiny village community, this part-brick, part-timber pub has remained largely unspoilt since it was built around 500 years ago. The two traditional bars, with their wooden and quarry-tiled floors and open fires, draw in a friendly, mixed clientele from a wide area, including families and, on Sunday evenings, a young and lively crowd. Among the collection of domestic and agricultural implements on show, an unusual carpet cleaner stimulates the most comment. There is a separate room where children are welcome, and additional seating is provided on benches in the flower-decked courtyard in front of the pub. Darts, dominoes, shove halfpenny and crib can be played, although the pool table is reserved for club members only. On Sunday evenings groups offering all kinds of music can be heard, and a folk club meets on alternate Thursdays. Butcombe and Thwaites Bitters are served, along with guest beers from the likes of Bunces, Shepherd Neame and Smiles. Toasted sandwiches are on offer at £1 to £2.50 and, as a starter, corn on the cob at £1.25. Also on the menu are omelettes at £1.50 to 2.25, salmon en croûte with broccoli at £6 and Provençale nut Wellington at £5.75, with sweets like blackberry and apple pancake rolls at £1.25 to round off the meal. A twin room, furnished in country style, is available for one or two people.

Brewery: Free house
Licensee: Mrs Sheila Roberts
Opening hours: 11am-2.30pm, 7-11pm but flexible, depending on trade; Sun 12-3pm, 7-10.30pm
Bar food: As opening hours within reason (except Sun evening)
Accommodation: (Price per room) single £25, double £40
Children: Preferably in room without bar

☞ LITTLE TUMBLING SAILOR
42 Mill Lane, Kidderminster DY11 6YJ. Tel 0562 747527

Kidderminster

Like the other houses owned by the Little Pub Co, this cheery, efficiently run pub gives excellent value for money with its huge helpings of well cooked food. The choice of starters includes half a pint of prawns at £2.25 and calamari at £3, while typical main courses are Cradley porkers (two outsized sausages) with vegetables and gravy at £4.25, Desperate Dan Pie at £4.85 and courgette and Stilton bake at £3.95. Chocolate roulade and lemon meringue pie, both at £1.60, are among the sweets available. On tap are

Brewery: Free house
Licensees: Roy and Anthea Wilkes
Opening hours: 11am-3pm, 6-11pm; Sun 12-3pm, 7-10.30pm
Bar food: 12-2.30pm, 6-10pm; Sun 12-2.30pm, 7-9.30pm
Children: Welcome anywhere until 8.30pm if well behaved;

Tetley Best and Lumphammer, which is brewed for the Little Pub Co chain by Ind Coope's Burton Brewery. Dating from 1850, the square, white-painted pub attracts a mixed clientele, its large, comfortable, L-shaped bar with flagstone floor serving several rooms likewise jam-packed with naval memorabilia. The nautical theme continues out on the patio, where a wave machine and a sandpit keep young children amused. On Monday evenings the pub plays host to pop, folk and jazz singers.

outdoor play area

Credit cards: Access, Visa

⊜ TALBOT
Knightwick, near Bromyard WR6 5PH. Tel 0886 21235

Knightwick

A hamlet close to the River Teme is the attractive setting for this pub, belying its proximity to a trunk road. Tubs of potentilla adorn the front of the substantial, white-painted building, dating from the late 15th century but with modern additions, while at the back a patio gives on to a large garden. Locals and business people frequent the two bars, which, with carpeted floors, cushioned benches and the choice of an open fire or a huge stove, are comfortable if slightly tired-looking. Upstairs, an inviting lounge is open to guests staying in the seven double and three single rooms, which are beamed in the main building and neat and functional in the modern extension. Bass, Banks's Bitter, Marston's Pedigree and Boddingtons are the beers on sale, while the extensive wine list matches the menu for cosmopolitan variety. The imaginative dishes, which make it advisable to book for the restaurant, include Genoese pesto pasta at £4.25, pigeon breast with sherried apricots at £3.95, braised rabbit, gin and lime pie at £5.95 and aubergine and tomato casserole with basmati rice at £6.95. Pool, darts, dominoes and cards are on offer, and the pub hosts regular displays of Morris dancing and occasional folk music.

Brewery: Free house
Licensee: J P Clift
Opening hours: 11am-11pm; Sun 12am-3pm, 7-10.30pm
Bar food: 12-2pm, 6.30-9.30pm; Sun 12-2pm, 7.30-9pm
Restaurant: Times as bar food
Accommodation: (Price per room) single £23, double £52.50
Children: Welcome anywhere at landlord's discretion
Credit cards: Access, Visa

CROWN AND ANCHOR
Cotts Lane, Lugwardine, near Hereford HR1 4AB. Tel 0432 851303

Lugwardine

Inventive cooking and value for money attract a good mix of customers, including regulars, families and business people, to this friendly, well-run pub. On offer as starters are delights like quails' eggs on a bed of leaves with celery mayonnaise at £2 and lamb and black olive pâté at £2.40, while typical main courses are watercress and asparagus tart at £4.75, rabbit with ginger and garlic at £5.50, chicken with apple and brandy at £6.25 and warm duck-breast salad at £7. The sweets, all at £2.25, are equally unusual. Bass, Worthington Best Bitter and Hook Norton Best Bitter are on sale, and the wine list has recently been expanded. Unusually, a cup of tea is served on request throughout opening hours. Dating from 1750, the pub is a pleasant black-and-white cottage built on a rise in the heart of the village. Rustic seats are set out on the terrace at the rear, overlooking a charming garden adorned with shrubs and flowers. The bar, part-carpeted but mainly quarry-tiled, is divided into cosy sections furnished with benches and tables and chairs, with decoration provided by fishing rods, cricket bats and scythes.

Brewery: Free house
Licensees: Nicholas and Julie Squires
Opening hours: 11.30am-11pm; Sun 12-3pm, 7-10.30pm
Bar food: 12-2pm, 7-10pm
Children: Welcome anywhere at landlord's discretion; outdoor play area

⊕ KINGS ARMS
Ombersley, near Droitwich WR9 0EW. Tel 0905 620315

Ombersley

A favourite destination for West Midlands day-trippers, this village pub concentrates on providing a varied menu which offers value for money. To this end, it employs five chefs to conjure up starters like goose pâté with Sauternes, smoked haddock and egg terrine at £3.95 and a choice of nine soups. In addition to light meals - for example, pasta with a spicy sauce of bacon, mushroom and tomatoes at £3.95 and crabmeat in béchamel sauce with tarragon vinegar at £4.25 - it also serves more substantial dishes. These include cod-based trawlerman's stew at £6.25, salmon and broccoli Mornay at £7.25 and beef, beer and mustard sausages at £4.50, as well as vegetarian dishes like mixed bean and vegetable chilli at £5.50 and garlic and mushroom quiche at £5.25. Among the sweets, all at £1.95, are fresh fruit tartlets and bread-and-butter pudding. Bass and Boddingtons Mild are on sale, along with a wide selection of malt whiskies. Some 600 years old, the pub is an impressive black-and-white building with a courtyard in front and a garden at the back. Inviting, with its three open fires, the bar is embellished with weapons and, between the ceiling beams, coats of arms which include that of Charles II.

Brewery: Free house
Licensees: Chris and Judy Blundell
Opening hours: 11am-2.45pm, 5.30-11pm; Sun 12-3pm, 7-10.30pm
Bar food: 12-2.15pm, 6-10pm (Sun from 7pm)
Children: Not permitted under eight years, and must be eating
Credit cards: Access, Visa

⊕ NEW INN
Market Square, Pembridge HR6 9DZ. Tel 05447 427

Pembridge

Black-and-white and thus in keeping with most of the showpiece of a town in which it stands, this large, creeper and rose-clad pub dates from the 13th century. A cobbled courtyard with tables and chairs faces the market square, while the two beamed bars, warmed in winter by log fires, are furnished in traditional style with settles and dark tables and chairs. Friendly and efficiently run by two sisters, the pub offers a varied and sensibly priced menu, complemented by an extensive, well balanced wine list. The starters include smoked chicken, bacon and croutons and avocado and crab salad, both at £3.95. Leek and mushroom coustarde at £3.75 and, both at £4.25, lamb casserole with redcurrant and red wine sauce and kidneys in sherry, mushrooms and onions, are typical main courses. Sweets, including bread-and-butter pudding and toffee meringue, are £1.75 and the coffee is good. Beer drinkers' needs are met by Ruddles County and Best, John Smith's, Wadworth 6X and Courage Directors, ciders from Stowford Press and Bulmer's are on sale and there is a choice of malt whiskies. The accommodation comprises three double rooms, including a large family room , two twin rooms and one single - all beamed, charmingly lopsided and furnished with old-fashioned pieces.

Brewery: Free house
Licensee: Jane Melvin
Opening hours: 11am-3pm, 6-11pm; Sun 12-3pm, 7-10.30pm
Bar food: 12-2pm, 7-9.30pm
Restaurant: Times as bar food
Accommodation: (Price per person) single and double £16
Children: Welcome anywhere except main bar; family room

ANCIENT CAMP
Ruckhall, near Hereford HR2 9QX. Tel 0981 250449

Ruckhall

Set high above the luxuriant Wye valley, this popular pub enjoys one of the most outstanding views in the county, if not in the country; so much so that the bath has been raised in one of the guest rooms to allow visitors to enjoy the vista while soaking. The long, low building, known to have been a cider house in 1835 but undoubtedly older, is a haven of peace, thanks to the absence of passing traffic. Outside, the small terrace is equipped with tables looking along the valley, while the single bar, with flagstone floor and two open fires, is furnished with cushioned settles, benches and comfortable armchairs. Inevitably tourists figure prominently among the clientele, although the quality and variety of the food also brings in business trade at lunchtime. Taramosalata and salad at £3.75 and avocado with prawns at £3.95 are typical starters, and the main courses include oxtail casserole at £6.50 and, both at £5.75, Greek shepherd's pie and cannelloni with ricotta cheese and spinach. Wood Parish Bitter and West Country Pale Ale are on sale, along with a

Brewery: Free house
Licensees: David and Nova Hague
Opening hours: 12-2.30pm, 6-11pm; Sun 12-2.30pm, 7-10.30pm; closed Mon lunchtime and all day Mon in winter
Bar food: 12-2pm, 7-9.30pm (except Sun and Mon)
Restaurant: Times as bar food
Accommodation: (Price per room) single £35, double £48-£55; children under eight years not permitted
Children: Welcome anywhere during the day, but in the evening only if eating

choice of malt whiskies and an above-average wine list. Four double rooms, one with twin beds, are available for one or two people. Light and airy and with white furniture, the rooms are all comfortable and those at the front offer the bonus of excellent views.

LOUGH POOL INN
Sellack, near Ross-on-Wye HR9 6LX. Tel 098987 236

Sellack

Formerly a chef, the enthusiastic new owner of this pub makes it his business to serve generous portions of well-prepared food. Home-made soup at £1.60 and stuffed mushrooms with garlic mayonnaise are among the starters, and the main courses include jumbo sausage and chips at £3.50, spinach, cheese and mushroom pie at £5.50 and a choice of steaks ranging from £6.95 to £10.50. A handsome, timbered building of the 16th and 17th centuries, previously a wheelwright's workshop, the pub stands on a quiet back road, fronting an attractive lawn provided with picnic tables. Inside, a flagstone floor, open fires and, for decoration, dried flowers, sporting prints and farm implements, lend a traditional flavour to this friendly pub. The pool of the inn's name is across the road, hidden by trees. On tap are Wye Valley's Hereford Supreme and Stones Best Bitter and Bass, along with Weston's Vintage and Stowford Press ciders. Low-alcohol ciders are also on sale, and there is a wide choice of malt whiskies.

Brewery: Free house
Licensee: Philip Moran
Opening hours: 12-3pm, 6.30-11pm; Sun 12-3pm, 7-10.30pm
Bar food: 12-2pm, 7-9.30pm
Restaurant: Times as bar food
Children: In restaurant only
Credit cards: Access, Visa, Diners

⊕ PLOUGH
Shenstone, near Kidderminster DY10 4DL. Tel 056277 7340

Shenstone

What this pub lacks in choice - only one beer is on offer, Bathams Best, and no food whatsoever - it certainly makes up for in atmosphere. A complete mix of customers, among them doctors, jockeys, solicitors and car dealers, fall under the spell of the jovial landlord, who, if he enjoys anything more than teasing his guests, likes to know that everyone is having a good time. A member of one of only four families who have run the pub in the last century and a half, he has himself been in charge for nearly 40 years. The brick-built house, dating from 1840 and situated in a quiet village, has sprouted several additions which would not go down well with purists. There is no garden, although a few benches are set out around the pub. Inside, the two crowded bars are comfortably furnished and lack nothing by way of decoration or diversion, being filled by the exuberant personality of the host.

Brewery: Bathams
Licensee: James Rose
Opening hours: 11am-3pm, 6-11pm; Sun 12-3pm, 7-10.30pm
Children: Not permitted inside

⊛ BATEMAN ARMS
Shobdon, near Leominster HR6 9LX. Tel 0568 708374

Shobdon

Wisely offering a separate menu of seven vegetarian dishes, this 15th-century pub reaps the benefit of making a proper choice of food a priority. A friendly place, with a clientele of regulars, families, business people and a younger crowd, it is particularly popular at lunchtime. The starters include cheese and prawn fritters at £4.50 and egg mayonnaise dressed with anchovies at £2.25, while typical main courses are medallions of lamb in orange and tarragon sauce at £6.25 and spicy beef and mushroom stir fry at £5.95. Norfolk treacle tart at £2.50 and brandy-snap basket at £2.95 are among the sweets. A wide range of wines and a selection of malt whiskies are on sale, and the beers are Flowers Original and Wood Parish Bitter, and Boddingtons Best in the summer. Built in traditional black-and-white style and formerly a farmhouse, the pub stands at the edge of the village. It offers the choice of two bars - one with a pool table, darts and dominoes, the other with carpeted floor, open fires, settles and Windsor chairs. The garden is shaded by apple trees, while roses adorn the terrace. Two spacious, beamed rooms are available, one with twin beds

Brewery: Free house
Licensee: Derek Yeoman
Opening hours: 12-2.30pm, 7-11pm; Sun 12-3pm, 7-10.30pm
Bar food: 12-2pm, 7-10pm
Restaurant: Times as bar food
Accommodation: (Price per person) double £22.50
Children: If well behaved
Credit cards:
AMERICAN EXPRESS®, Access, Visa

⊛ RHYDSPENCE INN
Whitney-on-Wye, near Hay-on-Wye HR3 6EU. Tel 04973 262

Whitney-on-Wye

Its position beside a stream forming the boundary with Wales makes this the first and last pub in England. Built in 1390, partly in the black-and-white style, and offering views over the Wye valley and the Black Mountains, it is well run and deserves the praise it customarily receives in the guidebooks. The well tended gardens incorporate lawns, areas planted with shrubs and wide terraces with flowers in tubs. A mixed clientele frequents the two bars, which are carpeted and furnished with wall benches and comfortable library chairs. Decoration is provided by a miscellany of guns, swords, farm implements and dairy equipment, and cooking utensils. The food, well prepared, filling and reasonably priced, includes seafood fettuccini at £5.75 and, both at £4.95, spinach and mozzarella crunch and the 'landlord's favourite' - chunks of ham or fish in cheese sauce. The extensive wine list matches the menu for choice, there are a dozen malt whiskies on offer and beer drinkers can plump for Bass, Marston's Pedigree or Robinson's Best Bitter. White walls and black beams preserve the inn's traditional character in the comfortable rooms - one single and three doubles, one of which has a four-poster bed.

Brewery: Free house
Licensees: Peter and Pam Glover
Opening hours: 11am-2.30pm, 7-11pm; Sun 12-3pm, 7-10.30pm
Bar food: As opening hours
Restaurant: Times as bar food
Accommodation: (Price per person) single £27.50, double £55-£65
Children: Welcome anywhere
Credit cards:
AMERICAN EXPRESS®, Access, Visa (£2 standard surcharge with each)

⊕ SUN INN
Winforton, near Hay-on-Wye HR3 6EA. Tel 0544 327677

Winforton

This pleasant, well-kept pub offers a wide-ranging and imaginative menu, making it a far better place for a meal than a quick drink. Among the starters are prawn and crab dumplings at £3.50 and Madeleine of mushrooms with smoked bacon, onions and herbs at £2.88, while the main courses include lamb casserole with lime and ginger at £6.99 and, each at £7.99, salmon, lava bread and bacon, beef in black bean sauce and wild rabbit braised in cider. Sweets like Welsh treacle tart, summer pudding and gin and lemon sorbet, all at £2.75, round off the meal, along with good, fresh coffee with cream. Felinfoel Double Dragon, Wood Parish Bitter, Sam Powell's Parish Bitter, Marston's Pedigree and Jennings Cumberland Ale alternately slake the thirst of an assortment of customers in the carpeted bar, which is furnished cottage-style and embellished with horse-brasses and farm implements. Darts, quoits and cribbage are to hand, and in winter a quiz is held on Sunday evenings. Situated in the heart of the village, the white-painted, early 18th-century pub has outdoor seating at picnic benches in the garden.

Brewery: Free house
Licensees: Brian and Wendy Hibbard
Opening hours: 11.30am-3pm, 6-11pm; Sun 12-3pm, 7-10.30pm; closed Tue in winter
Bar food: As opening hours
Children: In eating area only; outdoor play area

⊕ BUTCHERS ARMS
Woolhope, near Fownhope HR1 4RF. Tel 0432 860281

Woolhope

A peaceful setting just beyond the village adds to the appeal of this timbered and tiled 14th-century pub, which occasionally plays host to Morris dancers in the evening. Inside, cushioned settles and beams decked with hops reinforce the rustic character of the two bars, where the main attraction is the food and friendly service. Typical starters are smoked cod's roe pâté and leek and hazelnut terrine in vine leaves, both at £2.35, while among the main courses are chicken curry at £4.95 and, both at £5.25, smoked haddock and bacon in cheese sauce and lamb and cranberry casserole in red wine. The sweets include frozen ginger and coffee meringue cake and Malakoff (almond pudding with coffee and brandy), both at £1.75. A wine list complements the menu, the beers are Marston's Pedigree and Hook Norton Best and Old Hooky, along with a guest ale at weekends, and there is a choice of malt whiskies. There is additional seating in the garden at the back and a couple of picnic benches on the grass in front of the car park. Two double rooms and one single are available - all bright and comfortable.

Brewery: Free house
Licensee: Charlie Powers
Opening hours: 11.30am-3pm, 7-11pm (Fri and Sat 6.30pm); Sun 12-3pm, 7-10.30pm
Bar food: 12-2pm, 7-10.30pm
Restaurant: Fri and Sat 7-10pm
Accommodation: (Price per person) single £25, double £19.50
Children: Welcome anywhere

CROWN
Woolhope, near Fownhope HR1 4QP. Tel 0432 860468

Woolhope

O ver the past six years the enthusiastic owners of this village pub have built up a flourishing trade not only by providing good-value meals and friendly, efficient service, but also by valuing customers who just want a drink. Generous portions of smokies (smoked haddock in white wine and mushroom sauce) and garlic mushrooms, both at £2.50, are popular starters, while similarly unstinting are main courses such as double lamb chop with chasseur sauce at £5.25 and chicken and asparagus lasagne at £4.50. Crème brûlée and blackcurrants and apricot clafouti, both at £1.70, are among the adventurous selection of sweets. Best for burgundies, the wine list is well thought out and reasonably priced and Bass, Hook Norton Best and Smiles Best are on tap.Usually crowded with regulars and hungry youngsters, the bar is divided into three sections (one of which is a no-smoking area) furnished with upholstered seating and decorated with wildlife photographs. An open fire burns in winter, while in warmer weather customers may prefer to sit on the terrace in front of the 300-year-old pub.

Brewery: Free house
Licensees: Neil and Sally Gordon
Opening hours: 12-2.30pm, 6.30-11pm (winter 7pm); Sun 12-3pm, 7-10.30pm
Bar food: 12-2pm, 6.30-10pm (winter and Sun 7pm)
Children: Welcome anywhere if well behaved

⊕ ANCHOR
Wyre Piddle, near Pershore WR10 2JB. Tel 0386 552799

Wyre Piddle

T he landlord of this popular riverside pub is a chef, and his imaginative special dishes, served in addition to the brief daily menu, give him the chance to show off his skills. The starters on offer include Stilton and port pâté at £2.25 and terrine of fresh salmon and smoked mackerel at £3.25. Among the main courses, likewise good value for money, are venison casserole at £7, grilled halibut steak at £7.25 and chicken and mushroom curry Madras at £6.25. Prepared to the same high standard are the sweets, which include an outstanding fresh raspberry crème brûlée at £2.35 and black cherries in brandy and cream at £2.10. Fittingly, there is an excellent, well-balanced wine list, although beer drinkers are not overlooked, with Flowers Original, Boddingtons Bitter and Banks's Bitter on tap, plus a guest beer each month . The low, white-painted pub, part of which dates back to the 17th century, faces the main road at the front, while at the back a terraced garden drops down steeply to the Avon, giving views across the river to the Vale of Evesham. Inevitably, regular river users, as well as holidaymakers - who can moor their narrow boats overnight without charge - supplement the mixed clientele who crowd into the two beamed and carpeted bars.

Brewery: Whitbread
Licensee: Michael Senior
Opening hours: 11am-2.30pm, 6-11pm; Sun 12-3pm, 7-10.30pm
Bar food: 12-2.30pm, 7-9.30pm; Sun 12-2pm, 7-9pm
Restaurant: Times as bar food (except Sun evening)
Children: Welcome anywhere away from bar
Credit cards: Access, Visa

HERTFORDSHIRE

⊜ BUSHEL AND SHRIKE
Mill Street, Ashwell, near Baldock SG7 5LY. Tel 0462 742394

Ashwell

This very impressive inn, masterminded by a landlord who is eager to do everything not merely properly but with style, is notable for the huge selection of freshly prepared, imaginative dishes served in both bar and restaurant from a regularly changing menu; deep-fried squid (£3.60), for example, might be followed by venison pie (£6.25) and Pavlova (£2.25) - and even a simple sandwich is first class, with ham boiled by the local butcher and locally baked bread. A wide range of wines is available (40 by the bottle, three by the glass) as well as cask conditioned beers (Adnams Broadside and Wells Eagle IPA and Bombardier), three guest beers in rotation, and Guinness and Murphy's Stout. Draught beverages also include a choice of lagers and Scrumpy Jack cider. Light, open-plan bars feature an interesting array of furniture, and the restaurant - particularly popular for its wonderful 'eat all you like for £9.95' Sunday buffets - was once the meeting house of a local friendly society. The pub building itself, set in a pleasant garden down a narrow lane off the village high street, dates back several hundred years in parts, but its well kept, white painted walls and black woodwork present an attractively fresh appearance.

Brewery: Charles Wells
Licensees: F A and S A Lynch
Opening hours: 12-2.30pm, 6.30-11pm; Sun 12-3pm, 7-10.30pm
Bar food: As opening hours
Restaurant: Times as bar food
Children: Welcome in buffet bar and in restaurant area (reserved for families until 1pm Sat)
Credit Cards: AMERICAN EXPRESS®, Access, Visa

⊜ ROSE AND CROWN
High Street, Ashwell SG7 5NT. Tel 0462 742420

Ashwell

Colourful in summer with window boxes, hanging baskets and patio pots filled with Busy Lizzies, this rambling, yellow-painted, 15th-century building on the village high street is flanked by a small terrace and backed by a wonderful shrub garden. The availablity of 25 to 40 different malt whiskies at any one time must feature high on its list of attractions, while draught beers include Guinness as well as Greene King IPA, Rayments Special Bitter and Abbot. The menu, served in both bar and non-smoking restaurant is supplemented by a range of blackboard specials (£3.50 to £11.25), and there is always a vegetarian alternative to such dishes as steak, kidney and ale or salmon and broccoli pies. The two welcoming open-plan bars attract both regular local drinkers and restaurant users from a wide area.

Brewery: Greene King
Licensee: J Starling
Opening hours: 12-2.30pm, 6.30-11pm (Sat from 5.30pm); Sun 12-3pm, 7-10.30pm
Bar food: As opening hours (except Mon)
Restaurant: Times as bar food
Children: Welcome any age in dining area if eating; not permitted under 14 years in bar
Credit Cards: AMERICAN EXPRESS,® Access, Visa, Diners

⊜ BROCKET ARMS
Ayot St Lawrence, near Welwyn AL6 9BT. Tel 0438 820250

Ayot St Lawrence

A wide range of draught beers is featured at this friendly, cheerful pub at the centre of a prosperous village, two or three guest beers (Eldridge Pope Royal Oak or Thomas Hardy Country Bitter, for example) supplementing Bass, Marston's Pedigree Bitter, Wadworth 6X, Greene King IPA and Abbot, and two draught lagers. Good-value bar meals include dishes like scampi (£4.50) and steak and chips (£9) - though there will not necessarily be a vegetarian option - while the evening menu in the candlelit restaurant offers à la carte (£16.95) and blackboard (£15.95) choices. Beamed bars with rustic furniture and an inglenook fireplace are adorned with paintings, prints and sketches of local interest (some for sale). The pleasant atmosphere attracts weekend visitors from London and even further afield, as well as local customers, and on summer Sundays and bank holidays afternoon tea, from 3.30pm to 6pm, is also popular. Bedrooms in the 14th-century main building reflect its age in their beamed ceilings and interesting shapes, while those in a converted stable block are more modern in design; two rooms have four-poster beds.

Brewery: Free house
Licensee: Toby Wingfield Digby
Opening hours: 11am-3pm, 6-11pm; Sun 12-3pm, 7-10.30pm
Bar food: 12-2pm, 7.30-9pm (except Sun and Mon)
Restaurant: Times as bar food
Accommodation: (Price per room) single from £40, double £40-£65
Children: In restaurant only; outdoor play area
Credit Cards: Access, Visa

The Original AK
The great red-brick citadel of McMullen's dominates Hertford today, as it has since 1891. The company is much older, founded in 1827 by Peter McMullen and still in the family after six generations, the only survivor of 39 independent breweries in Hertfordshire at the beginning of this century. The same oak fermenting vessels, lined with copper, have been used since the 1890s and McMullen's Original AK, of which the brewery is particularly proud, has been made in the same way for over 100 years.

⊜ FOX AND HOUNDS
High Street, Barley, near Royston SG8 8HV. Tel 0763 848459

Barley

A spacious car park and a cheerful garden with trestle tables, swings and a wooden castle surround this very easy-going and friendly village-centre pub which dates back in parts to 1450 and runs its own brewery, producing aptly named beers like Flamethrower and Old Dragon. The rambling bar divides naturally into several separate areas, centred on a huge inglenook fireplace, and here a clientele drawn from within a 15-mile radius gathers, the pub's minibus service ensuring that they can appreciate to the full an excellent range of draught beers. Theakston Old Peculier, XB and Best Bitter are regulars, with a guest selection that

Brewery: Free house
Licensee: R J Nicholson
Opening hours: 12-2.30pm, 6-11pm; Sun 12-3pm, 6-10.30pm
Bar food: As opening hours
Restaurant: Times as bar food times; licensed till 12 midnight
Children: Welcome in the separate dining areas; own menu available; outdoor play area

over the years has featured 297 different brews, including
Jennings, Chiltern, Marston's Border and 'recession' beers
like McEwan 70/- for the hard-up; Becks and McEwans
lagers are also available on draught, as are two 'rough'
ciders. A meal chosen from the extensive bar menu might
start with garlic mushrooms (£2.35) or whitebait (£2.88) and
continue with a steak (from £6.75 to £13.75) or aubergine
bonne femme (£4.75).Vegetarians receive more than usually
sympathetic consideration. A list of puddings (from £1.60)
features a variety of ice creams as well as favourites like
raspberry Pavlova and Death by Chocolate. For added
entertainment there are dominoes, bar billiards, shove
halfpenny, cards and a skittle alley.

THREE HORSESHOES
Winkwell, Bourne End, near Hemel Hempstead HP1 2RZ. Tel 0442 862585

Bourne End

This very pretty roadside pub - a white painted 16th-
century building with black woodwork and a garden
which is ablaze with flowers in summer - is situated down a
tiny road by a petrol station. Set in lovely surroundings
overlooking the canal, it provides a cosy, comfortable and
very friendly environment in which to enjoy a choice of
draught beers which includes guests as well as Tetley,
Greene King IPA, Wadworth 6X, Benskins Best Bitter and
Burton Ale. Three bar menus offer main dishes (most served
with fries and a salad) like rump steak (£5.95), steak and
kidney pudding (£4.95), a succulent seafood platter (£4.95)
or jumbo sausage in crispy bread (£3.60) as well as a daily
changing vegetarian option and sandwiches (from £1.95). A
mixed clientele of businessmen, families and young people
mingles in the two beamed, tiny-windowed bars - one with a
huge fireplace, both decked with relics of the carthorse era
like harnesses and horse-brasses - where a singer or
guitarist sometimes entertains on Sunday evenings.

Brewery: Benskins
Licensee: Priscilla Anne Palmer
Opening hours: 11.30am-3pm,
5.30-11pm (Fri and Sat 11am-
11pm); Sun 12-3pm, 7-10.30pm
Bar food: 12-2.30pm, 7-9.30pm
(except Sun and Mon)
Children: Welcome anywhere

⊕ HORNS
Bull's Green, near Datchworth SG3 6RZ. Tel 0438 79367

Bull's Green

Deliberately promoting an olde worlde image, in keeping
with its reputed age of 500 years, this small white-
painted pub with black shutters and doors stands at the
centre of the hamlet of Bull's Green, overlooking the green
itself. A good-sized garden to the front is set with wooden
tables, and hanging baskets and tubs of flowers provide a
colourful show in summer. Two bars serve a selection of
draught beers (Boddingtons, Brakspear, Flowers Original,

Brewery: Whitbread
Licensee: Peter Metherall
Opening hours: 11.30am-
2.30pm (Sat 3pm), 5.30-11pm;
Sun 12-3pm, 7-10.30pm
Bar food: 12-2.30pm, 7-10pm;
Sun 12-2.30pm
Children: Welcome anywhere

McMullen Wethered Bitter) and Murphy's and Guinness, and the bar menu offers a range of such starters as deep-fried mushrooms at £3.25 or hot mussels at £3.55 before main courses like chilli con carne or cottage pie (both at £3.95). Vegetarians and children alike are adequately catered for. On Sundays there is a traditional Sunday lunch with roast beef at around £5.00 as well as the normal bar menu. In summer there is occasional entertainment - by a jazz trio, for example.

Credit Cards: Access, Visa

☻ WOODMAN
Chapmore End, near Ware SG12 0HF. Tel 0920 463143

Chapmore End

A place for drinking and talking - its bar menu restricted to bacon (£1.20), sausage (£1) or vegetarian grill (£1.10) in a roll - this small, square pub in the middle of a quiet hamlet has a reputation for good beer, gravity-delivered straight from the barrel, that brings enthusiasts from far and wide, though their choice is limited to Guinness and Greene King IPA and Abbot Ale. The two brick-floored bars are very small, but some seating is provided in the front garden, while the area at the rear contains swings and a slide. Morris dancing and similar 'country-style' entertainment takes place outside during the summer months.

Brewery: Greene King
Licensee: John Elliott
Opening hours: 12-3pm, 6-11pm; Sun 12-3pm, 7-10.30pm
Bar food: 12-2pm, 6-9pm (except Sun)
Children: Not permitted inside; outdoor play area

☻ WHITE HORSE
33 Castle Street, Hertford SG14 1HH. Tel 0992 501950

Hertford

An excellent choice of well kept draught beers is provided by this small white pub tucked away in a row of terraced buildings on the edge of the town centre, opposite the castle grounds: Hook Norton Old Hooky, Greene King IPA and Fuller's ESB, the house beers, are augmented by guest ales - Fuller's London Pride, Hoskins & Oldfield Little Matty, Mole's Brew 97 and Blackawton 44 Special being on sale at the time of visiting. Scrumpy cider is also available. The bar menu is short and simple, with toasted sandwiches from £1.25 and ham, egg and chips, lasagne or quiche at £2.95, but food is freshly prepared, bread is baked on the premises and a vegetarian dish always provided. A good cross-section of customers gathers in the two tiny, neat bars to enjoy good beer and conversation, customers bringing their own instruments along to join in Sunday lunchtime entertainment on guitar, banjo or even serpent.

Brewery: Free house
Licensees: I W S and J E Harvey
Opening hours: 12-3pm, 5.30-11pm (Sat 7-11pm); Sun12-3pm, 7-10.30pm
Bar food: 12-2pm only
Children: In family room only (space limited)

⊜ NAGS HEAD
The Ford, Little Hadham, near Bishop's Stortford SG11 2AX. Tel 0279 771555

Little Hadham

Chatty locals and a very friendly, relaxed staff make this pub a pleasant rendezvous for a night out. The low, mustard-coloured building, set at the centre of a village which sprawls along a country lane and fronted by an attractive little patio with hanging baskets and tubs of flowers, offers two bars - the small, dimly lit but cosy Public and a low-ceilinged, beamed Lounge displaying collections of brasses, guns and old photographs of the villag. A few steps lead down to the neat dining area. Bar and restaurant menus are identical at lunchtime, with starters like mussels in garlic (£3.75) or mushroom croutons (£3.50) preceding a range of main courses which includes steaks from £7.25 and half a chicken at £5.50. A good-value ploughman's at £2.50 and vegetarian dishes are also available, and the Sunday roast is so popular that booking is essential; in the evenings the dining area has a separate menu. Greene King IPA, Abbot and Rayments Special Bitter, as well as Guinness, are sold on draught.

Brewery: Greene King
Licensees: Michael and Kay Robinson
Opening hours: 11am-2.30pm, 6-11pm; Sun 12-3pm, 7-10.30pm
Bar food: 12-2pm, 6-9pm (Fri and Sat 9.30pm); Sun 12-2pm, 7-9pm
Restaurant: Times as bar food
Children: Welcome at lunchtime in dining area; children's dishes available

LYTTON ARMS
Park Lane, Old Knebworth SG3 6QB. Tel 0438 812312

Old Knebworth

A wide choice of imported beers, as well as British, is served in this large, attractive and friendly 19th-century pub where some 500 real ales have been sold over the past four years. Five regularly changing guest beers are available on draught together with Bass, Young's, Theakston XB, Adnams Broadside and Banks & Taylor Shefford; for the keen cider drinker there are two real scrumpies. The service of bar food is flexible, the landlord always being ready to oblige someone who comes in at the last moment if he can, and old-fashioned sweets like Spotted Dick or bread-and-butter pudding (both at £1.90) follow main courses which range from sausages with bread and pickles (£4.25) to ham and pineapple risotto (£3.80) or mixed grill (£7.25). Set on the outskirts of Knebworth, in a good walking area, the pub attracts businessmen during the week, families at weekends, and a steady stream of riders, hikers and cyclists. Seating provided in the garden and on patios (that at the rear sheltered by canvas) is popular during the summer months, while beamed bars with big log fires, piped music, a piano and a quiz machine are particularly welcoming in winter.

Brewery: Free house
Licensee: Stephen Nye
Opening hours: Thu-Sat 11am-11pm; Mon-Wed 11-3pm, 5-11pm; Sun 12-3pm, 7-10.30pm
Bar food: 12-2pm, 6.30-9.30pm (times flexible); Sun 12-2pm, 7-9.30pm
Restaurant: Times as bar food; booking advisable at weekends
Children: Welcome if eating; outdoor play area
Credit Cards: AMERICAN EXPRESS,® Access, Visa

⊜ CABINET
High Street, Reed, near Royston SG8 8AH. Tel 0763 848366

Reed

Set in a large garden, with weeping willows to its right and a front patio enhanced by a breathtaking flower display, this white weatherboarded pub - an ale house since 1712, though the building may be older - stands at the centre of the sprawling village. The restaurant serves the same menu as the bar, popular dishes, all home-made on the premises, including soup at £1.20, skinny dips, battered mushrooms, and spicy chicken wings or chicken Kiev at £3.95. On Sundays there is a very good value three-course Sunday lunch at around £6.50 to £7. White-walled, low ceilinged bars with open fires are cosy and cheerful, offering piped music as well as traditional games and attracting both businessmen and locals with their range of real ales - Greene King IPA and Abbot, Banks & Taylor Shefford Mild and Bitter, Adnams Best Bitter and two guest beers.

Brewery: Free house
Licensee: Miss Katie Brennan
Opening hours: 11am-3pm, 6-11pm; Sun 12-3pm, 7-10.30pm
Bar food: 12-2.15pm , 7-9.30pm (except Sun-Tue evening)
Restaurant: Times as bar food
Children: Welcome anywhere

GOAT
37 Sopwell Lane, St Albans AL1 1RN. Tel 0727 833934

St Albans

This 500-year-old, Grade II listed pub with its slightly overhanging first floor stands just off the city centre in a narrow residential street lined with interesting little buildings. A delightful atmosphere pervades the two beamed bars which are divided into cosy areas by brick columns; panelled walls are hung with an abundance of pictures, prints, sketches and old photographs. Here, customers of all ages gather to enjoy Sunday lunchtime jazz, Sunday evening quizzes or live music from a reasonably unobtrusive group on alternate Mondays. A large selection of draught and bottled lagers supplements the draught beers which include Hook Norton, Greene King Abbot and IPA, Marston's Pedigree Bitter, Wadworth 6X and Murphy's and Guinness. The bar menu offers daily specials - mousaka, for example, at £3.75, and beef goulash or roast beef at £3.95 - as well as such standard main courses as seafood tagliatelle (£3.95) or chicken Kiev (£5.75)and a range of starters or snacks and puddings.

Brewery: Devenish
Licensee: Mr A Ginn
Opening hours: 11am-3pm, 5.30-11pm; Sun 12-3pm, 7-10.30pm
Bar food: 12-2.30pm, 6.30-9pm; Sun 12-2.30pm only
Children: In or around eating area only

YE OLDE FIGHTING COCKS
Holmhurst Hill, St Albans AL3 4HE. Tel 0727 865830

St Albans

This interesting old building, developed from a 14th-century pigeon house, was first used as an ale house in 1600 and stands in the city centre, by a lake near the cathedral, its beamed white façade brightened by hanging baskets and shrubs. Not primarily a drinking pub, it offers draught Wadworth 6X, Benskins Best Bitter and Burton Ale, Tetley and Guinness. Its food is popular, a range of blackboard specials like Fighting Cock pie (£4.25) and cauliflower and broccoli bake (£3.95) supplementing ploughman's (£3), salads (£3 to £4) and jacket potatoes (average price £2.50). The low-ceilinged bar with its nooks and crannies is a favourite meeting place for young people in the evenings, its lunchtime trade appealing mainly to businessmen and older couples. In summer the terraced patio and the sloping garden behind it are very popular.

Brewery: Benskins
Licensee: Joe Campanella
Opening hours: 11am-3pm, 6-11pm; Sun 12-3pm, 7-10.30pm
Bar food: 12-2pm daily, Mon-Thu 6.30-9pm
Children: Welcome if eating at lunchtime or early evening; family room; outdoor play area

☙ GEORGE AND DRAGON
High Street, Watton-at-Stone, near Hertford SG14 3TA. Tel

Watton-at-Stone

This attractive old pub on the high street of the village has no outside seating area - the only garden being a narrow strip of grass where boules is played - but its two pleasantly furnished, comfortable bars attract a well-to-do clientele. Its speciality is food, the restaurant offering three-course set meals at £18.50 while the bar menu selection may offer as snack or starter hot avocado with a spicy tomato concassé (£4.50) or Corsican fish soup (£3.60), and as main dishes Aberdeen Angus rib eye steak (£9) and liver and bacon in Madeira wine (£5); among the sweets are a rich lemon and ginger cheesecake, chocolate roulade and sticky toffee pudding. A vegetarian dish is usually available, but there is no special children's menu. Greene King Abbot Ale and IPA, Murphy's and Guinness are on draught and there is the usual range of lagers.

Brewery: Greene King
Licensee: K Dinn
Opening hours: 11am-2.30pm, 6-11pm; Sun 12-3pm, 7-10.30pm
Bar food: 12.15-2pm, 7.15-10pm
Restaurant: 12.15-2pm; 7.30-9.30pm (except Sun and Mon evening)
Children: In small dining room, and the main one if eating
Credit Cards:
AMERICAN EXPRESS ®, Access, Visa, Diners

The Campaign for Real Ale
CAMRA, the Campaign for Real Ale, was founded in 1971 to stop traditional cask conditioned beer being driven out of the British pub by keg beers, including lager. Its success in inspiring the real ale revival of the last 20 years has been a dramatic example of an effective consumer group in action. With its headquarters in St Albans and a membership of 35,000 people, CAMRA vigorously opposes the closing down of traditional breweries and the destruction of historic and characterful pubs by the theme-pub concepts of the big brewers' marketing departments. It publishes the annual Good Beer Guide and other books, and the monthly newspaper Whats Brewing, and organises upwards of 100 beer festivals every year.

OXFORDSHIRE

⊕ MAYTIME INN
Asthall, near Burford OX18 4HW. Tel 0993 822068

Asthall

An attractive location in an unspoilt village adds to the charm of this 15th-century, vine-clad inn. Of local Cotswold stone, inside it is surprisingly light and airy, thanks to a high ceiling with elm beams where, unexpectedly, perch huge stuffed toys. A varied clientele frequents the single bar, with its cushioned benches and elm tables and chairs, where Youngers Tartan Special, Wadworth 6X and Beamish are on sale, with Sol and the highly potent Elephant among the foreign bottled beers. There is a no-smoking area. The imaginative main menu, complemented by a wine list which includes New World wines, offers starters such as grilled goat's cheese with crispy bacon at £4.25 and home-made chicken-liver pâté at £3.55. Main courses include, both at £8.25, a large Burford leg of lamb steak grilled pink with rosemary and served on orange, port and redcurrant sauce and baked seafood Thermidor with sole, prawns, mussels, with white wine and cream and topped with cheese. There is also a separate bar menu. Benches are set out in front of the pub, giving a view of the pretty village, and at the back there is a patio with seating. Six double rooms are available - pleasantly furnished and each with a television.

Brewery: Free house
Licensee: Tim Morgan
Opening hours: 11am-3pm, 6-11pm; Sun 12-3pm, 7-10.30pm
Bar food: 12-2.30pm, 7-10pm; Sun 12-2pm (Sun lunch or snacks only)
Accommodation: (Price per room) single £43.60, double £56.50
Children: Welcome anywhere
Credit cards: AMERICAN EXPRESS®, Access, Visa

⊕ BOTTLE AND GLASS
Binfield Heath, near Henley-on-Thames RG9 4JT. Tel 0491 575755

Binfield Heath

Pretty with its thatched roof and shuttered lattice windows, this village-centre pub dates from the 15th century. Its two smallish bars are fittingly simple, with their low beams, mixture of flagstones and bare boards and furniture which includes a fine long bench of old oak. Brakspear Bitter, Special and Old Ale, some 15 decent wines and a wide range of whiskies are on sale. Diners among the mixed clientele can choose between dishes like large mussels in garlic and herb butter and brown bread at £4.25, a vegetarian meal of the day at the same price and game casserole at £5.50. In the garden, which is lit at night, tables and chairs are set out beneath thatched parasols.

Brewery: Brakspear
Licensees: Anne and Mike Robinson
Opening hours: 11am-3pm, 6-11pm; Sun 12-3pm, 7-10.30pm
Bar food: 12-1.45pm, 7-9.30pm (except Sun evening)
Children: Not permitted inside

🍺 LAMB
Sheep Street, Burford OX18 4LR. Tel 099382 3155

Burford

With older customers forming the majority of its clientele, this attractive, vine-clad pub, built in mellow Cotswold stone over 550 years ago, offers an appropriate degree of comfort. It has two bars - one traditional, with wooden benches, the other furnished with armchairs, grandfather clocks and other antique pieces. Both rooms offer cosy privacy, with oriental rugs on stone flags, low ceilings, prints and paintings and generous log fires. Outside, there is seating at tables in a pleasant courtyard garden adorned with flowers, shrubs and trees. The menu is brief but the food is of high quality and includes home-made cream of celery and mushroom soup with granary bread at £2.50, terrine of salmon, prawns and spinach with watercress mayonnaise at £4.25 and sautéed chicken livers and bacon with granary bread at £4.50. Smoking is not permitted in the restaurant. Between 60 and 70 wines are listed, while beer drinkers have the choice of Guinness and 6X or Henry's Original IPA, both from Wadworth. Chintz curtains and oak beams lend a cottagey feel to the accommodation. Some of the rooms have substantial, oak-framed beds, while some also have televisions.

Brewery: Free house
Licensee: Richard De-Wolf
Opening hours: 11am-2.30pm, 6-11pm; Sun 12-2.30pm, 7-10.30pm
Bar food: 12-2pm (except Sun)
Restaurant: 7.15-9pm; Sun 12.30-1.45pm, 7.15-9pm
Accommodation: (Price per room) single £32.50-£35, double £70-£75
Children: Welcome anywhere
Credit cards: Access, Visa

🍺 TITE INN
Mill End, Chadlington, near Chipping Norton OX7 3NY. Tel 060876 475

Chadlington

Families are especially welcome at this friendly and unpretentious village pub, a Cotswold-stone building with a garden with benches and tables to one side. It dates from the 16th century and the single bar, although carpeted, retains its plain stone walls and a stone fireplace. Benches stand alongside copper-topped and plain wooden tables, and a small collection of marquetry is on show. Once a month, on a Sunday evening, the bar plays host to folk music. Adnams Bitter, Flowers Best, Murphy's and a guest beer are served, along with Byland Blackjack cider and nearly 20 wines. Half a dozen escargots at £3.50 and smoked salmon at £4.95 are among the starters on offer, while main courses include grilled pink trout with almonds at £5.95, chicken breast in a cider and honey sauce at £6.25 and a daily vegetarian dish.

Brewery: Free house
Licensees: Michael and Susan Willis
Opening hours: 12-2.30pm, 6.30-11pm (winter from 7pm); closed Mon; Sun 12-3pm, 7-10.30pm
Bar food: 12-2pm, 6.30-9pm; Sun 7-9pm
Restaurant: 7-9pm (except Sun and Mon)
Children: Welcome anywhere

BELL
Shore Street, Charlbury OX7 3PP. Tel 0608 810278

Charlbury

For somewhere offering ten double, two twin and two single rooms, this 17th-century pub has a smallish bar, although it is light and airy and, thanks to its congenial atmosphere, enjoys a varied clientele. A flagstone floor, a log fire, an old clock and a shotgun, a collection of bells and prints of bygone local life together preserve a traditional rural flavour. Outside the stone-built pub there is seating on the patio at the back and in the large garden adjoining the car park. Guinness, Hook Norton Best Bitter, Wadworth 6X and McEwan Export are on offer, along with a choice of nearly 70 wines. Snacks such as omlettes (£3.35 to £3.75), soup (75p) and a hot dish (£3.75) are served in the bar, while in the restaurant main courses include roast leg of lamb with a rosemary gravy at £5, poached salmon and vegetables at £5.25 and baked baby chicken in mushroom sauce at £4.95. The two-star accommodation is spacious, and the traditionally furnished rooms each have a television

Brewery: Free house
Licensee: Juan Claramonte
Opening hours: 11am-3pm, 7-11pm; Sun 12-2.30, 7-10.30pm
Bar food: 12.30-2.15pm, 6.30-8.30pm (Sun from 7pm)
Restaurant: 12.30-2pm, 7.30-9pm
Accommodation: (Price per room) single £50-£55, double £75-£85
Children: In restaurant, if eating, and the Lounge
Credit cards: AMERICAN EXPRESS®, Access, Visa, Diners

⊜ BLACK HORSE
Checkendon, near Reading RG8 0TE. Tel 0491 680418

Checkendon

This 17th-century pub has hung on to its rustic simplicity, partly because it stands almost alone in the depths of the countryside but mainly because the landlady, who has run it for 40 years, has kept it that way. The red-brick building adjoins a barn of the same material, and dates back to the 17th century. The single bar serves three small rooms which have beams, walls of a dark yet warm yellow, ancient benches and modest armchairs. Outside there is seating at benches on the veranda and in the small garden. Aided by her daughter, the landlady, at 86, still welcomes a wide variety of customers, who are drawn simply by the honest appeal of the place and the beer - Brakspear Bitter straight from the barrel - for no food is served.

Brewery: Free house
Licensee: Mrs Margaret Saunders
Opening hours: 11am-2pm (but flexible, so telephone to check); 6.30/7-11pm; Sun 12-3pm, 7-10.30pm
Children: Welcome anywhere

CLANFIELD TAVERN
Brampton Road, Clanfield, near Faringdon OX18 9RG. Tel 036781 223

Clanfield

A pretty flower garden with benches and tables lends charm to the front of this friendly Cotswold-stone pub. Dating from the 17th century, it was originally a coaching inn and stands at the heart of the village. An assortment of customers use the three cosy rooms, which are served by one bar. Decorated with shooting and racing prints, these

Brewery: Free house
Licensee: Keith Gill
Opening hours: 11.30am-3pm, 6-11pm; Sun 12-3pm, 7-10.30pm
Bar food: As opening hours
Accommodation: (Price per

have stone walls, low ceilings with hefty oak beams, flagstones, carpet or bare boards, generous log fires and solid traditional benches and tables. Upstairs there are three vast double bedrooms, with white walls, beams in unexpected places, chintz furnishings and a television in each. On offer in the bar are Morrells Varsity, Hook Norton Best Bitter, Morland Original Bitter and Murphy's, along with Stowford Press cider. Soup of the day, at £1.95, may be followed by main courses like steamed steak pudding at £6.15, spinach and scrambled egg stuffed into flat mushrooms with a spicy sauce at £5.70 and deep-fried whitebait at £4.95.

room) £50-£65
Children: Welcome anywhere
Credit cards: Access, Visa

⊛ BARLEY MOW
Clifton Hampden, near Abingdon OX14 3EH. Tel 086730 7847

Clifton Hampden

A thatched roof, lattice windows and low-pitched gables bestow great charm on this 600-year-old pub, which is featured in Jerome K Jerome's humorous novel *Three Men in a Boat*. But inside, while the past is similarly evoked by a beamed ceiling twisted beyond belief, oak panelling, benches, log fires, old lamps and hunting prints, the effect is to some extent spoiled by a fruit machine and tired-looking sofas. In addition to the single bar, where Webster's, Ushers Best and Ruddles County, as well as a dozen malt whiskies, are on sale to a mixed clientele, there is a garden at the back generously supplied with benches and tables. Beef in ale, chicken tikka and vegetable lasagne, all at £4.25, are among the dishes served in the bar. There are two double and two single rooms, cottage-like with their beams, pine furniture, pictures and flowers, and each with a television.

Brewery: Chef & Brewer
Licensees: Annette and Bob Mathias
Opening hours: 11am-11pm; Sun 12-3pm, 7-10.30pm
Bar food: 12-2pm, 7-9pm (except Sun)
Restaurant: 7-9.30pm
Accommodation: (Price per room) single £36, double £56
Children: Welcome anywhere
Credit cards: Access, Visa

⊛ GEORGE
High Street, Dorchester-on-Thames OX10 7HH. Tel 0865 340404

Dorchester-on-Thames

The stagecoach standing outside recalls this town-centre pub's former role as a coaching inn. A substantial, whitewashed building dating from the 15th century, it offers accommodation of 14 double and four single rooms. The majority are spacious and all are well furnished and decorated in traditional style and have a television. This feel of a comfortable hotel is reflected in the bar, with its ancient beams, large open fireplace, thick chintz curtains, sofas and old leather chairs. The food, complemented by an impressive list of 130 wines, in addition to Brakspear Bitter and a weekly guest beer and 12 malt whiskies, is of a high standard and all the more enjoyable for the relaxed

Brewery: Free house
Licensee: Brian Griffin
Opening hours: 11am-3pm, 6-11pm; Sun 12-2.30pm, 7-10.30pm
Bar food: 12-2pm, 7-9.30pm (Sun 7-9pm)
Restaurant: 12-2pm, 7-9.30pm
Accommodation: (Price per room) single £62, double £75-£100
Children: Welcome anywhere

surroundings and friendly mix of customers. On offer are home-made soup at £2.50 and main courses such as pan-fried lamb's liver and bacon with red-wine gravy, and wild mushroom and Stilton crumble, both at £4.95, and grilled salmon steak with parsley butter at £5. Sweets such as Dutch apple flan and rich chocolate mousse are £2.50.

Credit cards:
AMERICAN EXPRESS®, Access, Visa, Diners

WOODMAN
Fernham, near Faringdon SN7 7NX. Tel 0367 820643

Fernham

The landlord of this village pub in the Vale of the White Horse has been here for over 20 years, with a mission to serve the finest-condition ales. Consequently, straight from the barrel come four to six beers from a range which is frequently changed but always includes Morland Original Bitter and Theakston Old Peculier. The whitewashed, lattice-windowed pub, with gardens back and front, dates from the 16th century and has a single bar. With a clientele of locals and a good number of tourists, this serves a series of rooms which likewise retain their stone walls and heavy beams. Portraits of the pub's best-loved customers decorate the walls, and in winter a pot of stew hangs enticingly over the logs blazing in the huge fireplace. Mousaka at £4.20 and brown bean chasseur and fisherman's pie, both at £4, are among the other dishes on offer.

Brewery: Free house
Licensee: John Lane
Opening hours: 10.30am-3pm, 6-11pm; closed Mon lunchtime; Sun 12-3pm, 7-10.30pm
Bar food: 12-2pm, 7-9.30pm
Children: Welcome anywhere

FALKLAND ARMS
Great Tew, near Chipping Norton OX7 4DB. Tel 060883 653

Great Tew

Like the surrounding village, which can be seen from its garden, this vine-clad, 16th-century pub is built of the local golden stone. Popular with tourists as well as locals and business people, it serves well prepared home-made fare such as lamb and apricot pie, mushrooms and vegetables at £5.50 and, both at £4 and with salad, cheese, tomato and onion quiche with jacket potato and mushrooms in cider topped with cheese and a bread roll. Among the nine real ales sold are the regular Donnington Best, Wadworth 6X, Hall & Woodhouse Tanglefoot and Hook Norton Best, and there are 50 malt whiskies and 14 country wines to choose from. Hundreds of jugs, tankards and mugs hang from the low ceiling of the cosy bar, which also displays a collection of pipes and snuff. Stone walls and floor, a huge inglenook fireplace and rustic settles, benches and tables likewise preserve the rural character of the bar, where live folk music can be heard on Sunday evenings. Four beamed double rooms are available,- one with a four-poster bed.

Brewery: Free house
Licensee: John Milligan
Opening hours: 11.30am-2.30pm, 6-11pm; closed Mon lunchtime; Sun 12-2, 7-10.30pm
Bar food: 12-2pm (except Sun and Mon)
Accommodation: (Price per room) double £45
Children: Not permitted inside; outdoor play area

⏚ KING WILLIAM
Hailey, near Wallingford OX10 6AD. Tel 0491 680675

Hailey

At the same time as preserving its rustic character, this 16th-century pub lays great emphasis on the beer, serving Brakspear Old Ale, Special and Pale, but no draught lagers and only scrumpy besides. Nor is food a high priority: ploughman's at £3, hot minced beef pie at 75p and Cornish pasty at 85p are all that is usually on offer. The large garden behind the whitewashed farmhouse offers a fine view of the Chiltern Hills and has a display of old agricultural implements. This theme continues in the bar, where hundreds of farming tools from bygone days, along with the odd stuffed animal, decorate the exposed-brick walls and the low-beamed ceiling alike. The rigours of wooden benches are amply offset by the friendly mix of customers and the general cosiness of the bar, which is all the more welcoming in winter with its large open fire. Morris dancing and folk music occasionally take place of an evening.

Brewery: Brakspear
Licensee: Brian Penny
Opening hours: 11am-2.30pm, 6-11pm; Sun 12-2.30pm, 7-10.30pm
Bar food: 12-2pm only
Children: Welcome anywhere; outdoor play area

BLUE BOAR
Tucur Lane, Longworth, near Abingdon OX13 5ET. Tel 0865 820494

Longworth

A thatched roof which nearly touches the ground at the back lends great charm to this Elizabethan village-centre pub. The compact, Cotswold-stone building has one bar, with oriental rugs on a tiled floor, old wooden settles and a log fire. Cricketing and other prints adorn the stone walls, while from the ceiling hangs a collection of rare old skis. Locals and visitors mix comfortably, enjoying Morrells Best and Varsity, or sampling a menu which includes wild smoked salmon at £4.95 and boar burger at £3.75, followed by sweets like lemon meringue pie and fudge brownies, both at £1.95. There is a small back garden where barbecues are occasionally held.

Brewery: Morrells
Licensee: Paul Dailey
Opening hours: 11am-2.30pm, 6-11pm; Sun 12-3pm, 7-10.30pm
Bar food: 12-2pm, 7-9.45pm
Children: Welcome anywhere
Credit cards:
AMERICAN EXPRESS®, Access, Visa

Black Country Best
The Black Country has a reputation for good traditional beer and 'Unspoilt by Progress' is the motto of Banks' and Hanson's, which brew under the umbrella of Wolverhampton and Dudley Breweries. The Banks firm, established in Wolverhampton in 1875, amalgamated with two other local companies in 1890. One of them was Thompson's of Dudley and Edwin John Thompson became managing director. His great-grandson was the managing director a century later. The firm bought another Dudley brewery, Hanson's, in 1943.

TROUT

Godstow Road, Lower Wolvercote, near Oxford OX2 8PN. Tel 0865 54485

Lower Wolvercote

L it up after dark in summer, this Cotswold-stone pub's garden, where peacocks roam, is set on the banks of the Isis. On warm evenings the atmosphere is often lively, with music from a classical quintet or a jazz group an occasional added attraction. Tourists, above all, flock to the long, rambling building, which started life in 1138 as a hospice. Its interconnecting, oak-beamed rooms have inglenook fireplaces and oak or stone floors and are decorated with stuffed trout, hunting scenes and views of Oxford. Particularly impressive is the converted stable room, with its high ceiling. The two bars serve Bass Charrington IPA, Worthington Best and Guinness, as well as a regularly changed guest ale, while the simple menu includes quiche at £3.90, chicken and ham pie at £4.50 and smoked trout at £5.50, plus a range of hot dishes at £4.50.

Brewery: Bass
Licensee: Warren Zilch
Opening hours: Summer 11am-11pm; winter 11am-3pm, 5-11pm ; Sun 12-3pm, 7-10.30pm
Bar food: 12-2.30pm, 6.30-9pm (Sun 7-9pm)
Children: Welcome anywhere
Credit cards: AMERICAN EXPRESS®, Access, Visa

🍺 FIVE HORSESHOES

Maiden Grove, near Henley-on-Thames RG9 6EX. Tel 0491 641282

Maiden Grove

A fine view of the Chiltern Hills can be had from the pleasant garden of this secluded country pub. Built about 1700, the vine-covered, red-brick cottage offers its varied clientele the choice of two bars and a new conservatory which is used as a dining room. The bars, low-ceilinged, mainly carpeted and with large fireplaces, one with a wood-burning stove, are decorated with old tools, photographs and prints, while a collection of banknotes from around the world makes for an eye-catching ceiling. Brakspear Bitter and Special, Guinness, seven malt whiskies and a similar number of fine brandies are on sale. A list of over 50 wines complements the food, which is of good quality and includes starters such as Stilton soup at £2.50 and smoked trout pâté at £4.50, and main courses like pan-fried fresh king scallops on a bed of spinach cream cheese at £8.50 and stir-fried beef at £6.95.

Brewery: Bass
Licensee: Graham Cromack
Opening hours: 11am-2.30pm, 6-11pm; Sun 12-3pm, 7-10.30pm
Bar food: 12-2pm, 7-9.45pm (limited snacks only on Sun evening)
Children: Not permitted under 14 years inside
Credit cards: Access, Visa

Substantial Citizens

Henley-on-Thames was already a famous place for inns when Robert Brakspear founded his brewing firm there in 1779. An ex-publican, he experimented with his beers, shrouding his notes in the secrecy of shorthand. He died in 1812, when his son William Henry was only ten, but the boy grew up to expand the company substantially. A prominent citizen of Victorian Henley, with his enormous nose and protruding chin, he died in 1882 at the age of 80. His family has continued to produce its admirable beers ever since.

⊜ SEVEN STARS
Marsh Baldon, near Oxford OX44 9LP. Tel 086738 255

Marsh Baldon

Generous portions of well cooked food, along with Morland Old Speckled Hen and Original Bitter, Guinness and a guest ale draw locals and business people to this village pub, which comprises a 15th-century, red-brick part and more recent additions. Two adjoining rooms, carpeted and with wooden benches and tables, are served by one long bar, and there is additional seating in the uncultivated garden to the side and back, where the occasional hen clucks past. Among the starters on offer are chicken wings marinated in ginger, garlic and white wine at £2.25 and country mushrooms cooked in a sauce of tarragon, wholegrain mustard and soured cream at £2.75. Typical main courses are feuillette, a puff-pastry parcel of prawns and Stilton, at £5.50, chicken en croûte and pork chop stuffed with Stilton in a cider sauce, both at £6.95, while the sweets include raspberry crunch at £2.50.

Brewery: Free house
Licensees: Phil Morton and Mark Genders
Opening hours: 11.30am-2.30pm, 7-11pm; Sun 12-2.30, 7-10.30pm
Bar food: 12-2pm, 7-9.30pm (Sun 9pm)
Children: Welcome anywhere

⊜ BEETLE AND WEDGE
Ferry Lane, Moulsford-on-Thames, near Goring OX10 9JF. Tel 0491 651381

Moulsford-on-Thames

The stretch of the Thames on which this pub stands inspired Kenneth Grahame's *The Wind in the Willows*, and the river still provides an agreeable setting for a drink or a meal inside or on the terrace. The extended red-brick boat-house, part of which dates back to the 12th century, is more of a restaurant than a pub. A mixed clientele gathers in the single bar, with its Italian and Spanish floor tiles, beams and exposed brickwork softened by a few well chosen prints, where a wide range of dishes is grilled on an open charcoal fire. Starters include moules marinières à la crème at £5.50 and melon with fresh strawberries and white port at £4.95, while among the main courses are medallions of venison with chanterelles and fresh figs at £13.75 and baked monkfish tail with peppers, garlic and ginger at £10.95. An extensive wine list is available on request, while beer drinkers have the choice of Wadworth 6X, Hall & Woodhouse Tanglefoot, Adnams Bitter and Guinness. Occasional live music is provided by a jazz band. Ten light, spacious rooms are available, all with thick carpet and high-quality furnishings.

Brewery: Free house
Licensees: Kate and Richard Smith
Opening hours: 11am-2.30pm, 6-11pm; Sun 12-3pm, 7-10.30pm
Bar food: 12.30-2pm, 7.30-10pm (Sun 9.30pm)
Restaurant: 12.30-2pm, 7.30-10pm (except Sun evening)
Accommodation: (Price per room) single £70-£100, double £85-£125
Children: Welcome anywhere
Credit cards: AMERICAN EXPRESS®, Access, Visa, Diners

TURF TAVERN
4 Bath Place, Holywell Street, Oxford OX1 3SU. Tel 0865 243235

Oxford

To its mix of regulars, many of them students, this pub is a hidden treasure, accessible only on foot along alleys which burrow through the ancient heart of the city. Built into the old city walls, its two connected rooms have low oak beams and simple benches and tables, while outside two additional drinking areas are linked by a passageway. On tap are Flowers Original, Archers Headbanger and Golden Bitter and Boddingtons, and guest beers, with Westons Scrumpy and a range of country wines also on offer. Standard pub fare is served, including cottage pie, vegetarian lasagne and Cotswold chicken, all at £4.85.

Brewery: Whitbread
Licensees: Biff and Pam Griffin
Opening hours: 11am-11pm; Sun 12-3pm, 7-10.30pm
Bar food: 12-3pm, 6-9pm (Sun from 7pm)
Children: Welcome anywhere
Credit cards: Access, Visa

LAMB INN
Shipton-under-Wychwood, near Burford OX7 6DQ. Tel 0993 830465

Shipton-under-Wychwood

Unusually, this popular, 17th-century pub operates a buffet system for its assorted clientele. The chef serves good, wholesome food from the table on which it is displayed, although diners may help themselves to salad. Home-made soup is the only starter on offer, but the main courses include smoked trout and rolled duck, both at £7.50, and scallops in cream sauce at £4.50. Gooseberry brûlée and berry tartlet, both at £2.50, are among the sweets available. This compact pub, situated near the village centre, is built of local stone and has a patio and a small garden at the back. Hunting prints and beer tankards decorate the bar, which is traditional in character, with its stone walls, beamed ceiling, oak floor and wooden benches and chairs. Guinness, Hook Norton Best and Wadworth 6X are on sale, along with a choice of some 50 wines. Upstairs, five pleasantly furnished double rooms are available, all with beams, pictures of flowers on the walls and a television.

Brewery: Free house
Licensees: Vivien and Luciano Valenta
Opening hours: 11am-3pm, 6-11pm; closed Mon; Sun 12-3pm, 7-10.30pm
Bar food: 12-2pm, 7-10pm (except Mon)
Restaurant: 7-9.30pm (except Mon); Sun 12-2 only
Accommodation: (Price per room) single £48, double £65
Children: Not permitted inside
Credit cards: AMERICAN EXPRESS®, Access, Visa

SHAVEN CROWN
Shipton-under-Wychwood, near Burford OX7 6BA. Tel 0993 830330

Shipton-under-Wychwood

Originally a hospice for nearby Bruern Abbey, this substantial building in honey-coloured Cotswold stone dates back to 1350. Tapestries, hunting prints, photographs and odds and ends lend interest to the carpeted bar, which has a high, beamed ceiling, wooden benches and partitions and a log fire. In warmer weather the courtyard garden, with its flowers and vines, is a pleasant alternative to sitting inside. On tap are Hook Norton Best, Morland Old Masters,

Brewery: Free house
Licensee: Trevor Brooke
Opening hours: 12-2.30pm, 7-11pm; Sun 12-2.30pm, 7-10.30pm
Bar food: 12-2pm, 7-9.30pm (Sun 9pm)
Restaurant: 7-9.30pm; Sun 12-

Bentley's Yorkshire Bitter, Murphy's and a guest beer, along with Bylands Blackjack cider. A choice of some 60 wines complements the menu, which includes hot croissant with leek, ham, mushroom sauce with salad at £3.95, whitebait with lemon and brown bread at £3.25 and home-baked ham and salad at £4.95. Spacious, and attractive with their beams, mullioned windows and pine furniture, the seven double and one single room are all equipped with tea and coffee-making facilities and television.

⊕ SIR CHARLES NAPIER
Spriggs Alley, near Chinnor OX9 4BX. Tel 0494 483011

Spriggs Alley

Built in Chilterns style of flint and brick, this stylish 18th-century village pub is not so much a place for a drink - even though Wadworth IPA is served straight from the barrel - as a restaurant. In summer it is especially pleasant to eat on the vine and wisteria-draped terrace, but at weekends at any time of the year booking is advisable. The enticing menu includes starters such as wild mushrooms with ciabatta and Hollandaise sauce at £5.50 and artichoke salad with rocket and avocado at £5, while typical main courses are char-grilled loin of veal with rosemary and pan-fried salmon and scallops with ginger cream, both at £12.50, and pigeon breast on a bed of spinach with port sauce at £8. A remarkable choice of 400 wines is available, along with freshly squeezed fruit juices. A wide variety of customers rubs shoulders in the comfortable, informal bar, which has rugs, armchairs and benches and a log fire, and displays work by local artists and sculptors to a background of classical music. Outside there are the simpler diversions of a large croquet lawn and a paddock.

2pm only
Accommodation: (Price per room) single £33, double £66-£82
Children: Welcome anywhere, but not permitted under five years in restaurant in the evening
Credit cards: Access, Visa

Brewery: Free house
Licensee: Mrs Julie Griffiths
Opening hours: 11.45am-3pm, 6-11pm; Sun 12-3pm; closed Sun evening and all day Mon
Bar food: 12-2.30pm, 7.30-10pm; Sun 12.30-3.30pm
Children: Welcome anywhere at lunchtime, but not permitted under eight years in the evening
Credit cards: Access, Visa

⊕ RED LION
South Street, Steeple Aston OX6 3RY. Tel 0869 40225

Steeple Aston

Unusual etchings and prints adorn the bar of this friendly village pub, reflecting the owner's interest in art, while old clocks bolster the traditional atmosphere created by the beamed ceiling and log fire. Part plain Cotswold stone and part whitewashed, the 17th-century building is decked with vines and flowers, and has a pleasant, secluded patio. Wadworth 6X, Hook Norton Best, Beamish Stout and Hall & Woodhouse Tanglefoot are on sale, as well as Bitburger German bottled beer and a good selection of malt whiskies. To accompany the food, which includes, in winter, hoppel poppel (ham and smoked sausage topped with sour cream)

Brewery: Free house
Licensee: Colin Mead
Opening hours: 11am-3pm, 6-11pm; Sun 12-2.30, 7-10.30pm
Bar food: 12-2pm (except Sun)
Restaurant: 7.30-9pm (except Sun and Mon)
Children: Welcome anywhere
Credit cards: Access, Visa

and Koningsberger klops (pork and beef dumplings flavoured with anchovies and served with caper sauce), both at £3.80, there are 120 wines to choose from. In summer there might be fresh salmon or crab salad for £4.65.

⊛ NORTH STAR
The Causeway, Steventon, near Didcot OX13 6SG. Tel 0235 831309

Steventon

Named after the locomotive North Star, this friendly, unpretentious pub celebrates the Age of Steam by having a railway signal bearing its sign outside and pictures of historic engines inside. A pretty, whitewashed building, dating from1460, it stands just off the village green and has a small garden with tables and chairs. The single room, with low oak beams, traditional mustard-coloured walls and simple furniture, has no more than a foot of bar, and the beer - Morland Original Bitter and Mild - is drawn straight from the cask. No hot food is available - only sandwiches and rolls.

Brewery: Morland
Licensee: A Cox
Opening hours: 12-3pm, 7-11pm; Sun 12-3pm, 7-10.30pm
Bar food:12-2pm (except Sat and Sun)
Children: Not permitted under 14 years inside

PEYTON ARMS
Stoke Lyne, near Bicester OX6 9SD. Tel 0869 345285

Stoke Lyne

The beer in this friendly, unspoilt pub is drawn straight from the barrel, as in days gone by, although the building itself is not that old, dating from the last century. Of local Cotswold stone and situated in the heart of the village, it attracts mainly locals, there strictly for the beer - Hook Norton Best, Mild and, in winter, Old Hooky - for no food is available. One bar serves two small, cosy rooms which retain their simple rural character, thanks to low beams, shuttered windows and wooden benches. Lining the walls are photographs and prints of steam engines and local life, while among the other diversions on offer are darts, dominoes, shove halfpenny and Aunt Sally. For families and others who might prefer to drink outside, benches are set out in the good-sized garden.

Brewery: Hook Norton
Licensee: Norman Oxlade
Opening hours: 11am-2.30pm, 6-11pm; closed Mon lunchtime; Sun 12-3pm, 7-10.30pm
Children: Welcome anywhere

⊛ CROOKED BILLET
Newlands Lane, Stoke Row RG9 5PU. Tel 0491 681048

Stoke Row

This rural gem, enjoying splendid isolation, underlines the changes suffered by many less fortunate country pubs. Used as a location for many films, the handsome, white-painted brick-built pub dates from 1642 and in the 19th century gained a red-brick extension which is now covered

Brewery: Brakspear
Licensee: Paul Clerehugh
Opening hours: 12-3pm, 7-11pm; Sun 12-2.30pm, 7-10.30pm

in vines. An unspoilt meadow of a garden offers a view of the fine surrounding countryside. There is no bar; Brakspear Bitter, Old Ale and Special are served straight from the cask. A mixed clientele frequents the two snug rooms, where low ceilings, a large inglenook fireplace and wooden benches echo the traditional exterior, while oriental rugs add comfort to the parquet floor and accomplished paintings and photographs decorate the walls. Food is a priority here, and of a standard to match, although the visitor who wants just a beer or two will not feel unwelcome. Starters include terrine of local rabbit with salad and blackcurrant coulis and smoked goose breast with spring onion salad, both at £4.95, while typical main courses are escalope of wild Scottish salmon on a cushion of spinach with a white wine sauce at £9.95, skewers of grilled chicken breast served with wild rice on peanut sauce at £8.70 and fricassée of mushrooms, shallots and garlic with tagliatelle at £6. Around 70 wines are available.

Bar food: 12-2.30pm, 7-10pm; Sun 12-10pm
Children: Welcome anywhere

SHROPSHIRE

⊜ THREE TUNS
Salop Street, Bishop's Castle SY9 5BW. Tel 0588 638797

Bishop's Castle

Records show that this pub held a licence to brew beer as early as 1642, although the origins of the building are considerably older, and a medieval chimney survives. However, the Grade I listed Three Tuns Brewery across the small courtyard from the pub was built in 1888 and is still in use. In the three bars, furnished with high-backed settles and warmed in winter by wood-burning stoves, the brick-built pub, set into the hillside, sells the brewery's XXX Bitter, Light Mild, Jim Wood's and Old Scrooge to a mix of regulars and business people. Among the dishes on offer are home-made soup at £1.50, Shropshire blue-cheese ploughman's at £4.50, home-made fisherman's pie at £4.95 and ratatouille with melted cheese at £4.50. The sweets include treacle tart at £1.25 and carrot cake at £1.95. In addition, the landlord's sister specialises in Indian dishes - for example, onion bhajees at £2.50, beef Madras at £5.50 and prawn curry at £5.75. The pub has a snooker club, and darts and quoits can also be played, while occasional live music can be heard in the evenings.

Brewery: Free house
Licensee: Dominic E Wood
Opening hours: 11.30am-3pm, 7-11pm; Sun 12-3pm, 7-10.30pm
Bar food: 12-2pm, 7-9pm
Children: If eating and well behaved; half portions available

⊛ DOWN INN
Ludlow Road, near Bridgnorth WV16 6UA. Tel 0746 35624

Bridgnorth

Appetising, well presented and sensibly priced food attracts locals, families and, at lunchtimes in particular, business and retired people to this pub tucked away in the depths of the country. Typical starters are sweet cured herrings with dill mustard and Chinese dim sum, both at £2.90, while the main courses include smoked haddock in cheese sauce at £7.20, pan-fried calves' liver at £8.30 and Old English chicken pie at £6.70. A pub since the middle of the last century, the stone building has two carpeted bars, decorated with brass platters and mugs and furnished with comfortable, leather-upholstered chairs and carvers at small tables. The small side bar serves as a family room and there is additional seating on the pleasant patio. Beers include their own brew, called Down and Out, plus Flowers Original, Gale's Pompey Royal, Wadworth 6X and Marston's Pedigree. Scrumpy Jack cider and Murphy's Stout are also on sale, along with some 30 malt whiskies.

Brewery: Free house
Licensees: Bill Watson and Paul Millington
Opening hours: 10am-2.30pm, 6.30-11pm; Sun 12-2.30pm only
Bar food: 12-2pm, 7-9.30pm; Sun 12-2pm
Restaurant: Times as bar food
Children: Welcome anywhere; own menu and half portions available
Credit cards: Access, Visa

⊛ ROYAL OAK
Cardington, near Church Stretton SY6 7JZ. Tel 0694 771266

Cardington

A delightful position on a rise below the village church adds to the charm of this white-painted pub, brick-built over five centuries ago and adorned in summer with hanging baskets and roses. In the quarry-tiled bar, with its choice of Bass, M & B Springfield and Wadworth 6X, a mixed clientele, including a fair number of walkers and older customers, mingle beneath low, hop-draped beams. In winter the large open fire is irresistible, while in warmer weather the terraced garden beckons, with its tables set among the roses and shrubs. At lunchtime the food includes Shropshire fidget pie at £3.35 and lasagne (meat or vegetable) at £3.95, and in the evening dishes like chicken cobbler at £5.60 and chilli at £4.20 are served. To round off a meal, traditional sweets are on offer- for example, Spotted Dick and treacle sponge - as well as Bavarian lemon torte, all at £2.30. One bedroom, simply furnished, is available for either one or two persons.

Brewery: Free house
Licensee: John Seymour
Opening hours: 12-2.30pm, 7-11pm; Sun 12-2pm, 7-10.30pm
Bar food: 12-2pm, 7-8.30pm (except Mon); Sun 12-2pm only
Accommodation: (Price per room) single £22, double £33
Children: Welcome anywhere at lunchtime but, in the evening, only if eating

STABLES INN
Drury Lane, Hopesgate, near Minsterley SY5 0EP. Tel 0743 891344

Hopesgate

This stone pub with its small garden in front may look just like a cottage, but ever since it was built, in the 1690s, it has been an inn. The U-shaped bar offers a friendly atmosphere and the comfort of a carpeted floor, cushioned settles and an open fire to its clientele, who are mainly locals and retired people enjoying a reasonably priced meal. Food is served in the bar at lunchtime, when starters include hot local sausages with salad and crusty bread at £3.75, and in both the bar and the restaurant in the evening, with hot mushrooms à la Grecque and dressed Cromer crab in mayonnaise, both at £3.70, on offer. Main courses at lunchtime include cheese, tomato and aubergine bake at £4.60, and in the evening diced lamb with Mexican chilli bean sauce at £6, while those with a sweet tooth are catered for with local farmhouse ice cream and Norwegian cream (egg custard, apricot purée, cream and flaked chocolate). Along with a good selection of wines and half a dozen malt whiskies, Woods Special, Marston's Pedigree and Felinfoel Double Dragon, Bass and an occasional guest beer are on sale.

Brewery: Free house
Licensees: Denis and Debbie Harding
Opening hours: 11.30am-2.30pm, 7-11pm; closed Mon; Sun 12-2.30pm, 7-10.30pm
Bar food: 12-1.30pm; 7-8.30pm; Sun 12-1.30pm only
Restaurant: Wed-Sat 7-8.30pm; booking advisable
Children: Only if eating, and preferably not in the evening

CROWN INN
Hopton Wafers, near Cleobury Mortimer DY14 0NB. Tel 0299 270372

Hopton Wafers

A large, creeper-clad building dating back to the 16th century, this pub preserves its rural character inside, with a bar furnished with black settles, pews and cushioned seats, and oil paintings on the walls. Behind the inn, part stone, part brick and timber, is a large, lawned garden which has a duck pond and runs down to a stream, while outside the restaurant the patio garden's vine-covered arbour is an ideal spot for a drink before a meal or a coffee afterwards. Beer drinkers among the mix of customers can choose between Bass, Boddingtons, Flowers Original and Brains Dark, or from a selection of imported bottled lagers and malt whiskies. An extensive wine list and a good house wine complement a regularly changed choice of 15 special dishes, such as John Cope's spicy sausages at £5.25, Hopton mixed grill at £7.95 and whole baby plaice in lemon butter at £5.95. Sweets include stand-bys like treacle tart and plum pudding. Eight pleasant double rooms are available to either one or two persons.

Brewery: Free house
Licensee: John Price
Opening hours: 11am-3pm, 6-11pm; Sun 12-3pm, 7-10.30pm
Bar food: 12-2pm (Sat 2.30pm), 7-9.30 (Sat 10.30pm)
Restaurant: 7-9.30pm; bookings only at lunchtime
Accommodation: (Price per room) single £37, double £58
Children: Welcome anywhere; own menu available
Credit cards: Access, Visa

⊜ PHEASANT INN
Linley Brook, near Bridgnorth WV16 4TA. Tel 0746 762260

Linley Brook

In summer tourists boost the custom of this friendly country pub, whose regulars are mainly locals and include a fair number of youngsters, doubtless homing in on the bar billiards and electronic quiz machine. Stone-built 200 to 300 years ago, and with a modern brick extension, the appealing, white-painted inn consists of a single bar, furnished in traditional style and displaying local historical photographs and humorous cartoons, a dining area and a garden equipped with tables and chairs. On tap are Hook Norton Mild and Bitter, and usually two guest beers, along with Weston's range of ciders. An 8oz rump steak at £5.95, gammon and egg at £4.95 and home-made lasagne at £3.95 are included in the standard pub fare on offer.

Brewery: Free house
Licensee: Simon Reed
Opening hours: 11am-2.30pm, 6-11pm (winter 7-11pm); Sun 12-3pm, 7-10.30pm
Bar food: As opening hours
Children: In eating area, if well behaved; own menu available

⊜ GEORGE AND DRAGON
High Street, Much Wenlock TF13 6AA. Tel 0952 727312

Much Wenlock

Well prepared, well presented and reasonably priced food and a good range of beers bring a steady flow of locals, business people and youngsters to this small, town-centre pub. Among the home-cooked delights are spinach and cheese-stuffed pancakes at £2 (£4.85 as a main course), breast of chicken in Shropshire mead and cream at £6, spicy bean casserole at £4.85 and, in winter, rabbit pie and game pie at £4.50. Particularly good are the hot, sticky toffee pudding and chocolate truffle tart, both £2, like all the sweets. Hook Norton beers, Ruddles County, Titanic Captain Smith's Strong Ale, Courage Directors and Wells Bombardier are on sale in the single bar of this black and white pub, which is at least 400 years old. Brewing memorabilia, mainly pictures and posters, and a collection of jugs decorate the simply furnished, quarry-tiled bar, which from to time is enlivened by the landlady's son, who plays jazz guitar and folk music in the evening.

Brewery: Free house
Licensee: Mrs Eve Nolan
Opening hours: 11am-2.30pm, 6-11pm (Jan-Mar 12-2.30pm, 7-11pm); Sun 12-3pm, 7-11pm
Bar food: 12-2pm, 6.30/7-9.15pm (except Sun evening)
Restaurant: Times as bar food
Children: In restaurant at lunchtime if well behaved, but babies and toddlers discouraged

---

Skittles

Skittles is a far older game than darts or dominoes, on record in London since the 15th century, when it was banned. Henry VIII enjoyed it and had his own skittle alley, but governments kept vainly trying to stop ordinary people playing, because they ought to have been practising their archery and because they gambled so heavily. Even so, the game became popular enough to make 'beer and skittles' proverbial. Basically, three wooden balls are propelled at nine pins to knock them down, but there are sharp variations in the rules between different areas and pubs. Varieties include London or Old English Skittles, West Country Skittles, Long Alley and Aunt Sally, as well as ten-pin bowling and several types of table skittles.

∰ TALBOT INN
High Street, Much Wenlock TF13 6AA Tel 0952 727077

Much Wenlock

The comforts of a mainly middle-aged to elderly clientele are attended to by the friendly staff of this town-centre pub, built as a coaching inn some 600 years ago. Ruddles Best and Webster's Yorkshire, a good wine list including an excellent house wine, and six malt whiskies complement a varied menu. Typical starters are Greek salad and bacon, mushroom and Stilton bake, both at £2.95, while main courses, each at £5.25, include lamb and apricot casserole, stuffed courgette, cheese and potato and Chinese-style pork. For those with room, bread-and-butter pudding or raspberry roulade, both at £2.25, round off a meal nicely. Traditional in character, with beams, log fires, dark furniture and banquettes, the carpeted bar has a nostalgic atmosphere courtesy of piped music from dance bands of the 1930s. Three double, one single and two twin rooms are available, all spacious and simply furnished, and with a television and tea-making facilities.

Brewery: Free house
Licensee: Timothy Lathe
Opening hours: 10am-2.30pm, 6-11pm; Sun 12-3pm, 7-10.30pm
Bar food: 11.30am-2pm, 6.30-9.30pm; Sun 12-2pm, 7-8.30pm
Restaurant: Times as bar food
Accommodation: (Price per person) £40-£45 including dinner; no children under 12 years
Children: Welcome anywhere if well behaved, but no babies, prams or pushchairs
Credit cards: Access, Visa

∰ HUNDRED HOUSE HOTEL
Norton, near Shifnal TF11 9EE. Tel 0952 271353

Norton

Located in the heart of the village, this well run hotel and pub is of Georgian vintage and incorporates a thatched, Grade I listed courthouse from the 14th century. The main building, three storeys in rose-clad red brick, has one bar, which has beams, exposed brickwork and open fires and is embellished with cast-iron pots and pans and herbs from the herb garden hanging from meat hooks. Well stocked, attractively laid out and offering a pleasant outlook, the main garden is reserved for residents, whose children will no doubt be fascinated by the two donkeys. The mixed clientele have the choice of Phillips Heritage or Old Ale or a guest beer, three draught ciders and a range of malt whiskies, plus 30 or so wines. On sale in the bar are regularly changing snacks and meals, with the latter also served in the restaurant and including courgette and leek pancake at £3.95, Black Country black pudding at £2.75 and spinach and mushroom roulade at £6.95. There are nine rooms - five family, three double and one twin - furnished in grand yet cottagey style, with patchwork quilts and, in some cases, half-tester beds.

Brewery: Free house
Licensees: Henry, Sylvia and David Phillips
Opening hours: 10.30am-2.30pm, 6-11pm; Sun 12-2.30pm, 7-10.30pm
Bar food: 12-2.30pm, 6-10pm; Sun 12-2pm, 7-9pm
Restaurant: Times as bar food
Accommodation: (Price per room) single £59-£69, double £69-£79
Children: Welcome anywhere; outdoor play area
Credit cards: Access, Visa

WHITE HORSE
Pulverbatch, near Shrewsbury SY5 8DS. Tel 0743 718247

Pulverbatch

The choice of Flowers Original, Castle Eden Ale and Boddingtons is supplemented in this white-painted, 16th-century village pub by a selection of reasonably priced wines and a remarkable array of 115 malt whiskies. A wide variety of customers uses the two bustling, fortunately spacious, bars, which are carpeted and comfortably furnished and sport old fire plaques. These indicated, in the early days of insurance, that a building had fire cover and was thus entitled to the assistance of the fire brigade in the event of a blaze. The extensive bar food menu offers soup at 95p and smoked trout pâté at £2.75, both home-made, lemon sole goujons at £4.25, curries at £5.50 and steaks from £6.50. Sweets include White Horse Whotsits (ice cream based) at £2.15 and pecan and treacle pie at £1.95.

Brewery: Free house
Licensee: James MacGregor
Opening hours: 11am-3pm, 7-11pm; Sun 12-3pm, 7-10.30pm
Bar food: 12-2pm, 7-10pm; Sun 12-1.45pm, 7-10pm
Children: Welcome, subject to legal restrictions
Credit cards: Access, Visa

CASTLE VAULTS
16 Castle Gates, Shrewsbury SY1 2AB. Tel 0743 358807

Shrewsbury

Built in 1829 on the side of a hill in the busy town centre, this black-and-white pub is very near Shrewsbury Castle and so attracts tourists as well as local professional people. The bright, cheerful bar, carpeted and furnished with small tables, is divided into sections, giving comfort and privacy, and the roof garden, in the shadow of the castle, is open to overnight guests and pub customers alike. The dining room is a no-smoking area. Snacks are available at lunchtime, including grilled steak sandwich at £2.60 and tagliatelle Niçoise at £3.30, while in the evening the speciality is Mexican food - for example, a taco at £2.30 and Pancho's layered dip (avocado dip layered with spicy beans and mince at £3 for a regular portion and £4.25 for a large). Ruddles Best, Courage Directors, Marston's Pedigree, Buckley's Dark Mild and Beamish are on sale, along with wines from Tanners and several malt whiskies. Four double rooms and three single rooms, are available.

Brewery: Free house
Licensees: George and Mary Mitchell
Opening hours: 11.30am-3pm, 6-11pm; Sun 12-3pm only
Bar food: 11.30am-2.30pm, 6-10pm; no food Sun
Accommodation: (Price per room) single £20, double £38-£40
Children: Welcome anywhere away from bar

⊜ WENLOCK EDGE INN
Hilltop, Wenlock Edge, near Much Wenlock TF13 6DJ. Tel 0746 36403

Wenlock Edge

Originally a quarryman's cottage dating from about 1700, this white-painted, local-stone inn has been a public house since 1920. Blessed with rural seclusion and ringed by a stone wall, it offers the choice of two bars - one with tables and benches, the other with chapel pews - in which to savour Robinson's Best, Webster's Yorkshire or a guest beer, or one of the 20-odd malt whiskies on offer. Alternatively, there is a flowery terrace with picnic benches. Well cooked and good value for money, the food includes starters such as garlic mushrooms at £2.75 and tomato and sweet red pepper soup at £1.75, main courses like smoked chicken breast and salad and fresh-baked salmon, both at £6.80, and, at £2.10, sweets like chocolate chimney and lemon pudding. A mixed bag of customers enjoys a friendly, informal atmosphere and is entertained once a month by the Wenlock Tailors' Storytelling Club. Three double rooms are available, one with twin beds.

Brewery: Free house
Licensee: Stephen Waring
Opening hours: 11am-2.30pm, 6-11pm; closed Mon lunchtime except BHs; Sun 12-2.30pm, 7-10.30pm
Bar food: 12-2pm, 7-9pm (except Mon)
Restaurant: Times as bar food
Accommodation: (Price per room) single £35, double £48
Children: Welcome anywhere but not permited under ten years in restaurant after 8pm on Sat; half portions available
Credit cards: Access, Visa, Switch

⊜ PLOUGH
Wistanstow, near Craven Arms SY7 8DG. Tel 0588 673251

Wistanstow

Luckily, the unpromising exterior of this brick-built pub, dating from the 1770s, contrasts with the warmth of the welcome inside. Popular with locals, families, retired folk, business people at lunchtime and youngsters in the evening, it sells Wood Parish, Special and Wonderful, along with Weston's Scrumpy and Vintage cider, and offers a wide-ranging menu. Starters include baked giant New Zealand mussels at £3.50, pâté at £2.20 and garlic mushrooms at £2.50. Among the main courses served at lunchtime are rack of lamb with gooseberry and redcurrant sauce at £6.50, while in the evening the imaginative offerings include baked John Dory with lime and cream sauce at £7.20 and pan-fried duck breast in a fresh plum and kirsch sauce at £6.95. Fifteen good-quality wines are sold by the glass, and there is an extensive range of bottled wines. The three bars are carpeted, except for the combined Snug and games area, where darts, pool, dominoes and cards can be played. Comfortable modern Windsor chairs, and banquettes in the window bays, are provided in the Lounge Bar, outside which is a small patio with picnic benches.

Brewery: Free house
Licensee: Robert West
Opening hours: 11.45am-2.30pm, 7-11pm; closed Mon lunchtime; Sun 12-2pm, 7-10.30pm
Bar food: 11.45am-1.45pm, 7-9pm (except Sun evening in winter)
Children: In games area or in dining area if eating; half portions available; outdoor play area

STAFFORDSHIRE

⊛ GEORGE
Alstonefield, near Ashbourne DE6 2FX. Tel 033527 205

Alstonefield

In amongst the network of lanes, the tall trees and the stone houses that make up Alstonefield there are two small village greens. Facing on to one of them is the George, a delightful old building that dates back to the mid-17th century. There is a really warm welcome here for everyone, walkers, tourists and regulars (try and spot them in the pictures on the walls of the bar). Old tiles, cushioned settles and an open fire create a relaxed atmosphere in which to enjoy the Burtonwood Dark Mild and Forshaw's Bitter and Guinness draught beer, or perhaps the Iced Dragon cider. The menu is standard, but the food is well cooked and portions are generous. There is soup for £1.50, lasagne, meat and potato pie or Spanish quiche for £4.40 and (this is close to the Derbyshire border) an apple Bakewell tart for £2.20. There is a garden at the rear.

Brewery: Burtonwood
Licensee: R Grandjean
Opening hours: Summer 11am-2.30pm, 6-11pm (winter 7-11pm); Sun 12-3pm, 7-10.30pm
Bar food: 12-2pm, 7-10pm
Restaurant: Times as bar food
Children: Welcome anywhere away from the bar; outdoor play area

---

⊛ RISING SUN INN
Knowle Bank Road, Shraley Brook, Audley, near Stoke-on-Trent ST7 8DS. Tel 0782 720600

Audley

Back in the 18th century this was a wheelwright's cottage. If he was a drinking man, he would no doubt have appreciated a glass or two of the ale that is brewed on his premises nowadays. The beers are potently named: there is Total Eclipse, Sun Stroke, Solar Flare, Rising and Setting, and the bar also offers guest beers, a wide selection of bottled beers and no less than 125 malt whiskies. The Rising Sun is an altogether lively and enjoyable establishment, popular with all sorts. The food too is excellent. A typical menu might feature garlic mushrooms at £2.50, beef casserole (cooked, of course, in Solar Flare) at £5.50, venison at £8.50 or sirloin steak at £7.50, and a choice of desserts priced from £1.60 to £1.80. Thursday nights is Folk and Ballads Club night in the function room and, for sunnier days, there is a large garden.

Brewery: Free house
Licensee: Mrs G Holland
Opening hours: 12-3.30pm, 6.30-11pm (Sat 11am-11pm); Sun 12-3pm, 7-10.30pm
Bar food: 12-2.30pm, 6.30-10.30pm; Sun 12-2pm, 7-9.45pm
Restaurant: Times as bar food; licensed to midnight
Children: Welcome until 9pm

☺ BLACK LION INN
Butterton, near Leek ST13 7SP. Tel 0538 304232

Butterton

The Black Lion is a lovely old, stone-built village pub with magnificent views from the terraced garden over the Peak National Park. It is a traditional, unsophisticated and friendly place, popular with walkers and anglers as well as locals. Built in 1782, it has exposed beams, stone walls, open fires and several nooks and crannies in which to enjoy a peaceful drink (as peaceful, that is, as the resident parrot will allow). Small bands play occasionally and there is a variety of pub games. Draught beers on offer are Theakston Old Peculier, Best and Traditional Mild, McEwan 70/- and Younger No 3. The bar food menu includes dishes such as home-made soup at £1.40, gammon steak at £4.95 or breaded scampi at £4.45 and puddings such as Black Forest gâteau at £1.75. Ploughman's are served at lunchtime (£3.50) and there is a separate Carvery restaurant. There are three comfortable bedrooms, recently and attractively decorated.

Brewery: Free house
Licensees: Ron and Derek Smith
Opening hours: 12-3pm, 7-11pm; Sun 12-3pm, 7-10.30pm
Bar food: 12-2pm, 7-9.30pm
Restaurant: Fri and Sat 7-10pm; Sun 12-2pm
Accommodation: (Price per person) £20/25
Children: Welcome anywhere except the front room; family room
Credit cards: AMERICAN EXPRESS® (accepted for accommodation and in the restaurant)

☺ YEW TREE
Cauldon, Waterhouses, near Stoke-on-Trent ST10 3EJ. Tel 0538 308348

Cauldon

However long the drive, it will be worth it. The Yew Tree is unique. What makes it unique is the quite amazing collection of antiques and junk. There are grandfather clocks, there are bicycles, there are polyphons - you name it, you can find it here. The pub is about 300 years old, a traditional Staffordshire stone-built building situated between two vast quarries. The ancient yew tree after which it is named still stands outside. Inside, an old wireless plays in the background while local regulars, families and business people imbibe the atmosphere and the 105 per cent Glen Farclas whisky or the draught Bass M & B Mild and Burton Bridge XL . Snacks only are served at the bar, simple and good value. But then it's not the bar food that draws people to this wonderful Victorian emporium of a pub.

Brewery: Free house
Licensee: Alan East
Opening hours: 10am-2.30pm (Sat 3pm), 6-11pm; Sun 12-3pm, 7-10.30pm
Bar food: As opening times until 9.30pm
Children: Welcome in the polyphon room

GREEN MAN
Clifton Campville, near Tamworth B79 OAX. Tel 082 786 262

Clifton Campville

Clifton Campville is a village at the meeting of several minor roads in an area of rolling Staffordshire countryside that borders Derbyshire, Warwickshire and Leicestershire. At the village centre is this old, whitewashed brick pub, its large garden looking out over open fields. The building is believed to date to the 15th century and is heavily

Brewery: Ansells
Licensee: Wendy Connolly
Opening hours: 11am-2.30pm, 6-11pm; Sun 12-3pm, 7-10.30pm
Bar food: 12-2pm, 6-9.30pm; Sun 12-2pm, 7-9.30pm

beamed - its Lounge Bar is carpeted and fitted out with upholstered benches and stools, its Public Bar more basic. The food is fairly average pub fare, the menu featuring dishes such as pâté (£1.75) or garlic mushrooms (£2.50), cottage pie (£3.75) or lasagne (£3.75), fruit pie or banana split (£1.75). The beer is Ansells and there are guest beers.Various games (darts, pool, dominoes, electronic) are provided in a separate bar and quiz evenings are held occasionally.

Children: Welcome in Public Bar and Snug; family room; outdoor play area

SWAN
Fradley Junction, Alrewas, near Burton upon Trent DE13 7DN. Tel 0283 790330

Fradley

The junction of the Trent & Mersey Canal and the Coventry Canal makes a beautiful setting for this old pub. It is a whitewashed brick building right on the towpath, thought to have been built as warehouses in about 1770. Today, catering to the needs of the tourists, local regulars and business people who patronise its bars, it is just as busy as it must have been in the heyday of the canal era. The bars are fitted out with plush banquettes and stools, wooden or zinc-topped tables and carpets. Outside, tables, chairs and umbrellas are set out on the towpath. The bar food is reasonably priced but standard pub fare. Typically the menu might feature prawn cocktail at £2, rump steak at £5.75 or chicken Kiev at £5.45 and ice cream or cheese and biscuits at £1.50. There is a good selection of wines and malt whiskies and the beer on tap is Burton Ale and and Ansells Bitter.

Brewery: Ansells
Licensee: William Smith
Opening hours: 11am-3pm, 6-11pm; Sun 12-2.30pm, 7-10.30pm
Bar food: 12-2pm, 6.30-9.30pm; Sun 12-2pm, 7-9.30pm
Children: Permitted in cellar room only
Credit cards: Access, Visa

⊜ SWAN WITH TWO NECKS
Brook End, Longdon, near Rugeley WS15 4PN. Tel 0543 490251

Longdon

Although run by a Frenchman, this 16th-century, whitewashed, low-beamed inn is a typical English village pub, patronised by the locals and by business people in the area. The bar has tiled floors, cushioned benches and wooden tables and boasts a collection of bottled beers. There is a small, tidy garden at the back, with tables, for the warmer months. On draught is Ansells Bitter, Burton Ale and Lloyds Country Bitter, and there is a good selection of malt whiskies. The bar menu includes dishes such as ravioli au gratin (£2.90) or soup (£1.10) as starters, fillet of hake (£4.30), seafood platter (£4) or chicken schnitzel (£4.10) as main courses, and puddings like jam roly-poly or treacle tart (£1.30).

Brewery: Ansells
Licensee: Jacques and Margaret Rogue
Opening hours: 12-2.30pm, 7-11pm; Sun 12-2pm, 7-10.30pm
Bar food: 12-2pm, 7-9.30pm; Sun 7-9pm
Restaurant: Fri and Sat 7-9pm only
Children: Over six-year-olds welcome at lunchtime if eating; over 14-year-olds welcome in the evening if eating; outdoor play area

🍺 JERVIS ARMS
Onecote, near Leek SE13 7RU.Tel 0538 304206

Onecote

Standing next to the bridge over the River Hamps in this Peak National Park village, the Jervis Arms (named after Admiral John Jervis, under whom Nelson served) is a fine old stone pub noted particularly for its large and attractive garden on the banks of the river. This is one of the features of the pub that make it so popular with families. (Note, however, that the river can be dangerous and you are asked to supervise children in the garden.) Children have their own menu and there are always several vegetarian dishes (priced at £4). The main menu is fairly standard and includes starters such as egg mayonnaise at £1.25 and main course dishes such as plaice and chips or cottage pie at £3.25 and12oz sirloin steak at £7.25, with a variety of puddings at £1.75. There is a good choice of draught beers: Bass, Ruddles County, Webster's Yorkshire, Theakston Old Peculier, XB and Mild, Younger Scotch Bitter and Guinness.

Brewery: Free house
Licensee: Robert Sawdon
Opening hours: 12-2.30pm, 7-11pm; Sun 12-3pm, 7-10.30pm
Bar food: 12-2pm, 7-10pm
Children: Welcome anywhere except near the bar; family room; outdoor play area

HORSESHOE INN
Tatenhill, near Burton upon Trent DE13 9SD. Tel 0283 64913

Tatenhill

This is a charming old building that dates back to the 18th century or earlier, set in the centre of a quiet village just a few miles from the centre of Burton upon Trent. It has an attractive garden, with shady trees and flowery borders. Indoors there is a wood-burning stove for wintry nights and the friendly, efficient, bustling atmosphere throughout the year attracts a broad range of people. The pub specialises in wines from the Beaujolais and Macon regions of France, boasting probably the largest selection of Beaujolais in the area and there is also a good selection of malt whiskies, while draught beers on offer are Marston's and Guinness. The bar food is well presented and reasonably priced, with the menu including items such as breaded mushrooms at £2.20, steak and kidney pie at £3.85, prawn omelette at £4.25, sirloin steak at £5.60, and profiteroles at £2.80. Booking is essential for the traditional Sunday lunch.

Brewery: Marston's
Licensee: M J Bould
Opening hours: 11am-3pm, 5.30-11pm; Sun 12-3pm, 7-10.30pm
Bar food: 12-2; 12-2, 6-9.15pm (except Mon evening); Sun 12-1.30pm
Restaurant: Times as bar food
Children: Welcome in family room; outdoor play area
Credit cards: Access, Visa, Switch

🍺 MAINWARING ARMS
Whitmore, Newcastle under Lyme ST5 5HR. Tel 0782 680851

Whitmore

This one-time coaching inn stands opposite the distinctive half-timbered parish church, notable for its unique timbered bell-turret. It is a friendly country pub, some 150 years old, with a collection of old brewery and farming

Brewery:Free house
Licensee: S Hastings
Opening hours: 11am-2.30pm, 5.30-11pm (Fri and Sat 11am-

implements to emphasise the rustic ambience. There are two bars, four open fires in winter and a large patio at the back. A mixed clientele enjoys the upmarket facilities. The bar food, served at lunchtime only, is of excellent quality and very good value. Typical main courses might be steak and onion in Yorkshire pudding at £3.50, ham, turkey and asparagus bake in Stilton sauce at £4.25 and home-made lasagne at £3.95. The beer on tap is Bass, Boddingtons and Marston's Pedigree and there is also a good range of bottled beers and lagers.

11pm); Sun 12-3pm, 7-10.30pm
Bar food: 12-2pm only
Children: Welcome in two rooms, away from the bar, until 8pm

WARWICKSHIRE

⊕ BELL
Alderminster, near Stratford upon Avon CV37 8NY. Tel 0789 450414

Alderminster

An adventurous menu offering a high standard of home cooking, with a wine list to match, is the main attraction of this 17th-century roadside pub. Regulars and families form the majority of the clientele, who can choose between Marston's Pedigree and Flowers Best and Original, and from well presented main courses like rogan josh with rice and a poppadom at £7.75, minted lamb casserole with vegetables at £7.50 and hazelnut roast with a tomato sauce and vegetables at £5.95. Starters range from £2.25 to £5.25 and sweets are all £2.95. The spacious, cream-painted stone building has two beamed bars, with old, part-stone, part-wood floors, with prints and fresh flowers and, in the smaller, a collection of farm implements. Additional seating is available in the small garden.

Brewery: Free house
Licensee: Keith Brewer
Opening hours: 12-2.30pm, 7-11pm; Sun 12-2.30pm, 7-10.30pm
Bar food: 12-2pm, 7-9.30pm; Sun12-1.45pm, 7-9pm
Restaurant: Times as bar food
Children: Welcome anywhere
Credit cards: Access, Visa

FERRY
Alveston, near Stratford upon Avon CV37 7XQ. Tel 0789 269883

Alveston

Within easy reach of the tourist centre of Stratford upon Avon, and not far from the stately river, this friendly village-centre pub enjoys a good mix of customers, although young children are not encouraged. The Ferry is a cream-painted, Georgian-style building, with a small car park and a raised patio fronting the road, while inside, cream walls adorned with prints of fishes give the carpeted bar a light, airy feel. Well prepared and promptly served food is on offer at a range of prices, all representing value for money. Starters include home-made soup with French bread at £1.85 and chicken liver and Cognac pâté with garlic bread at £3.25,

Brewery: Trent Taverns Ltd
Licensee: D G Russon
Opening hours: 11am-2.30pm, 6-11pm; Sun 12-2.30pm, 7-10.30pm
Bar food: 11.45am-2pm, 6.30-9pm; Sun 12-2pm
Children: Not permited under five years inside
Credit cards: Access, Visa

while typical main courses are macaroni cheese with garlic bread at £3.50 and chicken tikka masala with rice and poppadoms at £5.95. Traditional favourites to round off the meal include treacle sponge and summer pudding, both at £1.95. Theakston Best, Bass, Wadworth 6X and Flowers Original are on sale, along with a selection of wines.

KINGS HEAD
Aston Cantlow, near Alcester B95 7HY. Tel 0789 488242

Aston Cantlow

This unspoilt, half-timbered pub gains both from standing among other ancient buildings in the heart of the village and, in summer, from its adornment of hanging vines and tubs of flowers. Long and low, it has an inviting bar with cushioned wall seats in the window bays, a beamed ceiling and an open fireplace. Tables and chairs are set out in the small, well tended garden, some of them shaded by a large horse-chestnut tree. Beer drinkers have the choice of Marston's Pedigree, Flowers IPA, Boddingtons Bitter and Mild and Murphy's Stout, and there is a reasonable selection of wines. Among the bar meals on offer are hake bake, ham, mushroom and leek pie and vegetarian lasagne, all at £5.75.

Brewery: Whitbread
Licensees: J and D Saunders
Opening hours: 12-2.30pm, 7-11pm; Sun 12-2.30pm, 7-10.30pm
Bar food: As opening hours (except Sun and Mon evening)
Children: Not permitted under 14 years in bar

⊕ BROOM TAVERN
High Street, Broom, near Bidford-on-Avon B50 4HL. Tel 0789 773656

Broom

This busy village pub, dating back to the 17th and 18th centuries, owes much of its popularity to its food, for it offers a wide choice of specials in addition to the regular menu, and the dishes are well prepared, unstinting and served without delay. There is also an extensive wine list. Black pudding with salad at £3.20 and smoked salmon mousse at £4 are typical starters, and the main courses include beef bourguignon at £6.20 and, both at £6, seafood Mornay and cottage pie. Sticky toffee meringue, tiramisu and cherry Bakewell tart, at £2.50 each, are among the sweets on offer. There are two traditional, beamed bars in this creeper-clad, timber and brick-built pub, decorated with horse-brasses and pictures on the walls, and serving Bass, Flowers Best and Murphy's Stout to a friendly, well assorted clientele. In front of the pub there is a small lawn set out with tables and chairs and - ideal for families with young children - a bouncy castle.

Brewery: Whitbread
Licensees: Mr and Mrs Zdanko
Opening hours: 11am-3pm, 6.30-11pm (Sat 6pm); Sun 11am-3pm, 7-10.30pm
Bar food: 12-2pm, 7-10pm
Restaurant: Times as bar food
Children: Welcome anywhere; outdoor play area
Credit cards: Access, Visa

MALT SHOVEL
Lower End, Bubbenhall, near Coventry CV8 3BW. Tel 0203 301141

Bubbenhall

The licensee of this quiet village pub pays tribute to his native Italy by serving dishes like ravioli at £2.75, while also offering items such as mushroom omelette at £3.25 and steak chasseur at £7.50 - likewise well prepared and good value for money. Although Italian wines are a speciality here, beer drinkers will not be disappointed, since Ansells Bitter and Mild, Bass and Tetley Bitter are on tap, along with Löwenbrau, Castlemaine XXXX and Skol lagers. Dating from the 16th century, the brick and timber pub has a small patio with seating at the front, as well as a garden adjoining a bowling green. Locals, business people at lunchtime and tourists in summer relax in the two pleasant, beamed bars.

Brewery: Ansells
Licensee: Antonio Cardellino
Opening hours: 11.30am-2.30pm, 6-11pm; Sun 12-2.30pm, 7-10.30pm
Bar food: 12-2pm, 6.30-9.30pm; Sun 12-2pm
Children: Welcome anywhere at lunchtime and in the early evening if supervised

CASTLE INN
Edge Hill, near Banbury OX15 6DJ. Tel 0295 87 255

Edge Hill

This unusual pub was built in 1747 as a folly in the form of a castle to commemorate, somewhat belatedly, the centenary of the battle of Edge Hill, which took place in 1642. It is said to stand on the spot where Charles I watched the battle, the first of the Civil War. Thoughtfully modernised to incorporate a display of memorabilia connected with the battle, it also displays a collection of farming implements. In the two comfortable bars, carpeted and with cushioned settles - there is additional seating in the large garden - the mixed clientele savour Hook Norton Old Hooky, Best Bitter or Best Mild, or Murphy's Stout. There is also a good selection of malt whiskies and fruit wines. Fillet of turkey breast at £6.50, steak and kidney pie at £4.75 and a huge mixed grill at £10.75 are among the bar meals on offer. Starters range in price from £3 and sweets from £1.75

Brewery: Hook Norton
Licensee: Mr Blann
Opening hours: 11.30am-2.30pm, 6.30-11pm; Sun 12-3pm, 7-10.30pm
Bar food: 12-2pm, 6.30-9pm; Sun 12-2.30pm, 7-9pm
Children: Only if eating; own menu available; outdoor play area
Credit cards: Access, Visa

CHEQUERS
Ettington, near Stratford upon Avon CV37 7SR. Tel 0789 740387

Ettington

This vine-clad village pub, once a favourite port of call for drovers, is now a friendly meeting place for its regulars, business people, families and tourists. The food, skilfully prepared and presented, includes Warwickshire sausage, chips and salad at £4.60, seafood platter at £6.25 and a 16oz Scotch T-bone steak with chips, salad and vegetables at £12.45. Snacks and starters range from £1.85 to £5.90, desserts from £1.95 to £2.85. Beer drinkers have the choice

Brewery: Free house
Licensee: Jan Williams
Opening hours: 10.30am-2.30pm, 6-11pm; Sun 12-2.30pm, 7-10.30pm
Bar food: 12-1.45pm, 6.30-9.30pm (Fri and Sat 9.45pm); Sun 12-1.45pm, 7-9.30pm
Children: Welcome anywhere if

of Adnams Bitter, Marston's Pedigree, Everards Tiger and
Beacon plus some guest ales, and there is a wide selection of
malt whiskies. Built about 1770, part stone, part white
painted, the pub has two carpeted, half-panelled bars with
open fires and settles and chairs, as well as a patio and a
garden where children can play. Darts and pool are on offer,
and during the Stratford Festival there is sometimes live
entertainment in the afternoons and evenings.

supervised; outdoor play area

⊜ CASE IS ALTERED
Case Lane, Five Ways, near Hatton CV35 7JD. Tel 0926 484206

Five Ways

A quiet location in a small village makes this 18th-century,
cottage-style pub a relaxing and popular place for a
drink. Flowers Bitter, Ansells Bitter and Mild, Samuel Smith
OBB and Burton Ale are dispensed from interesting old
pumps, but no food is served. The Public Bar, with a beamed
ceiling, tiled floor and the choice of chairs or cushioned
benches, has an ancient bar-billiards table which takes old
sixpences, available on request. At weekends the Lounge
Bar is open, and outside there are two tables in the small
courtyard. Although the clientele is well mixed, families with
young children are not encouraged.

Brewery: Free house
Licensee: M G Jones
Opening hours: 11.30am-
2.30pm, 6-11pm; Sun 12-2pm,
7-10.30pm
Children: Not permitted inside

⊜ HOWARD ARMS
Lower Green, Ilmington, near Shipston-on-Stour CV36 4LN. Tel 0608 82226

Ilmington

D ating from the 17th century and extended during the
18th, this inviting, stone-built pub enjoys a pleasant
setting overlooking the village green. Beams, a stone floor,
open fires and settles preserve the traditional character of
the spacious bar, while the garden, also sizeable, provides
adequate seating and shade. Good, home-cooked food is on
offer: well presented and unstinting, it includes starters and
snacks at £2 to £3, lasagne at £4.75, lamb pie with rosemary
at £4.95, rump steak at £7.75; desserts cost £2.50 and a four-
course Sunday lunch costs £10.75. An extensive wine list
complements the menu, along with Marston's Pedigree,
Flowers Best and guest ales like IPA. For overnight stays
there are two light and airy rooms, one double and one twin,
with television and facilities for making tea and coffee.

Brewery: Free house
Licensee: Mr D Smart
Opening hours: 11am-2.30pm,
7-11pm (summer 6.30pm); Sun
12-3pm, 7-10.30pm
Bar food: 12-2pm, 7-9pm (Fri and
Sat 9.30pm); Sun 12-2pm
Restaurant: 7-9pm (except Sun
and Mon); Sun 12-2pm
Accommodation: (Price per
person) single £25; (price per
room) double £40
Children: Welcome anywhere if
supervised
Credit cards:
AMERICAN EXPRESS®, Access,
Visa

NAVIGATION
Old Warwick Road, Lapworth, near Solihull B94 6NA. Tel 0564 783337

Lapworth

A well tended garden giving on to the Grand Union Canal helps to make this a busy pub with a mixed bag of customers. Attractively clad with ivy and flowering creeper, it dates from the middle of the 18th century and consists of a single bar, decorated with stuffed fish and canal ware, with a friendly, comfortable feel which is helped along in winter by open fires. Mitchells & Butlers Mild and Brew XI, Bass and a weekly changing guest beer are served, along with dishes such as lamb Madras, rice and nan bread and beef, Guinness and mushroom pie with chips and vegetables, both at £4.35, or half a chicken, chips and vegetables at £4.50. In summer there is a Sunday lunchtime barbecue outside, and bar food at other times of the year.

Brewery: Mitchells & Butlers
Licensee: Andrew Charles Kimber
Opening hours: 11am-2.30pm, 5.30-11pm (Sat 11am-3pm, 6-11pm); Sun 12-3pm, 7-10.30pm
Bar food: 12-2pm, 6-9pm; Sun 12-2pm, 7-9pm
Children: In room beyond bar only

Nine Men's Morris

A certain eeriness clings to one of the world's oldest games, which was played in Ancient Egypt 3,000 years ago and in Ireland in prehistoric times. It involves moving pegs or counters to form rows of three on a board or playing surface with 24 holes marked on it in an intricate pattern. In A Midsummer Night's Dream Shakespeare spoke of the nine men's morris and the quaint mazes on the wanton green as things from an earlier England. This has contributed to a belief that the moves in the game were once thought to be related to the mysterious forces and patterns underlying the way events move in the world.

FLEUR DE LYS
Lowsonford, near Henley-in-Arden B95 5HJ. Tel 0564 782431

Lowsonford

Long, cottage-like and dating from about 1800, this popular pub benefits from a waterside garden with access to the rural Stratford upon Avon Canal. Customers of all types mix in the two pleasant bars, although visitors with young children will feel particularly welcome, since there is a family room with toys and high chairs and the garden has a play area and rabbits in hutches. Boddingtons Bitter, Flowers Original and Best, and two regularly changing guest beers are on tap, for example Wadworth 6X and Gale's Wethered Winter Royal, and there is a wide selection of wines, including a number from Australia and New Zealand. Expertly cooked, promptly served and good value for money, the imaginative food includes starters like lightly curried parsnip soup at £1.50 and deep-fried Brie in breadcrumbs at £2.95. Typical main courses are swordfish steak with walnut butter at £5.99 and lamb meatballs with barbecue sauce in pitta bread at £3.95. Among the enticing desserts are cappuccino log with cream at £1.95 and and strawberry, redcurrant and yoghurt cheesecake at £2.10.

Brewery: Whitbread
Licensee: Russell Proctor
Opening hours: 11am-11pm; Sun 12-3pm, 7-10.30pm
Bar food: 12-3pm, 6-9.30pm (in summer, 12-9.30pm); Sun 12-2pm, 7-9.30pm
Children: In family room only; outdoor play area
Credit cards: Access, Visa

☞ HOLLY BUSH
Holly Bush Lane, Priors Marston, near Rugby CV23 8RW. Tel 0327 60934

A wide selection of beers helps draw a mixed clientele to this friendly pub, tucked away down a back lane in a quiet village. Bass and Bass Special Bitter, Flowers Original and IPA, Hook Norton Best, Theakston Old Peculier, Marston's Pedigree and Murphy's Stout are on offer, along with three ciders, including scrumpy. The 16th-century stone building has one long bar, with stone walls and beams and an unusual brick and timber serving area. A carpeted floor and open fires make it comfortable, and it is all the more relaxing because the bar billiards and darts are in a separate room. About four times during the year, on a Thursday evening, there is live music and on summer Sundays and holiday Mondays a whole pig may be spit-roasted (outside) and served either outside or in the bars from 8pm. There is also a regular bar menu offering, for example, goujons of plaice and Brie baked with almonds, both at £2.50, beefburger and chips at £2.95, various omelettes at £3.25, vegetarian tagliatelle and lasagne at £3.95 and salmon steak with lemon butter sauce at £7.95. The restaurant offers a wide menu, with main courses ranging in price from £6.25 to £10.75 and complemented by a huge list of wines from all over the world. There are additional seats on the patio and in the garden, where there is a hitching rail for horses.

Priors Marston

Brewery: Free house
Licensee: Mark Hayward
Opening hours: 12-3.30pm, 5.30-11pm (Fri and Sat 12-11pm); Sun 12-3pm, 7-10.30pm
Bar food: 12-2pm, 7-9.30pm; Sun 12-2pm, 7-9.30pm
Restaurant: Times as bar food, but last orders 10pm
Children: Welcome anywhere; outdoor play area
Credit cards: Access, Visa

☞ ROSE AND CROWN
Ratley, near Banbury OX15 6DS. Tel 0295 878148

This pub's setting near to the church in a remarkably pretty hamlet combines with its great antiquity (it is said to trace its history back to 1098) to make it very special. Parts of the ancient stone structure survive, including the bread oven in the bar, where old beams, stone walls, window seats and an inglenook fireplace create a cosy haven. Charles Wells Bombardier and Eagle IPA, along with guest beers such as Wadworth 6X and Adnams Broadside, attract locals as well as visitors, but a further attraction is the food, which is well cooked, well presented and good value for money. Among the choice of meals are chilli con carne with rice or chips and Mexican tacos, both at £4.95, and a selection of salads at £3.95, while to follow there are traditional sweets like Spotted Dick and lemon sponge, both served with custard, at £1.95. On Sundays in winter there is a traditional Sunday lunch at £4.95, as well as bar meals. This is a lovely pub, rescued by the present owners in spring 1992 from a two-year closure.

Ratley

Brewery: Free house
Licensee: Derek Hickson
Opening hours: 12-3pm, 6-11pm; Sun 12-3pm, 7-10pm
Bar food: 12-2.30pm, 6-10pm; Sun 12-2.30pm, 7-9.30pm
Children: Welcome anywhere if well behaved

⊜ WHITE BEAR
High Street, Shipston-on-Stour CV36 4AJ. Tel 0608 661558

Shipston-on-Stour

Brewery: Mitchells & Butlers

Licensee: Paul Ross

Opening hours: 11am-3pm, 6-11pm; Sun12-3pm, 7-10.30pm

Bar food: 12-2pm, 6.30-9.30pm (Fri and Sat 10pm) except Sun

Restaurant: Times as bar food

Accommodation: (Price per room) single £35, double £47

Children: Welcome anywhere

Credit cards: Access, Visa

Dating from the 17th century but in parts possibly older, this white-painted, brick-built pub stands in the centre of a small market town and is used by locals and visitors alike. A selection of the more serious newspapers is provided in the two carpeted bars, which are furnished comfortably in character with the aged beams and stone walls. Bass and Mitchells & Butlers Mild and Brew XI are the regular beers, with some guest ales, three draught lagers, three ciders and a wide choice of malt whiskies. For those who like to drink outside, there are a few scats on the small patio. The food is prepared to a high standard, and includes some dishes not often served in pubs, such as black-peppered skate wing at £7. Among the starters on offer are honeydew melon with Parma ham at £3.50 and warm salad with tomato and mozzarella cheese at £3.75, while typical main courses are seafood lasagne and salad at £4.50 and rack of lamb with blackcurrant sauce at £8. Nine double rooms and one single are available - all light and airy and furnished mainly in pine, and each with a television and facilities for making tea and coffee.

OLD MINT
Coventry Street, Southam CV33 0EP. Tel 0926 812339

Southam

Brewery: Free house

Licensee: Geoffrey Wright

Opening hours: 11am-3pm, 6.30-11pm (Sat 11am-11pm); Sun 12-3pm, 7-10.30pm

Bar food: 12-2pm, 7-10pm (Sat 12-3pm, 6-10pm); Sun 12-2.30pm, 7-9.30pm

Restaurant: Times as bar food

Children: In small bar and restaurant only

This stone pub was used as a mint by Cromwell during the Civil War, when it had already been in existence for three centuries. Situated in the town centre, it attracts an assorted clientele including business people at lunchtime and tourists and families at all times. An unusually wide choice of beers is on offer, including Wadworth 6X, Whitbread Original and Best Bitter, Bass, Marston's Pedigree, Hook Norton Bitter, Boddingtons Bitter, Taylor Landlord, a regularly changing guest beer and Murphy's Stout. Bar meals such as scampi at £4.35 and vegetarian quiche at £3.95 are served, along with special dishes for pensioners. The separate restaurant offers chicken supreme at £8.50, whole Dover sole at £13.75 and, on Sundays, a three-course meal at £6.95. An extensive wine list, including English country wines, complements the menu, and special reserve cider is also available. Traditional in style, the two carpeted bars are furnished with settles, stools and chairs beneath beamed ceilings, and the main bar has a fine collection of antique weapons - pikes, swords, guns etc. Seating is provided in the large garden, which has an attractive pool and miniature watermill; there is usually a bouncy castle to keep young children amused.

🍺 ROYAL OAK
Whatcote, near Shipston-on-Stour CV36 5EF. Tel 0295 680319

Whatcote

Thick stone walls and tiny windows testify to the great age of this pub which claims a history going back to 1168. Another evocative reminder of its colourful past is the hidey-hole in the chimney, reached by iron rungs. The three bars, with beams, settles and open fires, are used by a friendly mix of customers including tourists, many of them American. Coach parties are welcome by appointment. Situated in the heart of a quiet village, the ivy-clad pub has a patio at the front and a small garden at the back, both with seats. Three real ales are alternately on offer: Castle Eden Ale, Marston's Pedigree, and Boddingtons Bitter. There is also Murphy's Stout and an extensive wine list. Bar food ranges from snacks and starters priced from £1.45 to typical main courses such as fresh salmon at £6.80, mushroom and leek bake at £5 and mixed grill at £6.05.

Brewery: Free house
Licensee: Catherine Matthews
Opening hours: 10.30am-2.30pm, 6-11pm; Sun 12-3pm, 7-10.30pm
Bar food: 12-2pm, 6-10pm; Sun 12-2pm, 7-10pm
Children: Permitted inside only if eating; outdoor play area

🍺 SWAN HOUSE HOTEL
The Green, Wilmcote, near Stratford upon Avon CV37 9XJ. Tel 0789 267030

Wilmcote

Within easy reach of Stratford upon Avon and near Mary Arden's House, the family home of Shakespeare's mother, this village pub inevitably plays host to a large number of tourists. Many of the other customers are local business people who drop by for lunch. The three-storey, white-painted building is adorned in summer with flowers in hanging baskets and tubs, and has at the front a small terrace with tables and at the back a partially shaded garden with a children's play area. Inside, the comfortable bar is carpeted throughout and has cushioned benches and chairs and an open fire. A feature has been made of an old well near the serving area. Live jazz can be heard on some evenings, and an organist on Saturdays, while snooker, darts and dominoes can be played in a separate room. The accommodation comprises seven double rooms, one with a four-poster bed, and one single. All are fresh and comfortable and have television and radio and tea- and coffee-making facilities. Beer drinkers' needs are met by Theakston XB and Hook Norton Best Bitter, along with a good selection of bottled ales and lagers. Soup and crusty bread at £1.75 and savoury pancake at £3.50 are among the starters on the menu, while the main courses include chicken curry at £4.70 and steak on a stone from £9.95. The separate restaurant is not open regularly at the moment but, depending on demand, this may change.

Brewery: Free house
Licensees: Ian and Diana Sykes
Opening hours: 11am-11pm; Sun 12-2pm, 7-10.30pm
Bar food: 12-2.30pm, 7-9.30pm
Accommodation: (Price per room) single £36, double £56-£66
Children: Welcome anywhere; outdoor play area
Credit cards: AMERICAN EXPRESS®, Access, Visa

WEST MIIDLANDS

⊜ WILLIAM IV
1059 Foleshill Road, Coventry CV6 6ER. Tel 0203 686394

Coventry

On the left of the B4113 as you leave the city, 2 1/2 miles from the centre, this large and very pleasant pub dating from between the wars offers ample car parking space at both the front and rear of the building. An across-the-board clientele gathers in two carpeted, comfortably furnished bars where Bass Special Bitter, M&B Brew XI, Guinness and Tennent Extra are available on draught and superb, home-cooked bar food represents excellent value for money. The menu includes a vast range of genuine Indian dishes - chicken curry and rice at £2.90, for example, mausimi subsi (fresh vegetables cooked in north Indian style) at £2.50 or balti chicken with jal frizes at £4.50 - as well as a selection of starters and sweets. A garden round the rear car park provides extra seating during the warmer months.

Brewery: Mitchells and Butlers
Licensee: Perminder Singh Bains
Opening hours: 11am-2.30pm, 6-11pm (Fri and Sat 11am-3pm, 5-11pm); Sun 12-3pm, 7-10.30pm
Bar food: As opening hours
Children: Welcome if eating with adults

⊜ CROOKED HOUSE
Coppice Mill, Himley near Dudley DY3 4DA. Tel 0384 238583

Himley

Tourists and businessmen frequent this local curiosity, known locally as the Glynne Arms - a 19th-century building affected by subsidence to the point where its floors, walls and doors all slope noticeably! Three bars in Victorian style serve draught Banks's Bitter and Mild; bar menus offer snacks and salads alongside a range of dishes (steak and kidney pie at £3.30, faggots at £2.55 or seafood platter at £2.85, for example) with chips and peas. In country setting, though bordering on a former industrial area, the pub provides ample outdoor seating on side and front patios as well as in the garden.

Brewery: Banks's
Licensee: Mr Ensor
Opening hours: 11am-11pm; Sun 12-3pm, 7-10.30pm
Bar food: 12-2pm
Children: Permitted only if having meals; no prams

WHITTINGTON INN
Kidderminster Road, Kinver, near Stourbridge DY7 6NY. Tel 0384 872110

Kinver

This delightful inn, a house built in 1310 by the grandfather of Richard (Dick) Whittington, acquired a wealth of historical associations before it was converted to pub use in 1783: the childhood home of Lady Jane Grey (said to haunt the first floor to this day), it was also visited by Charles II on his escape from Worcester to Boscobel and by Queen Anne, whose iron seal (one of only two extant) is still

Brewery: Free house
Licensee: Craig Harrison
Opening hours: 11am-2.30pm, 5.30-11pm; Sun 12-3pn, 7-10.30pm
Bar food: As opening hours

fixed to the front door. Four beamed and panelled bars retaining many original features and displaying collections of Toby jugs and militaria attract a wide cross-section of customers who can enjoy a range of 12 to 15 malts as well as Flowers IPA and Original, Courage Directors and John Smith's Bitter on draught. Bar food of excellent quality represents good value for money in an extensive menu that includes sandwiches, salads and baked potatoes alongside dishes like chicken, ham and walnut pie (£5.85) or broccoli cheese bake (£4.99); meals are also served in a sub-contracted bistro-style restaurant. Entertainment includes folk and jazz on Tuesday nights and Wednesday games evenings in winter, while in summer the part walled garden and Tudor bricked patio with fountain provide relaxing surroundings.

Restaurant: Times as bar food
Children: Welcome anywhere
Credit Cards: Access, Visa

BREWERY
Station Road, Langley, near Oldbury B69 4LU. Tel 021 544 6467

Langley

The maximum price for any meal (including beef stew in the colder months) is £1.80 at this early Victorian pub in an industrial area beside the canal. A range of dishes like steak and kidney pie with vegetables or faggots and peas are served with crusty bread which is obtained from the little local bakery whenever possible; quality is excellent, and most children will find something to their taste - though vegetarians should note that there will not necessarily be anything suitable for them. Draught Castlemaine XXXX and Lowenbrau lagers and Olde English cider are served alongside cask-conditioned HP & D (Allied) Entire and Mild and Tetley Bitter. Displays of local memorabilia help to attract visitors as well as regulars to the two bars with their Victorian decor and open fire. The function room is used as an overflow bar at busy times, and a courtyard provides outside seating in summer.

Brewery: Holt, Plant and Deakin
Licensee: A J Stanton
Opening hours: 11am-2.30pm, 6-11pm; Sun 12-3pm, 7-10.30pm
Bar food: 12-2pm (except Sat and Sun); occasional evenings (subject to bread supply!)
Children: Welcome anywhere at landlord's discretion

⊕ SHOVEL INN
Pedmore Road, Lye, near Stourbridge DY9 8DZ. Tel 0384 423998

Lye

Set beside the busy A4036 in the town centre, a typical Black Country pub, converted from William IV houses, can provide only street parking 100 yards away during the day, though the facilities of a neighbouring optician's and factory can be used in the evening. An excellent range of draught beers (including different guest beers each week alongside Batham Best Bitter, Hook Norton Old Hooky, Everards Bitter, Ruddles Best Bitter and Banks's Mild) more

Brewery: Free house
Licensee: Stephen David Allen
Opening hours: 12-3pm, 6-11pm; Sun 12-3pm, 7-11pm
Bar food: 12-2pm, 6-9pm; Sun 12-2pm, 7-9pm
Children: Welcome with landlord's permission

than makes up for its undistinguished exterior, as does a wide-ranging menu of well cooked, value-for-money dishes like steak and Guinness pie (£3.75), faggots and peas (£2.50) or vegetable curry (£3.25). Four rooms are grouped round a central bar area, adorned with old photographs and offering attractive games as well as darts and dominoes, and outside seating is available in the courtyard.

LITTLE DRY DOCK
Windmill End, Netherton, near Dudley DY2 9HU. Tel 0384 235369

Netherton

The front door wings of this canalside Victorian pub are narrowboat rudders, and its brightly painted, typical O'Rourke exterior gives on to two drinking areas decked with canal memorabilia; the bar itself is well worth seeing, being an authentic narrowboat, and the floor covered with lino and sawdust is an effective reminder of another era - the whole forming an effective setting for live Irish folk music on Monday evenings. The value-for-money menu of good, home-cooked food includes a range of starters and old-fashioned sweets (bread-and-butter pudding and treacle roly-poly, for example, both at £1.60) as well as dishes like beef curry Bangalore (£4.20) or Cradley porkers (£3.85). Mad O'Rourke's Little Lumphammer beer is available on draught alongside Holts Mild and Entire. The whole area abounds with industrial archaeology - Cobb's engine house and Netherton tunnel being within easy reach - and this accounts for the predominance of tourists among the pub's clientele.

Brewery: Little Pub Company (Mad O'Rourke)
Licensee: Philip J Slater
Opening hours: 11am-3pm, 7-11pm; Sun 12-3pm, 7-10.30pm
Bar food: 11am-2.30pm, 6-10pm; Sun 12-3pm, 7-9.30pm
Children: Welcome anywhere
Credit Cards:
AMERICAN EXPRESS®, Access, Visa, Diners

CHURCH TAVERN
High Street, Quarry Bank, near Brierley Hill DY5 2AA. Tel 0384 68757

Quarry Bank

The ample portions of plain but tasty bar food served in the very clean and well maintained bar of this early Victorian 'local' in the town's high street represent excellent value for money; such starters as soup or egg mayonnaise can be followed, for example, by faggots and peas, cheese pie or steak, accompanied by a choice of chips or jacket potatoes and vegetables or salad, at prices ranging from £2 to £4.50. It should be noted, however, that a vegetarian alternative is not always offered. HP & D (Allied) Entire, Bitter and Mild are available on draught. The atmosphere is quiet and pleasant, the only entertainment being the traditional pastimes of darts, dominoes, cards and cribbage, and the predominantly business clientele evident at lunchtimes gives way to family groups in the evening. Though the pub's own parking facilities are limited, there is a large public car park near by.

Brewery: Holt, Plant and Deakin
Licensee: Mrs Janet Holt (manageress)
Opening hours: 11am-3pm, 5-11pm (Fri and Sat 11am-11pm); Sun 12-3pm, 7-10.30pm
Bar food: 12-2pm for main meals; snacks at other times
Children: Not permitted under 14 years inside

MANOR HOUSE
Hall Green Road, Stone Cross, near West Bromwich B71 2EA.
Tel 021 588 2035

Stone Cross

Many original features are preserved in this timbered 13th-century manor house, set in extensive grounds and entered through a gatehouse over the moat. Five carpeted bars, retaining much of the character of the manorial hall in beams, exposed timbers, shields and banners, are furnished in a style appropriate to their period, and a small museum displays artefacts found in the moat; less appropriate, perhaps, are the Wednesday karaoke evenings, but at other times entertainment is restricted to subdued background music and a quiz machine strategically placed in the corridor. Lunchtime sees a mainly business clientele, with families and tourists in the evenings (some coach parties being accepted with advanced booking). Well known locally for its cask-conditioned ales, the Manor House offers Harp, Grolsch and Kronenberg 1664 lagers on draught as well as Banks's Mild and Bitter. Fresh, home-cooked bar food always includes a vegetarian option alongside such dishes as steak and kidney pie, lasagne and plaice Mornay (£4- £4.50) and the separate restaurant provides a three-course meal at prices ranging from £6.85 from the Carvery to around £10 for a full menu choice. Booking is not normally essential, but two weeks' notice is required for Sunday lunch.

Brewery: Wolverhampton and Dudley breweries (Banks's)
Licensee: Mr Capner
Opening hours: 11.30am-2.30pm, 7-11pm; Sun 12-2.30pm, 7-10.30pm
Bar food: 12-2pm, 7-10pm
Restaurant: 12-1.45pm, 7-9. 30pm (except all day Mon, Sat lunch and Sun evening)
Children: Welcome anywhere; small side room suitable when pub crowded
Credit Cards: AMERICAN EXPRESS®, Access, Visa

⊜ MAD O'ROURKES PIE FACTORY
Hurst Lane, Tipton, near Dudley DY4 9AB. Tel 021 557 1402

Tipton

Brightly painted and typically O'Rourke in style, with life-sized model pigs and cows on roof and walls, this town pub-with-a-difference offers superb value in well cooked and generously served bar food, meals of the day supplementing such standard items as Dan pie (enough for two) at £4.95, its vegetarian alternative allotment pie (£4.25) and puddings like jam roly-poly (£1.60) or blackcurrant cheesecake (£1.75). Little Pub Company wines are served alongside draught Mad O'Rourkes Little Lumphammer, Holts Entire and Ansells Mild. The four bars - which reflect the pie-making theme in machinery, imitation sides of meat, pudding basins and so on are furnished with old chairs and settles on a lino and sawdust floor, and the spotless kitchen is open to view. Outdoor seating is provided on a small terrace bordering the extensive car park.

Brewery: Little Pub Company (Mad O'Rourke)
Licensee: David Henaghan
Opening hours: 11am-3pm, 6-11pm; Sun 12-3pm, 7-10.30pm
Bar food: During opening hours until one hour before closing
Children: Welcome anywhere
Credit Cards: Access, Visa

NORTHERN ENGLAND

Cheshire

❖

Cleveland

❖

Cumbria

❖

Co Durham

❖

Humberside

❖

Lancashire

❖

Greater Manchester

❖

Merseyside

❖

Northumberland

❖

Tyne & Wear

❖

Yorkshire

❖

CHESHIRE

SHROPPIE FLY
The Wharf, Audlem CW3 0DX. Tel 0270 811772

Audlem

Set beside the Shropshire Union Canal, on the edge of Audlem village, this pub - the product of a 70s conversion of a 200-year-old granary warehouse - retains industrial features like its mill and wharf, while customers (the majority of whom are holidaymakers) relax on a patio and terrace with the original canalside bricking. One of the two relaxed and welcoming bars incorporates the boat from which the pub takes its name, and collections of ceramic plates and canal memorabilia are displayed. Electronic games and a juke box supplement such traditional pursuits as cards, darts and table football, and a good range of drinks includes bottled Manns Brown Ale, Newcastle Brown, Diamond White, Kaltenherg Pils and Red Rock Cider as well as Boddingtons Bitter, Bentley's Yorkshire Bitter, Whitbread Mild, Guinness, and Murphy's Stout. Bar food is detailed on a daily changing blackboard menu, and meals are also served in a separate restaurant. A typical choice might include garlic mushrooms (£1.65) followed by rainbow trout (£4.25) and apple pie (£1.95). Vegetarian alternatives and children's dishes are always available, and dishes generally are both reasonably priced and generously served.

Brewery: Free house
Licensee: Malcolm Goodwin
Opening hours: 12-3pm, 6-11pm; summer school holidays 12-11pm; closed lunchtime in winter
Bar food: 12-2.30pm, 6.30-10pm
Restaurant: Times as bar food
Children: Welcome anywhere; family room
Credit cards: Access, Visa

WHITE LION INN Barthomley *see page 341*

⊕ BEARS HEAD
Brereton Green, near Sandbach CW11 9RS. Tel 0477 35251

Brereton Green

This extended black-and-white Tudor building at the edge of the village boasts a garden with tennis court and crazy golf as well as a patio area made attractive by hanging baskets and a fountain. Guests - predominantly business and commercial - relax in two bars which have a Continental atmosphere though their exposed beams and brasses are typically English in appearance. Burtonwood Ales and Bass are served on draught, and there are 12 malts on offer as well as a wide selection of wines and champagnes. The menu includes specials like black pudding with whisky sauce (£5.25) and fillet of plaice caprice (£5.50) which have earned the pub a gastronomic award from a Spanish newspaper, but

Brewery: Free house
Licensee: R Tarquini
Opening hours: 11am-3pm, 6-11pm; Sun 12-3pm, 7-10.30pm
Bar food: Times as bar food (except Sun evening)
Restaurant: 12.30-2pm, 7.30-10pm; Sun 12.30-2pm
Accommodation: (Price per room) single from £47, double from £59.50
Children: Not permitted by the

there are also vegetarian dishes. Overnight accommodation is provided in modern bedrooms, and service friendly and efficient throughout.

bar; own menu available
Credit Cards:
AMERICAN EXPRESS®, Access, Visa

WHITE LION INN
Barthomley, near Crewe CW2 5PG. Tel 0270 882242

Barthomley

This 17th-century black-and-white thatched building standing beside an original cobbled cart track has been an inn since 1614; a seige site in the Civil War, it has had only 18 landlords since that time. No electronic games, piped music or live entertainment are to be found in the single bar, the range of draught ales is limited to Burtonwood Mild, Bitter and Forshaw's Bitter, and a very restricted menu offers only pies and gravy (with no concessions to the requirements of vegetarians). Its charm, however, lies in the simplicity of its traditional quarry tiling and open fires, in old-fashioned amusements like dominoes, darts, crib and shove halfpenny, and in the excellence of its beers. Beamed bedrooms are both comfortable and charming, and the pub provides useful overnight accommodation for travellers on the M6, being within easy reach of junction 16.

Brewery: Burtonwood
Licensee: Terence Cartwright
Opening hours: 11.30am-3pm, 6-11pm (Sat 11.30am-11pm); Sun 12-3pm, 7-10.30pm
Bar food: 12-2pm (except Sat and Sun)
Accommodation: (Price per person) single from £20, double from £35
Children: Not permitted in bar

YE OLDE KINGS HEAD
48-50 Lower Bridge Street, Chester CH1 1RS. Tel 0244 324855

Chester

Built in 1623, this listed black-and-white Tudor building stands in the town centre close to the River Dee. A town pub atmosphere prevails downstairs, customers - who are mostly tourists, with young couples at weekends and family parties on a Sunday - enjoying the video juke box and electronic games, but the first-floor area is characterised by taste and quality; both beamed bars feature plush wall seating and display a collection of old prints. A selection of whiskies and wines is sold alongside draught Davenports, Greenalls Original Bitter, and Stones Best Bitter; Scrumpy Jack cider is also available on draught, and on a daily changed bar menu main courses like pork supreme (£4.25) are followed by such desserts as Death by Chocolate (£1.50). Overnight accommodation is provided in luxurious rooms with Liberty decor, these reflecting a period charm that even claims a resident ghost!

Brewery: Greenalls
Licencee: Mierion Perring
Opening hours: 11am-11pm; Sun 12-3pm, 7-10.30pm
Bar food: 12-2pm
Restaurant: 12-2pm, 6-9.30pm; Sun 12-9pm
Accommodation: (Price per room) single from £45, double £50-£60
Children: Welcome, but not permitted under 14 years in bar
Credit Cards: AMERICAN EXPRESS®, Access, Visa, Diners

Strange Games

Competitiveness and ingenuity have thrown up a rich variety of pub games besides the best-known ones, from lawn billiards to maggot racing to clay pipe smoking contests, where the object is to keep a pipeful of tobacco alight longest. Cribbage and other once popular card games are not seen so often nowadays, but bagatelle is alive and well in Chester and Coventry. In Knur and Spell up North the players hit a small ball (the knur) as far as possible with a bat. Bat and Trap, an odd variety of cricket, has a history going back at least to the 16th century in Kent. In Sussex the game of Toad in the Hole involves pitching flat discs into a hole in a table and in Lincolnshire they throw pennies into a hole and call it gnurdling. For all the video games and one-arm bandits, older and more convivial pastimes are still alive in British pubs.

⊜ CHOLMONDELEY ARMS
Cholmondeley, near Malpas SY14 8BT. Tel 0829 720300

Cholmondeley

A conversion of a late Victorian school building, this pub stands in the depths of the country bordered by a garden with picnic tables, a climbing frame and a swing. The single cosy bar with its pastel painted walls, antique pine, pictures, ceramics and bric-à-brac provides a peaceful atmosphere, undisturbed by electronic games or piped music, in which customers can enjoy draught Flowers IPA, Boddingtons Bitter, Marston's Pedigree and a weekly guest bitter. The real emphasis, however, is on the food - notable for both quality and presentation - served in the airy, comfortable eating area; a typical meal might comprise baked prawns with sour cream (£3.65), Thai green curry

Brewery: Free house
Licensees: Julian and Ginny Harrison and Guy and Carolyn Ross-Lowe
Opening hours: 12-3pm, 7-11pm (Sat from 6.30pm); Sun 12-3pm, 7-10.30pm
Bar food: 12-2.15pm, 7-10pm
Accommodation: (Price per person) single from £30, double from £20
Children: Welcome except in

(£6.25) and hot fudged bananas (£3.15), with vegetarian and children's dishes always available, and a fine, world-wide wine list including Antipodean and South American labels to choose from. Cottagey accommodation is provided in comfortable, cheerful rooms with a floral theme.

main bar room; outdoor play area
Credit cards: Visa

⊜ PHEASANT INN
Higher Burwardsley, near Tattenhall CH3 9PF. Tel 0829 70434

Higher Burwardsley

This inn, a 300-year-old half-timbered sandstone building commanding views across the Cheshire Plain to Wales from its elevated setting on the top of the Peckforton Hills, stands in a large garden which incorporates a play area and flagged terrace with seating. The beamed bar is traditional in style, featuring a huge log fire and decorated with pictures, jugs and foxes' masks. Here customers (including tourists and walkers and local farmers) are given a choice of over 40 whiskies as well as draught Bass Worthington and Guinness. The daily blackboard menu lists dishes such as cod in white wine (£4.50) and beef and Guinness pie ((£4.30), withvegetarians always catered for; choice is good and the hearty, well presented fare reasonably priced. The original farmhouse kitchen has been turned into a separate restaurant which offers additional specials in the evening, and a converted barn provides bedrooms with modern facilities and, in most cases, views of the countryside. Welcoming, efficiently run and enjoying a lovely setting (which visitors can appreciate to the full by taking advantage of a horse and trap ride), the pub was winner of the Heinz 1992 Pub Award and the Cheshire Environmental Award for Quality and Innovation.

Brewery: Free house
Licensee: David Greenhaugh
Opening hours: 12-3pm, 7-11pm; Sun 12-3pm, 7-10.30pm (Sunday teas 3-5.30pm in summer)
Bar food: As opening hours
Restaurant: 7-10pm; Sun 12-2.30pm, 7-10pm
Accommodation: (Price per person) single from £30, double from £40
Children: Welcome in conservatory, but not permitted under 14 years in bar
Credit cards: AMERICAN EXPRESS,® Access, Visa, Diners

BIRD IN HAND
Knolls Green, near Mobberley WA16 7BN. Tel 0565 873149

Knolls Green

This busy 18th-century village pub welcomes all comers to the friendly, relaxed atmosphere of its beamed, carpeted central bar and the cosy rooms, warmed by open fires, off it; darts, dominoes and electronic games provide entertainment, and a choice of draught beverages including Samuel Smith Old Brewery Bitter, Museum Ale and Cider Reserve, Ayingerbrau low alcohol lager and Pils is backed up by a premium range of export beers and lagers - Taddy Porter, Oatmeal and Imperial Stout, for example - and a selection of malt and blended whiskies. A daily changing blackboard menu offers dishes as diverse as pan-fried black pudding (£3.95) and chicken tikka (£5.50), while the full

Brewery: Samuel Smith
Licensee: Andrew Towers
Opening hours: 11am-3pm, 5.30-11pm (Sat 11am-11pm); Sun 12-3pm, 7-10.30pm
Bar food: 12-2pm, 7-9.30pm; Sun 12-2.30pm, 7-9.30pm
Children: Welcome generally, but not permitted under 14 years near bars
Credit cards: Access, Visa

English breakfast served on Sunday mornings (£5.95) comes complete with newspapers; generous portions offer value for money, vegetarians are always catered for, and children usually so. Rustic benches and tables provide pleasant outdoor seating on warmer days.

⊛ BELLS OF PEOVER
The Cobbles, Lower Peover, near Knutsford WA16 9PZ. Tel 0565 722269

Lower Peover

This Grade I listed building dating back to 1296 is idyllically set in its own garden facing the village church, wisteria hanging over its porchway entrance and American and British flags displayed on a side wall as they have been since a visit by General Patton during the war. A stone-paved area with hanging baskets in front of the pub provides additional seating in fine weather, while the bar, with its elegant period decor and displays of Toby jugs, prints, plates, copper and brass, has a luxurious feel. Guinness and Greenalls Keg Mild, Bitter and Original are served, together with extensive and connoisseurs' wine lists which include French-bottled house red and white. A good blackboard menu (featuring, for example, steak and kidney pie at £4.75, lasagne at £4.60 or filled jacket potatoes from £3.60) caters for vegetarians and a separate restaurant offers restricted opening hours.

Brewery: Greenalls
Licensees: David and Margaret Barker
Opening hours: 11.30am-3pm, 5.30-11pm; Sun 12-3pm, 7-10.30pm
Bar food: 12-2pm, 6.30-8.30pm (except Sat); Sun 12-2pm
Restaurant:: Wed,Thu,Fri 12-2pm, 7-9.30pm; Sat from 7pm; Sun 12-2pm
Children: Not permitted under 14 years except in restaurant
Credit cards: Access, Visa

⊛ STANLEY ARMS
'Bottom of the Oven', Macclesfield Forest, near Macclesfield SK11 0AR. Tel 0260 252414

Macclesfield Forest

A small paved terrace outside this 19th-century farmhouse makes the most of its exceptional views - set as it is in the middle of magnificent Peak District countryside. The atmosphere inside is pleasant, with flowers in all the rooms, and a mixed sample of visitors to the area congregate in the comfortable bar and two other rooms reserved for eating. In addition to draught Marston's Pedigree and Best and Marston's lager, bottled Newcastle Brown Ale and UK Stein Beers are on sale, and a good selection of malt whiskies is available. Separate lunchtime and evening menus include starters like home-made soup (£1.65) or half a Scottish crab (£3.25), with main courses such as local rainbow trout or Italian-style lasagne (both at £5.95) and a range of desserts.

Brewery: Marston's
Licensee: Alan James Harvey
Opening hours: 11.30am-3pm, 7-11pm; Sun 12-3pm, 7-10.30pm
Bar food: 12-2.30pm, 7-10pm
Restaurant: Times as bar food; booking necessary
Children: Restricted access to bar area; own menu available
Credit cards: Access, Visa

⊕ BOWLING GREEN
The Gullet, Nantwich CW5 5DA. Tel 0270 626001

Nantwich

A 300-year-old town-centre building in an attractive traffic-free setting, its extensive garden a winner in the Nantwich in Bloom contest, this efficiently run and relaxing pub is popular with a mixed amd lively clientele which includes beer enthusiasts who appreciate the good selection (Courage Directors, Webster's Yorkshire Bitter, John Smith's Bitter, Marston's Pedigree, Beamish Irish Stout and Guinness) available on draught; a wide choice of lagers, ciders and bottled beverages is also sold, as are ranges of malt whiskies and house wines. The large L-shaped bar with its exposed timbers is warm and welcoming, featuring electronic games as well as darts, dominoes and pool, with folk music on Wednesday evenings; lunchtime bar food - much of it home-made on the premises - includes a value-for-money special each day as well as dishes like gammon steak with egg (£3.95), scampi (£3.25) and pizzas from £3. Overnight accommodation is provided in country-style bedrooms.

Brewery: Courage
Licensee: Mandy Pratten
Opening hours: 11am-11pm; Sun 12-3pm, 7-10.30pm
Bar food: Lunchtimes as opening hours; evening bookings by arrangement
Restaurant: As opening hours; booking necessary for evenings
Accommodation: (Price per person) single from £16.50, double from £15
Children: Welcome in family room; outdoor play area
Credit cards: Access, Visa

CHESHIRE HUNT
Spuley Lane, Rainow, near Macclesfield SK10 5BA. Tel 0625 573185

Rainow

A cattle auction site in the 1700s, the pub was originally called The Quiet Woman; its present name is a reference to the East Cheshire Drag Hunt, which meets in this lovely country setting on the edge of the village, close to the 'Grit stone Trail'. Two carpeted bars with open fires, wooden pews and piped music, together with a terrace commanding fine views, attract a cross-section of customers who gather to indulge in draught Boddingtons Bitter, Marston's Pedigree and Murphy's Stout, a good selection of whiskies and an extensive choice of wines. A weekly changing blackboard menu offers simple pub food at reasonable prices, a typical main course at lunch being home-made steak and kidney pie at £4.50, with options like the Cheshire Hunt mixed grill at £7 in the evening; vegetarians should find something to their taste too. Live entertainment is sometimes staged in the useful function room.

Brewery: Free house
Licensee: Roger Barton
Opening hours: 12-3pm, 5.30-11pm
Bar food: 12-2pm, 6-10pm; Sun 12-2pm, 7-10pm
Children: Welcome except in bar
Credit cards: Access, Visa

Great Tew

⊜ HIGHWAYMAN
Rainow, near Macclesfield SK10 5UU. Tel 0625 573245

Rainow

There are spectacular views over the western Peak District from this stone-built 300-year-old country pub, one wall of which features a distinctive black horse painting. Efficiently run by friendly staff, relaxed and cosy, it is popular for the well kept beer (Thwaites hand-pumped Bitter and Dark Mild) served in three comfortable, olde worlde bars decked with copper and brass ware and warmed in winter by open fires. Bar meals feature traditional black pudding with bread and butter (£1.80) as well as home-made steak and kidney pie, lasagne and chilli con carne (all at £4.15) and a variety of pizzas at £2.80.

Brewery: Thwaites
Licensee: Mr Frank Jones
Opening hours: 12-3pm, 7-11pm; Sun 12-3pm, 7-10.30pm
Bar food: 12-2pm, 7.15-9.30pm (Fri and Sat 9.45pm)
Children: Not permitted in main bar; families welcome lunchtimes and evenings until 8.30pm if dining

⊜ SWETTENHAM ARMS
Swettenham, near Congleton CW12 2LF. Tel 0477 71284

Swettenham

Peacefully set in idyllic surroundings beside the village church and close to Daffodil Dell, a local beauty spot, this 300-year-old pub features a large beer garden as well as a small walled garden with paved patio. Visiting walkers, cyclists, fishermen and tourists, as well as regulars, congregate in two traditional, beamed and stone-walled bars where entertainment includes live Cajun music once a month as well as the more predictable pool and electronic games. Speciality malts - Highland Park and Talisker, for example - are served alongside a good range of draught beverages, such beers as Banks's Bitter and Traditional Mild, Marston's Pedigree, Camerons Strongarm and Hanson's Keg. Additive-free meals based on fresh local produce whenever possible are cooked to order, both bar and restaurant featuring freshly made pasta. Service is efficient and dishes are fairly priced - a meal comprising, for example, potted shrimps at £3.50, roast duckling at £9.50 and chocolate roulade at £3.50. There is a separate vegetarian menu.

Brewery: Wolverhampton and Dudley Breweries
Licensee: John Irlam
Opening hours: 12-3pm, 6-11pm; Sun 12-3pm, 7-10.30pm
Bar food: 12-2.30pm, 7-9.30pm; Sun 12-2.30pm, 7-9pm
Restaurant: Times as bar food; booking necessary at weekends
Children: Welcome anywhere

⊜ FARMERS ARMS
Chapel Lane, Wilmslow SK9 5JH. Tel 0625 532443

Wilmslow

A roomy car park, a courtyard and a large, pretty garden set with picnic tables surround this pub - a double-fronted black-and-white Victorian building (originally two houses) on the edge of the town. Friendly staff create a congenial atmosphere, and two homely bars with hanging brasses, etched windows and sewing machine tables attract a good following of regulars (including families) and their pets

Brewery: Boddingtonss
Licensee: Jean Dunbar
Opening hours: 11am-11pm; Sun 12-3pm, 7-10.30pm
Bar food: 11.30am-2.15pm (except Sun)
Children: Welcome anywhere

- the landlady being an animal lover. Traditional entertainments like darts, cards and dominoes are supplemented by quiz evenings in spring and autumn, and a range of whiskies (Talisker and Oban, for example) is served alongside Boddingtons Mild and Bitter, Guinness and Murphy's Stout on draught. A blackboard menu of bar food follows soup of the day (90p) or egg mayonnaise (£1.50) with main courses like a giant Yorkshire pudding with beef and mushrooms (£2.25), chilli and pitta bread (£2.50) or home-made sausages (£2.65).

CLEVELAND

POT AND GLASS

Church Road, Egglescliffe, near Stockton-on-Tees TS16 9DQ. Tel 0642 780145

Egglescliffe

Fulfilling generously the role of a traditional village local, this pub fields not one but two cricket teams. The small, whitewashed building, some 260 years old, stands tucked away opposite the ancient church in a village on the edge of a larger town. Its original layout is retained, and the two beamed rooms, comfortably furnished with cushioned settles, both have intricately carved bar fronts, the handiwork of a former landlord. Beer drinkers among the mixed clientele can choose between Bass, Stones Best Bitter and Worthington Best Bitter, while diners are offered delicious home-cooked food representing excellent value for money. Among the meals on offer are steak pie with chips or jacket potato and salad, and gammon steak, egg and pineapple with chips or jacket potato, both at £3.65. Booking is necessary on Sundays, when a lunch of roast beef and Yorkshire pudding, with a sweet, is served at £3.95. Outdoor seating is provided in the large, south-facing courtyard, where two barbecues are set out on the flagstones.

Brewery: Century Inns Ltd
Licensee: Mr W Taylor
Opening hours: 12-3.30pm, 5.30-11pm; Sun 12-3.30pm, 7-10.30pm
Bar food: 12-2pm
Children: Welcome in family room; outdoor play area

VANE ARMS

Darlington Road, Long Newton TS21 1PE. Tel 0642 580401

Long Newton

With its large garden to the side and rear incorporating a play area, this pleasant pub welcomes families with young children. Situated at the end of a late Victorian terrace on the edge of the village, it occupies what were once two cottages. The updated interior, furnished with dark-wood chairs, benches and stools, consists of an island bar serving

Brewery: Century Inns Ltd
Licensee: Angela Bramley
Opening hours: 11.30am-3pm, 5-11pm (Sat 11am-11pm); Sun 12-3pm, 7-10.30pm
Bar food: 12-2pm, 7-10pm

an open-plan lounge and a separate bar-cum-taproom. Beer drinkers among the clientele of locals, business people and tourists have the choice of Bass or Stones Bitter and a wide selection of bottled beers to accompany dishes like home-made steak pie, lasagne and beef and chicken curry, all at £3.50, or a three-course roast at £4.75.

(except Mon evening); Sun 12-2pm
Children: Welcome anywhere; outdoor play area

⊜ SHIP
Saltburn, Langbaurgh TS12 1HF. Tel 0287 622361

Saltburn

Standing at the foot of towering cliffs, and overlooking a fine bay, this pretty, whitewashed pub attracts a friendly assortment of customers, although notably few youngsters. The building, dating from 1450, comprises a seaward terrace - a delightful place to sit and enjoy the view - and two bars, rich in mellow wood and offering the traditional comforts of cushioned settles and open fires. On tap are Tetley Imperial Bitter, along with a choice of four draught lagers and Olde English cider. Good value for money is given by the wide-range of well prepared meals, including dishes such as goujons of cod at £6.95 or the more inventive turkey and mushroom kebab at £4.25 and gammon and minted pear at £4.95. Sweets are £2. Once a month the restaurant holds a theme night - for example, a French evening. Next door to the pub, a joint venture by the brewery and the local council has turned a derelict cottage into a museum telling the story of the smugglers of Saltburn.

Brewery: Joshua Tetley & Son Ltd
Licensee: Mr Ronnie Scott
Opening hours: Summer 11am-11pm; winter 11am-3pm, 6-11pm; Sun 12-10.30pm
Bar food: 12-2.30pm, 7-10pm (except Sun evening in winter)
Restaurant: Times as bar food
Children: In restaurant only; children's menu available; outdoor play area
Credit cards: Access, Visa

⊜ STAINTON INN
Meldyke Lane, Stainton TS8 9AZ. Tel 0642 599902

Stainton

A mixture of regulars, business people and tourists use this friendly village-centre pub, brick-built in 1897 and extended a few years ago into adjoining cottages of the same period which have been carefully refurbished in Victorian style. It is spacious, with a single, open-plan bar serving several rooms, comfortably furnished with cushioned and plain dark-wood chairs, and with a large area set aside for diners. There is additional seating on the patio at the rear. Camerons Strongarm and Traditional Bitter and Banks's Bitter are the beers on offer, while the food includes pork in a Stilton and walnut sauce at £4.25 and duckling at £8.75. Fresh fish, when available, is a speciality.

Brewery: Camerons
Licensee: Richard Mervin Taylor
Opening hours: 11am-3pm, 6-11pm; Sun 12-3pm, 7-10.30pm
Bar food: 12-2.15pm, 7-10pm
Children: Welcome anywhere
Credit cards: AMERICAN EXPRESS®, Access, Visa

CUMBRIA

ROYAL OAK INN
Bongate, Appleby in Westmorland CA16 6UN. Tel 07683 51463

Part of this pub dates from the 14th century, while the rest of the old stone building is a relatively modern 300 years old. It's a good place for real ales, with Theakston Best Bitter, Yates Bitter and Premium, Deuchars IPA, Younger Scotch Bitter, and Draught Bass, as well as guest ales. The freshly cooked food is another major attraction, with delicious dishes like beef in beer pie and coriander curried chicken at £4.95, and leeky links - leek and cheese sausages - costing £3.75. Marinated herring in sour cream makes a reasonably priced starter and vegan dishes are also available. Over 80 wines are listed, and there are 50 malt whiskies to sample. This is a popular place to eat or drink, and the two bars offer typical old English comfort with plenty of exposed wood. Flower tubs add a splash of colour to the outside, and there are eight spacious bedrooms in keeping with the style of the pub.

Appleby in Westmorland

Brewery: Free house
Licensee: C F Cheyne
Opening hours: 11am-3pm, 6-11pm; Sun 12-3pm, 7-10.30pm
Bar food: As opening hours
Restaurant: Times as bar food
Accommodation: (Price per person) single £19.50, double £27.50
Children: Welcome anywhere
Credit cards: AMERICAN EXPRESS®, Access, Visa, Diners

PUNCH BOWL INN
Askham, Penrith CA10 2PF. Tel 0931 712443

A picture-book village complete with river, church and castle is the lovely setting for this popular late 17th-century inn. Lowther Castle is just a few minutes' walk away, and the village green is spread out in front of the inn. The beamed bar is the preferred choice of eating place, though the same food is served in the restaurant. Starters like Stilton fries at £3.35 and smoked salmon and prawn bake at £2.80 feature on the international menu, and there are main courses such as fisherman's pot (£7.50) and Chinese pork kebabs at £5.80. Whitbread Castle Eden Ale and a guest beer are on tap, and four rooms offer overnight accommodation.

Askham

Brewery: Free house
Licensees: Frances and David Staff
Opening hours: 11am-3pm, 6-11pm; Sun 12-3pm, 7-10.30pm
Bar food: 12-2pm, 6.30-9.30pm; Sun 12-2pm, 7-9pm (summer 9.30pm)
Restaurant: Times as bar food
Accommodation: (Price per room) double £37
Children: Welcome anywhere
Credit cards: Access, Visa

⊕ DRUNKEN DUCK
Barngates, neasr Ambleside LA22 0NG. Tel 05394 36347

Barngates

This hearty hunting and fishing inn attracts visitors to its very rural location throughout the year. Set beside crossroads (B5286 Hawkshead/Ambleside road and follow Barngates signs) with views over the fells and on to distant Lake Windermere, the relaxed atmosphere is especially popular with families. The food is home-made except for the scampi, and tasty starters include port and Stilton or spicy pepper pâtés at £2.95. Main dishes like fennel, orange and butterbean bake for vegetarians at £4.95 feature on the menu, with Gressingham duck and beef goulash both at £5.50. Syrup roly-poly and lemon sponge pudding are £2.50. On tap are Marston's Pedigree, Theakston XB and Old Peculier, and real ales from Jennings, Yates and Boddingtons, as well as Murphy's and Guinness. There are 60 malt whiskies. Foxes' masks and fishing flies adorn the pine and oak bar, where seating is on comfortable cushioned settles around an open fire. Nine very smart bedrooms decorated in 'Laura Ashley' style have lovely views.

Brewery: Free house
Licensee: Stephanie Barton
Opening hours: 11.30-3pm, 6-11pm; Sun 12-3pm, 7-10.30pm
Bar food: 12-2pm, 6.30-9pm (Sun 7pm)
Accommodation: (Price per room) double £65
Children: Welcome in rooms other than the bar
Credit cards: Access, Visa

WHITE HART
Bouth, near Ulverston LA12 8JB. Tel 0229 861229

Bouth

Georgian bow windows were a later addition to this old Lakeland building which has been serving good beer since the 17th century. It is still a haunt for beer lovers, with Tetley Mild and Bitter, Theakston XB, Boddingtons and Guinness on tap in the low-ceilinged bar. Window seats and an open fire add to the cosy, happy atmosphere, and a collection of memorabilia includes old clay pipes, newspapers, antlers and farm implements. Bar food is standard fare, with pizzas, steak and kidney pie, fish and chips and Cumberland sausage all costing under £5. Sloping ceilings and beams lend character to the five bedrooms.

Brewery: Free house
Licensee: Ross Hogan
Opening hours: Mon-Thu 12-3pm 6-11pm; closed,Tue lunchtime; Fri and Sat 11am-11pm; Sun 12-3pm, 7-10.30pm
Bar food: 12-2pm (except Tue), 6.30-9pm; Sun 12-2pm, 7-8.30pm
Accommodation: (Price per person) single £15, double £15-£20
Children: Welcome, but not after 9pm

Brewing's Capital

The fame of Burton upon Trent rests on the hard water of its springs. The monks made good beer here in the Middle Ages and by the 17th century Burton beer was being exported to London. The 18th-century improvement of the River Trent navigation opened a route through Hull to the Baltic and Russia, where Catherine the Great was exceedingly fond of strong, sweet Burton ale, while the Mersey and Trent Canal led to Liverpool and the passage to India. The railway's arrival in 1839 spurred vigorous expansion, led by the Bass dynasty. Other famous Burton names included Worthington, Allsop, Marston and Evershed, and firms from London and the South built Burton breweries to use the local water. Ind Coope has been there for many years. Today the Bass Museum of Brewing and the Heritage Brewery Museum open windows on the industry's past.

⊛ COLEDALE INN
Braithwaite, near Keswick CA12 5TN. Tel 07687 78272

Braithwaite

Serious hikers and casual walkers converge on this solid no-frills pub where several real ales are waiting to refresh them, for example McEwan 70/- (Younger Scotch), Yates Bitter and Guinness. Bar food is freshly cooked and plentiful, and includes dishes like Borrowdale trout and beef in beer both at £5.40, and Cumberland sausage for £4.35. There are two bars - one lofty with high ceilings and cushioned seats, the other smaller and more snug. Superb views are to be had from the garden and patio, and there are 12 Victorian-style bedrooms.

Brewery: Free house
Licensees: Peter, Geoffrey and Michael Mawdsley
Opening hours: Summer 11am-11pm; winter Mon-Thu 6.30-10.30pm (closed lunchtimes); Fri and Sat 12-3pm, 6.30-11pm; Sun 12-3pm, 7-10.30pm
Bar food: 12-2pm, 6.30-9pm
Accommodation: (Price per person) double £23
Children: Welcome anywhere; family room; outdoor play area
Credit cards: Access, Visa

☻ ABBEY BRIDGE INN
Lanercost, Brampton CA8 2MG. Tel 06977 2224

Brampton

An ancient converted smithy houses this atmospheric little pub which manages to combine a host of superlatives: warmest welcome, cosiest bar, first-class beer and excellent food. The setting is exceptionally attractive too, next to a river, with a sheltered patio near the old bridge, and close to the old Lanercost Priory in a wooded valley. The inn has been in operation since 1850, but the blacksmith's business dates back to 1670 when the house was built. The tiny bar is heavily beamed, the floor is flagged, and a huge stove dominates the room. Here a regularly changing series of guest ales (examples are Yates, Wadworth, Butterknowle) is on tap, and there's also a wide range of malt whiskies, many of them little-known names. A spiral staircase leads from the bar to a balconied restaurant, open in the evenings, where an à la carte menu is served, offering appetising starters like smoked trout mousse at £3.25, and as a main course, perhaps steak in whisky cream sauce (£8.99). Bar meals (served at lunchtime) are also good value, with dishes like quiche with potatoes and salad (£4.35) and savoury-filled potatoes (£3.35). On Sundays, a traditional roast is served. Accommodation is available in seven comfortable bedrooms.

Brewery: Free house
Licensee: Philip Sayers
Opening hours: 12-2.30pm, 7-11pm (10.30pm Sun)
Bar food: 12-2pm
Restaurant: 7-11pm
Accommodation: (Price per person) £19-£25
Children: Welcome anywhere; half portions available
Credit cards: Access, Visa

☻ BRIDGE HOTEL
Buttermere CA3 9UZ. Tel 07687 70252

Buttermere

Parts of this Cumberland stone building date back to the 11th century, though additions made several hundred years later form the greater part of what is now a hotel set in the centre of the village. Once a cornmill, its current role is to play host to the many walkers, locals and business people who descend on it for food, drink and accommodation. Traditional and friendly hospitality is on offer in the two bars, where oak beams and cushioned chairs help to create a very welcoming atmosphere. An almost bewildering selection of real ales is served here, including Black Sheep Best Bitter, Theakston Best Bitter, XB, and Old Peculier, Younger No 3 and Scotch Bitter and McEwan 80/-, as well as Guinness and Murphy's. Good local food is also available, with dishes like Cumbrian hotpot and 'tatie ash' - lamb and potatoes - both costing £4.50, and beef and Old Peculier pie for £4.75. There is also a special menu for vegetarians. In addition to a list of 85 wines, there are 13 malt whiskies to choose from. Outside is a stone patio with superb views, and 22 bedrooms decorated in traditional style offer accommodation; there are also self-catering possibilities.

Brewery: Free house
Licensees: Peter and Janet McGuire
Opening hours: 11am-11pm; Sun 12-3pm, 7-10.30pm
Bar food: 12-2.30pm, 6-10.30pm; Sun 12-2.30pm, 7-9.30pm
Restaurant: 7-8.30pm
Accommodation: (Price per person, inc dinner) single £54.50, double £47
Children: Welcome anywhere

⊜ MASONS ARMS
Strawberry Bank, Cartmel Fell, near Cartmel Over Sands LA11 6NW.
Tel 05395 68486/68686

Cartmel Fell

There's a huge selection of beers from all around the world on sale at this popular whitewashed inn which is the home of the Lakeland Brewery Company. Fans of Arthur Ransome's novels will recognise the beer names - Big Six and Amazon, and you can also try a home-made damson beer in winter or home-pressed farmhouse cider alongside the more familiar names: Theakston XB, Thwaites Bitter and a selection of guest beers. The range of bottled and canned beers, reckoned to number around 400, is also remarkable. The wide range of bar food includes unusual but tasty dishes like vegetable burritos at £5.75, Cajun chicken for £7.25, hummus with pitta bread and salad at £4.75, as well as the more familiar fish soup at £3.65 and chicken and mushroom pie for £7.25. At weekend lunchtimes the bar gets very busy, as walkers, families and tourists all jostle for attention. Set on the side of a fell with wonderful views over the open countryside, the inn is even more popular in the summer. The bar offers comfortable seating on lovely old settles, and the stone floors, wooden furnishings, open fires and ranges are all in keeping with its early 18th-century character. Outside, a paved patio with wooden seats makes best use of the views, and heaters mean it need not be out of action even on very cold days. Four two-person self-catering apartments and two four-person cottages are available.

Brewery: Free house
Licensee: Helen Stevenson
Opening hours: 11am-3pm,
6-11pm; Sun 12-3pm, 7-10.30pm
Bar food: 12-1.45pm, 6-8.45pm;
Sun 12-2pm, 7-8.45pm
Accommodation: From £158
per week
Children: Welcome if eating with
parents

⊜ PHEASANT
Casterton, near Kirkby Lonsdale LA6 2RX. Tel 05242 71230

Casterton

Those who come to this 200-year-old coaching inn for a quiet drink or two can browse through the newspapers and magazines provided in the bar. Oak beams, antique furniture, open fires and a carved wooden bar make a very pleasant place to relax, and there's a warm welcome from the friendly landlord. Locals and tourists alike take advantage of the hospitality, and on tap are Jennings and Tetley bitters with another guest beer in summer. There is also a good range of malt whiskies, reflecting the landlord's previous career in the whisky trade. Food is highly praised, and there is always a daily special in addition to the everyday fare. Home-made beef steak and kidney pie at £5.25 is popular, as are Cumberland gammon and egg at £5.95 and vegetarian pasta for £4.50. Sticky toffee pudding is one of several desserts at £2.50. There are ten good-sized bedrooms.

Brewery: Free house
Licensees: Melvin and May
Mackie
Opening hours: 11am-3pm,
6-11pm; Sun 11-3pm, 6-10.30pm
Bar food: 12-2pm, 6.30-9pm
Restaurant: 6.30-9pm
Accommodation: (Price per
room) single £37.50, double
£52.50
Children: Not permitted in bar;
family room
Credit cards: Access, Visa

⊕ SUN INN
Main Street, Dent, near Sedbergh LA10 5QL. Tel 05875 208

Dent

Two locally brewed real ales attract much custom to this traditional stone-built pub in an almost idyllic village setting in the midst of beautiful Dentdale countryside. Dent Bitter and Ramsbottom Strong Ale are on tap along with Younger Scotch, and in summer the garden is packed with real-ale drinkers from near and far sampling this local delight. Inside the old building, which dates back to 1640 and was once a smithy, cracks in the oak beams are stuffed with coins, and seating comes in a great variety of periods and styles. This pub is big on dominoes, and a game is invariably in process at the special table. Bar food is fairly standard but it is all freshly cooked and the generous portions are good value for money. Try full size rump steak for £4.95, Cumberland sausage at £3.75, and home-made pasties for £2.95. Accommodation is available in three good double rooms, furnished in the style of the pub.

Brewery: Free house
Licensees: Jacky and Martin Stafford
Opening hours: Summer 11am-11pm; winter 11am-2.30pm, 7-11pm; Sun 12- 2.30pm, 7-10.30pm
Bar food: 12-2pm, 7-8.30pm (Sat from 6.15pm); Sun 12-2pm, 7-8.30pm
Accommodation: (Price per room) £31
Children: Welcome anywhere
Credit cards: Access, Visa

⊕ BRITANNIA INN
Elterwater, near Ambleside LA22 9HP. Tel 09667 210

Elterwater

This long, low, whitewashed pub dates back to 1600, and was once a farmhouse, but its function now is to accommodate the great numbers of people who come to sample the food and drink, and it is usually very busy. Tourists and walkers far outnumber the locals, and parking can be difficult in the summer. There is a good atmosphere in spite of the crowds, heightened by the two comfortable bars with their settles, Windsor chairs, window seats and low ceilings. Naval memorabilia, maps and photographs make the interior interesting, but there are lovely views through the windows too. Outside, a garden is next to the pretty village green, where chairs and slate-topped tables provide al fresco seating. The food is very popular, and includes starters like herrings in Madeira sauce and vegetable samosa and onion bhajee both at £1.85. There are main dishes such as Cumberland fish pie at £4.60, pizza for £3.60, and pork chop baked with cider for £4.90, and sticky toffee pudding and chocolate heaven cake are both £1.85. To help wash it all down, or drink on its own, are real ales like Marston's Pedigree Bitter, Jennings Mild and Bitter, Boddingtons Bitter, and Wheelwrights LA Bitter. Afternoon tea is served, and there are five nicely decorated bedrooms.

Brewery: Free house
Licensee: David Fry
Opening hours: 11am-11pm; Sun 12-3pm, 7-10.30pm
Bar food: 12-2pm, 6.30-9pm
Restaurant: 7.30pm (one sitting)
Accommodation: (Price per person) single £17.50-£43, double £17.50-£29.50
Children: Welcome anywhere; family room
Credit cards: Access, Visa

BOWER HOUSE
Eskdale Green, near Holmrook CA19 1TD. Tel 09467 23244

Eskdale Green

Families and couples, visitors and locals, all mingle together in this warm, welcoming and very relaxed old inn. The landlord and staff are helpful and friendly, and provide a pleasant oasis in this lush but sparsely populated part of the Lake District. The large bar is interesting and comfortable with low ceilings and exposed beams, and there are sporting and hunting prints on the walls. On tap are Robinson's Hartleys XB, Theakston Best Bitter and Younger Scotch. Food here is special, too, and completely home-made. Starters like soup and rolls at £1.50, and chef's pâté with French bread for £3 might be followed by steak with mushrooms, grilled plaice or vegetable lasagne, all served with chips. An excellent chef's selection is always available in the bar, and there is a full vegetarian menu. For a more formal meal and setting the restaurant (smoking discoraged) is open every day. Outside, a lovely rambling garden has a small stream, and there are sheltered wooded areas and open lawns for walking or sitting. Charming and comfortable overnight accommodation is available.

Brewery: Free house
Licensee: Derek Connor
Opening hours: 11am-3pm, 6-11pm; Sun 11am-3pm, 7-10.30pm
Bar food: As opening hours
Restaurant: Times as bar food
Accommodation: (Price per person) single £39.25, double £26.75
Children: Welcome anywhere
Credit cards: Access, Visa

⊕ STRING OF HORSES
Faugh, near Carlisle CA4 9EG. Tel 0228 70297

Faugh

A network of narrow lanes leads from several directions to this large whitewashed pub which dominates a tiny village in the midst of rolling countryside. The building dates back to the late 17th century, and inside the two bars its character speaks for itself: big stone fireplaces, oak beams, and wooden benches and stools help create a relaxing, mellow atmosphere. Several inter-connecting rooms are dark and cosy, and full of brasses and coppers. Another attraction is the good food, and the pub draws country regulars, families and business people from a wide area. The bar menu caters for all tastes, and features dishes like Madras curry at £5.25 alongside the similarly priced goujons of chicken, and steak and oyster pie at £5.50. Other choices include starters like eggs Benedict for £4.25 and soup at £1.75, and main course pork calypso for £5.75. Bread-and-butter pudding and apple pie are both £1.95. There's a daily changing special and a help-yourself lunchtime buffet. On tap are Jennings Cumberland Ale and Mild, Theakston Best Bitter, Federation and McEwan 80/- as well as Murphy's and Guinness, and there's a good range of malt whiskies. Bedrooms offer sumptuously furnished accommodation, including four-poster beds.

Brewery: Free house
Licensee: Mrs A M Tasker
Opening hours: 11.30am-3pm, 5.30-11pm; Sun 12-3pm, 7-10.30pm
Bar food: 12-2pm, 7-9.30pm
Restaurant: Times as bar food
Accommodation: (Price per room) single £58-£72, double £65-£95
Children: Welcome anywhere
Credit cards: AMERICAN EXPRESS®, Access, Visa, Diners

⊕ METAL BRIDGE INN
Floriston, near Carlisle CA6 4HG. Tel 0228 74206

Floriston

A beer garden and conservatory look out over the River Esk at this former fishing house, but the metal bridge of the pub's name is nowhere to be seen. Set near the Scottish border and the sea, the pub stands on its own on the river bank. Alterations have opened out the original layout and obscured the exact age of the building, but some of the old features remain. The decor in the bar is modern, and a collection of stuffed fish in cases and fishing implements form an interesting memento of its past. Families, country regulars and business people rub shoulders comfortably in the pleasant atmosphere. Bar food is fairly standard, but tasty and offering good value, with dishes like scampi at £3.95, Cumberland sausage for £3.85 and sirloin steak for £7.95. On tap in the bar are Theakston Best Bitter, Younger Scotch Bitter and Guinness. Outside the square white building, the restaurant and overnight accommodation, consisting of three bedrooms in country-pine style, are housed in attractive old red sandstone outbuildings.

Brewery: Scottish and Newcastle
Licensee: Alan Miller
Opening hours: 11am-3pm, 5.30-11pm; Sun 12-3pm, 7-10.30pm
Bar food: 11.30am-2pm, 5.30pm-9.30pm; Sun 12-2pm, 7-9.30pm
Restaurant: 7-9.30pm
Accommodation: (Price per room) single £32, double £45
Children: Welcome anywhere; half portions available
Credit cards: AMERICAN EXPRESS®, Access, Visa, Diners

⊕ GEORGE AND DRAGON
Garrigill, near Alston CA9 3DJ. Tel 0434 381293

Garrigill

L ocals generally have this cosy country pub to themselves in the winter, but once the weather warms up the place undergoes a dramatic change. Walkers, families, fishermen and tourists discover or rediscover it in the summer, and receive a warm welcome. The old stone building overlooking the village green dates back to 1621, and many of the original features can still be seen in the bar. Old wooden fittings, open fires, flagstone floors and a leather-cushioned settle help to create a relaxing country atmosphere, and there are brasses and George and Dragon memorabilia. Real ales on tap include Theakston Best Bitter, XB and Old Peculier, Younger Scotch Bitter (McEwan70/-), and Guinness. Bar food is good and wholesome, and typical dishes might be a seafood in puff pastry starter for £2.60, and main courses include traditional Yorkshire pudding with various fillings (£1.20 to £3.15), home-made steak pie with chips and peas for £3.85, and country lentil crumble for £4.50. Hot fudge sundae costs £2.10. Outside, an enclosed stone courtyard has seating, and there is a bunk house to sleep the walkers who wander in off the fells. There are also two double and two single good-sized bedrooms, furnished in traditional style.

Brewery: Free house
Licensee: Brian Holmes
Opening hours: 11am-3pm, 6.30-11pm; Sun 12-3pm, 7-10.30pm
Bar food: 12-2pm, 7-9pm (except Mon evenings)
Restaurant: Times as bar food
Accommodation: (Price per person) £14; bunk house £3; children not permitted under five years
Children: Not encouraged after 9.30pm

⚬ WASDALE HEAD INN
Wasdale Head, near Gosforth CA20 1EX. Tel 09467 26229

Gosforth

Climbers and walkers make the most use of this remote inn at the head of a beautiful, isolated valley. The lakeside road ends here, and the magnificent peaks of Scafell Pike, Great Gable and Pillar rise up behind it. Many people use it as a base for negotiating these and other summits, while others enjoy a day here away from the more populated lakes. The atmosphere inside is relaxed and friendly, with the basic decor and furniture that befits its rugged role. Pictures of famous mountaineers, and walking and climbing memorabilia make inspiring perusal. The Public Bar has a flagstoned floor, seating at wooden tables and benches, and open fires, and at the entrance piles of boots tell their own story. Bar food is available throughout the day in summer, and the menu offers dishes like fellman's lunch at £4.50, locally smoked mackerel for £4.25, Cumberland sausage at £5.95, and potted shrimps at £3.50. Home-made soup is £1.70, and puddings like chocolate fudge cake and apple pie are £2.50. On tap in the bar are Theakston Best Bitter and Old Peculier, Jennings Bitter, Yates Bitter and Murphy's. Ten bedrooms (cots can be provided for small children) offer comfortable accommodation, some with views of the famous peaks.

Brewery: Free house
Licensee: G R M Carr
Opening hours: Summer 11am-11pm; Sun 12-3pm, 7-10.30pm; winter (weekends only) Fri and Sat 11am-3pm, 5.30-11pm; Sun 12-3pm
Bar food: As opening hours
Restaurant: Times as summer opening hours
Accommodation: Mar-Nov and two weeks New Year (price per person, inc dinner) single £55, double £53
Children: Welcome anywhere; family room
Credit cards: Access, Visa

⚬ OLD CROWN
Hesket Newmarket, near Caldbeck CA9 8JG. Tel 06998 288

Hesket Newmarket

Five real ales brewed at this unspoilt village pub have proved to be a powerful draw to beer drinkers. Doris's 90th Birthday Ale, Skiddaw Special Bitter, Blencathra Bitter, Old Carrock Strong Ale and Great Cockup Porter, produced by the Hesket Newmarket Brewery, are all highly praised, and people come from far and wide to sample them. Old world charm is much in evidence in the two bars, with their

Brewery: Hesket Newmarket
Licensees: Jim Fearnley and Liz Blackwood
Opening hours: 12-3pm, 5.30-11pm; Sun 12-3pm, 7-10.30pm
Bar food: 12-3pm, 6.30-8.30pm; Sun 12.30-2.30pm, 7-8.30pm

exposed beams, sturdy wooden furniture, old prints and open fires. In the summer customers often spill out on to the village green with their drinks and bar meals, as there is no garden, and the setting is idyllic. The stone-built pub nestles below the Caldbeck fells in this typical English village in the depths of the Cumbrian countryside. Food covers two different ranges - traditional British and Indian cooking - and local produce is used wherever possible. The result is meals of a very high standard: local salmon and home-cooked ham both cost £4.50, steak and kidney pie, or the vegetarian Indian dahl with cashew nuts and sweet potatoes, are £3.95, and rogan josh is £4.20. At lunchtime during the week only soup and sandwiches are available, and on Sundays there is a set three-course lunch with coffee for £5.50. A terraced cottage adjoining the pub offers two bedrooms with good views.

Restaurant: 6.30-8.30pm; Sun (set lunch or sandwiches) 12-2pm, 7-8.30pm
Accommodation: (Price per person) £14.50
Children: Welcome anywhere except main bar; half portions available
Credit cards: Diners (for restaurant and accommodation only)

⊕ SNOOTY FOX TAVERN
Main Street, Kirkby Lonsdale LA6 2AH. Tel 05242 71308

Kirkby Lonsdale

Farming and brewing antiques make an interesting display at this 17th-century tavern just off the square in the small market town of Kirkby Lonsdale. The three bars, with their flagged floors, wooden beams and open fires, are cosy and fresh flowers add a fragrant touch, much appreciated by locals and tourists. Staff are friendly and helpful. Hartleys XB, Theakston XB, and Timothy Taylor Landlord are on tap, and fruit wines like damson, elderberry and elderflower are also popular. Food is fresh and home-made, and includes choices such as marinated pork ribs in sweet and sour sauce at £3.75, old-fashioned Lakeland bacon, apple and sage crusty pie for £5.25, roast guinea fowl at £5.95, and hot pancake with ricotta cheese and spinach for £3.50. Booking is advisable for dinner at the weekend. A pretty walled garden provides outdoor seating, and there is accommodation in five beamed rooms, unfussily furnished in country style; cots are available for young children.

Brewery: Free house
Licensees: Jack Shone, David and Wendy Moses
Opening hours: 11am-3pm, 6-11pm; Sun 12-3pm, 7-10.30pm
Bar food: 12-2.30pm, 7-10pm
Restaurant: Times as bar food
Accommodation: (Price per room) single £21-£26, double £36-£46
Children: Welcome anywhere; family room; outdoor play area

⊕ KIRKSTILE INN
Loweswater, near Cockermouth CA13 0RU. Tel 0900 85219

Loweswater

An isolated whitewashed stone building at the foot of the fells, this 16th-century pub is ideally situated to quench the thirsts of passing walkers. Jennings Bitter, Younger Scotch and Guinness are on tap to do the job, and there's also a good selection of wines and malt whiskies. Food here is freshly cooked, and includes fairly standard dishes like

Brewery: Free house
Licensee: Ken Gorley
Opening hours: 11am-11pm; Sun 12-3pm, 7-10.30pm
Bar food: 12-2.30pm, 6-9pm; Sun 12-2.30pm, 7-9pm

Cumberland sausage and omelette, both at £4.50, and scampi for £5.25. There is always a special dish for vegetarians. The bar is as attractive as the location, with its oak beams and open fires, and there are plenty of traditional pub games to play, like shove halfpenny, dominoes, cards, pool and darts. Chairs and tables are set up in the garden, and the setting in the depths of the countryside attracts many tourists, especially in summer. Ten bedrooms, decorated in keeping with the style of the pub are available.

Restaurant: 7-8pm (except Sun)
Accommodation: (Price per room) double £40-£50
Children: Welcome anywhere; family room
Credit cards: Access, Visa

⊕ FARMERS ARMS
Lowick Green, near Ulverston LA12 8DT. Tel 0229 861277/861376

Lowick Green

Two wonderfully preserved examples of old Lakeland bars can be seen at this rambling pub - originally a farm - parts of which date back to 1350. One bar has rough plastered walls, a beamed ceiling and old comfortable furniture, while the other has flagged floors, open fire and settles and is broken up by alcoves; both have lovely old leaded windows. The decor is a mixture of bric-à-brac, stuffed birds, old brasses, plates and paintings, and the friendly staff create a relaxed atmosphere. Cribbage, darts and pool can be played and there's also a skittle alley. The inn is set at a crossroads in the heart of the countryside with marvellous views, and its position as much as its ambience attracts all comers, from business people during the week to families, walkers and country sports enthusiasts at weekends. On tap are Theakston XB, Younger Scotch Bitter, McEwan, and Guinness, and there's a great selection of single malts and liqueurs. Very large portions of good plain food are served, including ploughman's platter at £4, farmer's roast of the day for £5.25 and ocean pie at £4.85. Puddings like apple blossom pie and chocolate orange Seville are £1.75. There are 11 bedrooms, decorated in country style.

Brewery: Scottish and Newcastle
Licensee: Alan Lockwell
Opening hours: 11am-11pm; Sun 12-3pm, 7-10.30pm
Bar food: 12-2pm, 6-9pm; Sun 12-9pm (supper licence)
Restaurant: 7-9pm; Sun 12-2pm
Accommodation: (Price per person) single £32.50-£45, double £35-£55
Children: Welcome anywhere before 9pm; children's menu available
Credit cards: AMERICAN EXPRESS®, Access, Visa

The Red Triangle

Bass's simple red triangle is the world's oldest registered trademark. The firm was founded in Burton upon Trent in 1777 by a carrier named William Bass and was built up by three formidable successors - his son, grandson and great-grandson. When the son, Michael Thomas Bass, died a multi-millionaire, at today's values, in 1827, production was approaching 10,000 barrels a year. By 1877 it was close to one million barrels a year. Michael Thomas Bass II died in 1884. His successor, Michael Arthur, a notable local benefactor, art collector and close friend of King Edward VII, was created Lord Burton before his death in 1909. The Bass firm took over numerous rivals, including Worthington's, Charrington's and Tennent's, and is now the country's biggest brewer, supplying more than one-fifth of Britain's beer.

⊕ SHEPHERDS INN
Melmerby, near Penrith CA10 1HF. Tel 0768881 217

Melmerby

Food is one of the main attractions at this typical Cumbrian sandstone pub, particularly the excellent range of sweets and cheeses. Everything is home-baked, from starters like local freshwater eel in garlic butter at £2.50 and Stilton and gammon pasta bake for £2.90 through to the main courses and puddings. Venison and Roquefort crumble (£6.95), Cumberland sausage hot pot for £4.80 and chicken Leoni, £6.25, are all cooked to a high standard. Jennings Cumberland Ale and Sneck Lifter, Marston's Pedigree and two guest ales are on tap, and there are 46 malt whiskies and a good choice of wines. The pub sits at the foot of the Pennines, and there's a friendly welcome for visitors and regulars alike. Exposed beams and stone floors add to the unspoilt atmosphere in the two bars, and there are open fires and sheep prints by a local artist. Accommodation can be arranged in the village.

Brewery: Free house
Licensee: Martin Baucutt
Opening hours: 10.30am-3pm, 6-11pm; Sun 12-3pm, 7-10.30pm
Bar food: 11am-2.45pm, 6-9.45pm; Sun 12-2.45pm, 7-9.45pm
Children: Welcome if eating and accompanied by adults; half portions available
Credit cards: AMERICAN EXPRESS®, Access, Visa

⊕ TOWER BANK ARMS
Near Sawrey, near Hawkeshead LA22 0LF. Tel 05394 36334

Near Sawrey

A traditional slate-flagged floor and big cooking range in the cosy bar make this 17th-century Lakeland pub a popular choice for tourists. Low ceilings with exposed beams, old settles and a grandfather clock add to the old-world atmosphere, and next door is the home of Beatrix Potter, now owned by the National Trust. The pretty village is a magnet for Peter Rabbit and Jemima Puddleduck fans, as well as fishermen and walkers, and all are welcome at this fine black-and-white hostelry. Theakston Best Bitter, XB and Old Peculier are on tap in the bar, along with Younger Scotch Bitter and Guinness, and there's a good range of malt whiskies including a 'malt of the month'. There's plenty of choice on the bar food menu, too, and the results are tasty: potted shrimps at £3.50 and soup for £1.40; cream cheese and broccoli bake, and steak and onion pie, both at £4.25, and grilled salmon steak and asparagus at £6.25. Sweets like sherry trifle and banana cream bash are £1.80. A small garden and patio to the side of the pub make a pleasant spot for outdoor eating and drinking, and there are striking views to be had from the three comfortable bedrooms.

Brewery: Free house
Licensee: Philip Breadley
Opening hours: 11am-3pm, 5.30-11pm (from 6pm in winter); Sun 12-3pm, 7-10.30pm
Bar food: 12-2pm, 6.30-9pm; Sun 12-2pm, 7-9pm
Restaurant: Times as bar food
Accommodation: (Price per room) single £32, double £40; children not permitted to share parents' room
Children: Lunchtime in eating area only; dinner in restaurant only
Credit cards: AMERICAN EXPRESS®, Access, Visa

⊛ WHITE HORSE
Threlkeld, near Keswick CA12 4SY. Tel 07687 79241

Threlkeld

Surrounded by fells and set midway between Penrith and Keswick, this old-fashioned pub attracts a mixed crowd of locals, tourists and business people, who are drawn by the unspoilt, cosy old bar with its oak beams, hunting prints and blazing log fires in winter. Outside nothing much has changed since it was built 320 years ago, and there are stunning views of the fells and Blencathra or Saddleback. A few chairs and tables at the front make the most of these. On tap are Jennings Bitter, Marston's Pedigree and Guinness, and there's a reasonable range of malts and wines. The food is as much an attraction as the pub's beautiful setting, and a consistently high standard is maintained. Portions are large, and there's an excellent choice at lunchtime - for example - sirloin steak with herb and garlic or blue Stilton savoury butters at £9.75, local chicken with lemon sauce and rice at £8.50, and rainbow trout poached in white wine at £7.75.

Brewery: Free house
Licensee: Larry Slattery
Opening hours: 11am-3pm,
6-11pm; Sun 12-3pm, 7-10.30pm
Bar food: 12-1.45pm, 7-8.30pm
Children: Welcome in two Snug
Bars; half portions available
Credit cards: Access, Visa

MORTAL MAN
Troutbeck, near Windermere CA23 1PL. Tel 05394 33193

Troutbeck

Locals and tourists enjoy the friendly reception at this whitewashed 17th-century Cumbrian stone building, whose beautiful location guarantees a constant stream of visitors to its panelled bar, where oak beams and cushioned chairs makes a pleasant resting place. Pub food is standard but well cooked and tasty, and includes choices like venison casserole at £5.50, hotpot for £5.80, and Cumberland sausage for £5.20. There is also a vegetarian dish. A wine list with over 45 choices complements the food, and Theakston Best Bitter and Younger Scotch are on tap. In the summer months, tables and chairs are arranged on the lawn outside, and for simple overnight accommodation there are 12 bedrooms.

Brewery: Free house
Licensee: C J Poulsom
Opening hours: 12-2.30pm,
5.30-11pm; Sun 12-2.30pm,
7-10.30pm
Bar food: 12-1.50pm, 6.30-9pm
(except Mon); Sun 12-1.50pm,
7- 9pm
Restaurant: 7.30-8pm
Accommodation: (Price per
person, inc dinner) double £50
Children: Welcome anywhere
but not permitted under five
years

⊛ BAY HORSE INN
Canal Foot, Ulverston LA12 9EL. Tel 0229 583972

Ulverston

The landlord of this 17th-century coaching inn is also an accomplished chef who previously worked at the renowned Miller Howe hotel, and his food attracts a great deal of attention, inspiring many people to drive through the unpromising industrial estate to reach this isolated pub which stands on the edge of the estuary with superb views

Brewery: Free house
Licensee: Robert Lyons
Opening hours: 11am-11pm;
Sun 12-3pm, 7-10.30pm
Bar food: 12-2pm (except Mon)
Restaurant: 12-1.30pm, 7.30pm

across the water to Morecambe Bay. With a guide it is possible to walk across the treacherous sands, but this is not recommended for the uninitiated. There's a stone horse's head in the bar in case anyone forgets the inn's name, and black beams, a marbled fireplace and lots of brasses add to the traditional atmosphere. Here Mitchell's Fortress and Best Bitter are on tap along with Murphy's and Guinness, and Everards Tiger Bitter is one of the real ales which makes a guest appearance. There is a huge variety of New World and European wines available to go with the wonderful food. Examples of daily specials from the bar menu, all costing around £7, might be bobotie, a Cape Malay dish of spiced minced lamb covered with a savoury custard and baked, or mushrooms and courgettes with garlic and sage served with fettucini au gratin, or tomatoes provençale baked with sliced fennel, leeks and water chestnuts topped with Emmenthal cheese and savoury custard. There is, of course, a separate restaurant menu.There are six bedrooms and all have views over the estuary.

for 8pm (one sitting)
Accommodation: (Price per person, inc dinner) single £75, double £65
Children: Welcome if over 12 years and only if eating
Credit cards: Access, Visa

CO DURHAM

RED WELL INN
Harmire Road, Barnard Castle DL12 8QJ. Tel 0833 37002

Barnard Castle

Although surrounded by industry, this well run pub retains the atmosphere of a country inn as a result of being situated on the edge of sheep-farming Teesdale. A much extended farm cottage, the substantial whitewashed pub dates from the mid-19th century and has two bars, frequented mainly by locals, business customers and passing trade. One bar serves a taproom furnished in traditional style and the other serves the remainder of the pub, which comprises several carpeted lounge areas of different size and a separate restaurant. Simple bar meals, including filled pancake at £4.65 and steak and kidney pie at £5.45, as well as daily specials, are available in the taproom. More elaborate meals are on offer in the other bar, while the restaurant serves à la carte dishes and four-course dinners at £10 to 13.50. Butterknowle Conciliation Ale, Newcastle Brown and a guest beer are on sale, along with over 30 wines. Pool, dominoes, cards and electronic games can be played, and outdoor seating is provided on a small terrace in front of the pub. There are seven double rooms, all with modern furniture complemented by a pale decor.

Brewery: Free house
Licensee: Michael Rudd
Opening hours: 11.30am-2.30pm, 6.30-11pm; Sun 12-2pm, 7-10.30pm
Bar food: 12-1.45pm; 7-9pm (Mon 8.30pm); Sun 12-1.45pm, 7-8.30pm
Restaurant: Times as bar food
Accommodation: (Price per person) single £29.95-£38, double £42-£49.50
Children: Welcome anywhere
Credit cards: Access, Visa

☺ LORD CREWE ARMS
Blanchland, near Consett DH8 9SP. Tel 0434 675251

Blanchland

Situated in an attractive village surrounded by high moorland, this friendly pub began life as a monastery in 1165, but it is not known when it became an inn. A bar with an arched stone ceiling and a flagstone floor preserves the building's simple, traditional character inside, where an unusual feature for a pub is a small library of fascinating old books. Additional seating is provided in a pleasant garden behind the pub. Beer drinkers among the well assorted clientele, which includes many famous visitors, are offered the choice of Vaux Samson, Newcastle Exhibition and McEwan Scotch Bitter, while an extensive wine list complements the menu. Well prepared and good value for money, the food includes enticing items such as crispy coated garlic and herb king prawns at £4.90, sautéd pork fillet dipped in horseradish and with fresh tomato sauce at £5.50 and smoked salmon and prawn cornets at £7.50. Eighteen rooms are available, all decorated and furnished in traditional country style, and one with the bonus, or otherwise, of a ghost.

Brewery: Free house
Licensee: Mr P R Gingell
Opening hours: 11am-3pm, 6-11pm; Sun 12-3pm, 7-10.30pm
Bar food: 12-2pm, 7-9.30pm
Restaurant: Times as bar food
Accommodation: (Price per person) single £70, double £47
Children: Welcome anywhere except bar
Credit cards: AMERICAN EXPRESS®, Access, Visa, Diners

☺ FOX HOUNDS
Cotherstone, near Barnard Castle DL12 9PF. Tel 0833 50241

Cotherstone

This Tees valley village pub, built about 1750, is popular with both locals and visitors, including tourists, many doubtless drawn by its reputation for good food and its comprehensive wine list. Fish and seafood figure prominently on the menu - for example, grilled fresh lemon sole at £8.45 and baked crab at £9.45 - and local specialities are served, including chicken Cotherstone at £8.95. John Smith's Bitter and Magnet, and Hambleton Best Bitter, along with a wide range of malt whiskies, are served in the beamed bar, which is decorated and furnished in traditional rural style. The three double rooms, with their country pine furniture and the odd more solid period piece, are in keeping with the bar.

Brewery: Free house
Licensees: P C and J L Crawley
Opening hours: 11.30am-2.30pm, 6.30-11pm; Sun 12-2.30pm, 7-10.30pm
Bar food: As opening hours
Restaurant: Times as bar food
Accommodation: (Price per person) single or double £27.50; children under ten years not permitted
Children: Welcome anywhere; children's menu available
Credit cards: Access, Visa (three per cent supplement added)

DUKE OF YORK
Fir Tree, near Crook DL15 8DG. Tel 0388 762848

Fir Tree

Built in 1749 to serve drovers and coaches plying between England and Scotland, this pub still attracts a good amount of passing trade in addition to its regulars. Its whitewashed walls set off by black, shuttered windows, the handsome building stands in five and a half acres, including a large landscaped garden at the rear. Three rooms, carpeted and furnished with spindlebacked chairs and oak tables, are served by two bars. The interior was modernised in 1966 with the help of the furniture maker 'Mouseman' Thompson, who fitted out the former stables as bars and whose mouse trademark appears on the stools and bar fittings. Decoration is provided by hunting rifles, African spears, and pictures and prints, some depicting Stone Age subjects. Draught Bass and Bass Best Scotch Bitter, and Stones Best Bitter are on tap, along with two draught lagers and one cider, and there is a wide selection of bottled beers. The food, all fresh and prepared to the unique recipes of the proprietor, includes speciality dishes such as gammon in sherry and steaks for about £10, as well as simpler dishes, and is complemented by an extensive wine list.

Brewery: Free house
Licensee: G R Suggett
Opening hours: Summer 10am-11pm; winter 10am-3pm, 6.30-11pm; Sun 7-10.30pm
Bar food: As opening hours
Restaurant: 11am-2pm, 6-10pm (Sun from 7pm)
Children: Welcome anywhere
Credit cards: Access, Visa

MORRITT ARMS HOTEL
Greta Bridge, near Barnard Castle DL12 9SE. Tel 0833 27232

Greta Bridge

An imposing building dating from 1774, this pub stands beside a bridge over the River Greta, in beautiful countryside near where the smaller river meets the Tees. With their armchairs and open fires, and a mixed, largely older clientele of regulars and visitors, the two beamed bars are comfortable and relaxing. The Dickens Bar, embellished with murals depicting characters from the novelist's works, and displaying a collection of models and antiques, opens on to a pleasant garden equipped with picnic tables. Butterknowle Conciliation Bitter, Younger Scotch Bitter and Newcastle Exhibition are the beers on sale. Simple, but freshly prepared, the bar meals include jumbo sausage and fried egg at £4.75, various omelettes at £4.80 and grilled rump steak at £10. Sandwiches are on offer at all times outside bar meal hours. Furnished and decorated in the modern country style, five single and 12 double rooms are available, one of the latter complete with a four-poster bed.

Brewery: Free house
Licensees: David and John Mulley
Opening hours: 11am-3pm, 6-11pm; Sun 12-2pm, 7-10.30pm
Bar food: 12-2pm
Restaurant: 7-8.45pm; Sun 12-2pm
Accommodation: (Price per room) single £36, double £64
Children: Not permitted under six years in public areas after 7pm, and in dining room for breakfast only; outdoor play area
Credit cards: AMERICAN EXPRESS®, Access, Visa, Diners

KIRK INN
Romaldkirk, near Barnard Castle DL12 9ED. Tel 0833 50260

Romaldkirk

A good variety of well kept beers - Clark's Burglar Bill, Castle Eden Ale, Boddingtons Bitter and Butterknowle Conciliation Ale - is the main attraction of this little village pub. Built about 1700 on the green, near the Saxon church, it is frequented mainly by regulars and families, and has a cosy bar, simply furnished and retaining its original beams. At lunchtime sandwiches and light meals starting at £3.95 are available, while in the evening the food, likewise skilfully cooked, is more substantial. Among the main courses, served at the same price in the bar and in the small dining room, are fillet steak in red wine and mushroom sauce at £8.95, poached fillet of salmon with prawns at £7.25 and breast of chicken filled with honey and almonds at £6.95. Dominoes can be played, there is a collection of toys to keep young children amused, and on alternate Wednesday evenings a quiz is held.

Brewery: Free house
Licensee: Dennis Frampton
Opening hours: 12-3pm, 6-11pm; closed Tue lunchtime; Sun 12-3pm, 7-10.30pm
Bar food: As opening hours
Restaurant: Times as bar food
Children: Welcome anywhere; half portions available

☻ ROSE AND CROWN INN
Romaldkirk, near Barnard Castle DL12 9EB. Tel 0833 50213

Romaldkirk

Two distinct groups of customers - regulars and families in the Public Bar and business people in the Hotel Bar - use this former coaching inn, and both enjoy its friendly, relaxed atmosphere. Built in 1733 and one of three pubs overlooking the green, where the old stocks can still be seen, the inn stands in a village set astride the main road through Teesdale. A huge open fireplace is among its surviving original features, while period furniture, objects from the worlds of hunting and farming, and a collection of brass kettles contribute to the traditional look of the pub. Theakston Best Bitter and Old Peculier are on sale, along with an extensive range of malt whiskies and an excellent choice of wines. The wide choice of food, all prepared on the premises and very good value for money, includes a large open sandwich of Greenland prawns at £4.85, and pan-fried steaks: sirloin at £9.50 and fillet at £10.85. The 12 double rooms and one single are furnished in a modern style.

Brewery: Free house
Licensee: Mr C Davey
Opening hours: 11.30am-3pm, 5.30-11pm; Sun 11.30am-3pm, 7-10.30pm
Bar food: 12-1.30pm, 6.30-9.30pm (Sun from 7pm)
Restaurant: 7.30-9pm
Accommodation: (Price per room) single £48, double £70
Children: Welcome anywhere; children's menu available

⊜ SUN
Beamish Open Air Museum, Stanley DH9 0RG. Tel 091 3701699

Stanley

Brewery: Free house
Licensee: Mrs W Allison
Opening hours: Summer 10am-5.30pm; winter 10am-4.30pm; closed Mon in winter
Bar food: As opening hours
Children: In back room only

Originally established as an ale house in the late 17th century, nowadays this friendly little pub gives a wide variety of visitors a fascinating glimpse into the more recent past. A recreation of a miners' pub in Bishop Auckland, it is situated in a typical small northern mining town and has a single bar which incorporates the original furniture and style of decoration. Sunderland lustre jugs, stuffed animals, old mirrors and nostalgic prints further help to conjure up the bygone days. Theakston Best Bitter, Younger No 3 and Scotch Bitter, Newcastle Exhibition and Beamish Stout are on sale, along with McEwan lager, Blackthorn cider and bottled Newcastle Brown. Sandwiches are available during the week, and at lunchtime on Sundays local specialities are free at the bar: black pudding, pease pudding and cheese and pickles. From time to time the pub plays host to traditional musicians, dancers or singers.

⊜ BRIDGE INN
Whorlton, near Barnard Castle DL12 8XD. Tel 0833 27341

Whorlton

Brewery: Free house
Licensee: Mr F T Hawkswell
Opening hours: Summer 11am-2pm, 6.30-11pm; winter 7-11pm; Sun 12-3pm, 7-10.30pm
Bar food: As opening hours
Restaurant: Times as bar food
Children: In dining room only; children's menu available

Square and built in stone, probably around 1800, this pub stands at the corner of a small, attractive village set above a gorge of the River Tees. Although its clientele is very mixed, embracing both locals and foreign visitors, the atmosphere is friendly in the single bar, with its wooden tables and chairs, cushioned benches and interesting collection of teapots. Picnic benches are set out on a grassed area in front of the pub, giving a view of the village green. John Smith's Bitter and Magnet are on sale, along with Beamish Stout and two lagers. All home-cooked to a high standard, the food gives good value for money. Meals are served in both the bar and the separate dining room, and include starters such as mussels in white wine at £2.60 and main courses like chicken in orange sauce or chicken with apricot and ginger, both at £6.50.

Machine-Gun Brown Ale

Closures in the Co durham coalfield in the 1960s convinced the Vaux Group that the North East beer market would decline, and it diversified into hotels, property and shops. Cuthbert Vaux founded his first brewery in Sunderland in 1837 and several generations of his family succeeded him. The company's Maxim Ale was named after Major Ernest Vaux's maxim-gun detachment in the Boer War, and it also produced Vaux's Highly Nourishing Stout. The last Vaux to be chairman died in 1927. The firm grew steadily and is now one of Britain's largest independents.

GREATER MANCHESTER

⊕ ROYAL OAK
729 Wilmslow Road, Didsbury M20 0RH. Tel 061 445 3152

Didsbury

An extensive and impressive selection of cheeses and pâtés (£2.50) - probably the best on any bar menu in the country - is featured by this very popular, traditional, street-corner pub which has stood in the town centre since the 19th century. Draught beverages include Fosters, Swann and Heineken lagers as well as Marston's Pedigree Bitter and Banks's Mild, and two comfortable, carpeted bars where the flock wallpaper is adorned with theatrical hand bills are always crowded with a mixture of business folk and local regulars; tables on the street provide outdoor seating.

Brewery: Marston's
Licensee: A Gosling
Opening hours: 11am-3pm, 5-11pm (Sat 11am-11pm); Sun 12-3pm, 7-10.30pm
Bar food: 12-2pm (except Sat and Sun)
Children: Not permitted inside

NURSERY INN
Green Lane, Heaton Norris, near Stockport SK4 2NA. Tel 061 432 2044

Heaton Norris

A bowling green and beer garden make this 1930s suburban inn a popular summer venue. The interior of the pub displays material relating to its history, and the traditional Public Bar displays mementoes of the local football team, whose headquarters it is. Four comfortable seating areas include a separate dining room serving value-for-money lunches - soup and hot bread at £1, for example, followed by sirloin steak (£4) and summer pudding (£1.20), with a vegetarian option always available - which make good use of fish, and a reasonable choice of wine supplements draught Guinness and Hydes' Anvil Bitter and Mild.

Brewery: Hydes
Licensee: George Lindsay
Opening hours: 11.30am-3.30pm, 5.30-11pm (Sat 11.30am-11pm); Sun 12-3pm, 7-10.30pm
Bar food: 12-2.15pm (Sat 3pm) except Sun
Children: Welcome if dining Mon to Fri only

⊕WHITE HOUSE
Blackstone Edge, Littleborough OL15 0LG. Tel 0706 378456

Littleborough

The restaurant of this 17th-century coaching inn is reserved for private functions, but the wide range of dishes served in its two comfortable, open-fired bars represents excellent value for money, a starter like mushrooms and garlic (£2) being followed perhaps by prawn and plaice Mornay (£4.75) and apple pie (£1.20). Such meals, together with the availability of a good choice of ales - John Smith's Bitter, Taylor Landlord, Courage Directors and a guest selection - on draught, a friendly, relaxed atmosphere and a wonderful moorland setting with impressive views, make the pub a popular venue for both business people and family parties.

Brewery: Free house
Licensee: Neville Marney
Opening hours: 11.30am-3pm, 7-11pm; Sun 12-3pm, 7-10.30pm
Bar food: 11.30am-2pm, 7-10pm; Sun 12-2.30pm, 7-10pm
Restaurant: Available for private functions only
Children: Welcome until 9pm

LASS O'GOWRIE
Charles Street, Manchester M1 7DB. Tel 061 273 6932

Manchester

The ornate tiled exterior of this very attractive 19th-century city pub hides an interesting interior where a lively clientele (largely comprised of students) can enjoy draught beer of an excellent quality, own brew LOG 35 and 42 being served as well as Murphy's and Chester's (Exchange); Scrumpy Jack cider is also available on draught. Bar snacks, though simple (soup at £1, for example, with a range of ploughman's at £3), represent good value for money, and the bar itself is very unusual, being gas lit, with exposed brickwork, beams, a wood floor and windows looking on to the brewing area.

Brewery: Whitbread
Licensee: Raymond Wilson
Opening hours: 11.30am-11pm
(Sat 11.30am-3pm, 6-11pm); Sun
12-3pm, 7-10.30pm
Bar food: 11.30am-2.30pm (Sat
2pm); Sun 12-2pm
Children: Welcome over two
years old; must not approach bar

MR THOMAS'S CHOP HOUSE
52 Cross Street, Manchester M2 7AE. Tel 061 832 2245

Manchester

The frontage of this 19th-century city-centre pub is very small, but its tiled exterior is both attractive and original, and a bar with lots of atmosphere and a style reflecting the building's Victorian origins attracts both business folk and shoppers - particularly at lunchtime, when it tends to become crowded. A superior wine list is available, and champagnes, as well as more than 20 malt whiskies, are served alongside a wide choice of draught beverages which includes Stella Artois and Heineken lagers as well as Murphy's Stout, Chester's (Exchange), Webster's Yorkshire Bitter, Boddingtons and Ruddles beers. Basic bar food (soup at £1.50, for example, with hot roast beef sandwiches and chips at £2.50 and sausage and chips at £1.40) may not include anything suitable for vegetarians or children, but restaurant meals are recommended.

Brewery: Free house
Licensee: Richard Davies
Opening hours: 11am-11pm
(Sat 11am-3pm, 7.30-11pm; Sun
12-3pm, 7-10.30pm
Bar food: 12-3pm (except Sun)
Restaurant: 12-3pm (except Sat
and Sun)
Children: Not permitted inside
Credit cards:
AMERICAN EXPRESS®, Access,
Visa

⊛ DEVONSHIRE ARMS
Longhurst Lane, Mellor, near Stockport SK6 8PP. Tel 061 427 2563

Mellor

Stone-built, attractive and comfortable, this pub on the edge of the village boasts a well kept garden and a stone-flagged patio with benches and tables; most of the present building is 19th-century, but ales have been sold here for the last 200 years. Today's customers - a mixture of businessmen and locals, with families at weekends - can choose from a range of over 50 malt whiskies and an extensive wine list as well as Robinson's beer and Tennent lager on draught; bar food is available at lunchtimes throughout the week (evenings by arrangement), good value main courses like

Brewery: Robinson's
Licensee: Brian Harrison
Opening hours: 11am-3pm,
5.30-11pm (Sat from 7pm); Sun
12-3pm, 7-10.30pm
Bar food: 12-2pm, evenings by
arrangement
Children: Welcome in separate
room

lambs' kidneys in red wine sauce (£4.35) or vegetarian curry (£3.95) being preceded by soup and garlic bread (95p) or fresh hot prawns (£2.65), for example. In the relaxed atmosphere of the recently refurbished Victorian-style bar patrons can enjoy live jazz on Thursday evenings as well as the more traditional pursuits of cards, dominoes or shove halfpenny.

OLDE BOARS HEAD
111-113 Long Street, Middleton M24 3UE. Tel 061 643 3520

Middleton

This well managed, character, town pub - a timber-framed Elizabethan building dating from 1590 - has been attractively restored to retain many original features. Three very comfortable beamed bars attract an across-the-board mixture of customers who gather to enjoy a choice of draught beverages comprising Guinness, Lees Mild and Bitter, Lees Pilsner, light and strong lagers and Strongbow cider; a short, value-for-money bar menu based on fresh ingredients and offering sandwiches (£1.50) and salads (£3.10) as well as a full meal like prawn cocktail (£2) followed by minced beef and tomato pie with chips (£3.10) and one of a range of puddings at £1.10; the needs of vegetarians are also considered. Live music will be provided by jazz/blues groups on Thursday evenings, Monday is quiz night, and on summer Sundays a brass band regales those eating or drinking on the patio.

Brewery: Lees
Licensee: Mr M T Reeves
Opening hours: 11.30am-3pm, 7-11pm; Sun 12-3pm, 7-10.30pm
Bar food: 12-2pm (except Sun)
Children: Welcome at lunchtimes if having a meal

MARK ADDY
7 Stanley Street, Salford M57 1EJ. Tel 061 832 4080

Salford

Bar snacks at this very attractive canalside pub - carefully converted from former passenger waiting rooms - are limited to cheeses and pâtés served with granary bread (£2.30) and a range of desserts (£1); the extensive range of cheeses is renowned, however, and large portions represent excellent value for money. Food, together with draught Marston's Pedigree and Boddingtons Bitter, is served in an attractively comfortable, wide-windowed bar with brick bays and cast-iron pillars, historic artefacts of river and canal life providing a display in keeping with the setting. Outside tables and benches provide a pleasant waterside seating area for warmer days.

Brewery: Free house
Licensee: Philip Mead
Opening hours: 11.30am-11pm; Sun 12-3pm, 7-10.30pm
Bar food: 11.30am-8pm (except Sun evening)
Children: Welcome anywhere, but must not approach bar

BAKER'S VAULTS
Market Place, Stockport SK1 1ES. Tel 061 480 3182

Stockport

A popular venue for live music, with jazz, rock or blues every evening except Saturday, this busy 19th-century pub in the market place offers Tennent and Einhorn lagers as well as Robinson's Best Mild and Bitter on draught. The comfortable, traditional bar attracts shoppers, market traders and businessmen as well as regulars - not least by an extensive, value-for-money menu which offers more imaginative dishes like Cajun chicken (£4.15) alongside such established favourites as battered fish (£3.45) or beef and mushrooms in Guinness (£3.85), both served with chips; there is a vegetarian dish every day.

Brewery: Robinson's
Licensee: Ian Brookes
Opening hours: 11am-11pm;
Sun 12-3pm, 7-10.30pm
Bar food: 12-2.30pm (Fri and Sat
5-8.30pm); Sun 12-2.30pm
Children: Not permitted inside

CROSS KEYS
Runningate, Uppermill, near Saddleworth OL3 6HA. Tel 0457 874626

Uppermill

The garden of this attractive, stone-built, 18th-century pub, though basic, does include a children's play area and a patio set with tables; its moorland location overlooking Saddleworth church also commands marvellous views. Well known both as a folk venue and a good drinkers' pub, it combines rustic charm with a traditional atmosphere, the two very attractive period-style bars - which have been used in television programmes - attracting climbers and walkers as well as locals and lovers of folk music (Wednesdays) or jazz (occasional). Draught beverages are limited to Lees Mild and Bitter, Lees lager and Strongbow cider, while the lunchtime bar menu, though simple, offers satisfying main courses - ideal after a walk on the moors! - like curry and rice or steak and kidney pie and chips (both at £3.35), followed perhaps by pie and cream (£1) or fudge cake (£1.35).

Brewery: Lees
Licensee: Philip Kay
Opening hours: Summer 11am-11pm; winter 11am-3pm, 6.30-11pm; Sun 12-3pm, 7-10.30pm
Bar food: 11am-2pm; Sun 12-2pm
Children: Welcome anywhere; outdoor play area

HUMBERSIDE

WHITE HORSE INN (NELLIE'S)
Hengate, Beverley HU17 8BN. Tel 0482 861973

Beverley

Nothing much has changed at this roadside pub for about 100 years, although the building itself dates back to 1585. Some of its rooms are still gas lit - one even uses candles - and there's a wonderful collection of old furniture, including iron ranges, an ancient gas cooker, huge mirrors and Victorian pictures. The six bars are unspoilt and quite basic, and they attract a lively mixed crowd: in the evening the place is full of regulars and at lunchtime all kinds of people come to experience its renowned friendliness. Weekly jazz and folk evenings are also popular. Samuel Smith Old Brewery Bitter and Museum Ale are on tap, and there's a good selection of bottled beers and lagers. The bar food is interesting, and includes dishes like chicken en croûte for £4.95, pepper and mushroom pie for £4.25, and steak and ale pie at £3.95. Outside the low shuttered building a cobbled patio and courtyard provides bench seating.

Brewery: Samuel Smith
Licensee: John Southren
Opening hours: 11am-11pm;
Sun 12-3pm, 7-10.30pm
Bar food: 12-2pm, 6-9pm (except
Sun and Mon evenings)
Children: Welcome anywhere
except bar
Credit cards: Access, Visa

☙ FLEECE INN
Bishop Wilton, near York YO4 1RU. Tel 07596 251

Bishop Wilton

This family-run inn - rebuilt in 1925 on an older pub site - usually caters for locals but there's a very warm welcome too for visitors. Outside, hanging flower baskets lend a splash of colour to the brick building, and there are a couple of benches in the old stable yard. Inside cushioned settles and carpets make the lounge cosy, and there are a number of horse-brasses, water jugs and Guinness prints. Country and western evenings are held every Friday. Real ales from John Smith and Tetley are on tap as well as Guinness and Carlton LA, and there are 25 whiskies. Typical lunchtime bar food dishes include steak pie and chips at £3.75, pizza and chips for £2.55 and ploughman's for £3.15. In the evening the menu is more extensive, with choices like rump steak for £6.45, and seafood platter and vegetable lasagne both at £4.95. The converted stable block provides seven simple bedrooms with mock timbering.

Brewery: Free house
Licensee: L Wells
Opening hours: 12-3pm,
6-11pm; Sun 12-3pm,
7-10.30pm
Bar food: 12-2pm, 7-9pm (Sat
6-9.30pm); Sun 12-2pm,
7-9.30pm
Restaurant: Times as bar food
Accommodation: (Price per
person) single £25, double £20
Children: Welcome anywhere

⊜ RED LION
High Street, Broughton DN20 0NY. Tel 0652 652560

Broughton

This typical 1930s brick-built pub offers an interesting variety of bar food at not too expensive prices. Chicken hussar at £5.95, kleftiko at £4.25, and sirloin steak for £6.95 make tasty main dishes, and whitebait is a good starter at £2.15. A vegetarian dish can be cooked on request even if there is not one on the menu. On tap in the bar are Mansfield Riding Traditional Bitter, Riding Dark Mild, Old Baily and Guinness, and several malt whiskies are on sale. Seating in the carpeted Lounge and in the Public Bar is on cushioned settles, and there's a collection of china plates. Pool, darts and dominoes are played here.

Brewery: Mansfield
Licensee: Mel Beniston
Opening hours: 11am-3pm, 6-11.30pm (Fri and Sat 11am-11pm); Sun 12-3pm, 7-10.30pm
Bar food: 12-2pm, 7.30-9.30pm (except Mon); Sun 12-2pm
Children: In Lounge if eating

⊜ BOOT AND SHOE INN
Ellerton, near York YO4 4PB. Tel 0757 288346

Ellerton

This attractive 16th-century Saxon longhouse is set in a quiet village deep in the Vale of York. The very low rendered building looks small from the outside, but appearances are deceptive here. Inside are three bars with open fires and exposed beams propping up low ceilings, and seating is a mixture of cushioned settles and wooden chairs. Ducks of all shapes and sizes are on display. This peaceful pub becomes very lively at weekends when a mixed clientele descends on it, particularly for the food. Starters like cheese and herb pâté at £1.80, and corn on the cob for £1.40 are popular, followed by home-made dishes like beefsteak in Guinness for £4.50, breaded haddock at £3.75, and sirloin steak for £6.25. Cheesecake is £1.25. Snaith Old Mill and real ales from John Smith as well as Guinness are on tap. The inn is set in two-thirds of an acre of gardens.

Brewery: Free house
Licensee: Patrick McVay and D Gregg
Opening hours: 7-11pm; Sat 12-3pm, 7-11pm; Sun 12-3pm, 7-10.30pm
Bar food: 7.30-9pm; Sat 12-2pm, 7-9.30pm; Sun 12-2pm, 7-9.30pm
Children: Welcome anywhere

⊜ LIGHT DRAGOON
34 Main Street, Etton, near Beverley HU17 7PG. Tel 0430 810282

Etton

This white-painted brick pub is set in the centre of a peaceful estate village. The quiet atmosphere is only slightly disturbed on the first Tuesday of every month when the 'Processed Pea' folk club meets in the Lounge Bar. At other times this friendly pub, which dates from the 18th century, is the favourite haunt of several regulars. Under a mock timbered ceiling, real ales such as Youngers IPA and No 3, Theakston Best Bitter, McEwan Export and Guinness are on tap, and seating at the wooden tables is on cushioned settles and chairs. The bar food is reasonable and not too

Brewery: Younger
Licensee: James Bell Weatherhead
Opening hours: 12-2.30pm, 7-11pm; Sun 12-3pm, 7-10.30pm
Bar food: 12-2pm, 7-9.30pm
Restaurant: 12-2pm; 7-9.30pm (except Mon and Tue evenings)
Children: Welcome anywhere; children's menu available;

expensive, and includes dishes like fried haddock and chips at £4.25, steak pie for £4.50, and chicken and broccoli au gratin for £5.25. Prawn Figaro is a tasty starter at £3.25, and desserts cost £1.95. A vegetarian dish usually features on the menu. Outside a small terraced garden and grassed area has benches.

outdoor play area
Credit cards: Access, Visa

☺ HALF MOON
16 Main Street, Skidby HU16 5TG. Tel 0482 843403

Skidby

Man-sized Yorkshire puddings with a variety of accompaniments are the speciality of this old pub, and they are sure to satisfy all but the most demanding of appetites. There are seven different gravies and fillings to go with these feather-light giants, from minced beef and mushroom to lamb chops and onion gravy. Prices range from £2.20 to £4.15. The menu offers plenty of other large or small choices, and the bar food makes this place a popular night out. A bowl of chilli or curry is £2.60, home-made steak and kidney pie costs £3.60, and various burgers range from £2.20 to £3.25. Puddings like gorgeously gooey gâteau and bramley apple pie are under £1.50. On tap in the busy and basic but comfortable bars are John Smith's Bitter and Chestnut Mild, and there are 24 whiskies to sample. This 300-year-old pub has been much extended over the years, and there's a large garden well away from the road.

Brewery: John Smith's
Licensee: Pete Madely
Opening hours: 11am-11pm; Sun 12-2.30pm, 7-10.30pm
Bar food: 12-2pm, 7-10pm; Sun 12-2.30pm, 7-10pm
Children: Welcome anywhere; outdoor play area
Credit cards: Access, Visa

☺ PIPE AND GLASS
West End, South Dalton, near Beverley HU17 7PN. Tel 0430 810246

South Dalton

This lovely old country inn is set in a picturesque Wolds village overlooking Dalton Park. Parts of the pantile and white-painted brick building date back to before 1750, but most of it has changed over the years. Outside in this superb location a pleasant fenced garden is shaded by an old yew tree. Indoors, huge open fires and cushioned settles make the two bars comfortable and appealing. Bar food is very well presented here, and includes starters like chicken wings and sesame mayonnaise at £2.65, and Yorkshire pudding and onion gravy for £1.65. Main dishes like pork and apple lattice pie, and ploughman's lunch, both cost £4.25, and vegetarian lasagne is £4.50. Puddings like passion cake crumble and custard cost £2.35. There is a good range of liqueurs and brandies, and on tap are Castle Eden Ale, Ruddles Best Bitter and John Smith's Bitter. Sunday night is usually quiz night.

Brewery: Free house
Licensee: Adrian Wilkinson
Opening hours: 11.30am-2.30pm, 7-11pm; Sun 12-3pm, 7-10.30pm
Bar food: 12-2.30pm, 5.30-10pm; Sun 12-2.30pm, 7-9.30pm
Restaurant: Times as bar food
Children: In restaurant and one bar only; outdoor play area
Credit cards: Access, Visa

PARK DRAIN HOTEL
Park Drain, Westwoodside DN9 2EN. Tel 0427 752255

Westwoodside

This imposing red-brick Victorian hotel sits rather oddly in the midst of miles of flat agricultural land. Its isolated setting does not prevent it from being very popular, however, and the main reason for this is its food. Bar meals and the interesting restaurant menu offer excellent quality and very good value for money. Bar starters like garlic mushrooms or whitebait are both £1.75, and there are main courses such as rack of lamb at £4.95, and steak and mushroom pie for £3.50. On tap to wash it all down are John Smith's Bitter, Stones Best Bitter, Wilson's Original Mild, Riding Dark Mild and Guinness. A selection of over 30 whiskies is also on sale. Choices on the restaurant menu are more sophisticated, and include starters like stuffed mushrooms at £2.95 and goujons of fresh halibut at £3.95. There's a wide range of steaks, and main dishes like chicken in walnut sauce for £7.95 and sweebreads in black pepper for £6.95. Locals mainly frequent the fairly basic bar that remains virtually unchanged since the days of its Victorian origins, while the plusher Lounge Bar attracts a wider assortment of people. A rather Spartan patio at the front of the building offers some seating.

Brewery: Free house
Licensee: Nick Sutherton
Opening hours: 11am-3.30pm, 5.30-11pm; Sun 12-3pm, 7-10.30pm
Bar food: As opening hours (except Mon); Sun 12-2pm, 7-9pm
Restaurant: 12-2pm, 7-9.30pm (except Mon evening); Sun 12-2pm, 7-9pm
Children: Welcome in rooms other than Public Bar

LANCASHIRE

MOORCOCK
Gisburn Road, Blacko, near Nelson BB9 6NF. Tel 0282 614186

Blacko

This old whitewashed Lancashire farmhouse is set on the wide open moors with marvellous views in all directions. Set close to the Pendle walk, it's more a family eating place than just a pub, with standing room only at the bar for those who have come just for a drink. On tap are real ales from Thwaites and Guinness, and there are a few malt whiskies. Around five or six special dishes feature daily on the popular menu, including choices like liver and onions at £3.95, and lamb chops for £5.25. Regular dishes are starters like soup at £1.50 and garlic prawns for £3.75, and main dishes such as wheat and walnut bake, £3.95, and Austrian goulash or schweinschnitzel, both at £4.95. There are several inter-connecting rooms that share the same bar, each with attractive large windows and lots of bric-à-brac. Toby jugs, Torquay pottery, old plates and brasses help to make this a jolly place.

Brewery: Thwaites
Licensee: Elizabeth Holt
Opening hours: 11.30am-2.30pm, 6.30-12 midnight; Sun 12-11pm
Bar food: 12-2pm, 7-10.30pm
Restaurant: As bar food times
Children: Welcome anywhere

⊕ ASSHETON ARMS
Downham, near Clitheroe BB7 4BJ. Tel 02060 41227

Downham

Very little has changed in this lovely old village since it was bought by the Assheton family over 400 years ago. The pretty pastoral views can be enjoyed from tables and seats in front of the pub where it sits opposite the village church. Inside the bar a warm atmosphere is created by the big open fire and low ceilings, and there are sturdy wooden settles and stools to sit on. It's a popular place with young people and families from local towns as well as its own regulars. On tap are Bentley's Yorkshire Bitter, Castle Eden Ale and Marston's Pedigree Bitter as well as Murphy's. Bar meals and snacks are tasty and generous, with starters like Stilton pâté at £2.60, and gravlax at £5.50. Very filling main dishes include cauliflower and mushroom Provençale, £4.50, game pie at £6.10, and poached salmon for £6.95. Orange and curacao sundae is £2.75, and chocolate fudge Pavlova is £1.75.

Brewery: Whitbread
Licensees: David and Wendy Busby
Opening hours: 12-3pm, 7-11pm; Sun 12-3pm, 7-10.30pm
Bar food: 12-2pm, 7-10pm
Children: Welcome anywhere; own menu available
Credit cards: Access, Visa, Diners

⊕ TH'OWD TITHE BARN
The Wharf, Church Street, Garstang PR3 1BA. Tel 0995 604486

Garstang

Narrow-boats are moored alongside the canal when their owners come to this pretty flower-covered pub in a converted tithe barn. A patio right next to the water's edge makes a pleasant place to sit and watch the ducks and boats. This interesting pub, which dates from 1710, has plenty of character, and is proving a popular pull for boat people and land-based families alike. In the bar, pitch-pine church pews and great long tables are arranged in friendly fashion on the flagged floor, and there's a collection of agricultural implements. Old-fashioned serving wenches take orders for food, and bring dishes like steak and kidney pie at £4.10, vegetarian quiche at £4.20, and roast pork for £4.55. Home-made soup and pâté both cost £1.95, and there are sweets like cheesecake and lemon meringue pie for £1.95. On tap are Mitchell's Best Dark Mild, Best Bitter and ESB, and Murphy's . There's a large selection of fruit wines including mead, blackberry and damson.

Brewery: Mitchell's
Licensee: Kerry Matthews
Opening hours: 11am-3pm, 7-11pm (Sat from 6pm); closed Mon; Sun 7- 10.30pm
Bar food: 12-2.30pm, 7-10pm (Sat from 6pm); Sun 12-2.30pm, 7-9.30pm
Restaurant: Times as bar food
Children: Not permitted under 14 years except in dining area

On the Dry Side
Temperance hotels were a product of the powerful 19th-century reaction in Britain against public drunkenness and the evils of drink. Most common in the northern industrial towns, they were places where teetotal sales representatives and other travellers could put up for the night in modest comfort without temptation or embarrassment. Some of them survived into the 20th century, though in many cases they relaxed the rules sufficiently to allow guests to order drink from outside.

BUSHELLS ARMS
Church Lane, Goosnargh, near Preston PR3 2BH. Tel 0772 865235

Goosnargh

Good food and the right wine to complement it makes this pub a popular place, and queues sometimes form outside. The proprietor is very interested in wine (as reflected in the extensive list), and the food has won several awards. Soup comes in unusual varieties like shrimp and pumpkin, excellent at £1.30, and tandoori wings are also good at £2.50. Main dishes include chicken Olympus, and salmon and broccoli parcels, both £6, smoked cod pasta with mushrooms at £5, and vegetable pasties for £4.50. Puddings include 18th-century chocolate and rum pie, and raspberry shortcake. The food is served in the comfortable interconnecting bar areas, where lots of bare stone and exposed beams create a cosy atmosphere, helped by several pot plants and soft lighting. On tap are Preston Pride, Whitbread Trophy, and Murphy's . This Georgian pub has a pleasant garden with tables, and here the cooking herbs are grown.

Brewery: Whitbread
Licensees: David and Glynis Best
Opening hours: 12-3pm, 6-11pm; Sun 12-3pm, 7-10.30pm
Bar food: 12-2.30pm, 7-10pm
Children: Only until 9pm in eating area of bar

HEATONS BRIDGE INN
Heaton's Bridge, near Ormskirk L40 8JG. Tel 0704 840549

Heaton's Bridge

A traditional working man's pub with no frills and no ambitious attempts to take it upmarket. Women are not often to be seen in the cosy dark and smoky areas around the bar, and in many ways it's reminiscent of what pubs used to be like. Tourists and travellers do venture inside with the regulars from time to time, however, and they are rewarded with Tetley Walker Best Bitter and Tetley Mild on tap. Interesting curios, bric-à-brac, teapots and brasses all add to the old-fashioned atmosphere, and there is plenty of comfortable furniture to relax in. Bar food is served at lunchtime only, and includes dishes like steak pie, roast chicken and curries, all served with mixed vegetables, and all very reasonably priced at £1.50. There is also a specials board. This very pretty canalside pub which dates back 170 years has a cobbled forecourt with tables and chairs next to the road and car park.

Brewery: Tetley Walker
Licensee: Fred Hook
Opening hours: 11am-11pm; Sun 12-3pm, 7-10.30pm
Bar food: 12-2pm
Children: Not permitted under 14 years inside

HARK TO BOUNTY INN
Slaidburn, near Clitheroe BB7 3EP. Tel 02006 246

Slaidburn

From the 14th century until the 1930s the upstairs of this old building was used by travelling justices as the only courtroom between York and Lancaster. Nowadays this impressive room witnesses nothing more entertaining than

Brewery: Scottish & Newcastle
Licensees: Linda Smith and Phillip Hofman
Opening hours: 11am-11pm;

parties and weddings. Set in the middle of a picturesque village, this historic pub is popular with locals and families, and at weekends it gets very busy. Predictably there's a wonderful atmosphere in the bar, where old-fashioned settles and exposed beams blend in with tapestries, old maps and pictures. Theakston Old Peculier and Matthew Brown Bitter are on tap, and there's a good wine list and selection of malt whiskies. The food comes highly recommended, and venison, rabbit and juniper berry casserole at £5 is a good example of what's available on the bar menu. Starters include hot black pudding at £2.75 and soup for £1.50, and passion cake and raspberry russe are typical desserts. Booking is necessary for the set Sunday lunch. There's a different menu in the restaurant, with starters like smoked salmon and trout terrine, and prawns with Stilton dip both at £4, and main dishes rack of lamb and guinea fowl costing £7.50. Eight bedrooms offer country-style accommodation.

Sun 12-3pm, 7-10.30pm
Bar food: 12-2pm, 6-9pm; Sun 12-2pm, 7-9pm
Restaurant: 7-9pm
Accommodation: (Price per room) single £20-£24, double £45
Children: Welcome in areas other than the bar; own menu available; games room

EAGLE AND CHILD
Church Road, Wharles, near Kirkham PR4 3SJ. Tel 0772 690312

Wharles

There's a very pleasing and relaxing atmosphere at this thatched and whitewashed country pub. Set along a country lane in the little village of Wharles, the pub dates from the 17th century and there are plenty of reminders of its great antiquity. In the bar a carved oak chimney piece matches the collection of furniture including some antique oak settles and seats. Country implements, advertising mirrors and other antiques are all comfortably at home here, and an old coal stove and grandfather clock are not at all out of place. On tap in the bar are real ales from Cains, and there are also regularly changing guest beers and draught Murphy's, plus a range of bottled beers. The pub attracts a wide mixture of clientele from local regulars to tourists and business people. It serves no food at all. The Eagle and Child has been a frequent winner of the CAMRA Pub of the Year Award.

Brewery: Free house
Licensees: Brian and Angela Tatham
Opening hours: 7-11pm; Sat 12-3pm; Sun 12-3pm, 7-10.30pm
Children: Not permitted under 14 years in bar

INN AT WHITEWELL
Whitewell, Forest of Bowland, near Clitheroe BB7 3AT. Tel 02008 222

Whitewell

This appealing old manor house is surrounded by trees and has wonderful views down to the river and over the hills. Dating back to the 14th century, it has also been a sporting lodge, and first became licensed in the late 18th century. Nowadays it houses an 'own label' shirt-making business, an art gallery and a wine merchants, as well as the

Brewery: Free house
Licensee: Richard Bowman
Opening hours: 11am-3pm, 6-11pm; Sun 12-3pm, 7-10.30pm
Bar food: 12-2pm, 7.30-9.30pm
Restaurant: 7.30-9.30pm

serious business of providing good food and drink. The gracious rooms include a tap room and sitting room as well as the bar, and throughout there's a fine collection of interesting antiques. Beams and leaded windows lend a comfortable, relaxing air, and there's a selection of newspapers. Regulars and families mingle with shooting and fishing parties, and there are eight miles of fishing waters. The food served here is imaginative and delicious; and everything is cooked to order. Soup at £1.40 and fish mousse for £4 make tasty starters, and there are main dishes like gourmet fish pie at £5.60 and courgette lasagne for £4.80. There are also specials like grouse and sea bass, and a great selection of hand-made British cheeses. Real ales from Boddingtons are on tap, as well as Guinness and Murphy's , and there's an extensive wine and champagne list. Peat fires burn in the nine luxurious bedrooms.

Accommodation: (Price per person) single £38-£77, double £49-£90
Children: Welcome anywhere; half portions available
Credit cards: AMERICAN EXPRESS®, Access, Visa, Diners

PLOUGH AT EAVES
Eaves Lane, Woodplumpton, near Broughton PR4 0BJ. Tel 0772 690233

Woodplumpton

There's a pleasant, welcoming atmosphere at this traditional country pub that appeals to all tastes. Set in the centre of a little village, it dates back to 1625. The front of the pretty whitewashed building is bright with flowers in the summer, and a large garden offers seating with views over open fields. Inside the two bars there's a comfortable old world feel, enhanced by the low ceilings with exposed beams and traditional pub furniture. Bric-à-brac and a collection of shotguns make an interesting display, and Thwaites Bitter and Craftsman are on tap. There's a good range of bottled beers, and over 35 malt whiskies are on sale. In addition to a good selection of special dishes, the menu offers Cumberland sausage at £3.25, beef in beer for £3.55, and country lentil crumble at £4.35. Sandwiches cost from £1.85, and sweets are £1.50. Starters like country pâté and soup cost under £1.50.

Brewery: Thwaites
Licensee: June Daniel
Opening hours: 12-3pm, 6.30-11pm; Sun 12-3pm, 7-10.30pm
Bar food: 12-2.30pm, 6.30-9.30pm; Sun 12-2.30pm, 7-9pm
Restaurant: 12-2pm, 6.30-9.30pm; Sun 7-9pm
Children: Welcome anywhere; games room; outdoor play area
Credit cards: AMERICAN EXPRESS®, Access, Visa, Diners

⊕ NEW INN
Yealand Conyers, near Carnforth LA5 9SJ. Tel 0524 732938

Yealand Conyers

This old creeper-covered building set in the small, pretty village of Yealand Conyers was first licensed as a public house in the 16th century. Beneath low ceilings with exposed beams there is still a traditional atmosphere here, cosily enhanced by carpets and country furniture. Out of season it's mostly frequented by locals and business people, but in summer many tourists return again and again, drawn

Brewery: Free house
Licensees: Colin and Vicki Gilham
Opening hours: 11.30am-2.30pm, 6-11pm; Sun 12-3pm, 7-10.30pm
Bar food: 11.30am-1.45pm,

by the warm and friendly welcome they receive. Wheelwrights' tools adorn the walls, and on tap in the bar are Robinson's Bitter, Hartleys XB and Mild, and Guinness. There's a good selection of ploughman's lunches and salads on the bar menu, and other choices include lamb and leek pie and vegetables for £3.75, lasagne at £3.25, and rump steak with vegetables for £5.95. There are different sweets every day. Seating is available in the leafy, shaded beer garden.

6-8.45pm (except Mon evenings in winter); Sun 12-2pm, 7-8.45pm
Restaurant: Times as bar food
Children: Not permitted under ten years, and in restaurant only

MERSEYSIDE

⊕ SEVEN STARS
Church Road, Thornton Hough L63 1JW. Tel 051 336457

Thornton Hough

Travellers using the nearby toll bridge used to be given shelter at this white-painted pub in the centre of the village. Nowadays its function is purely social, and a mixture of locals and visitors come to enjoy its comforts. Framed manuscripts relating to the village's history and that of the surrounding area hang on the walls in the two bars along with pictures of local scenes, and both rooms are carpeted and well furnished. Very good fresh food is brought by efficient waitress service, and there is value for money in bar starters like pâté or deep-fried mushrooms at £1.95. Main dishes include sirloin steak for £7.95, lamb chops for £4.50, and chicken Kiev at £6.90. There are also daily specials, and a vegetarian choice is always available. On draught are Castle Eden Ale, and beers from Flowers and Thwaites, and there's a wide selection of wines too.

Brewery: Whitbread
Licensee: M M Nelson
Opening hours: 11.30am-3pm, 5.30-11pm; Sun 12-3pm, 7-10.30pm
Bar food: 12-2pm, 7-10pm
Children: Welcome anywhere

India Pale Ale

As the British extended their sway over India, there came a growing, almost anguished demand for beer to quench the thirst of soldiers and officials. It needed to be light and pleasantly bitter and able to withstand the long voyage. The firm of Bass in Burton upon Trent developed a successful East India Pale Ale, later India Pale Ale, later still simply IPA, and shipped it out in enormous quantities from Hull and Liverpool. It so happened that in 1827 a ship carrying 300 casks of this excellent fluid was wrecked in the Irish Sea. The salvaged casks were auctioned off in Liverpool. Sold in this country, they created a new British demand for this type of beer.

NORTHUMBERLAND

⊛ MINERS ARMS INN
Main Street, Acomb, near Hexham NE46 4PW. Tel 0434 603909

Acomb

Buchanan's Original, Big Lamp Bitter, Morrells Variety Bitter, Federation Best Bitter, Robinson's Bitter, Courage Directors, Bass, Beamish Stout - all these, plus guest beers, are served in this popular village pub. And the three-day beer festivals held here in the spring and October confirm that the licensees are passionate champions of real ale. Stone-built, and dating from 1610, the pub stands in an old farming village, although it takes its name from the coal-mining which was carried on hereabouts in more recent times. The compact, beamed bar, cosy with its cushioned benches and open fires, enjoys a well assorted clientele embracing local people and visitors, teenagers and octogenarians. The food, simple, well cooked and unstinting, includes steak and vegetable pie at £3.65 and, both at £3.95, home-battered cod and miner's brunch, a generous fried breakfast. Traditional musicians provide occasional entertainment, and behind the pub is a pleasant, south-facing garden with a barbecue area.

Brewery: Free house
Licensee: Keith Millar
Opening hours: Summer 11am-11pm; winter 11am-4pm, 5-11pm; Sun 12-3pm 12-10.30pm
Bar food: As opening hours. Breakfast available 8-9.30am by booking
Restaurant: Times as bar food
Children: In Lounge and restaurant only; half portions available

⊛MANOR HOUSE INN
Carterway Heads, near Shotley Bridge DH8 9LX. Tel 0207 55268

Carterway Heads

Built in 1860, this substantial pub stands in isolation high up on the moors, on the scenic road from England to Scotland. Offering a view of the Derwent Reservoir and, from the small, neat garden, of the river valley, it is a welcome haven for travellers through a rugged part of the country. It is also deservedly popular with local people, for the food is excellent and very good value for money. Changed frequently, the menu offers interesting items such as Brie and smoked salmon croissant at £3.95, baked sea trout in mint butter at £6.75 and pasta gratin with tomatoes and basil at £4. Fuller's London Pride, Butterknowle Bitter, McEwan Scotch Bitter, Beamish Stout and two guest beers are on sale in the two bars, which remain largely unaltered, with their beams, open fires and cushioned benches. Also on tap are Thatcher's draught cider and two lagers.

Brewery: Free house
Licensee: Anthony Pelly
Opening hours: 11am-3pm, 6-11pm; Sun 12-3pm, 7-10.30pm
Bar food: 12-2.30pm, 7-9.30pm (Sun 9pm)
Restaurant: Times as bar food
Children: In one bar and dining room only, but preferably not after 9pm; children's menu available
Credit cards: Access, Visa

⊜ PERCY ARMS
Chatton, near Alnwick NE66 5PS. Tel 06685 244

Chatton

A creeper-clad exterior and views over the village green to distant hills together make this pub's sunny, south-facing garden a very pleasant place for a drink or a meal. It is equally inviting inside, its two bars refurbished but retaining their traditional character courtesy of beams, open fires and cushioned benches. Although situated in a village surrounded by beautiful countryside, the pub is not overrun by visitors to the area, most of its trade being supplied by locals and families. The beer - Theakston XB, Newcastle Exhibition, IPA and Scotch Bitter - is the perfect partner for the straightforward fare, which includes home-made shepherd's pie at £3.95 and, both fresh and locally caught and at £4.95, crab (salad) and trout. The accommodation consists of seven double rooms.

Brewery: Free house
Licensee: Kenneth Topham
Opening hours: 11am-3pm, 6-11pm; Sun 12-3pm, 7-10.30pm
Bar food: 12-1.30pm, 6.30-9.30pm (Sun from 7pm)
Restaurant: 6.30-9.30pm (Sun from 7pm); lunchtimes by arrangement
Accommodation: (Price per person) £20
Children: Welcome anywhere; children's menu available

⊜ JOLLY FISHERMAN
Haven Hill, Craster, near Alnwick NE66 3TR. Tel 0665 576461

Craster

In summer this pub numbers holidaymakers among its customers, along with regulars and families, since the fishing village in which it stands is in sight of the dramatic remains of Dunstanburgh Castle, on an unspoilt stretch of coast. Dating from 1847, the solid-looking building stands on a rock above the harbour, and is fronted by a grassed area with tables where visitors can sit and look out to sea. Wards Sheffield Best Bitter, Vaux Samson and Lorimers Best and Beamish Stout are on sale in the two bars, furnished with cushioned benches and lent a traditional character by beams and plenty of dark wood. A good selection of malt whiskies is also available, but the food is limited to sandwiches (crab, salmon, ham and cheese) at £1.50 and snacks (pizzas and burgers)at £1.10.

Brewery: Vaux
Licensee: Albert George
Opening hours: 11am-3pm, 6-11pm; Sun 12-3pm, 7-10.30pm
Bar food: As opening hours
Children: Welcome anywhere

⊜ DIPTON MILL
Dipton Mill Road, near Hexham NE46 1YA. Tel 0434 606577

Dipton Mill

Part of the charm of this little pub is its secluded position on the banks of a river in quiet countryside. It was originally a mill house, built around1750, to which a cottage was added in Victorian times. Locals, business people and tourists relax in the bar, with its panelled walls, low ceiling and dark furniture, or play pool in the separate room, both rooms being heated in winter by open fires. Through the attractive garden and patio flows a small stream which joins

Brewery: Free house
Licensee: Geoffrey Harry Brooker
Opening hours: 12-2.30pm, 6-11pm; Sun 12-3pm, 7-10.30pm
Bar food: As opening hours (limited in the evenings)
Children: Not permitted inside

the river near by and gives its name to one of the beers brewed and sold by the pub: Devils Water. Also served are Hexhamshire Bitter and Lowquarter, and Hadrian Gladiator and Emperor Ale, and there is a good choice of bottled beers. Among the few meals on offer are Lincolnshire hotpot at £3.25 and prawn salad at £3.50.

COTTAGE INN
Dunstan Village, near Embleton NE66 3JZ. Tel 0665 576658

Embleton

A row of whitewashed, single-storey cottages dating from the last century was converted in recent years to create this well run pub and hotel, and apart from the inn sign, the building still looks residential. Locals and tourists mingle in the spacious, carpeted bar, where the oak panelling is matched by the traditional dark furniture. An open fire, plates and jugs, and old photographs and prints of local subjects, all add to the impression of a long-established village pub. By contrast, the conservatory, with its modern furniture, is light and airy, and gives on to a sheltered, south-facing patio and a one-acre lawned garden. The beamed and oak-panelled restaurant is decorated with large, colourful murals depicting local events in medieval times. Skilfully cooked and presented, and sensibly priced, the food includes lamb stew at £4.20, roast beef, Yorkshire pudding and vegetables at £4.95 and fisherman's platter at £5.75. Dinner is served at £12.95, and the restaurant offers a comprehensive à la carte menu, complemented by an extensive wine list. McEwan Scotch, Webster's Yorkshire Bitter and Ruddles Bitter are on tap, along with Scrumpy Jack cider and two lagers.

Brewery: Free house
Licensee: Lawrence Jobling
Opening hours: 11am-3pm, 6-11pm; Sun 12-3pm, 7-10.30pm
Bar food: 12-2.30pm, 6-9.30pm; Sun 12-2.30pm, 7-9pm
Restaurant: 7-9pm
Accommodation: (Price per room) double £57; reduced winter rates
Children: Welcome anywhere
Credit cards: Access, Visa

⊛ BLACK BULL
Etal, near Berwick upon Tweed TD12 4TL. Tel 0890 820200

Etal

S et in the middle of an early 18th-century row of cottages in an unspoilt estate village, from the outside this thatched pub typifies the village inn of old, so little has it changed. Not that it has been spoilt inside, although sensible concessions have been made to the modern demand for comfort. Nowadays many pubs, particularly those in attractive settings, cater for tourists as well as village folk, as does this one. Vaux Lorimers Best Scotch is on sale, along with three lagers and Scrumpy Jack cider, in the single bar, which runs the length of the pub and is furnished with dark Windsor chairs and fixed benches. At lunchtime light meals are available (scampi and chicken, for example, both at

Brewery: Vaux
Licensee: Thomas Hails
Opening hours: Summer 12-3pm, 6-11pm; winter 12-2pm, 7-11pm; Sun 12-3pm, 7-10.30pm
Bar food: 12-2pm, 6-9pm
Children: Not permitted under 14 years inside

£4.25) and in the evening the choice is supplemented by dishes like sirloin steak at £7.90, farmhouse gammon at £5.60 and chilli con carne at £4.30. The pub has no garden, but in the summer customers may sit on the lawned area in front of the village hall, next door.

⊜ GENERAL HAVELOCK
Haydon Bridge, near Hexham NE47 6ER. Tel 0434 684376

Haydon Bridge

Having maintained a high standard of cooking over many years, the restaurant of this friendly village pub is deservedly popular. All kinds of customers except youngsters are drawn by offerings like hot Shields smokie - smoked cod in cheese sauce - at £2.40 and, both at £5.70, roast loin of pork with apple sauce and fillet of plaice baked in butter with lemon and parsley. On tap are Tetley beers. Built in 1840 in a village straddling the Newcastle-to-Carlisle road, the pub blends into the street in which it stands, and has a pleasant south-facing patio and garden on the banks of the South Tyne. The bar, incorporating a lounge area, offers the comforts of cushioned benches and open fires, and in so doing doubtless stimulates the flow of good conversation often to be enjoyed here.

Brewery: Free house
Licensee: Ian Clyde
Opening hours: 11am-2.30pm, 7-11pm; Sun 12-2pm, 7-10.30pm
Bar food: Wed-Sat 11am-2.30pm
Restaurant: Times as opening hours (except Sun evening and all day Mon and Tue)
Children: In restaurant only; half portions available

⊜ FEATHERS
Hedley-on-the-Hill, near Stocksfield NE43 7SW. Tel 0661 843607

Hedley-on-the-Hill

Little changed on the outside from the brick-built farmhouse it once was, this village-centre pub has been thoughtfully restored inside, its open fires, traditional furniture and simple decor evoking its late 18th-century origins. Regulars provide most of the trade, their numbers swelled by visitors at weekends and in the summer, although unusually the pub is not open at lunchtime from Monday to Friday. Boddingtons Bitter and Murphy's Stout and a guest beer are on sale, along with Scrumpy Jack cider, and 20 to 25 malt whiskies are always available. Bar food is served at weekends only and includes sandwiches and home-made soups, pâtés and pasta. Other dishes include savoury pancake at £3.95 and pancake with prawns at £4.25. Darts, skittles, dominoes and shove halfpenny are to hand, and there is a separate children's room.

Brewery: Free house
Licensee: Marina Atkinson
Opening hours: 6-11pm; Sat 12-3pm, 6-11pm; Sun 12-2.30pm, 7-10.30pm
Bar food: 12-2.30pm, 6-9.30pm weekends only
Children: Welcome anywhere; children's menu available

⊕ GRANBY
Front Street, Long Framlington, near Morpeth NE65 4DP. Tel 0665 570228

Long Framlington

Locals and families supply this popular village pub with most of its custom, fully appreciative of the value for money offered by its extensive menu. Steak and kidney pie at £4.10, rump steak at £8.25 and, for a special treat, lobster salad at £15.45, are among the choice of well prepared meals, along with a wide range of vegetarian dishes. The beers are Stones Best Bitter and Bass Best Scotch. Some two centuries old, the pub is a pleasantly compact stone building situated in a small farming community on the edge of moorland. Despite being busy, the bar enjoys a relaxed atmosphere, and is comfortably furnished with cushioned benches and dark tables and chairs, while there is outdoor seating on the small, south-facing patio in front of the pub. Seven double rooms and one single are available, all with modern decor and furniture.

Brewery: Free house
Licensee: Mrs Anne Bright
Opening hours: 11am-2.30pm, 6-11pm; Sun 12-2.30pm, 7-10.30pm
Bar food: As opening hours
Restaurant: 7-8.30pm
Accommodation: (Price per person) single or double £26.75; children under 14 years not permitted
Children: Welcome, but at landlord's discretion
Credit cards: Access, Visa

⊕ SHIP
Low Newton by the Sea, near Alnwick NE66 3EL. Tel 0665 576262

Low Newton by the Sea

Invitingly situated just above the beach, and overlooking Newton Haven, this friendly, unassuming pub is popular with holidaymakers in summer and with local people all year round. Families find it ideal, since children can play on the beach and picnic tables are set out on the village green at the front. Part of a three-sided group of former fishermen's cottages built around 1800, the pub has one bar serving two rooms, one of which offers pool, darts and dominoes. Both rooms are simply furnished with cushioned benches and dark furniture, and warmed in winter by open fires. There is the choice of Webster's Yorkshire Bitter, Newcastle Exhibition or Drybroughs Scotch Bitter to accompany a crab, prawn or salmon sandwich at £1.15, or to follow home-made vegetable soup at £1.05. To finish off, there is apple pie with ice cream at 90p, for example.

Brewery: Free house
Licensee: Mr Garnett Hopper
Opening hours: Summer 11am-11pm; winter 11am-3pm, 7-11pm; Sun 12-3pm, 7-10.30pm
Bar food: As opening hours
Children: Not permitted under 14 years after 9pm

STAR
Netherton, near Thropton NE65 7HD. Tel Ex-directory

Netherton

Run by the same family since 1917, this unspoilt pub offers a glimpse of what a village local might have been like in early Victorian times. The square, stone building, dating from the 17th century, stands in a farming village at the foot of the Cheviot Hills, and has one bar, sparsely furnished with wooden benches, tables and chairs. Picnic tables are set out

Brewery: Free house
Licensee: Ms Vera W Wilson-Morton
Opening hours: Sun, Mon, Tue, Thu 7-10.30pm; Wed, Fri, Sat 7-11.30pm; open for a short period

on the south-facing grassed area in front of the pub. Regulars savour the only draught beer served: Whitbread Castle Eden Ale; nor is there any food. Instead, this unusual pub's appeal resides in its peaceful situation amid beautiful countryside and in its compelling respect for the past.

at lunchtimes
Children: Not permitted inside

Seahouses

⊛ OLDE SHIP
Main Street, Seahouses NE68 7RD. Tel 0665 720200

Inevitably, the seafaring life has inspired the decorations in this cosy harbourside pub. Brass, polished wood and leather abound in the two bars, where, in addition to numerous nautical odds and ends, a collection of model boats is on show, all made by a local man. In a village which gains its livelihood from fishing, seafarers provide most of the pub's trade, although tourists also happen upon it. Originally a stone-built farmhouse dating from the 17th century, the pub has sold beer since 1812. Nowadays it serves Theakston Best Bitter and XB, McEwan 80/- and Bass Best Scotch Bitter, Newcastle Exhibition and Bitter, as well as Longstone Bitter, from a small, recently established local brewery. It also boasts a good choice of malt whiskies. The home-cooked food embraces the traditional - for example, steak and kidney pie, and fillet of lemon sole with prawns and shrimp sauce - and the more cosmopolitan, like lamb curry masala - all at £4. Beside the pub there is a garden with its own putting green and views out to sea. Fourteen double rooms and one single are available, furnished and decorated in traditional style. A bonus for overnight guests is the 'boat gallery' in the residents' lounge, which displays some interesting ships' remnants.

Brewery: Free house
Licensee: Mr A C Glen
Opening hours: 11am-3pm, 6-11pm; Sun 12-3pm, 7-10.30pm
Bar food: 12-2pm
Restaurant: 12-2pm, 7-8.15pm
Accommodation: (Price per person) £31
Children: In family room and restaurant only; half portions available
Credit cards: Access, Visa

Seaton Sluice

⊛ WATERFORD ARMS
Colywell Bay, Seaton Sluice NE46 4QZ. Tel 091235 0450

Built in 1899 and typically late Victorian, this pub overlooks the harbour of a straggling coastal hamlet. It retains its original layout of two bars, one with pool, darts and dominoes, and both furnished with cushioned benches and traditional wooden tables. Locals and families provide most of the trade, enjoying home-cooked dishes like seafood platter at £6.95, prawn curry at £4.95 and roast beef at £4.65. Beer drinkers have the choice of Vaux Samson, Extra Special, Lorimers Best Scotch and Guinness. Three double rooms are available, with modern decor.

Brewery: Vaux
Licensee: Mrs Charlton
Opening hours: 11am-3pm, 7-11pm; Sun 12-3pm, 7-10.30pm
Bar food: As opening hours
Accommodation: (Price per person) £22
Children: Welcome anywhere

⊕ PHEASANT INN
Stannersburn, near Falstone NE48 1DD. Tel 0434 240382

Stannersburn

In summer the attractions of the Kielder Forest bring many visitors to this 360-year-old pub, which enjoys a mainly local trade the rest of the year. Standing alone in a hamlet next to the vast Kielder Water, and with a sheltered garden to the rear, the sturdy, stone building has been refurbished so as to retain the original layout and features. As a result, the two bars have a homely feeling, their horse-brasses and old farming implements evoking the bygone days of life on the land. On sale are Theakston Best Bitter and XB, along with a remarkable choice of 26 malt whiskies. The simple, home-made fare includes oven-crisped haddock, lasagne and steak and kidney pie, all at £5.25. Like the rest of the food, these are served in generous portions, giving good value for money. The six double and four single bedrooms are furnished and decorated in a modern style.

Brewery: Free house
Licensee: Walter Kershaw
Opening hours: 11am-3pm, 6-11pm; Sun 12-3pm, 7-10.30pm
Bar food: 12-2pm, 7-9pm
Restaurant: 7-9pm; Sun 12-2pm, 7-9pm
Accommodation: (Price per room) single £21, double £50
Children: In restaurant and games room only, and not after 8.30pm; half portions available; outdoor play area

WARENFORD LODGE
Warenford, near Belford NE70 7HY. Tel 0668 213453

Warenford

Luckily for this 200-year-old former coaching inn, the busy A1 bypasses it, leaving it and the hamlet in which it stands in a peaceful pocket of countryside. Yet being tucked away has done nothing to prevent the pub's reputation for excellent food from spreading. Indeed, there is a steady flow of visitors keen to sample a menu which includes imaginative regional dishes like venison cakes St Hubert at £6.70 and Northumberland fish soup at £7.55. On tap to partner the food are McEwan Best Scotch and Newcastle Exhibition. Regulars and families are also very much in evidence in the bar and lounge, which have been renovated without destroying the pub's character, and are furnished in traditional style with cushioned benches and wooden tables and chairs.

Brewery: Free house
Licensee: Mr R Matthewman
Opening hours: 12-2pm, 7-11pm; closed Mon; Sun 12-3pm, 7-10.30pm
Bar food: As opening hours
Children: In dining room only
Credit cards: Visa, Diners

⊕ MASONS ARMS
Dial Place, Warkworth NE65 0UR. Tel 0665 711398

Warkworth

Part of this mellow sandstone building dates back 600 years, but it is snippets of its history since it became a pub, around 1700, that are recorded in gilt lettering on its massive oak beams. Among other events, the first Jacobite rising is recalled, when 'On 8th October 1715, the Earl of Derwentwater and 40 of his followers dined in this house'. If the food was good enough for an earl then it is certainly

Brewery: Scottish & Newcastle
Licensee: Mr J mulligan
Opening hours: 11am-3pm, 6-11pm; Sun 12-3pm, 7-10.30pm
Bar food: As opening hours
Children: In dining area only; half portions available

appreciated now by its clientele of regulars and families. The keynote is freshness - all the fish comes from the nearby port of Amble - and the prices are very reasonable. Among the dishes on the straightforward menu are fresh cod at £3, steak pie at £3.50 and roast of the day at £3.75. For beer drinkers there is the choice of Theakston Best Bitter, Younger No 3, Newcastle Exhibition and McEwan Best Scotch to accompany the food. Polished wood and open fires lend a homely feel to the bar, part of which is given over to eating, while in summer there's the equally pleasant option of sitting in the sheltered garden. The surrounding village is one of the most attractive in the county.

⊛ FOX AND HOUNDS
Main Road, Wylam NE41 8DI. Tel 0661 853246

Wylam

Situated in a village on the north bank of the Tyne, just across the river from County Durham, this pub is used mainly by local people and by families. While the fabric of the whitewashed stone building dates from the 18th century, inside it has been renovated to form an open-plan room retaining some of the original features and reproducing others. Although spacious enough to accommodate a separate eating area, the bar remains cosy, with its carpet and spindlebacked chairs. Underlying the fact that the pub serves a rural community, a wealth of rustic odds and ends is on show, including a harness and horse-brasses. Vaux draught beer is on sale, as well as bar meals such as chilli con carne at £3.75, and, both at £6, fresh salmon and sirloin steak.

Brewery: Vaux
Licensee: Trevor Bellas
Opening hours: 11am-11pm; Sun 12-3pm, 7-10.30pm
Bar food: 12-2pm, 5.30-10pm;Sun 12-2pm, 7-10pm
Children: Welcome anywhere; outdoor play area

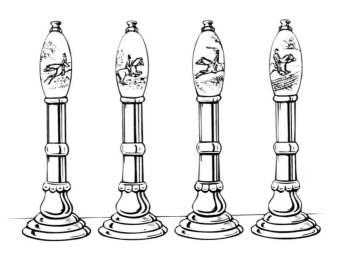

TYNE &WEAR

☻ BLACK BULL
Matfen, near Newcastle upon Tyne. NE20 0RP. Tel 0661 886330

Matfen

Some 200 years old, this handsome, stone-built pub stands in the middle of an estate village in the heart of the country, its front garden overlooking the green. It attracts a very mixed clientele - even its local customers range from labourers to aristocrats - with the restaurant accounting for much of its popularity. Cooked to a high standard and giving good value for money, the wide range of dishes includes chicken and leek pie at £4.25, oak-smoked trout fillets at £4.95 and spicy vegetable chilli at £3.95. The wine list is comprehensive, and Theakston Best Bitter and a guest beer, along with 28 malt whiskies, are on sale in the bar. Cushioned benches and wooden furniture and old photographs of the village and the surrounding countryside are in keeping with the traditional decor of the pub, which has a separate family room. Five double rooms are available, decorated in country style.

Brewery: Free house
Licensees: Colin and Michelle Scott
Opening hours: 11am-3pm, 6-11pm; Sun 12-3pm, 7-10.30pm
Bar food: As opening hours
Restaurant: Times as bar food
Accommodation: (Price per room) single £18, double £30
Children: In family room and restaurant only; children's menu available
Credit cards: Access, Visa

☻ CROWN POSADA
The Side, Newcastle upon Tyne NE1 3JE. Tel 091 2321269

Newcastle upon Tyne

A brass relief of the Spanish crown provides the sign for this city-centre pub, which is said to have been built by a Spanish merchant for his mistress nearly two centuries ago. But whether it was built as a private house, which it resembles outwardly, or an inn remains unclear, for 'posada' means the latter. Two fine, large stained-glass windows, probably depicting the couple, dominate the front of the pub, which is entered through wrought-iron gates and double doors. A long, narrow room incorporating a Snug, the bar features dark panelling, complemented by dark-wood furniture in mid-Victorian style. Boddingtons Best Bitter, Hadrian Gladiator Bitter, Butterknowle Conciliation Ale, McEwan Scotch Bitter, Theakston Bitter and Beamish Stout are on tap, and the pub's popularity seems to be unaffected by the fact that the only wines are French dry whites and the only food available is sandwiches at lunchtime. Business people and tourists provide much of the trade, and the place is particularly lively and full of atmosphere in the evenings.

Brewery: Free house
Licensee: Malcolm McPherson
Opening hours: 11am-3pm, 5.30-11pm; Sun 12-3pm, 7-10.30pm
Bar food: 11am-2pm, 5.30-7pm; no food Sun
Children: Not permitted inside

⊜ SHIREMOOR HOUSE FARM
Middle Engine Lane, New York NE29 8DZ. Tel 091 2576302

New York

Carried out five years ago, this imaginative conversion of derelict stone farm buildings not far from the coast has created a pub with a real flavour of the rural past. The bar combines the original features of a flagstone floor, stone walls and exposed beams with the comfort of easy chairs and sofas. What was the granary became a conservatory, while the cowshed was cleverly turned into a restaurant, and at the front of the building is a pleasant patio with tables. Old farm implements, on show everywhere, recall the origins of the pub, which is used by a mix of country regulars and business people. The beers on offer are Stones Best Bitter, Theakston Best Bitter and Old Peculier, Courage Directors, Bass and a guest ale. Well cooked, attractively presented and reasonably priced, the food includes rump steak in garlic cheese sauce and salmon sterak, both at £5.95, and rack of lamb with rosemary and redcurrant sauce at £5.25.

Brewery: Free house
Licensee: Bill Kerridge
Opening hours: 11am-11pm;
Sun 12-3pm, 7-10.30pm
Bar food: 12-2.30pm, 6-9.30pm
(Sun from 7pm)
Restaurant: 12-1.30pm,
7-8.30pm
Children: In conservatory and restaurant only; half portions available
Credit cards:
AMERICAN EXPRESS®, Access, Visa

YORKSHIRE (NORTH)

⊜ CRAB AND LOBSTER
Asenby, near Topcliffe YO7 3QL. Tel 0845 577286

Asenby

There's an eccentric antique shop feel to this intimate thatched pub, with its grandfather clocks, old telephones, leather cases and kilims casually arranged under low oak beams. More a haven for informal food and wine lovers than just beer drinkers, there are over 130 wines to choose from, and dishes of superb quality are written in chalk on the beams. The pub is one of the most popular in Yorkshire, and weekend bookings for the restaurant are made up to six weeks in advance. The main reason for its reputation can be found in starters like crab and lobster bisque at £2.50, and goat cheese, burnt onion and honeycomb in filo for £5. The high standards are sustained in main dishes like scallops langoustine with bacon tagliatelle at £9.50, chicken and garlic mushrooms en croûte for £7.95, and char-grilled lamb steak with mint béarnaise at £8.50. Puddings are all £3.25. Real ales from Youngers and Theakston are on tap in the bar.

Brewery: Free house
Licensees: Jackie and David Barnard
Opening hours: 11.30am-3pm,
6.30-11pm; Sun 12-3pm; closed Sun evening
Bar food: 12-2pm, 7-9.30pm
Restaurant: 11.30am-3pm, 6.30-11pm; Sun 12-3pm; booking necessary
Children: Welcome anywhere; family room
Credit cards:
AMERICAN EXPRESS®, Access, Visa, Diners

⊜ BIRCHALL INN
Beckhole, near Whitby YO22 5LE. Tel 0947 86245

Beckhole

Idyllically placed beside a ghyll in a small hamlet at the bottom of a lush green valley, this pub has much more than just its chocolate-box setting to recommend it. The whitewashed building - originally two small early 17th-century cottages - is beautiful in an unobtrusively rural way, and on the front wall a landscape painting by Algernon Newton adds an unexpected touch. Inside the two bars are full of character and charm. Decorated simply and sparsely adorned with various rural artefacts, both share a relaxed and very friendly atmosphere. One bar is so tiny that more than five people make it crowded, and the other is not much bigger, but somehow everyone manages to squeeze in. Locals and regular visitors love the uniqueness of this little pub, where Theakston Traditional Mild, Best Bitter and XB are on tap. Food is of the pie and sandwich variety, but it is available all day.

Brewery: Free house
Licensee: Colin Jackson
Opening hours: Summer 11am-11pm; winter 11am-3pm, 7-11pm; Sun 12-3pm, 7-10.30pm
Bar food: As opening hours
Children: In small bar only

⊜ MALT SHOVEL
Brearton, near Knaresborough HG3 3BX. Tel 0423 862929

Brearton

The altar and pulpit from an old church were rescued to make the bar at this pretty 16th-century pub, and years later a mixed crowd still congregates around them. There's a simple, relaxed atmosphere here, helped by the low oak-beamed ceilings, open fires and exposed stone walls, and beer tankards and rural objects make an eye-catching display. The pub is a family-run affair, with the friendly landlord serving behind the bar while his mother and sister organise the food side. On offer are dishes like fresh salmon with cucumber mayonnaise at £5.50, nut roast with tomato and fruit sauce for £4.25, and vegetable samosas with salad offering good value at £3.75. Banana fudge flan, and fresh fruit pies and crumbles are all £1.75. Daleside Bitter, Theakston Traditional Mild and Best Bitter and Guinness are on tap, as well as real ales from Tetley and Old Mill. Outside, the walls are soft yellow stone with vines growing on them, and there's a patio and small garden.

Brewery: Free house
Licensee: Leigh Trafford-Parsons
Opening hours: 12-3pm, 6.45-11pm (Fri and Sat from 6.30pm); closed Mon; Sun 12-3pm, 7-10.30pm
Bar food: 12-2pm, 7-9pm (except Sun)
Children: Welcome anywhere

☺ ABBEY INN
Byland Abbey, Coxwold, near Wass YO6 4BD. Tel 03476 204

Byland Abbey

Built of old Yorkshire stone and set in the countryside close to Byland Abbey, the interior of this inn combines originality with a spacious homeliness. An assortment of bric-à-brac, stuffed birds, fabrics and rugs is part of a fascinating collection which also includes pictures and paintings, old beer tankards and antiques. Seating is a mixture of benches and chairs set on flagstoned floors, and oak beams and open fires complete the cosy picture. The inn attracts a mainly mature crowd who enjoy the daily changing lunch and evening menus - to call the food bar meals would be an understatement. Dishes like garlic Mediterranean chicken and rice, venison pie, and smoked mackerel, all costing £6, are very well presented and tasty. Puddings including chocolate fudge cake and mincemeat crumble and custard are £2.50. Eldridge Pope EP Best Bitter, Theakston and Guinness are on tap.

Brewery: Free house
Licensee: Peter Handley
Opening hours: 10am-2.30pm, 6.30-11pm; closed Mon; Sun 12-3pm
Bar food: As opening hours
Children: Welcome anywhere

☺ FORESTERS ARMS
Carlton, near Leyburn DL8 2BB. Tel 0969 40272

Carlton

Tasteful fabrics, solid wooden furniture and a large farmhouse-style fireplace add to the appeal of this delightful traditional pub in the heart of the Dales. Built in 1630 of typical York stone, it has changed little over the years with its chunky oak beams, low ceilings and flagged floors. Sketches of local characters and scenes cover the walls, and a very mixed crowd rubs shoulders in the simple cosy bar. The food served there is anything but simple, however, and cooking standards are high. Dishes like home-made chicken liver pâté with green peppercorn and wild mushrooms and melba toast at £3.95 make a very tasty starter, with choices to follow like Vienna schnitzel at £8.95 and whole fresh lobster grilled with garlic or served cold with mayonnaise offering excellent value at £12.95. Two people can share paella Valenciana for £18.95. Apple strudel and tiramisu are just two of the puddings on the menu at £2.95. There's an extensive wine list, and real ales from Theakston and John Smith on tap, as well as Guinness. Five bright and pretty bedrooms are available, some with good views of the Dales, and there are lovely views to be had too from the seating at the front of the inn.

Brewery: Free house
Licensees: Helmfried Fehlow and Lesley Carlson
Opening hours: 11am-3pm, 6-11pm (from 7pm in winter); Sun 12-3pm, 7-10,30pm
Bar food: 11.30am-3pm, 6-10pm; Sun 12-3pm, 7-10pm
Restaurant: 7-9.30pm (except Sun and Mon in winter)
Accommodation: (Price per room) single £21.50, double £40
Children: Welcome anywhere; family room
Credit cards: Access, Visa

⊕ FAUCONBERG ARMS
Coxwold, near Wass YO6 4AD. Tel 03476 214

Coxwold

Gleaming brass and copper is much in evidence at this lovely old village pub, where real ales from Theakston, Tetley, John Smith's and Guinness are on tap. Tables at the front look on to the village street, while inside it's all traditional Yorkshire with beams, flagged floors and open fires. Food is well above average, including such dishes as stuffed aubergine with red lentils, cumin and apricot, and home-made steak and kidney pie, both at £4.95. Starters include deep-fried puff pastry parcels filled with creamy garlic for £2.95. Four flowery bedrooms offer cosy, well equipped accommodation.

Brewery: Free house
Licensees: Robin and Nicky Jacques
Opening hours: 11am-3pm, 6.30-11pm; Sun 12-3pm, 7-10.30pm
Bar food: 12-2pm, 7-8.45pm
Restaurant: 7-8.45pm (except Sun and Mon)
Accommodation: (Price per room) single £24-£40, double £40
Children: Welcome anywhere
Credit cards: Access, Visa

⊕ BLUE LION
East Witton, near Leyburn DL8 4SN. Tel 0969 24273

East Witton

Candlelight casts a gentle glow around this friendly pub in the evenings, and a well-heeled clientele basks in the general warmth. Service is very attentive, and the food is imaginative and interesting. Try starters like leeks in cream with Wensleydale cheese in bacon, or wild boar terrine, both under £3. Main dishes include salmon wrapped in filo pastry with beurre blanc at £7.55, and roast woodpigeon with thyme, shallots and smoked bacon for £6.25. The desserts are particularly good, with choices like white chocolate mousse with orange chocolate sorbet and orange sauce, and glazed summer fruit brûlée with almond nougat, both at £3.25. In the bar unusual portraits and prints, old china, a grandfather clock, dried flowers and old bottles add to the comfortable, homely feel, and these are set against a background of antique settles, oak panelling and flagged floors. On tap are Theakston Best Bitter, XB and Old Peculier, Younger Scotch Bitter and Murphy's. Nine cottagey bedrooms are available, furnished with stripped pine and tasteful fabrics. Outside, the pretty Georgian-style inn benches overlook the village green, and there is a garden at the back.

Brewery: Free house
Licensees: Helen and Paul Klein
Opening hours: 11am-11pm; Sun 12-3pm, 7-10.30pm
Bar food: 12-2pm, 7-9.30pm
Restaurant: 7-9.30pm (except Sun and Mon)
Accommodation: (Price per room) £50
Children: Welcome anywhere
Credit cards: Access, Visa

A Pint of Fed

A pint of Fed served in a North Country club is testimony to the success of an initiative taken during a beer shortage in 1919 in the wake of the First World War. The Federation Brewery supplies its beer not to pubs, or not in the main, but to clubs in the North of England. Operating for years in Newcastle, it moved to Dunston, Tyne & Wear, in 1975. It is owned by 540 member clubs and has won many awards for its beer.

⊜ STAR INN
Harome, near Helmsley YO6 5JE. Tel 0439 70397

Harome

This real gem of a 14th-century pub with its mixture of refinement and simplicity unsurprisingly appeals to all tastes, from the well-known visitor to the regular local. The intimate rural atmosphere is enhanced by tall old settles, stuffed animals and a French cooker, plus the traditional low oak-beamed ceiling and solid oak furniture. Classical music is played in the background, and plans are afoot to introduce classical soirées in the future. Diners in the restaurant are often invited to take their coffee in a loft built into the eaves of the thatched roof. Food is a cut above the usual, and includes dishes like fresh lemon salmon at £7.95, garlic chicken for £6.95 and vegetarian crêpe at £5.95. A good choice of real ales is on tap, including Theakston Best Bitter and Old Peculier, Timothy Taylor, Tetley, Guinness and an occasional guest beer. There is also a fine wine list, and some old ports and brandies.

Brewery: Free house
Licensee: Thomas Blackburn
Opening hours: 12-3pm, 6.30-11pm; Sun 12-3pm, 7-10.30pm
Bar food: 12-2pm, 7.30-9.30pm
Restaurant: 7.30-9.30pm (lunchtime if requested); Sun 12-2.30pm, 7.30-9.30pm
Children: Welcome anywhere; family room
Credit cards: Access, Visa

⊜ ANGEL
Hetton, near Skipton BD23 6LT. Tel 0756730 263

Hetton

Whether you pop into this pub for a quick drink or spend the evening over a long meal you'll be equally welcome and feel instantly at ease. It's as pretty inside as out, with the long ivy-clad York stone building leading to a tasteful and smart but essentially cosy bar. The clientele tends to be well heeled and mature, attracted in part by the delicious but inexpensive food which is complemented by around 350 wines. Parfait of foie gras and chicken livers with port wine sauce makes a tasty starter, with main course choices like confit of duck with blood orange and curacao sauce for £6.85, and hot poached Scotch salmon in white wine sauce at £6.50. Both are served with new potatoes and mangetouts. A vegetarian speciality might be fresh spinach noodles with garlic and basil. Theakston Best Bitter and XB are on tap, along with McEwan Scotch Bitter and Taylor Landlord. A patio at the front of the building affords very good views.

Brewery: Free house
Licensee: Denis Watkins
Opening hours: 12-2.30pm, 6-10.30pm; Sun 12-2.30pm, 7-10.30pm
Bar food: 12-2pm, 6-10pm; Sun 7-10pm
Restaurant: 7-10pm; Sun 12-2pm
Children: Welcome anywhere
Credit cards: Access, Visa

⊜ THWAITES ARMS
Horsehouse, near Leyburn DL8 4TS. Tel 0969 40206

Horsehouse

This totally unspoilt and unpretentious country pub is the regular haunt of local farmers, as well as being a 'find' for some intrepid summer visitors. The simple but cosy little bars, with their beams and benches, stone walls and open

Brewery: Free house
Licensees: Bruce and Sheila Powell
Opening hours: 12-2pm (Sat

fires, offer traditional hospitality, and interesting photos and prints depict local life and history. Theakston Traditional Mild, Best Bitter, and in summer Old Peculier are on tap, as well as John Smith's. Food is quite simple at lunchtime, except on Sundays when roast beef and Yorkshire pudding are served. In the evenings it's a bit more lavish, with home-made beef casserole in Old Peculier at £4.95, broccoli and cream cheese bake for £4.50, and chicken Kiev at £5.75. Puddings like apple crumble are £1.75. Compact and functional accommodation is available, and the remote Dales setting is worth admiring from the garden.

3pm, 7-11pm; closed Mon lunchtime; Sun 12-3pm; Sun 7-10.30pm
Bar food: 12-2pm, 7-9pm
Accommodation: (Per person) £16.50
Children: Welcome anywhere; family room

GEORGE INN
Kirk Gill, near Hubberholme BD23 5JE. Tel 0756 760223

Hubberholme

This rustic 'higgledy-piggledy' white stone-washed building dates back to 1600, and stands on its own overlooking a gill in the depths of the countryside. There's a lovely warm atmosphere inside, helped by the very friendly and amiable landlord. A wood-burning stove keeps the temperature up when it's cold outside, and the decor is simple but tasteful. It caters to all tastes, and the food is above average. Dishes like plaice filled with lemon and garlic butter cost £6.50, and chicken pie is £4.40. Quality house wines are on sale, with Younger Scotch Bitter and No 3 on tap. There are four compact rooms, one with a great view.

Brewery: Free house
Licensees: Marjorie Forster and John Fredrick
Opening hours: 11.30am-3pm, 7-11pm (Fri and Sat 6.30-11pm); Sun 12-3pm, 7-10.30pm
Bar food: 12-1.45pm, 7-8.45pm
Accommodation: (Price per room) £36; children under eight years not permitted
Children: Welcome anywhere

LION
Blakey Ridge, Hutton-le-Hole YO6 6LQ. Tel 07515 320

Hutton-le-Hole

Breath-taking views of the North Yorks Moors from the Lion give the heady feeling of being right on top of the world. Dating back to the 12th century, this pub is well away from anywhere, and even in summer when the tourist trade is at its height the atmosphere remains warm and relaxed. The cosy beamed bar contrasts strikingly with the dramatic bleakness of its beautiful surroundings, and on tap in here are real ales from Theakston, McEwan, Tetley, Younger and Guinness. Food is reasonably priced, with main courses like chicken and broccoli lasagne at £4.95 and haddock in breadcrumbs for £3.95. Treacle or jam roly-poly pudding with custard is not for the faint-hearted! A variety of modern and older rooms is available overnight, the former in a new extension and the latter with the same oak-beamed cosiness as the bar. Visitors can enjoy the outstanding views without restriction from a walled garden.

Brewery: Free house
Licensee: Barry Crossland
Opening hours: 11am-11pm; Sun 11am-10.30pm (supper licence)
Bar food: 12-10pm, inc Sun
Restaurant: 7-9.30pm; Sun 12-3pm, 7-9.30pm
Accommodation: (Price per person) double £15.50-£26.50
Children: Welcome anywhere
Credit cards: Access, Visa

⊜ TAN HILL INN
Keld, near Thwaite DL11 6ED. Tel 0833 28246

Keld

There's a uniquely convivial air to the 'highest pub in England', due in part, the staff claim, to the effects of its high altitude and partly, no doubt, thanks to their own witty and eccentric personalities! Whatever the cause, the atmosphere is lively and welcoming, helped by the bar's cosy log fire, stone walls and exposed beams. The 13th-century walls are decorated with photographs of the beautiful local scenery, postcards and various eccentricities, and seating is on wooden benches. Theakston Traditional Mild, Best Bitter, XB and Old Peculier are on tap, as well as Guinness, and there's a good range of malt whiskies. The bar menu offers choices like giant Yorkshire pudding with venison casserole inside at £8.95, broccoli and cream cheese pie for £4.50 and sirloin steak for £7.95. Sandwiches are available all day. The magnificent views are even more incredible from the seven bedrooms which are fitted out with modern furniture.

Brewery: Free house
Licensees: Margaret and Alec Baines
Opening hours: 11am-11pm; Sun 12-3pm, 7-10.30pm
Bar food: 12-2.30, 7-9pm
Accommodation: (Price per person) single £18.50, double £21.50
Children: Welcome anywhere

⊜ BLACKSMITHS ARMS
Lastingham, near Hutton-le-Hole YO6 6TL. Tel 07515 247

Lastingham

One of the oldest churches in England is a neighbour of this pub, whose own history goes back to 1647. Antiquity is evident everywhere, from the pretty York stone building itself to the flagged and beamed bar, and the range that houses the open fire is 200 years old. The friendly landlady creates a relaxed, homely atmosphere, drawing in a mixed crowd of locals and tourists. A regular guest beer is on tap along with real ales from Webster's, Bass, Stones Best Bitter and Guinness. Home-made soups and puddings like treacle roly-poly cost under £1.50, and main course choices include steak and kidney Yorkie at £4.05 and local sausage for £3.20. There are four cosy, cottagey rooms for those wanting to stay the night.

Brewery: Free house
Licensee: Sheila Frost
Opening hours: 11am-11pm; Sun 12-3pm, 7-10.30pm
Bar food: 12-3pm, 7-9.30pm
Restaurant: Times as bar food
Accommodation: (Price per room) double £17.50
Children: Welcome anywhere; family room; outdoor play area

Thwaites of Blackburn
Stern and comprehensively bearded, a former excise official named Daniel Thwaites founded a brewery by a natural spring in Blackburn, Lancashire, in 1807. He was succeeded by his son, Daniel Thwaites II, whose daughter married into the Yerburgh family, which has run the firm ever since. It is Blackburn's oldest company and its noble Shire horses still haul casks to the local pubs. The horses have won numerous awards, as have the brewery's mild and bitter. The Thwaites pubs are mostly in Lancashire.

⊕BLACK BULL
Moulton, near Richmond DL10 6QT. Tel 0325 377289

Moulton

The mainly business clientele who frequent this pub goes for the restaurant, which enjoys a good reputation, rather than just for a drink. Bar food is also available, and includes dishes like black pudding and pork sausage with caramelised apple at £3.25, and tagliatelle matriciana and Welsh rarebit and bacon, both for £4.25. An extensive wine list complements the food, and Theakston Best Bitter, Guinness and real ale from Tetley are on tap. The bar is small but attractive, with plenty of brass and copper on display and simple oak furnishings and benches. Paintings, prints and an old wooden chest create a cosy feel.

Brewery: Free house
Licensees: George and Audrey Pagendam
Opening hours: 12-2.30pm, 6-10.30pm (Fri and Sat 11pm); Sun 12-2pm, 7-10.30pm
Bar food: 12-2pm (except Sun)
Restaurant: 12-2pm, 7-9.30pm
Children: Not permitted inside under seven years
Credit cards: AMERICAN EXPRESS®, Access, Visa

⊕ FARMERS ARMS
Muker, near Thwaite DL11 6QG. Tel 0748 86297

Muker

Hearty traditional food at good prices is popular with the local farmers who frequent this cosy 17th-century pub in the centre of a typical Dales village. Dishes like vegetarian lasagne, chicken curry and home-made steak pie all cost £3.25, and to finish with there are puddings such as apple pie and peach melba, both at £1.50. Plenty of real ales are on tap to help wash it all down: Theakston Best Bitter and Old Peculier, John Smith's Magnet, Black Sheep Best Bitter, and ale from local brewery Butterknowle are all on sale here, plus Beamish Stout. The simple decor, with flagstone floors, pine settles, wooden beams and plenty of plates and tankards on display also appeals to the summer visitors who find their way to the attractive black-and-white building. Photographs and prints of local scenes and wildlife also enliven the walls. Outside on the terrace there are views of the village and the very rural landscape.

Brewery: Free house
Licensee: Jeffrey Bridel
Opening hours: 11am-3pm, 6.30-11pm (winter from 7pm); Sun 12-3pm, 7-10.30pm
Bar food: 12-2pm, 7-9pm
Children: Welcome anywhere; family room

⊕ THREE TUNS
Osmotherley, near Northallerton DL6 3BN. Tel 0609 883301

Osmotherley

Uncluttered and avoiding the usual brass and curio look, this 17th-century pub offers a tasteful and cosy atmosphere with white walls, cushioned settles, carpets and dried flower arrangements. It caters for varied tastes, from the regular locals to summer tourists, and the daily changing fresh fish menu is a great attraction to both groups. The friendly landlady and her husband will cater for children and

Brewery: Free house
Licensees: Juliet and Hugh Dyson
Opening hours: 12-2.30pm, 7-11pm; Sun 12-3pm, 7-10.30pm
Bar food: 12-2.30pm, 7-9.30pm; Sun 12-2pm

vegetarians on request, but otherwise there are starters like lobster and lettuce soup, and Californian pepperpot with bread board for £1.95. Main courses might include monkfish tail wrapped in bacon on a bed of fresh spinach for £9.95, and Whitby plaice and lobster with lobster sauce for £8.95. There is a good range of wines, and on tap are Theakston Best Bitter, XB and Old Peculier, Younger Scotch Bitter and No 3, and Beamish. There's a pretty walled garden, and new rooms from 1993.

Restaurant: 12-2.30pm, 7-9.30pm (except Sun)
Accommodation: (Price per room) single £38. double £50
Children: Welcome anywhere; family room available
Credit cards: Access, Visa

✆ NAGS HEAD
Pickhill, near Thirsk YO7 4JG. Tel 0845 567391

Pickhill

There's a tradition here of cutting the ties off unsuspecting visitors and displaying them in glass cabinets, so if you're wearing one when you arrive, tuck it out of sight! The quirky humour that is the hallmark of this pub is evident in other areas too: a giant draughts table is set into the floor and the game played with pints of beer, and a witty weather stone is worth having a look at. The unexciting front of the building belies the warmth and cosiness of the interior, with the flagged floors half carpeted, and an attractive open fire for cold days. As well as the notorious tie exhibits, a pictorial history of the pub and village dating back to the 19th century adorns the walls, and there are books and rural artefacts on display. The food is superior and the portions generous, with starters like smoked oysters sautéd with bacon on a warm salad for £3.60, and chilled melon with ginger sauce and raspberry at £2.95. Casserole of pheasant in blackcurrant and port makes an unusual main course (£8.25), and other choices include baked cod and prawn Florentine at £7.25. Puddings like vacherin glacé with hot chocolate sauce and baked upside-down pineapple sponge cost £2.50. On tap are Theakston Best Bitter, XB and Old Peculier, and ales from Younger and local brewers Hambleton.

Brewery: Free house
Licensees: Raymond and Edward Boynton
Opening hours: 11am-11pm; Sun 12-3pm, 7-10.30pm
Bar food: 12-2pm, 6-10pm; Sun 12-2pm, 7-9.30pm
Restaurant: 7-9.30pm; Sun 12-2pm
Accommodation: (Price per room) single £30, double £42
Children: Welcome anywhere; outdoor play area
Credit cards: Access, Visa

✆ MILBURN ARMS
Rosedale Abbey, near Pickering YO18 8RA. Tel 07515 312

Rosedale Abbey

Step through the doors of this large, pretty York stone pub which dates back to 1776 and you'll find an interior that is surprisingly up to date. Artificial beams prop up the ceiling beside some original ones, and the furniture and carpets are modern. Real ales from Theakston, Stones and Bass and Guinness are on tap, and there are several malt whiskies.

Brewery: Free house
Licensee: Terry Bentley
Opening hours: 11.30am-3pm, 6.30-11pm; Sun 12-3pm, 7-10.30pm
Bar food: 12-2pm, 7-9.15pm; Sat

Bar food includes starters like smoked mackerel and brandy pâté for £3, and main course choices might be vegetarian cannelloni at £3.95, and beef and Guinness casserole for £5.45. Eleven spacious floral rooms are available, and there's a pretty walled garden and patio.

and Sun 12-2pm, 7-10pm
Accommodation: (Price per person) single £37.50-£53.50, double £30-£46
Children: Welcome anywhere; family room
Credit cards: Access, Visa, Diners

✤ FOX AND HOUNDS
Starbotton, near Skipton BD23 5HY. Tel 0756760 269

Starbotton

A lovely limestone village is the setting for this simple 17th-century pub with a down-to-earth rural atmosphere. Theakston Best Bitter, XB and Old Peculier and Younger No 3 are on tap in the cosy, traditional bar, where plates and whisky jugs are on display. Food is reasonably priced, with starters like chicken liver pâté and pickled herring in dill both costing £2.50. Wine and nut loaf at £4.25 is an unusual dish, with other main course choices like Moroccan lamb for £5.50 and almond risotto and peanut sauce at £3.95. There's a good view from the front patio, and two attractive rooms are available.

Brewery: Free house
Licensees: James and Hilary McFadyen
Opening hours: 11.30am-3pm, 6.30-11pm; 12-3pm, 7-10.30pm
Bar food: 12-2pm, 7-9pm (except Mon evening)
Accommodation: (Price per person) £20
Children: Welcome anywhere

✤ BUCK INN
Thornton Watlass, near Ripon HG4 4AH. Tel 0677 422461

Thornton Watlass

Foxes' tails, stuffed heads of ducks, rabbits and otters, a bottle collection and paintings by local artists make impressive viewing at this mellow old pub. One bar dates back to the 17th century, and its thick oak joists and low ceilings create a cosy, unpretentious atmosphere. A new extension houses the second bar, where modern carpets and decor give a blander impression. The pub appeals to everyone from families to business people, and at weekends organ music and country and western nights are held. Whisky drinkers have 45 malts to choose from, and on tap are Theakston Traditional Mild and Best Bitter, and real ales from Tetley, Beamish and Carlton as well as a weekly guest beer. Avocado, orange and celery salad at £1.95 and garlic mushrooms for £2.25 are two starter choices, and main courses include baked aubergine and tomato Charlotte for £4.50, and home-made lamb mousaka at £5.25. Six functional bedrooms have good views.

Brewery: Free house
Licensee: Michael Fox
Opening hours: 11am-2.30pm, 6-11pm; 12-3pm, 7-10.30pm
Bar food: 12-2pm, 6.45-9.30pm; Sun 12-2pm, 7-9.30pm
Accommodation: (Price per person) single £25, double £20
Children: Welcome anywhere; outdoor play area
Credit cards: AMERICAN EXPRESS®, Access, Visa

⊜ WOMBWELL ARMS
Wass, near Thirsk YO6 4BE. Tel 03476 280

Wass

Very hospitable hosts create an easy-going atmosphere which draws a well-heeled middle-aged crowd to this 17th-century whitewashed stone pub. The bar and two dining rooms are an attractive mixture of flagstone floors, floral patterns, stripped pine and dried flowers, and open fires burn cheerfully in colder weather. A quality wine list complements bar meals like Dijon rabbit, and beef in orange and brandy, both at £6.95, and venison casserole for £7.50. Starters include duck and port pâté, and Wensleydale mushrooms at £2.75. Everards Old Original and Camerons Traditional Bitter are on tap in the bar, as well as draught Guinness, and drinkers can play Trivial Pursuit, monopoly and chess over their pints. Three light and airy rooms furnished in stripped pine and newly decorated in' Laura Ashley' style offer spacious accommodation.

Brewery: Free house
Licensees: Richard Alan and Lynda Evans
Opening hours: 12-2.30pm, 7-11pm; closed Mon; Sun 12-3pm, 7- 10.30
Bar food: 12-2pm, 7-10pm
Accommodation (Price per person) £21.50 (seasonal); children under eight years not permitted
Children: Welcome anywhere; family room
Credit cards: Access, Visa

⊜ SPORTSMANS ARMS
Wath in Nidderdale HG3 5PP. Tel 0423 711306

Wath in Nidderdale

There's peace and quiet aplenty at this attractive old pub set in its own grounds on the edge of a small village. The young staff are friendly, and a mature clientele is attracted in part by the relaxed atmosphere. The interesting menu is another bonus here, and the food enjoys a good reputation. Starters like melon sorbet at £3.50 and chicken liver terrine for £4.60 are popular, and the main menu offers dishes like turbot on a bed of spinach in white wine for £7.20, and grilled Scottish salmon with prawns at £6.65. The wine list is extensive, and there are plenty of malt whiskies and vodkas to try. Real ales from Younger, McEwan and Guinness are on tap. The bar is quite modern but tastefully furnished with high-backed cushioned seats, and pictures of local scenes line the pink walls. Benches and chairs are set out on the front driveway, and some of the seven pleasant rooms have views of the gardens and beyond.

Brewery: Free house
Licensee: Ray Carter
Opening hours: 12-2.30pm, 7-11pm; Sun 12-2.30pm, 7-10.30pm
Bar food: 12-2pm, 7-9.30pm; Sun 12-2pm, 7-8.30pm
Accommodation (Price per room) single £28-£30, double £47-£50
Children: Welcome anywhere;
Credit cards: Access, Visa

⊜ WHITE SWAN
Wighill, near Wetherby LS24 8XX. Tel 0937 832217

Wighill

A strong racing influence from nearby Wetherby and York pervades this pub, where many of the locals are involved with stables and lots of horsey pictures hang on the walls. Five log fires add to the charm of the three bars, and the friendly landlady supplies plenty of relaxed warmth herself. There's a mixture of oak beams, wooden benches and simple decorations, and on tap are real ales from Tetley and Stones, and Theakston Old Peculier. Bar food is fairly standard, and includes dishes like large prawns for £4.95 and grilled Aberdeen steak of the day at £7.50, both served with chips and salad, and smoked mackerel with bread and butter for £2.90. Soup is home-made, and so are the various sweets at £1.80. There's a good wine list to choose from. Outside tables and chairs on the front terrace look on to the village street, and there are two lawned gardens.

Brewery: Free house
Licensee: Rita Arundale
Opening hours: 12-3pm, 6-11pm; Sun 12-3pm, 7-10.30pm
Bar food: 12-2pm, 6-9.30pm; Sun 12-2pm
Restaurant: 6-9.30pm
Children: Welcome anywhere, family room; outdoor play area

BLACK SWAN
Peasholme Green, York YO1 2PR. Tel 0904 625236

York

This half-timbered black-and-white merchant's house is reputed to be the oldest inn in York. Dating back to 1417, it has been the home of several Lord Mayors of York and one of London, and still bears the distinct hallmark of its wealthy family origins. Now completely restored, the bar with its three connecting rooms is mainly wood panelled, with beamed ceilings supported by wooden posts. The historic atmosphere attracts a mixed crowd, from business people and tourists to a young and lively bunch in the evenings. On tap are Draught Bass, Stones Best Bitter and Worthington Best Bitter, and plenty of bottled beers are stocked. Bar food is basic but good value, and includes choices like giant Yorkshire pudding with beef and gravy, and lasagne and chips, both for £4.50, and steak and onion pie with chips for £3.90. Four standard bedrooms have the same atmosphere as the bar.

Brewery: Bass
Licensee: Joe Cahill
Opening hours: 11am-11pm; Sun 12-3pm, 7-10.30pm
Bar food: 12-2pm, 6.30-9pm; Sun 12-2pm
Accommodation: (Price per person) £45
Children: Not permitted inside under 14 years
Credit cards: Access, Visa

YORKSHIRE (SOUTH)

⊜ CADEBY INN
Main Street, Cadeby, near Doncaster DN5 7SW. Tel 0709 864009

Cadeby

A staggering selection of malt whiskies - over 200 of them - fine wines and several choices of real ale make this a drink-connoisseur's paradise. On tap are Courage Directors, John Smith's Bitter and Magnet, Samuel Smith OBB, Tetley Bitter, and Ind Coope Burton Ale. The converted farmhouse dates from 1700, and much of its character and atmosphere has been preserved. The two bars are spacious and busy, with displays of county cricket caps, sporting trophies, horsey articles and prints for sale. This popular family inn is set in a large garden with lawns and attractive shrubs. The bar menu is extensive, and as well as a Carvery with cuts of meat costing £4.55 there are dishes like battered scampi with salad, chips and peas for £4.25 and spinach and mushroom lasagne for £3.95. Sweets from the trolley are £1.50, and afternoon tea is served.

Brewery: Free house
Licensee: Bill Ward
Opening hours: 11am-3pm, 5-11pm (Sat 11am-11pm); Sun 12-3pm, 7-10.30pm
Bar food: 12-2pm, 6-10pm; Sun 12-2pm, 7-9.30pm
Children: In special area only; outdoor play area
Credit cards: Access, Visa

⊜GREEN TREE INN
Thorne Road, Hatfield Woodhouse, near Doncaster DN7 6NL. Tel 0302 840305

Hatfield Woodhouse

Although modernised and enlarged, the Green Tree has retained much of the character of the 17th-century coaching inn it once was. Its one large bar is composed of a series of connecting rooms with beamed ceilings and exposed timbers. Open fires, old prints and a collection of antique firearms on the walls make a pleasant setting in which to enjoy a pint of Wards Thorne Best Bitter or Vaux Samson to accompany the very enjoyable bar food. Popular dishes include fish and chips and roast lamb at £3.95, or sirloin steak at £4.95, with puddings like lemon meringue pie or fruit salad at £1.45. There is also a separate restaurant with its own à la carte menu, for which booking is advisable. There is a large garden at the rear of the pub, and here also are chalet-style buildings housing overnight accommodation which consists of four simply furnished but comfortable rooms.

Brewery: Wards
Licensee: Trevor Hagan
Opening hours: 11am-3pm, 6-11pm; Sun 12-3pm, 7-10.30pm
Bar food: 12-2.30pm, 7-10pm
Restaurant: 7-10pm (except Mon); Sun 12-2.30pm
Accommodation: (Price per room) single £25, double £35
Children: Welcome anywhere
Credit cards:
AMERICAN EXPRESS®, Access, Visa, Diners

SHIP INN
Hooton Road, Kilnhurst S62 5TA. Tel 0709 584322

Kilnhurst

Canopies and leaded windows lend a welcoming appearance to this white-painted pub which dates from the 1800s. A generous variety of real ales is on tap in the beamed bar, for example Whitbread Exchange Trophy, Stones Best Bitter, Marston's Pedigree Bitter, Castle Eden Ale, Boddingtons Bitter, Guinness and Murphy's. Popular items are the cocktails that the bar also specialises in mixing and serving. The food is fairly standard but cheap, with dishes like steak Canadian with onion at £1.75, and golden breaded scampi at £2.20. A set Sunday lunch costs £5.95.

Brewery: Whitbread
Licensee: Andrew House
Opening hours: 11.30am-11pm; Sun 12-10.30pm
Bar food: 12-2.30pm, 6-10pm; Sun 12-2.30pm, 7-9.30pm
Restaurant: Times as bar food
Children: Welcome anywhere

⊕ ROYAL OAK
Turnshaw Road, Ulley S31 0YG. Tel 0742 872464

Ulley

Heavy-horse harnesses and brasses decorate the dark woodwork and exposed beams of this stone-built village-centre pub. There's a very welcoming and pleasant country atmosphere in the two bars, both carpeted, with low, beamed ceilings, and there's a light and airy family room next to the children's playground. The pub draws mainly on passing trade with a few locals, and the good food is one of its chief attractions. The extensive and well presented menu includes dishes like steak and kidney pie or haddock, both at £3.75, and sirloin steak for £5.95. Starters like soup, melon and salmon cost between £1.20 and £2.20. On tap are real ales from Samuel Smith, and there's a short but decent wine list. A garden on two sides of the pub offers some seating outside the low and sloping-roofed building which dates back about 300 years.

Brewery: Samuel Smith
Licensee: David Hinan
Opening hours: 11am-3pm, 6-11pm; Sun 12-3pm, 7.30-10.30pm
Bar food: 12-2pm, 7-9.45pm
Children: Welcome anywhere; family room; outdoor play area; own menu available
Credit cards: AMERICAN EXPRESS®, Access, Visa

Inns, Taverns and Alehouses

As the Middle Ages wore on, a rough distinction grew up between three types of drinking-house: the inn, the tavern and the alehouse. At the top of the tree, the inn provided lodging, meals and drink for well-to-do travellers. The tavern was more like today's wine bar, with no accommodation. Usually in a town, it dispensed wine and sometimes food to prosperous customers. A bunch of evergreen leaves above the door might identify it and it was associated, in puritanical minds at least, with gambling, loose women and disreputable songs.

At the bottom of the ladder and far more numerous, alehouses catered for ordinary people. As the name implies, they were simply dwelling houses where ale was brewed and sold. Often kept by women, they were generally one-room, wattle-and-daub hovels which supplied a take-out service for the neighbours. Inside there was no bar-counter, customers and the alewife huddled close, pigs and chickens wandered in and out, and standards of hygiene would horrify patrons today. The quality of the ale was checked by a local official, the ale-conner, and the houses identified themselves with an alestake. This long pole with leaves at the end was the forerunner of today's pub sign.

🏰 FOX AND HOUNDS
Main Street, Wadsworth DN11 9AY. Tel 0302 853425

Wadsworth

The original 18th-century pub has been modernised and extended over the years to provide a comfortable, smart eating and drinking house. A collection of plates and crockery decorates the Lounge, a spacious room with dark wooden furniture, while the Public Bar has dark oak chairs and benches and wood panelling. A large restaurant overlooks the garden, which has a lawned area with benches. The pub serves good quality food, and there's excellent value for money in dishes like sirloin steak and mushrooms for £9.95, farmhouse grill, and halibut. Starters and snacks range from £1.20 to £2.20, and the set-price meal costs £5.95. On tap are Marston's Pedigree Bitter, John Smith's Bitter and Magnet, Beamish Stout and perhaps a couple of guest beers. The choice of bottled beers, malt whiskies and wines is also good. This village pub is set directly on the A60 and attracts a passing trade as well as business people and locals.

Brewery: Courage
Licensee: Ray Bradley
Opening hours: 11am-3pm, 6.30-11pm; Sun 12-2.30pm, 7-10.30pm
Bar food: 12-2pm, 7-9.30pm; Sun 12-2pm
Restaurant: Times as bar food
Children: Welcome if eating; children's menu available
Credit cards: Access, Visa, Diners

GEORGE AND DRAGON
Main Street, Wentworth S62 7TL. Tel 0226 742440

Wentworth

There's a charming, rustic atmosphere in this cosy beer lovers' pub which appeals for other reasons as well. Old stoves and rural artefacts enhance the traditional setting in the two bars, with their stone-flagged floors, low ceilings and exposed wooden beams. The old country pub, which dates from the 16th century, is packed with character, and is a popular outlet for the several real ales on draught: Oak Wobbly Bob and, exclusive to the George and Dragon, Dragon's Blood, Timothy Taylor Landlord and Best Bitter, Ind Coope Burton Ale and Tetley Bitter, as well as three guest beers. There's also a great selection of traditional country wines and imported beers. Bar food is served every lunchtime, with a choice of dishes like fresh salmon salad at £3.30, rump steak for £4.95, and Cumberland sausage with salad for £1.30. A vegetarian dish is usually on the menu. The annual beer festival is a well frequented event at this pub, and a camp site behind the old building provides temporary accommodation for the real ale aficionados who flock here. There's also a garden backing on to a field with horses and a barn.

Brewery: Free house
Licensee: Steve Dickinson
Opening hours: 12-3pm, 5-11pm; Sun 12-3pm, 7-10.30pm
Bar food: 12-2pm
Children: Welcome at lunchtime only

YORKSHIRE (WEST)

BINGLEY ARMS
Church Lane, Bardsley LS17 9DR. Tel 0937 572462

Bardsley

A lovely terraced garden filled with flowers makes a delightful place to sit on warm evenings at this old country pub. Dating back to AD953, it is crammed with historical interest from its ivy-clad outside walls to the very old-world atmosphere inside. Hunting prints are ranged around the walls, and several lamps brighten the two high-ceilinged bars. Exposed wooden beams and panelling, and cushioned settles make this quiet, roomy pub an attractive haunt for country regulars as well as visitors. Tetley Mild and Bitter are on draught and there's a good choice of interesting bar meals, including a vegetarian choice. Steak with red wine, lasagne verde and courgette wheels are all £4.25, and spare ribs make a filling starter or snack at £2.45 to £2.95. Puddings like profiteroles with chocolate sauce are £2. Booking is generally advised for meals in the restaurant.

Brewery: Tetley
Licensee: Angela Newton
Opening hours: 11am-3pm, 6-11pm (Fri and Sat 11am-11pm); Sun 12-3pm, 7-10.30pm
Bar food: 12-2pm, 6-8pm; Sun 12-2pm
Restaurant: Wed-Sat 6-9pm; Sun 12-2pm
Children: Welcome anywhere
Credit cards: AMERICAN EXPRESS®, Access, Visa

MALT SHOVEL
Harden Lane, Harden, near Bingley BD16 1B0 . Tel 0535 272357

Harden

This little pub nestles at the bottom of a wooded valley on the bank of the Harden Beck, just on the edge of the village. Dating back to the 16th century, and built of local stone, the pub is thought to have served at one time as the local court and lock-up and an original grilled window from this period survives. Nowadays, the atmosphere is considerably more hospitable and the two cosy bars, wood-panelled and warmed in winter by open fires, welcome locals, business people and tourists who appreciate the unspoilt charm. Tetley Bitter is on draught to accompany the simple, but good value, bar food served at lunchtime. Hot dishes such as steak and kidney pie, chilli con carne and breaded haddock all cost around £3, and giant Yorkshire puds, £2.70. Outside there is a large lawned garden, safely fenced and ideal for children in the summer.

Brewery: Tetley
Licensee: Keith Bolton
Opening hours: 11.30am-3pm; 5.30-11pm (Sat 11am-11pm); Sun 12-3pm, 7.30-10.30pm
Bar food: 12-2pm (except Sun)
Children: Welcome anywhere

KINGS ARMS
Heath Common, Kirthorpe, near Wakefield WF5 5SL. Tel 0924 377527

Heath Common

A display case of old and commemorative beers is a very appropriate feature of a pub that dispenses the locally brewed award-winning, ales from Clark's of Wakefield. Their Traditional Bitter and Ram's Revenge take pride of place in the gas-lit bars, along with real ales from Timothy Taylor and Tetley as well as regularly changing guest ales. Extensive mahogany panelling, oak beams, flagged floors and open fires give a comfortable feel to the Lounge and three small rooms which are linked by passageways. This friendly, well kept pub also comes highly recommended for its food, both in the bar and the restaurant. The quality is impressive, and portions extremely large. Authentic lasagne made by the Italian chef is good value at £3.25, and roast of the day costs £3.50. Heath Yorkshire pudding as a starter is £1.25, and Italian trifle is £1.50. Outside this building - a converted stables dating from the early 1700s - masses of dahlias bloom every year.

Brewery: Free house
Licensees: David Warthwaite and John Ridley
Opening hours: 11am-3pm, 6-11pm; Sun 12-3pm, 7-10.30pm
Bar food: 12-2pm, 7-9.30pm; Sun 12-2pm
Restaurant: Times as bar food
Children: Not permitted under 14 years in bar
Credit cards: Access, Visa

OLD HALL
New North Road, Heckmondwike WF16 9PD. Tel 0924 404774

Heckmondwike

B uilt as a farmhouse more than 400 years ago, this fascinating old building, once the home of the 18th-century scientist and cleric Joseph Priestley, has been beautifully restored and converted into a pub with an interesting interior displaying many of the original features, for example the open gallery of the main room and the elaborate plaster ceiling. The atmosphere is pleasantly relaxed and welcoming, attracting locals, families at weekends and business people during the week. Bar meals include standard favourites such as roast chicken (£3.85), fillet of plaice (£4.50) and sirloin steak (£7.50) as well as daily specials. Lemon cheesecake, Death by Chocolate or apple pie might be the choice of puddings. Samuel Smith OB is on draught.

Brewery: Samuel Smith
Licensee: Charles William Mole
Opening hours: 11am-2.30pm, 6-11pm; Sun 12-3pm, 7-10.30pm
Bar food: As opening hours
Children: Welcome anywhere
Credit cards: AMERICAN EXPRESS®, Access, Visa, Diners

Claims to Fame
One thousand eager drinkers can fit into the Downham Tavern in Bromley, Kent, Britain's largest pub. Candidates for the more appealing title of the country's tiniest pub include the diminutive Smiths Arms - originally the village smithy - at Godmanstone, Dorset, and the miniature Nutshell in Bury St Edmunds, Suffolk, while the Two Brewers in Rochester, Kent, is not big enough for three brewers. The highest pub in Britain is generally agreed to be the remote Tan Hill Inn in North Yorkshire, 1732ft (528m) up on the Pennine Way, built for local miners in the 18th century. Other elevated pubs include the Cat and Fiddle on the moors outside Buxton in Derbyshire and the Sportsman's Arms at Bylchau in Clwyd.

GARDEN GATE
Waterloo Road, Hunslet, near Leeds LS10 2NS. Tel 0532 700379

Hunslet

Most of the original fittings and decorations are still intact in this Victorian pub, where etched and cut glass room partitions give it a light and airy feel. Original bell pushes remain in place in the smoke room and bar, where fitted benches and half-panelled walls blend in well with cast-iron tables with marble and wooden tops. All of the rooms have open fires, and in some carpets replace the more traditional tiled floors. In the main room the same tiles line the bar and the fireplace. Food here is basic but good value, with dishes like pie and peas at £1, shepherd's pie, chips and peas for £1.95, and pizza from £1.70. Only slightly more expensive, at £2.25, are liver and onions, home-made lasagne and chips, and chilli con carne. Tetley Bitter is on tap, and a mixture of locals, business people and visitors enjoy the Victorian layout and setting that has remained virtually unchanged for over 200 years.

Brewery: Tetley
Licensee: Chris Ripley
Opening hours: 11am-11pm; Sun 12-3pm, 7.30-10.30pm
Bar food: 12-2pm (except Sat and Sun)
Children: Not permitted under 14 years unless eating

☺ CHEQUERS
Claypit Lane, Ledsham, near Castleford LS25 5LP. Tel 0977 683135

Ledsham

A unique six-day licence governs this ivy-clad pub which prevents it from opening on Sundays. Set opposite the church in the centre of the village, the 16th-century building has attractive bay windows, and an old-fashioned red phone box stands outside, making it easy to spot. One small bar serves several rooms, each warm and cosy with wood panelling, exposed beams, low ceilings and open fires. Country regulars tend to relax here, and dominoes can be played. Theakston Best Bitter, Younger Scotch Bitter and No 3, John Smith's Bitter and Guinness are all on tap, and there is a good choice of bar food. Yorkshire ham is £5.25, dieter's delight salad, £3.25, and lasagne £3.95. Country pâté costs £2.95, and there are puddings like fruit pie and cream for £1.50. In the evenings the separate Hastings restaurant is open. Outside, seating is available in the terraced garden where tables and chairs are set on a patio looking on to the rockery and flowered areas.

Brewery: Free house
Licensee: Chris Wright
Opening hours: 11am-3pm, 5.30-11pm (Sat 11am-11pm); closed Sun
Bar food: 12-2pm, 6-8.30pm
Restaurant: 7.30-9.45pm (except Sun and Mon)
Children: In two rooms only
Credit cards: Access, Visa

⊛ WHITELOCKS
Turks Head Yard, Briggate, Leeds LS1 6MD. Tel 0532 453950

Leeds

Tucked away down an alley in the city centre, this traditional pub has lots of character and dates back to 1715. The two bars hark back to the 19th century, however, with their wooden partitions, mirrored walls and Victorian decor. Stained-glass windows and historic advertising add a touch of colour, and drinks are served behind an attractive marble and brass bar. In the passageway outside the black-and-white timbered building barrel tables and benches make a pleasant seating area. Food is plain and straightforward, with main dishes like meat and potato pie with mushy peas and roast potatoes for £3.20. Beef sandwich with dripping and salad is £1, and jam roll with custard 80p. On tap are Younger Scotch Bitter, No 3, and IPA (McEwan 80/-), and there's a good selection of wines. The pub appeals to a good mix of people, but the young do not predominate.

Brewery: Scottish & Newcastle
Licensee: J Cliff
Opening hours: 11am-11pm;
Sun 12-3pm, 7-10.30pm
Bar food: 11am-6pm (except Sun)
Restaurant: 12-2.30pm, 5.30-8pm (Fri and Sat 7pm); Sun 12.30-1.45pm
Children: Not permitted under 16 years in bar
Credit cards:
AMERICAN EXPRESS®, Access, Visa

QUARRY HOUSE INN
Bingley Road, Lees Moor, near Keighley BD21 5QE. Tel 0535 642239

Lees Moor

There are panoramic views of the Worth valley from this converted early 19th-century farmhouse set in the depths of the countryside. The place is popular for its recommended food, and attracts a very varied clientele from families to business people. A mixed grill special is available for £5 every Wednesday, and the bar menu offers an extensive choice of well cooked food made from fresh produce. Waitresses serve dishes like broccoli and cream cheese pie for £4.15, asparagus and smoked salmon quiche at £4.85, and pork pie with mushy peas for £1.25. The separate restaurant menu might include wild Tay salmon with tomato and butter sauce at £7.95, and tenderloin of pork with dry cider sauce, Calvados and smoked bacon for £8.50. On tap in the bar that was once part of the furnishings of a church are Tetley Bitter, Timothy Taylor Landlord and Burton Ale, and there are over 40 wines. A small garden in front of the pub makes the most of the views.

Brewery: Free house
Licensees: Chris and Jean Smith
Opening hours: 12-3pm, 7-11pm; Sun 12-3pm, 7-10.30pm
Bar food: 12-2pm, 7.30-10.30pm
Restaurant: 12-3pm, 7.30-10.30pm
Children: Not permited under 14 years in bar
Credit cards:
AMERICAN EXPRESS®, Access, Visa

BULLS HEAD
Blackmoorfoot, Linthwaite, near Huddersfield HD7 5TR. Tel 0484 842715

Linthwaite

There's a cosy, cottage style to this stone-built pub, set back from the road in the village centre, which is enhanced by a collection of Toby jugs and irons, comfortable upholstered seating and exposed wooden beams. Although always busy, the atmosphere is friendly, and many tastes are catered for. Food is one of the main attractions, and there is a wholesome vegetarian slant to many of the well-cooked and highly recommended dishes. Baked pepper with spicy rice and nut and lentil stuffing offers good value at £3.50, tagliatelle with cod, prawn, salmon and pernod sauce is £4.20, and bobbotii - spiced African meatloaf - comes at £3.90. On tap are Stones Best Bitter, and Boddingtons Mild and Bitter, and there is a selection of whiskies and several bottled beers. A small patio provides some seating outside.

Brewery: Free house
Licensees: Stephen and Brenda Head
Opening hours: 11am-11pm; Sun 12-3pm, 7-10.30pm
Bar food: As opening hours (Sat 11am-3pm, 6-11pm); no food Sun
Children: Welcome anywhere; family room; outdoor play area

OLD BRIDGE INN
Priest Lane, Ripponden, near Sowerby Bridge HX6 4DF. Tel 0422 822595

Ripponden

Cottage-style flower boxes create a vivid splash of colour against the white pebbledash walls of this 14th-century inn, making it a striking feature of the picturesque Pennine village. This is just as well since the pub has no sign outside indicating its name. Inside the ancient building crooked walls and ceilings create a very old-world setting for the exposed beams and antique furniture. The three rooms are tastefully decorated, and the atmosphere is quiet and relaxed, attracting an appreciative clientele. There's a good choice of real ales, with Timothy Taylor Best Bitter and Golden Best, Samuel Smith OBB and Thwaites Bitter on tap. A wide range of imported bottled beers and malt whiskies is also available. Bar dishes include deep-fried Camembert for £2.75, salmon and broccoli pancakes at £3.25, and chicken, broccoli and Stilton pie for £3.95. On weekday lunchtimes there is a buffet at £6.95 and the separate restaurant is open in the evenings. There is also live entertainment in the form of fringe theatre and jazz evenings.

Brewery: Free house
Licensee: Ian Beaumont
Opening hours: 11.30am-4pm, 5.30-11pm (Sat 11am-11pm); Sun 12- 3pm, 7-10.30pm
Bar food: 12-2pm, 7-9.30pm (Sat 12-2pm only); no food Sun
Restaurant: 7-9.30pm (except Sun)
Children: Welcome at lunchtime only
Credit cards: AMERICAN EXPRESS®, Access, Visa (restaurant only)

Tadcaster and the Smiths

Two famous brewing firms are linked with the Wharfedale town of Tadcaster in Yorkshire. The Smith family, which acquired the Old Brewery here in 1847, made effective use of the local hard water to brew bitter whose quality was widely admired. When John Smith died childless in 1879, the business went to his nephew Samuel, while John's brother William opened a new brewery called John Smith's. Samuel Smith's has remained stoutly independent at the Old Brewery, while John Smith's joined Courage in 1970 and is now part of the Elders group.

THREE ACRES INN
Roydhouse, Shelley, near Huddersfield HD8 8LR. Tel 0484 602606

Shelley

Display cabinets of shoes and handbags make an unusual feature alongside a collection of Toby jugs at this large stone inn. The bars are open and roomy, with great views from the bay windows, and there are comfortable cushioned seats and open fires. This is a popular business hotel, as well as being a local for country regulars, and the food comes well recommended. Hearty portions of well cooked and flavoursome dishes include deep-fried Whitby haddock, and seafood coquille, both £5.95, and steak and kidney pie with vegetables. Hot blueberry pancakes with cream or ice cream are £2.50. There is a superior wine list, and some rare whiskies and brandies, as well as draught beers from Theakston, Timothy Taylor and Tetley Mild and Bitter. Accommodation is available in 16 comfortable bedrooms.

Brewery: Free house

Licensees: Neil Truelove and Brian Orme

Opening hours: 12-3pm, 7-11pm (Sat 11.30pm); Sun 12-3pm, 7-10.30pm

Bar food: 12-2pm (except Sat), 7-10pm

Restaurant: Times as bar food

Accommodation: (Price per room) single £25-£47.50, double £40-£57.50

Children: Welcome anywhere; family room

Credit cards:
AMERICAN EXPRESS®, Access, Visa

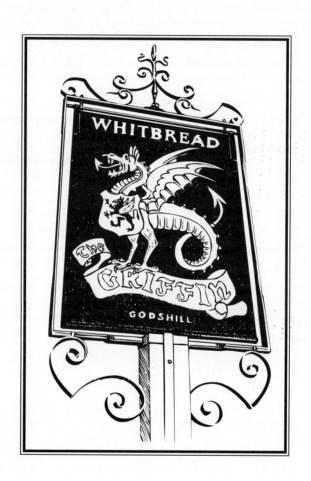

WALES

Clwyd

✜

Dyfed

✜

Glamorgan

✜

Gwent

✜

Gwynedd

✜

Powys

✜

CLWYD

FFARM HOTEL
Betws-yn-Rhos, near Abergele LL22 8AR. Tel 049 260287

Betws-yn-Rhos

Resembling a small castle, this former gentlemen's country residence sits in its own splendid grounds and has a distinctly up-market image. Set on the edge of the Denbigh moors in a pretty village, the 1880 building houses one bar, with a splendid staircase and a herringbone patterned wooden ceiling. Families and country regulars form the major part of the clientele, who often come for quality food, rather than for a drink. The bar is simply decorated with old prints and plates. Its food menu ranges from such starters as whitebait (£2.75) or smoked salmon (£4.95) to main courses such as buckwheat and vegetable bake (£5.50) or buttercrisp scampi (£6.25). Tetley Bitter is served on tap, and a good selection of whiskies is offered. Seating is available in the garden, but is little used.

Brewery: Free house
Licensee: R A Lomax
Opening hours: 7-10pm; closed Sun and Mon
Bar food: 7-10pm
Children: Welcome anywhere
Credit cards: Access, Visa

DINORBEN ARMS
Bodfari, near Denbigh LL16 4DA. Tel 0745 75309

Bodfari

Whisky-lovers will appreciate this pub, set next to the church in the village centre, which offers a range of over 100 brands. Four bars are contained within the 1640 buildings, serving Thwaites Bitter on draught, and there are several rooms to explore, furnished with old wooden benches. A choice of tasty and filling dishes is offered at the bar, with such examples as grilled salmon (£5.45), steak and kidney pie (£4.45) and ham salad (£4.75); vegetarian meals are available. Booking is advised for the separate restaurant; and there is an interesting wine list. A garden with a terrace and a pretty fountain has benches and tables for customers.

Brewery: Free house
Licensee: G T Hopwood
Opening hours: 12-3pm, 6-11pm; Sun 12-3pm, 7-10.30pm
Bar food: 12-2.30pm, 6-10.30pm; Sun 12-2.30pm, 7-10pm
Restaurant: 12-2.30pm, 6-11.30pm; Sun 12-2.30pm, 7-11pm
Children: Not permitted in bar areas; family room; outdoor play area
Credit cards: Access, Visa

⊕ SPORTSMANS ARMS
Bryntrillyn, near Bylchau LL16 5SW. Tel 0745 70214

Bylchau

Claiming the title of the highest pub in Wales, this exposed roadside pub looks out over open moors. Travelling here is quite a challenge, especially in winter months, and much of the pub's clientele consists of walkers, cyclists and other outdoor types, as well as regulars and families; all are given a warm welcome. Two carpeted and spacious bars, decorated with paintings and murals, serve Lees Bitter and GB Mild and Guinness. The bar food menu, including items such as home-made steak pie (£4.95) and sirloin steak (£7.95), as well as vegetarian and children's options, is supplemented by specials, which are chalked up on a board. This is a pub which has retained its genuine Welsh character, and on Saturday nights locals gather here to sing Welsh hymns. Although no accommodation is available in the building, overnight camping is occasionally permitted.

Brewery: J W Lees
Licensee: S E Jones
Opening hours: Summer 11am-11pm; winter 11am-3pm, 7-11pm (closed Mon lunchtime); Sun 12-3pm, 7-10.30pm
Bar food: 12-2.30pm, 7-9 30pm (except Mon lunchtime in winter)
Children: In dining area only

WHITE HORSE INN
Cilcain, near Mold CH7 5NN. Tel 0352 740142

Cilcain

Window boxes and hanging baskets decorate this picturesque 14th-century white pub, with a slate roof. Sitting at the centre of a small village at the edge of the Clwydian Hills, the White Horse has two comfortable bars. Four open fires keep them warm in winter; the main bar has an inglenook fireplace, and the back bar is tiled and decorated with brasses and photos. Tables are set outside in the summer. Bar food is served in generous portions; examples include cold roast turkey, chips and salad (£4.60), prawns and salad (£6.95) and prime rump steak with chips and salad (£7.45). Draught beers are Tetley and Ansells Bitter, Draught Bass, Marston's Pedigree Bitter, Boddingtons, Beamish and Guinness. Customers include locals and cyclists, but this is not really a pub for families, as children are not welcome.

Brewery: Free house
Licensee: P J Jeory
Opening hours: 12-3pm, 7-11pm; Sun 12-3pm, 7-10.30pm
Bar food: 12-2pm, 7.30-9.30pm (Fri and Sat 10pm); Sun 12-2pm
Children: Not permitted inside
Credit cards: Access, Visa

⊕ GOLDEN PHEASANT HOTEL
Dolywern, near Glyn Ceirog LL20 7BR. Tel 069172 281

Dolywern

A quiet air of up-market comfort is aimed for in this country hotel. Its two carpeted bars strike an appropriate note with their displays of sporting and hunting items and stuffed birds. The 1755 red-brick building sits on a crossroads at the edge of the village of Dolywern, and there

Brewery: Free house
Licensee: J T Gibourg
Opening hours: 11am-11pm; Sun 12-3pm, 7-10.30pm
Bar food: As opening hours

are splendid views from the spacious rooms (16 double and two single). All are well equipped, luxury rooms are available with Elizabethan four-poster beds and jacuzzis. Although this is not really a drinkers' pub, there is Bass Special Bitter on offer, as well as a good range of malts and brandies. Bar food is available all week; examples of the dishes include country soup (£1.95), crispy duckling (£5.95) and tagliatelle and kidneys (£4.50). Booking is advised for the restaurant, which opens only during evening hours. There is a central courtyard and a pretty garden with views extending down the valley.

Restaurant: 7.30-9pm
Accommodation: (Price per person) £40, inc dinner
Children: Welcome anywhere; outdoor play area
Credit cards:
AMERICAN EXPRESS®, Access, Visa, Diners

☺ BOAT INN
Erbistock, near Ruabon LL13 ODL. Tel 0978 780143

Erbistock

Set in the depths of the country on the banks of the River Dee, this pub has idyllic surroundings and an excellent menu of bar food. The tranquil 16th-century cottage, once a ferryman's house, has flowered gardens and a terrace overlooking the river and its swans; its bar, with two open fires, flagged floors and large wooden beams, has retained a great deal of character, and displays simple and tasteful pictures of the local area. Fish dishes are a speciality here, and the food is imaginative and a little out-of-the-ordinary, with such items as lemon sole (£7.95), sauté of chicken (£6.95) and beef Indienne (£7.95). Customers for the restaurants, open in the evenings, should book beforehand. Murphy's Stout is served at the bar and there are occasionally rare malt whiskies to be had.

Brewery: Free house
Licensee: Nick Shaw
Opening hours: 11am-3pm, 6-11pm; Sun 12-3pm, 7-10.30pm; closed Sun and Mon evenings in Oct and Nov
Bar food: 11am-3pm; Sun set lunch only
Restaurant: 7-9.30pm (except Sun and Mon in Oct and Nov)
Accommodation: (suite for up to four) £39
Children: Not permitted in bar area
Credit cards:
AMERICAN EXPRESS®, Access, Visa

Pilgrims, Shrines and Inns

All through the Middle Ages hospitality to strangers was considered a fundamental Christian duty and travellers could stay overnight free at monasteries or bed down with the servants in a nobleman's hall. Gradually, however, with growing prosperity and burgeoning trade, more people began to travel. Among them were pilgrims making their way to the shrines of saints, to acquire religious merit or be cured of sickness. The two most popular pilgrimage centres were the tomb of St Thomas à Becket at Canterbury and the Virgin Mary's shrine at Walsingham in Norfolk, but many other churches possessed wonder-working relics of great sanctity.

Monasteries put poor pilgrims up free in wooden sheds with rush-strewn floors, a brazier for warmth and a few benches, but with mounting affluence better-off pilgrims were ready to pay for greater comfort, a decent meal and congenial company. Scenting a profit, monasteries built inns to meet the demand and others were opened by local landowners and town merchants. Most of Britain's oldest inns go back to these beginnings..

⊜ BRITANNIA INN
Pentre Road, Halkyn, near Holywell CH8 8BS. Tel 0352 780272

Halkyn

A pub with character, the 500-year-old Britannia caters for all needs and types. Customers include tourists, international travellers, locals, families and coach parties, and there is a wide selection of wholesome food, ranging from simple sandwiches to large meals; typical dishes include garlic mushrooms (£3.30), casserole of chicken (£5.50) or beef in red ale (£5.20), and there are vegetarian and children's options. There are two bars in this stone corner building, which sits on the side of the Clwyd Hills, overlooking the Wirral and the River Dee. Each has an open fire, and small, cosy drinking areas, and there is a separate pool room. A bright, open patio outside gives views over the valley towards Merseyside. Lees Bitter, GB Mild and Moonraker and Guinness are served at the bar; there are 20 whiskies and a wide selection of wines, with monthly specials.

Brewery: J W Lees
Licensee: T O'Neil
Opening hours: 11.30am-3pm, 5.30-11pm (Sat and BHs 11am-11pm); Sun 11am-3pm, 7-10.30p
Bar food: As opening hours
Restaurant: 12-2.30pm, 6.30-10pm (Sun 7pm)
Children: Not permitted in bar area

WEST ARMS HOTEL
Llanarmon Dyffryn Ceiriog, near Glyn Ceiriog LL20 7LD. Tel 069176 665

Llanarmon Dyffryn Ceiriog

This converted 440-year-old farmhouse sits in the centre of an isolated village - birthplace of the celebrated Welsh poet Ceiriog - on the edge of the Berwyn Hills. Three open fires heat its two bars; luxurious cushioned armchairs furnish the carpeted lounge, which has the unusual feature of a 13th-century confessional box, while there are bench seats in the slate-floored Wayfarers' Bar. Business people, travellers, walkers and cyclists come to enjoy the relaxing atmosphere and the wide selection of good value food, ranging from sandwiches (from £1.75) or home-made soup (£2.40) to rump steak Dijonaise (£6.50). Boddingtons and Guinness are served at the bar, and there are 14 to 15 malt whiskies; 95 wines are available in the separate restaurant, where booking is advised. A rose garden is open to customers, and accommodation is offered in rooms whose traditional decor is in keeping with the rest of the pub's character.

Brewery: Free house
Licensees: M Price and G O Hughes
Opening hours: 11am-11pm; Sun 12-2.30pm, 7-10.30pm
Bar food: 12-2pm, 6.30-9pm; Sun 12-2pm, 7-9pm
Restaurant: 7-9pm; Sun 12-2pm
Accommodation: (Price per person) double £39-£44, single £60-£66
Children: Only if eating
Credit cards: AMERICAN EXPRESS®, Access, Visa, Diners

GREEN INN
Llangedwyn, near Oswestry SY10 9JW. Tel 0691 828234

Langedwyn

Beer-drinkers appreciate this pub, which serves Boddingtons, Guinness and Murphy's Stout, as well as three guest beers. There are three bars in all in the early 17th-century whitewashed farmhouse, which has an attractive rural setting, half a mile from a small village. A large log fire adds comfort to the main bar; a cosy back bar is furnished with fireside bench seats; and a sofa and chairs are set out in the lounge. Interesting displays include jugs, horns, brasses and African throwing sticks. Fish is a speciality on the good value bar menu; dishes include smoked mackerel (£1.75) as a starter, and substantial main meals such as sirloin steak (£6.50), as well as a separate vegetarian menu and specials chalked up on the blackboard. A list of 43 wines is available in the restaurant. A large garden with benches, across the road from the pub itself, offers views along the valley.

Brewery: Free house
Licensee: G Greenham
Opening hours: 11am-3pm, 6-11pm; Sun 12-3pm, 7-10.30pm
Bar food: 12-2pm, 6.30-10pm; Sun 12-2pm, 7-10pm
Restaurant: 7-10pm (except Mon); Sun 12-2pm; booking advisable
Accommodation: (Price per room) single £12, double £24
Children: In eating areas only
Credit cards: Access, Visa

BRITANNIA INN
Horseshoe Pass, Llangollen LL20 8DW. Tel 0978 860144

Llangollen

The location is an essential part of this pub's attraction. Set in the heart of the country at the foot of the famous hairpin ascent of Horseshoe Pass, tucked into the mountains near Llangollen, the 1462 building draws much of its custom from tourists and visiting families, particularly during the summer months, when crowds attend the International Eisteddfod at Llangollen. The two bars have modern pine furniture, and there is a prize-winning garden. Flowers IPA and Boddingtons Bitter are served on tap, and the bar food includes soup (£1.60), Britannia steak pie (£4.75), leek and mushroom crumble (£4.75) and desserts such as toffee apple pie or hot lemon meringue pie (each £1.60). A separate restaurant opens seven days a week for evening meals. Five double rooms are furnished in comfortable style and all have four-poster beds.

Brewery: Free house
Licensee: M Callaghan
Opening hours: 11am-3pm, 7-11pm; Sun 12-3pm, 7-10.30pm
Bar food: 12-2pm, 7-10.30pm
Restaurant: 7-10pm
Accommodation: (Price per room) £40
Children: Welcome anywhere
Credit cards:
AMERICAN EXPRESS®, Access, Visa, Diners

RED LION
Llansannan, near Denbigh LL16 5NG. Tel 0745 77256

Llansannan

It is well worth going inside this rather bland-looking white 13th-century house at the heart of Llansannan village. Two carpeted bars with open fires provide traditional comfort and plenty of interesting displays, including brasses, jugs and pictures. Despite limited hours, customers of all ages and

Brewery: J W Lees
Licensee: D L Morris
Opening hours: Mon and Wed 5-11pm; closed Tue; Thu and Fri

backgrounds come here to enjoy the high quality (and low-priced) bar food; examples include salmon mousse and toast (£1.75), corn on the cob or garlic mushrooms on toast (each 95p) as starters, and home-made steak and kidney pie with chips (£2.75) or grilled sirloin steak (£4.75) as main courses. Lees Bitter and Mild are served on tap. A large, pretty garden and a courtyard with benches, chairs and tables are open to customers. Three double rooms and three single rooms provide accommodation: some are furnished in keeping with the traditional style of the pub; others, in an extension, have a more modern look.

12-3pm, 5-11pm; Sat 11am-11pm; Sun 12-3pm, 7-10.30pm
Bar food: Mon and Wed 6-9pm; Thu-Sat 12-2pm, 6-9pm; Sun 12-2pm, 7-8.30pm
Accommodation: (Price per person) £30
Children: Welcome anywhere; outdoor play area

CERRIGLLWYDION ARMS
Llanynys, near Ruthin LL16 4PA. Tel 074578 247

Llanynys

A fine example of a Welsh country pub, this black-and-white building dating from 1400 sits in a quiet country lane and offers a particularly warm welcome. The two bars have comfortable benches and alcoves, with an inglenook fire, and have an unusual display of 200 teapots hanging from the ceiling, as well as jugs and horse-leathers. There are 100 malt whiskies on offer (the pub has a whisky club), and choices of snuff are available at the bar, where draught beers are Bass Bitter and Mild and Worthington, Crown Buckley Best Bitter and Dark Mild, and Guinness. An impressive range of dishes is served at the bar and in the separate restaurant (for which booking is necessary), including starters such as egg harlequin (£2), local trout (£2.50) or devilled crab (£3.25); main meals such as Elizabethan pork (£4.75) or chicken supreme (£5.75); and desserts such as raspberry Pavlova (£2.20) and Dutch apple pie (£2.45). The choice changes regularly, and a wide selection of vegetarian options is offered. A sheltered garden is open to customers across the road, and some evenings are enlivened with Welsh singing.

Brewery: Free house
Licensee: Chris Charles
Opening hours: 11.30am-3pm, 6-11pm; Sun 12-3pm, 7-10.30pm
Bar food: 12-2pm, 7-9.30pm; Sun 12-2pm, 7-9pm
Restaurant: 12-2pm, 7-9.30pm; Sun 12-2pm, 7-9pm
Children: Not permitted in bar area
Credit cards:
AMERICAN EXPRESS®, Access, Visa

⊜ ROCK INN
Lloc, near Holywell CH8 8RD. Tel 0352 710049

Lloc

A new bypass has brought tranquillity to this old miners' pub, which is set alongside the A55 in the hamlet of Lloc. Cushioned seats and exposed beams form the decor of the two bars, which are heated by a log fire on colder days, and show a display of teapots and bottles. Darts, dominoes, crib and chess can be played in a separate games room. Draught beers on offer are Burtonwood Best Bitter and Dark Mild and Forsham's. Good value bar food is served,

Brewery: Burtonwood
Licensee: C T Swift
Opening hours: 11am-11pm; Sun 12-3pm, 7-10.30pm
Bar food: 12-2.30pm, 6-9.30pm (except Tue evening)
Restaurant: Times as bar food, but weekends only in winter;

with dishes such as soup (£1.35) or smoked mackerel
(£2.25); rump steak (£8.35) or vegetarian chilli (£3.95); and
hot chocolate fudge cake (£1.65). Customers include
travellers, locals and families, and there are seating areas in
front of the pub and in the back garden.

booking necessary
Children: Welcome anywhere;
outdoor play area

SUN INN
Rhewl, near Llangollen LL20 7YT. Tel 0978 861043

Rhewl

This small, local pub was built in the 14th century as a
drovers' inn, and sits in the remote village of Rhewl,
close to the River Dee. Its low-ceilinged, carpeted bar draws
locals, families and tourists, and is well decorated with
artefacts reflecting the area's history. Felinfoel Double
Dragon is served on tap, and the excellent value bar food
menu includes local rainbow trout (£4.75) and Meg's home-
made beef in beer pie (£3.95), as well as vegetarian and
children's options. Darts, pool, dominoes and shove
halfpenny are available in the separate games room; this and
a small room without a bar are open to children. Log
furniture is set out in the pub garden, which is surrounded
by bushes. This is a place with genuine local character, and
regulars occasionally enjoy a singing session in the bar.

Brewery: Free house
Licensee: Alun Williams
Opening hours: 12-3pm,
6-11pm; Sun 12-3pm,
7-10.30pm
Bar food: 12-2.30pm, 6-10pm;
Sun 12-3pm, 7-10pm
Children: Not permitted in bar
area; outdoor play area
Credit cards: Access, Visa

DYFED

⊜ BLACK LION
Abergorlech, near Carmarthen SA32 7SN. Tel 0558 685271

Abergorlech

The flower-filled village of Abergorlech makes a pretty
setting for this 16th-century pub near the River Cothi.
Housed in a black-and-white gabled building, this is a strictly
traditional pub, with brasses and warming ladles on display,
a deep fireplace and comfortable window seats. The bar's
friendly atmosphere draws locals and tourists alike, and
there is a reasonably varied bar food menu, ranging from
simple starters such as soup (£1.35) or scampi tails (£2.85)
to chicken Kiev (£5.95) or salmon steak (£6.50), and
including vegetarian options. Dominoes, cards and darts are
all on offer, in keeping with the traditional emphasis, and
there is a spacious function room. Felinfoel Double Dragon
is available on draught, and bottled beer includes Newquay
Steam Bitter; there is also a standard but well represented
wine list. Across the road, a barbecue area has picnic tables
set on the grassy riverbank, offering pleasant views.

Brewery: Free house
Licensee: Brenda Entwistle
Opening hours: Summer 11am-
11pm; winter12-3pm, 7-11pm;
Sun 12-3pm, 7-10.30pm
Bar food: As opening hours
Children: Welcome anywhere;
outdoor play area
Credit cards: Access, Visa

⊕ CAREW INN
Carew, near Tenby SA70 8SL. Tel 0646 651267

Carew

Home-cooked food is high on the list of attractions of this early 19th-century pub. Locally caught fish often feature on the menu; Carew oysters are on offer for £3.50; desserts include chocolate hazelnut slice (£1.52) and rhubarb crumble (£1.50). The pub's impressive setting could be difficult for people with disabilities: the three-storey stone building sits high above Carew creek near the castle, and is reached by a steep flight of steps; however, a side entrance is accessible from the road. Inside, this is a small and cosy, well kept pub, with two bars - one of which is tiny - and appropriate decor. Three double rooms and one twin are available, all recently redecorated. Draught beers are Ind Coope (Allied) Burton Ale, Bass and Worthington Best Bitter. A terrace at the front of the pub has good views, and there is an attractive garden.

Brewery: Free house
Licensee: Mandy Hinchcliffe
Opening hours: Summer 11am-11pm; winter 11am-3pm, 5-11pm (Sat 11am-11pm); Sun 12-3pm, 7-10.30pm
Bar food: 12-2.30pm, 7-9.30pm (except Sun and Mon evenings)
Accommodation: (Price per room) £12.5
Children: Only if well behaved; outdoor play area

⊕ DROVERS ARMS
Lammas Street, Camarthen SA31 3AP. Tel 0267 237646

Carmarthen

A friendly welcome is guaranteed from the landlord of this old town pub - built nearly 300 years ago, and one of 18 licensed houses on one-way Lammas Street. Its brown and dark green frontage is typical of the area, and the panelled walls and beams and prints of rare livestock breeds all add to its traditional appeal. There is a distinctly local flavour to the bar food: fresh ingredients are used for such items as Crochan y Bugail (shepherd's hotpot, £3.75), drover's supper (a mixed grill, £5.95) and Myfanwy ginger sponge (£1.50); the Pampette house wine is a popular feature, and morning coffee and afternoon tea are available. (Booking may be necessary for the separate restaurant.) On tap are Felinfoel Bitter and Mild and Double Dragon. A lively mix of families, local business people and tourists come to enjoy the atmosphere - which is occasionally enlivened by a sing-song round the piano. There is no garden.

Brewery: Felinfoel
Licensee: Edward Evans
Opening hours: 11am-3.30pm, 5.30-11pm; Sun 12-3pm, 7-10.30p
Bar food: As opening hours
Restaurant: Times as bar food
Children: In family room only

⊕ WHITE HART/HYDD GWYN
Cenarth, near Newcastle Emlyn SA38 9JP. Tel 0239 710305

Cenarth

New fittings and furniture have changed much of the character of this once very simple old pub, but its low beams and whitewashed stone give evidence of its 16th-century origins. Set on the crossroads above the Cenarth Falls and the River Teifi, this is a pub with tourist appeal,

Brewery: Free house
Licensee: Terry and Linda Parsons
Opening hours: 11am-11pm; Jan and Feb 11am-3pm, 5.30-11pm;

drawing heavily on the visitors who come to watch leaping salmon and coracle fishing on the Teifi: a coracle provides an eye-catching display on the front wall. Inside, the formerly enclosed series of rooms has been opened out to centre on a large bar area with a wood-burning stove. A collection of 'Brass Monkey' brassware is on sale to customers at a discount. Draught beers available are Bass, Worthington Best and Dark and Beamish, and bar food includes particularly good Glamorgan sausages (£1.75). A beer garden and play area are set above the pub itself.

Sun 7-10.30pm
Bar food: 12-2.30pm, 6.30-9.30pm; Sun 12-2.30pm, 7-9.30pm
Children: Welcome in rooms other than bar; outdoor play area

✪ PICTON INN
Clarbeston Road, near Haverfordwest SA63 4UH. Tel 0437 731615

Clarbeston Road

Newly rebuilt in its original 19th-century style, this pub was named after the Picton family, who owned estates in many parts of southern Pembrokeshire. Despite its open-plan design, it has retained an old-fashioned air, with beams and rough stone walls, and an open fire. The enthuastic new tenants have introduced an inventive menu of bar food (booking is recommended), using local game and fish and offering dishes such as kidneys Preseli (£2.85) and ox tongue braised in real ale (£4.95). Special items are chalked up every day. Draught beers are Worthington Best Bitter and Bass. A grassy area behind the building is open to customers, and picnic tables are set up on the paved patio in front of the pub. The railway whose station is next to the pub is one of the few surviving local branches in the area, and nearby attractions include Llys-y-fran Country Leisure Park.

Brewery: James Williams
Licensees: Adrian Jones and Jane Lewis
Opening hours: 11am-11pm; Sun 12-3pm, 7-10.30pm
Bar food: 12-2.30pm, 6-9.30pm; Sun 12-2.30pm, 7-9pm
Children: Welcome anywhere; outdoor play area

✪ CRESSELLY ARMS
Cresswell, near Kilgetty SA68 OTE. Tel 0267 290221

Cresswell

For peace and quiet, this pub has the ideal setting, opposite its own quay - where there is seating -with views of a wooded creek. Its genial atmosphere draws a lively local trade, but for those preferring private contemplation there is a small room with good river views from a bay window. Originally a Georgian house, this is a stylish and comfortable building, covered in Virginia creeper and entered via the old kitchen door. The bar offers only the basics - there is no food, tea or coffee - and seems little changed since the days of its former owner, now aged 104 and living in one part of the building. Hancocks HB is available on tap and Worthington Best Bitter from the keg.

Brewery: Free house
Licensee: Maurice Cole
Opening hours: 11am-3pm, 5-11pm; Sun 12-3pm, 7-10.30pm
Children: Not permitted in bar area under 14 years

⊕ FREEMASONS ARMS
Dinas Cross, near Fishguard SA42 0UW. Tel 03486 243

Dinas Cross

Several cottages have been converted to create this low, two-storey building in a 19th-century terrace of houses on the main village road. Window boxes and climbing plants distinguish the pub, which is near the approach to the beach. The friendly local clientele and bar staff ensure that everyone feels at home here; former customers included the young King Hussein, on holiday with the Rothschild family. A quarry-tiled floor, displays of photographs and maps, and a hand-painted chair and settle (showing the pub name and a ship in full sail) add to the character of the interior. A reliable menu of bar food, much of it cooked on the premises, includes smoked pepper mackerel (£3.35) and seafood pasta (£4.65); Bass is available on tap, and keg beers are Worthington Best Bitter and Dark Mild. A pretty restaurant looks out on to a pleasant sheltered garden behind the pub.

Brewery: Free house
Licensee: Graham N Hitchings
Opening hours: 11am-3pm, 5-11pm; Sun 12-3pm, 7-10.30pm
Bar food: 12-2.30pm, 5.30-10pm; Sun 12-2.30pm, 7-9.30pm
Restaurant: 7-10pm; Sun 12-2.30pm, 7-9.30pm
Accommodation: (Price per room) single £18 (£13 outside peak season), double £13/£15
Children: Welcome in rooms other than bar; outdoor play area

⊕ PEN POMPREN
Drefach, near Llanybydder SA40 9YB. Tel 0570 480733

Drefach

The Welsh name of this pub means 'At the end of the footbridge', and it is, in fact, set by a bridge, on the A475. Leo Walmsley, the best-selling author of the 1920s and '30s, lodged here while writing his autobiography, *So Many Loves*, and described the pub in his account of life in West Wales during the Second World War, *The Happy Ending*. Open only during weekday evenings, the Pen Pompren is a plain, simple pub, which has been in the present licensee's family for 100 of its 200-year existence.It has no garden. A magnificent fireplace overmantle, brought from the nearby Highmead mansion, is one of few embellishments in the bar, which offers a wide range of organic and other wines, and Worthington Dark and Best Bitter from the keg. The licensee, who once worked for top chef Anton Mosimann, plans to open a restauran but there is no food at present A local folk group provides occasional live entertainment.

Brewery: Free house
Licensee: Hazel Ann Thomas
Opening hours: 7-11pm; closed Sat and Sun
Children: Not permitted in bar area after 9pm

⊜ DIAL INN
Lamphey, near Pembroke SA71 5NU. Tel 0646 672426

Lamphey

Elegant decor, an interesting past and excellent bar food and wine make this a pub worth visiting. Formerly the dower house to Lamphey Court, the 1830 building is decorated with a profusion of flowers all year; inside, a mix of families, young people and regulars enjoy the two bars, furnished with white-painted Britannia tables and displaying a fine collection of Shelley china. A cosmopolitan wine list includes good wine by the glass, and the imaginative menu offers dishes such as falafel with dip (£3.95) and deep-fried Camembert in gooseberry sauce (£2.25). Draught beers are Bass, Worthington Best Bitter and Hancocks HB, and bottled cider includes Brody, Autumn Gold, Red Rock and Diamond White. Behind the pub are squash courts and picnic tables on a grassy area with a view of the Bishop's Palace. At Christmas there is carol-singing and the annual ceremony of carrying in the Yule log.

Brewery: Free house
Licensee: Francis Parry
Opening hours: 11am-3.30pm, 6-11pm; Sun 12-3pm, 7-10.30pm
Bar food: 11am-3.30pm, 6-11pm; (May-October 7-10.30pm); Sun 12-3pm
Restaurant: 12-2pm, 6-10pm (winter 12-2pm, 7-9.30pm)
Children: Not permitted in bar area under 14 years; outdoor play area
Credit cards: Access, Visa

⊜ SWAN INN
Little Haven, near Haverfordwest SA62 3UL. Tel 0437 781256

Little Haven

Named after its original owners, this mid-17th-century pub is housed in a charming double-gabled building with bay windows. Its setting, near the harbour wall beside a small bay, is reflected in a collection of artefacts connected with sea life, and an old church font is among the other intriguing items on display. Good food is a high priority here: the present licensee has inherited an impressive standard of fresh cooking, which is being well maintained. Bar food includes fresh local crab (£5.50), rack of lamb in Madeira sauce (£9.95) and fillet steak with Brie and walnuts (£10.95); an interesting wine list offers two US Washington reds and a claret produced by a former local farmer, Château Banduc (1986). Draught beers are Worthington Best Bitter and Felinfoel Double Dragon. A quiet, civilised atmosphere draws regulars and locals as well as tourists, and a terrace in front of the pub makes the most of the bayside location.

Brewery: James Williams
Licensee: Glyn Davis
Opening hours: 11am-3pm, 6.30-11pm; Sun 12-3pm, 7-10.30pm (Aug 11am-11pm, inc Sun)
Bar food: 12-2pm
Restaurant: 7-9.30pm Wed-Sun (winter 7-10.30pm Wed-Sat)
Children: Only if well behaved; children under 14 years not permitted in bar area

⊜ BUTCHERS ARMS
Llanddarog, near Carmarthen SA32 8NS. Tel 0267 275330

Llanddarog

This exceptionally pretty 500-year-old pub is one of three which once drew their custom from Llanddarog's fair. Tucked in by the church wall, on a sharp turning off the main road, it is well worth seeking out. A collection of Toby jugs

Brewery: Free house
Licensee: David and Mavis James
Opening hours: 11am-3pm,

and old photographs of the area is displayed, and a cheerful log fire adds to the friendly and traditional atmosphere. The service here is always attentive, despite the pub's popularity: families travel from Swansea, Neath and Llanelli to enjoy the imaginative food, which is served in a separate bar meals area. The menu includes avocado and bacon salad (£2.40); pork fillet and garlic mushrooms (£8.30); duck breast, with a variety of sauces (£8.50) and stuffed chicken fillets (£6.50), and a wide range of specials is chalked up each day. About 12 malt whiskies are on offer at the bar, and Felinfoel Traditional and Double Dragon are available on tap. Bottled beer includes Theakston Best Bitter and Newcastle Brown. There is an outdoor seating area, decorated with flowers, between the front of the pub and the church wall, providing a safe place for children to play.

5.30-11pm; Sun 7-10.30pm
Bar food: 11am-3pm, 6-9.30pm (Sat from 5.30pm); Sun 7-9.30pm
Restaurant: Times as bar food
Children: Welcome anywhere during the day; only in restaurant during evening; outdoor play area
Credit cards: AMERICAN EXPRESS®, Access, Visa, Diners

☺ TORBAY INN
Heol Cennin, Ffairfach, Llandeilo SA19 6UL. Tel 0558 822029

Llandeilo

This unexpectedly traditional gabled pub sits on the outskirts of Llandeilo. Built in 1842 as the school house, it now has a downbeat but cosy charm, and offers bar food with an occasionally Polish flavour. Typical dishes are pan-fried cockles at £2, egg and prawn curry at £3.95 or plaice in batter at £3.75. A sunny covered garden has a Continental air, and is particularly attractive in the evening, when the tables are candlelit. A mix of tourists and local farmers form the clientele; during the winter, a quiz is held on Wednesday evenings. Available on tap are Buckley's Bitter and Great Western, Whitbread Welsh and Best Mild and Murphy's Stout.

Brewery: Free house
Licensee: Hugh and Jan Mulligan
Opening hours: 12-3pm, 6-11pm; Sun 12-3pm, 7-10.30pm
Bar food: 12-2pm, 6-9pm (Fri and Sat 10pm); no food Sun
Children: Welcome anywhere

☺ RED LION
Llandybie, near Ammanford SA18 3JA. Tel 0269 851202

Llandybie

Set in a rather gaunt, 200-year-old Georgian building, enhanced only by a pillared entrance, this is a pub whose reputation rests on its food and atmosphere. Originally a farmhouse and part of the Cawdor Estate (one room was used to collect estate rents), the pub relied on cattle drovers, en route to market, for its custom. Now it draws families and tourists from up to 25 miles around. Fish from Swansea harbour are among the ingredients used for an appetising menu: items include hake in orange and Cointreau sauce (£7.50); Indian meat balls with raita (£4.75); pan-fried loin of lamb in garlic sauce (£7.50) and deep-fried Brie and Camembert with tomato and garlic sauce (£3.25). Daily

Brewery: Free house
Licensee: Sara Priestland
Opening hours: 11.30am-3pm, 6-11.30pm; Sun 12-3pm
Bar food: As opening hours
Restaurant: Times as bar food
Children: Welcome anywhere except bar area; children's room; outdoor play area
Credit cards: AMERICAN EXPRESS®, Access, Visa, Diners

specials are chalked on a board. Stripped-pine tables and chairs and cream-washed walls give warmth to the potentially bleak high-ceilinged interior of the bar; there is also a separate restaurant and children's eating room. Draught beers are Original, Boddingtons, Castle Eden and Bass Red Triangle and morning coffee and afternoon tea are served.Outside seating is available next to the car park, and there is a grassed area for children.

SHIP INN
Llangranog, near Llandysul SA44 6SL. Tel 0239 654423

Llangranog

Set behind Llangranog beach, this 200-year-old pub has always been popular with the seaside tourist trade, although the large car park near by detracts from its pleasant location. A patio provides outdoor seating and a colourful mural of the galleon *Y Llund* decorates the gable end of the L-shaped building - a tribute to the local pirate Bartu Ddu (Black Bart, 1683-1722), who was actually associated with Little Newcastle, further inland. Recent modernisation has not spoiled the atmosphere of the interior, where memorabilia include a ship's wheel and Welsh cooking pots. Bar food provides a mix of standard frozen food and freshly prepared dishes: in season, these include a seafood platter of cockles, mussels, lobster, crab and whelks from the shore (£9.75); locally caught mackerel and skate are also featured. Burton and Worthington beers are available on draught.

Brewery: Free house
Licensee: Richard Box and Kevin Brown
Opening hours: Summer 11am-11pm; winter 11am-3pm, 6-11pm; Sun 12-3pm, 7-10.30pm
Bar food: 11am-3pm, 6-10pm; Sun 12-3pm, 7-9.30pm
Children: Welcome anywhere

⊕ FARMERS ARMS
Mathry, near Haverfordwest SA62 5HB. Tel 0348 831284

Mathry

Full of life and local character, this 13th-century pub is a favourite for local farmers from around the hilltop village of Mathry. The interior is clean, simple and cosy, and a small building next to the pub, converted from a former monks' brewery, offers serviced overnight accommodation and self-catering for longer stays (a child's bed and cot are provided). Bar food of a high quality is cooked on the premises and offered in generous portions: the 'snacks' on offer during evening hours are as filling as many bar meals. The menu includes ploughman's lunch with Llangloffan cheese and the pub's own ham (£4.25); fresh pollock in white wine sauce (£3.95), and home-made apple pie with cream or ice cream (£1.50). Draught beers are Worthington Best and Bass, and morning coffee and afternoon tea are served. A separate family room is available, and there is an enclosed grassy area outside.

Brewery: Free house
Licensee: Eric John
Opening hours: 11am-11pm; Sun 12-3pm, 7-10.30pm
Bar food: 12-3pm; snacks during evening hours (except Sun)
Accommodation: double with kitchen, sitting room and bathroom £15 for adults (children by arrangement)
Children: Welcome anywhere; outdoor play area

MAENLLWYD INN
Meidrim, near Carmarthen SA53 5QU. No phone

Meidrim

Entering this 17th-century pub, nearly a mile west of Meidrim, is like walking into the past. From the outside, the faded farm building looks uninhabited - its painted sign is almost illegible; the interior has retained its simple, plain air, with a black-leaded grate in one room and a portable gas heater in the other, which is the present landlord's own front room. The pub is run to fit in his work for the local council, and all drinks are kept in a small kitchen. There is no food available and no garden. Crown Buckley is available on draught; Colonel Buckley himself lived near by and because he was a regular visitor, the previous owners (the landlord's parents) made no changes to the structure or decor. Old china and a photograph of Buckley are displayed; the clientele is made up mostly of local farmers, who may well start up some spontaneous singing at the end of an evening.

Brewery: Free house
Licensee: Leonard Lewis
Opening hours: 6-11pm; closed Sun and Mon
Children: Not permitted in bar area under 14 years

⊛ TREWERN ARMS
Nevern, near Newport SA42 ONB. Tel 0239 820395

Nevern

Recent extensions have turned this 17th-century pub into a pub-cum-hotel and restaurant, but the many changes which have taken place since the 1950s (when its French chef brought it a high reputation) have always been in keeping with the original stone-built character. A beautiful riverside setting, with an old stone bridge near by, gives the building genuine charm and outside seating is provided in a grassy area surrounded with shrubs and flowers. The hotel and restaurant are reached from the front entrance, facing the river, while a side entrance leads from the extensive car park to the bar meals area. These days the bar food is standard and much of it is pre-cooked; the menu includes ploughman's platter with local Nevern cheese (£3.50), home-made steak and kidney pie (£4.90) and trout and almonds (£5.50). The restaurant offers an unremarkable but sound menu, and its generous helpings of grills, roasts and poultry with rich sauces are immensely popular with local people. In the original 17th-century bar a fascinating collection of old farm implements, Welsh cauldrons, horse chains, traps etc are suspended from the rafters, and lanterns tucked into the wall niches provide interesting lighting effects. Live entertainment is occasionally provided, and there is often Welsh singing to be heard in the back bar. Draught beers are Flowers Original, Castle Eden, Boddingtons and Whitbread Pompey Royal.

Brewery: Free house
Licensee: Ann Jones
Opening hours: 11am-3pm, 6-11pm; Sun 12-3pm, 7-10.30pm
Bar food: 12-2pm, 6-9pm; Sun 12-2pm, 7-9pm
Restaurant: Summer Tue and Thu-Sun 7-9pm; winter Thu-Sat 7-9pm, Sun 12-2pm
Accommodation: (Price per room) single £28 (no extra charge for single occupancy of double room), double £45
Children: Welcome anywhere; outdoor play area
Credit cards: Access, Visa

⊕ FFYNONE ARMS
Newchapel, near Newcastle Emlyn SA37 OEH. Tel 0239 841235

Newchapel

A true Welsh country pub, the Ffynone Arms takes pride in its unmodernised decor and lively local trade. The 17th-century dark stone building is set halfway through the village of Newchapel, by the old pump, and is decorated with flowers and window boxes all year round. There is a herb garden at the rear, and a large lawn at thefront. (Newchapel is close to the Nash mansion, Ffynone, now open to the public.) The well prepared and interesting menu (game dishes from £4, Glamorgan sausages £3.25, smoked duck £4.25) is complemented by a wide-ranging and carefully selected wine list. There are occasionally 'special' menu evenings (Greek, Spanish etc), often accompanied by live entertainment. Flowers Original and guest beers are on tap.

Brewery: Free house
Licensee: Danny Homer
Opening hours: Summer 11am-3pm, 6-11pm; winter 4-11pm; Sat 11am-11pm; Sun 12-3pm, 7-10.30pm
Bar food: As opening hours
Restaurant: 6-10pm
Accommodation: (Price per room) single £18 (in twin room), double £35,
Children: In restaurant only; outdoor play area

⊕ RISING SUN INN
Pelcomb Bridge, St David's Road, near Haverfordwest SA62 6EA. Tel 0437 765171

Pelcomb Bridge

Rebuilt about eight years ago on the site of an old coaching inn, the Rising Sun has nevertheless kept many original fittings, as well as a cheerful and relaxed atmosphere. Photographs of the reconstruction work, as well as of the area in the past, decorate the interior. A good mix of customers fills the three bars all through the year; the pub has a convenient setting on a well-trodden tourist route near Haverfordwest, with easy parking. A reliable menu of bar food cooked by a resident chef offers good value with dishes such as garlic mushrooms in cream sauce (£2.85), chicken galloise (£6) and beef Wellington (£8.95), and an upstairs function room, which has its own bar, takes up the surplus from the main bar during very busy periods. Tetley and Ind Coope Burton Ale are available on tap.

Brewery: Free house
Licensee: Robert Brown
Opening hours: Summer 11.30am-3pm, 6-11pm (winter from 7pm); Sun 12-3pm, 7-10.30pm
Bar food: Times as bar food
Accommodation: (Price per person) double £18.25, twin £22.50
Children: Welcome if well behaved

⊕ HALFWAY INN
Devil's Bridge Road, Pisgah, near Aberystwyth SY23 4NE. Tel 097084 631

Pisgah

A superb view of the Rheidol valley from the garden is the main attraction of this 150-year-old semi-timbered pub. The bar's sturdy wooden chairs and tables and rough stone walls are in keeping with its 'old inn' image, and pictures of birds emphasise the fact that this is red kite country. Bar food includes T-bone steak (£11.50) and chicken, ham and mushroom pie (£6.50); it is advisable to book for the restaurant. Available on tap are Flowers Best and Original,

Brewery: Free house
Licensee: Mr and Mrs Roger
Opening hours: Summer 11am-11pm; winter 11.30am-2.30pm, 6.30-11pm (Sat 11am-11pm); Sun 12-3pm, 7-10.30pm
Bar food: 12-2pm, 7-9pm
Restaurant: Times as bar food

Worthington Best Mild (keg), Felinfoel Double Dragon and Whitbread Pompey Royal, and there are guest bitters; there are also 17 whiskies on offer, and non-alcoholic elderflower 'champagne'. Two double rooms provide new and attractive furnishings.

Accommodation: (Price per person) single £17.50, double £12.50; children under 14 years not permitted
Children: In Stone Bar and dining room only; outdoor play area

⊜ SALUTATION INN
Pontargothi, near Nantgaredig SA32 7NG. Tel 0267 290336

Pontargothi

A traditional black-and-white half-timbered building with a portico entrance houses this typical country pub, formerly a smallholding. Exposed stone walls and beams give a convincing sense of its 300- to 400-year past, and a varied selection of food has given the pub a good reputation. As well as full Sunday lunch, the menu includes red mullet (£5) and venison noisettes (£7), and vegetarian options are readily available. A patio in front of the pub is set with picnic tables, but is unfortunately very close to the busy main road which leads through the village; inside, rural artefacts and horse-riding memorabilia decorate the bar, which is well run and attracts a mix of families, country regulars and tourists. Felinfoel Double Dragon, Bitter and Special Dark are available on tap.

Brewery: Felinfoel
Licensee: Gerald Chard
Opening hours: 11.30am-3pm, 6-11pm; Sun 12-3pm, 7-10.30pm
Bar food: 12am-2pm, 6.30-10pm; Sun 12-1.30pm, 7-9.30pm
Restaurant: Times as bar food
Children: Only if well behaved; not in bar area
Credit cards: Access, Visa

⊜ DYFFRYN ARMS
Pontfaen, near Fishguard SA65 9SE. Tel 0348 881 305

Pontfaen

K nown locally as 'Bessie's', this pub is something of a local legend, with a reputation for a warm welcome, and for its spontaneous outbursts of Welsh singing. A genuine part of the Gwaun valley community, it has a rather isolated roadside setting, with a steep hill rising behind the 1845 building - a plain, double-fronted West Wales house. Although no bar food is offered, morning coffee is served, and there is always the chance of a cup of tea in the kitchen! Bass and Burton are available on tap and served in a jug from a wall hatch. The simple interior offers no embellishments and is not smart, but both the pub itself and the landlady are enormously popular with locals. A garden with some flowers is open to customers on a small, sloping grassy area on either side of the building, and there is a separate family room where older children can go.

Brewery: Free house
Licensee: Bessie Davies
Opening hours: 12-11pm; Sun 3-7pm
Children: Not permitted inside under 14 years; separate family room for older children

FARMERS ARMS
Goat Street, St Davids SA62 6RF. Tel 0437 720328

St Davids

Three two-storey cottages have been knocked into one building to create this pub, whose gabled upper windows look over a steep street leading towards the cathedral. As a result there are several rooms at varying levels, all with rough stone walls, beams and windows offering a view of the street. One section of the bar is dedicated to the St Davids lifeboat crew, with photographs of the lifeboat's history and a ship's wheel on show. This is a busy and popular pub, drawing fishermen, families and tourists. The bar food is ordinary with a wider choice available during summer months: the best value is probably the Farmers Arms lunch: ham, cheese, pâté, pickles, salad and a roll for £3.50; crab salad is available in season (£5). Flowers Original and Boddingtons draught beers are available. A pleasant open area with picnic tables and outdoor lighting is set out behind the pub, offering views of the cathedral tower.

Brewery: Free house
Licensee: J W Braby
Opening hours: 11am-11pm;
Sun 12-3pm, 7-10.30pm
Bar food: 11am-3pm, 6-9.30pm;
Sun 12-3pm, 7-9.30pm
Children: Welcome anywhere;
outdoor play area

GLAMORGAN (MID, SOUTH & WEST)

BUTCHERS ARMS
Alltwen Hill, Alltwen, near Pontardawe SA8 3BP. Tel 0792 863100

Alltwen

Set on a steep hillside overlooking the Tawe valley, this low building consists of a pub and a restaurant extension. Spacious and comfortable, the long bar is a favourite with locals and families: conversation is easy, but there is plenty of room for those who prefer to find a quiet corner. The decor is dark but not oppressive, and drawings of the local views and of the area's industrial heritage decorate the walls. Bar food provides good value for money, with generous portions and an imaginative range, including lamb and mint pie (£4.25) and a staple option of garlic potatoes with each dish. Although food is available every day except Sunday evenings, availability depends on demand, and the kitchen may close early during quiet periods. A full à la carte menu is available in the restaurant, which is lighter and offers good valley views. Draught beers are Everards Old Original, Wadworth 6X, Courage Directors, John Smith's Bitter and a guest ale which changes three times a week. A few tables and benches are set outside, where there is a large gravel parking area.

Brewery: Free house
Licensees: Mr and Mrs Swords
Opening hours: 12-3pm, 6.30-11pm; Sun 12-3pm, 7-10.30pm
Bar food: 12-3pm, 6.30-11pm;
Sun 12-3pm; subject to demand
Restaurant: 12-3pm, 6.30-11pm; Sun 12-3pm
Children: Not permitted in bar area under 14 years
Credit cards: Access, Visa

COURT HOUSE
Cardiff Road, Caerphilly CF8 1FN. Tel 0222 888120

Caerphilly

A concealed entrance, between two major banks, leads into this pleasing pub, housed in a 14th-century Welsh longhouse. Its one bar and several rooms mix comfort with tradition: bare stone walls, inglenook fireplaces and flagstone floors retain a sense of the building's long history. A restaurant/café at the back of the pub offers a contrast, with glass walls and a modern design, and has excellent views over the moat to Caerphilly Castle. Carvery lunches are on offer all week, and a wide selection of food is displayed on the restaurant blackboard, including vegetable nut cutlets in spicy tomato sauce (£3.50), shepherd's pie (£3.50) and chicken breast chasseur in white wine sauce (£3.95). Draught beers are Courage Best Bitter, John Smith's Yorkshire Bitter, Directors and Ruddles Best Bitter. A grassy area and paved terrace at the back of the pub give more views of the castle; in the forecourt stands a well, which was discovered during reconstruction work.

Brewery: Free house
Licensees: Mr and Mrs Jenkin
Opening hours: 11am-11pm; Sun 12-3pm, 7-10.30pm
Bar food: 12-2.30; Sun 12-3pm
Restaurant/café: 9.30am-5pm, 6.30-9.30pm
Children: In restaurant only; outdoor play area
Credit cards: AMERICAN EXPRESS®, Access, Visa, Diners (over £10)

BLUE ANCHOR
East Aberthaw, near Barry CF6 9DD. Tel 0446 750329

East Aberthaw

Built as a farmhouse in 1380, this thatched stone building attracts a cross-section of local, touring, business and country custom. Inter-connecting rooms lead off the one bar, offering a range of moods and atmosphere: some dark and cosy, with fires and brasses, others light and airy, with bare stone walls. Separate rooms are available for games, and for families with children. Bar food is on offer during lunchtime hours, and a separate restaurant opens during the evenings. Dishes include children's items (ham, chips and beans, £1.60), vegetable pancake (£3.50) and fresh grilled sardines (£2.75). Draught beers available are Wadworth 6X, Marston's Pedigree Bitter, Crown Buckley Best Bitter, Flowers IPA, Theakston Old Peculier and Boddingtons Best Bitter.

Brewery: Free house
Licensee: Jeremy Coleman
Opening hours: 11am-11pm; Sun 12-3pm, 7-10.30pm
Bar food: 12-2pm
Restaurant: 7-10.30pm
Children: In family room only
Credit cards: Access, Visa

GRIFFIN
Gilfach Goch, near Trealaw CF39 8LY. No phone

Gilfach Goch

Sitting at the bottom of a steep, unsurfaced single-track road, this 19th-century former colliery office is now in the best no-nonsense, straightforward pub tradition. A mix of locals and people touring the area comes to enjoy views of the moors; inside, a fascinating array of memorabilia

Brewery: Free house
Licensee: Mrs J S Morgan
Opening hours: 11am-4.30pm, 6-11pm (Sat from 12 noon); Sun 12-3pm, 7-10.30pm (knock if

decorates the bar and separate lounge room, and the licensees are happy to relate the history of each item. Poultry is kept in the pub grounds and peacocks roam freely about; an open area in front of the building has tables and benches, but also acts as a car park. There is some moorland where children can play, but old mine-workings still exist near by and parents should be on hand to supervise. No bar food is available, in keeping with the licensees' traditional view of pub life, but rolls are occasionally on offer, and coffee is served in winter. Brains SA Best Bitter is available on tap.

front door locked during licensing hours)

Children: Not permitted inside; outdoor play area

⊜ PRINCE OF WALES
Kenfig, near Pyle CF33 4PT. Tel 0656 740356

Kenfig

History is an essential part of this pub's attraction, and is well respected by its proprietor. Set on the coast road, this two-storey pub is 745 years old and its upper floor serves as the village hall, Sunday school and functions area. The intriguing history of the ancient city of Kenfig, gradually buried by sand dunes, is readily related; the present village, east of the sand, centres around the pub building, originally the Guildhall and still displaying the old mace of the Parish Council. A good range of home-cooked bar meals, using local produce, includes smoked bacon and laverbread (£3.25), faggots and peas (£1.70) and fillet steak (£9.50), with plenty of seafood on offer. Booking is advised for Sunday lunches in the eating area, although food is served throughout the pub.Outside a courtyard is set with tables and chairs. A varying range of beers are available on tap: Draught Bass, Felinfoel Double Dragon, Worthington Best Bitter, Wadworth 6X, Marston's Pedigree and Courage Directors.

Brewery: Free house

Licensee: J M Evans

Opening hours: 11.30am-4pm, 6-11pm; Sun 12-3pm, 7-10.30pm

Bar food: As opening hours

Children: In eating area only

⊜ LLANGEINOR ARMS
Llangeinor, near Betws CF32 8RX. Tel 0656 870268

Llangeinor

According to the earliest records of this building, which dates back about 700 years, it was once used by monks from Margam Abbey; its superb location, on the old cattle road from Ogmore to Brecon, overlooking lush valleys and hills, is one of the pub's prime assets. Set in a hilltop village next to the church, the Llangeinor Arms makes little of its long history in pleasant but unremarkable decor. A Welsh grandfather clock stands near the main door; brasses and ceramics decorate the main bar, and a conservatory is furnished with garden chairs and tables. Bar food is available in generous portions, with dishes such as T-bone steak (£8.95), vegetable Stroganoff (£4) or chicken Kiev (£3.75),

Brewery: Free house

Licensee: J Payter

Opening hours: 11.30am-4pm, 7-11pm (Sat 11am-11pm); Sun 12-3pm, 7-10.30pm

Bar food: 12-2.30pm (except Sun)

Restaurant: 7.30pm-2am; Sun 12-5pm

Children: In conservatory only; not permitted in bar under 14 years; outdoor play area and a separate restaurant, the Ty Abbot, offers a full á la carte menu (booking necessary). Brains SA Best Bitter, Worthington Best Bitter and Hancock's HB are on tap, and bottled ales include Mann's Brown, Newcastle Brown and Toby Light. A fenced-off field in front of the pub has a climbing frame, swing and slide to keep children occupied.

Credit cards: Access, Visa

OLD HOUSE/YR HENDY
Llangynwyd, near Maesteg CF34 9SB. Tel 0656 733310

Llangynwyd

The Old House claims to be one of the oldest licensed houses in Wales, and makes the most of its interesting past. Wil Hopkin is said to have written the famous Welsh song 'Bugeilio'r Gwenith Gwyn' here, and this is one of the few places left in the country which still hosts the New Year's tradition of Mari Lwyd, in which a horse's skull is draped in sheets and decorated with flowers, and taken from door to door to the accompaniment of sung verse. The original 1140 thatched building now has a slate-roofed extension, and a restaurant building was formerly the first Nonconformist chapel in the Llynfi valley (1840). An extensive bar food menu includes a range of hot and cold starters, meat, fish and vegetarian dishes, desserts and children's options: examples are home-made steak and kidney pie (£3.50), salmon en croûte (£9.50), aubergine lasagne (£3.50) and steak au poivre (£9.75); there is also a full wine list. Dark wood furnishings, an inglenook fireplace and various nooks and crannies add to the cosy atmosphere of the two bars; a conservatory and a terrace overlooking the children's adventure playground offer alternative seating. On draught are Flowers Original and IPA and Brains SA Best Bitter.

Brewery: Whitbread
Licensee: Richard David
Opening hours: 11am-4pm, 6.30-11pm; Sun 12-3pm, 7-10.30pm
Bar food: As opening hours
Restaurant: Times as bar food
Children: Welcome in conservatory; outdoor play area
Credit cards: Visa

⊕ PLOUGH AND HARROW
Monknash, near Llantwit Major CF7 7QQ. Tel 0656 79209

Monknash

Although built originally as the chapter house of a monastery, this has been a pub for 500 of its 600-year existence. Its peaceful country setting, on the edge of a small village with views across the fields to the Bristol Channel, has attracted more than one film-maker looking for a likely location. Inside the low, whitewashed and slate-roofed building, a carpeted hallway leads to the lounge and bar, simply furnished with high wooden benches, flagstone floors and an open fireplace. On tap are Whitbread Best Bitter and Flowers Original, Murphy's Stout, Marston's Pedigree and Worthington Best Bitter. Morning coffee and afternoon tea

Brewery: Free house
Licensee: Gary Thomas
Opening hours: 11am-3pm, 6-11pm (Sat 11am-11pm); Sun 12-3pm, 7-10.30pm
Bar food: 11am-3pm, 6-11pm; Sun 12-3pm, 7-10.30pm
Children: Welcome anywhere

are served, and the bar menu offers standard dishes such as vegetable lasagne , steak and kidney pie with potatoes and vegetables and mushroom and nut fettucine (all £3.95). A walled off garden at the front of the pub has wooden benches and tables for customers.

⬤ GREYHOUND INN
Oldwalls, near Bishopston SA3 1HA. Tel 0792 390146

Oldwalls

Set near a hamlet in the middle of the Gower Peninsula, the Greyhound is a regular venue for the Swansea fringe festival in October, and for a Folk Club every Sunday. A relaxed and cheerful atmosphere brings in many families with children: nearly two acres of grassy paddock gives plenty of room to run about, and a separate family room is available. The Lounge Bar forms the original part of this building - a 200-year-old white-painted cottage - with wooden panels and an open fire; a large modern extension contains the restaurant. Seafood is a particular speciality, providing excellent value; items on the bar food menu include plaice (£4.75), Welsh cheese ploughman's lunch (£2.60) or home-made steak and kidney pie (£3.50). Coffee, tea and hot chocolate are served all day. Draught Bass and Flowers are among 40 beers rotated on six pumps.

Brewery: Free house
Licensee: Peter Green
Opening hours: 11.30am-11pm; Sun 12-3pm, 7-10.30pm
Bar food: 12-2.30pm, 6.30-9.30pm; Sun 12-2.30, 7-9.30pm
Restaurant: Apr-Sep 7-10pm
Children: Welcome anywhere; family room; outdoor play area
Credit cards: Access, Visa

⬤ RED LION INN
Penderyn, near Hirwaun CF44 9JR. Tel 0685 811914

Penderyn

Visitors who enjoy good beer in simple surroundings will love this pub, which is unable to offer food until renovation and extension work is complete. The licensee, a local man who has returned to the area from London, is currently establishing a reputation for a wide range of beers, and has instigated a great deal of structural work on the early 17th-century limestone building, which sits high in the mountains on the old drovers' road. Draught beers are Fuller's, Moorhouse's Old Speckled Hen, Draught Bass, Brains, Felinfoel Double Dragon, Boddingtons, Wadworth 6X, Marston's and Murphy's Stout. Antique furniture and forces memorabilia are on display in the bar, and a garden has picnic benches and superb views.

Brewery: Free house
Licensee: Keith James
Opening hours: 1-4pm (Sat 5pm), 7-11pm; closed Mon; Sun 12-3pm, 7-10.30pm
Children: Not permitted inside

⊜ CAPTAINS WIFE
Beach Road, Swanbridge, near Sully CF6 2UG. Tel 0222 530066

Swanbridge

This lively and popular pub sits on the seafront looking out towards Sully Island and the Bristol Channel, and makes the most of its maritime connections. The large, rambling bar, with a generous open fire at one end and an old stove at the other, is packed with displays of sea-life memorabilia, and a ship's figurehead is displayed next to the main door. This is definitely a family pub; a children's room leading off the bar has a cheerful, relaxed atmosphere, and simple, good quality food attracts a lot of weekend custom. Jacket potatoes with various fillings (£2) are available during the week, and Sunday lunchtime specials are particularly good value (Yorkshire pudding filled with beef, lamb or turkey, plus greens, £1.50). The Mariners restaurant opens on some days of the week, according to seasonal demand. Available on tap are Courage Real Ale, John Smith's Bitter, Directors and Best and one guest bitter.

Brewery: Freehouse
Licensee: D C R Jones
Opening hours: 11am-11pm;
Sun 12-3pm, 7-10.30pm
Bar food: 12-2.30pm
Restaurant: in season, Thu-Sat
7-11pm; Sun 12-3pm
Children: In family room only
Credit cards:
AMERICAN EXPRESS®, Access,
Visa

GWENT

⊜ LLANWENARTH ARMS
Brecon Road, Abergavenny NP8 1EP. Tel 0873 810550

Abergavenny

Three miles north-west of Abergavenny, the Llanwenarth Arms boasts beautiful views over the River Usk towards the Black Mountains. A modern extension has been added to the original 16th-century building, formerly known as Pantrhiwgoch, to create a pub-cum-hotel-restaurant. An impressive menu is changed daily and chalked up on the blackboard; the friendly and helpful staff run a flexible kitchen and will do their best to produce dishes which are not listed. Items such as smoked chicken breast (as a starter, £3.95), a half-rack of lamb (£11.95) and a selection of steaks (£10 to £12) are complemented by a wide range of wines; there are also good selections of malt whiskies and ports. Draught Bass and Wadworth 6X are on tap. Booking is advisable for the restaurant. The two bars are comfortably furnished with upholstered benches; one has an open fireplace. There are 18 rooms (double or twin), each offering a view of the river or of the lower slopes of the Sugar Loaf mountain, and two stretches of salmon and trout fishing are available for guests. A terrace and Victorian conservatory provide an equally enjoyable outlook.

Brewery: Free house
Licensees: D'Arcy and Angela
McGregor
Opening hours: 11am-3pm,
6-11pm; Sun 12-2pm, 7-10.30pm
Bar food: 12-2pm, 7-10pm
Restaurant: Times as bar food
Accommodation: (Price per
room) double £59, single
occupation £49 (children half
price); weekend rates (two nights
with full breakfast) double £99,
single £79
Children: In restaurant area and
conservatory only
Credit cards:
AMERICAN EXPRESS®, Access,
Visa, Diners

SKIRRID
Llanfihangel Crucorney, near Abergavenny NP7 8DH. Tel 0873 890258

Llanfihangel Crucorney

This fine stone building, looking out over fields to the Skirrid mountain, dates from 1110 and claims to be the oldest inn in Wales, as well as one of the foremost contenders for the title of the oldest public house in Britain. Its upper floor was formerly a court house; the condemned were hanged from the stairwell. Set on the old main road from Abergavenny to Hereford, with a fenced garden at the back, the Skirrid now enjoys the peace and quiet brought about by a new bypass, and offers a genuinely warm welcome. A mix of locals and travellers frequents the three spacious bars, which retain flagged floors, dark wood furnishings, stone walls and an open fire. A small restaurant in a separate room has elegant dark panelling, said to be salvaged from a man o' war; it may be shut during winter lunchtimes. The menu, offered in the bar or the restaurant, is unpretentious but imaginative and filling, and is chalked up in the bar as available; examples include Crucorney trout fillet (£5.25) and pan-fried swordfish steak (£7.50). A Skirrid wine is offered as red, rosé and white. Draught beers are Courage Best and Directors, John Smith's, Ushers Founders Ale, Best and Triple Crown. Accommodation is available in three rooms: one double room has a four-poster bed.

Brewery: Ushers of Trowbridge
Licensee: Steven Grant
Opening hours: 12-3pm, 7-11pm; Sun 12-3pm, 7-10.30pm
Bar food: 12-2pm, 7-9pm
Restaurant: Times as bar food
Accommodation: (Price per room) single £20, double £40-£50
Children: In restaurant only; outdoor play area

ABBEY HOTEL
Llanthony, near Abergavenny NP7 7NN. Tel 0873 890487

Llanthony

The unique appeal of this pub and hotel is immediately apparent: the tiny Cellar Bar is built into the ruins of a 12th-century Augustinian priory, and a Norman spiral staircase (62 steps and no lift) leads to the five rooms, converted from church ruins in 1790. Walkers and holiday groups come to enjoy the spectacular views in this isolated valley, and to wander around the ruins, though local heritage and culture plays little part in the character of the bar itself. No food is served in the bar, but a restaurant in the hotel offers a full menu. A wide range of draught beers, not all available at the same time, includes Ruddles County, Draught Bass, Wadworth 6X, Whitbread Flowers Original and Boddingtons. There is plenty of space for children to play in the priory grounds, although these are not actually part of the licensed premises.

Brewery: Free house
Licensee: I Prentice
Opening hours: Summer 11am-11pm; winter 11am-3pm, 6-11pm; Sun 12-3pm, 7-10.30pm
Restaurant: 12-2.30pm, 7-8.45pm
Accommodation: (Price per room) Fri and Sat £95 for two nights, Sun-Thu £41 per night. Rooms let as singles in quiet periods
Children: Not permitted inside under 14 years

Penallt, see Gloucestershire *page 282*

⊕ BEAUFORT ARMS HOTEL
Raglan, near Abergavenny NP5 2DY. Tel 0291 690412

Raglan

Although attached to a hotel, this is more than a hotel bar; the licensees have made a considerable effort to give it a character of its own. Hanging baskets decorate the doorway of the whitewashed building, which sits at the heart of a historic village and is named after the Beaufort family, owners of Raglan Castle. A mix of locals and visitors enjoy the Castle Country Bar and the carpeted lounge, with its exposed timbers, stone walls and ornately carved bar. On draught are Guinness, Beamish Stout, Courage John Smith's, Simons Bitter, Best and Directors. Bar food includes vegetarian options; examples of dishes offered are home-made soup (£1.50), fresh grilled salmon trout (£6) and boeuf bourgignon (£5.50). Accommodation is available in 12 double or twin rooms, two singles and one family room, and there is a patio at the front for outdoor drinking or eating..

Brewery: Free house
Licensees: Mr and Mrs P Dorey
Opening hours: 11am-3pm, 6-11pm; Sun 12-3pm, 7-10.30pm
Bar food: 12-2.30pm, 6.30-10pm; Sun 12-2.30pm, 7-10pm
Restaurant: 7-9.30pm; Sun 12-2pm
Accommodation: (Price per room) double/twin £45, single £35, family £55
Children: Not permitted in bar under 14 years
Credit cards: AMERICAN EXPRESS®, Access, Visa, Diners

⊕ CARPENTERS ARMS
Shirenewton, near Chepstow NP6 6BU. Tel 02917 231

Shirenewton

This gem of a pub, set on the Usk road in a valley below Shirenewton, has no fewer than seven bars to explore, as well as a multitude of nick-nacks and memorabilia (although outside seating is limited to roadside benches). In one room, a collection of chamber pots hangs over the customers' heads; in another, large bellows are displayed, from the former smithy which forms part of the pub. Decor ranges from flagstone to carpeted floors, some rooms having open fireplaces, some offering wide valley views. Game and fish are specialities on the excellent bar food menu; dishes are home-made using fresh produce, and are chalked up on a blackboard. Examples are leek and potato soup (£1.75) or whitebait (£2.50) as starters; spinach and mushroom lasagne (£4.25) or chicken in leek and Stilton (£5.25); and bread-and-butter pudding (£2) or apple crumble (£1.75) as desserts. A range of 20 malt whiskies is offered at the bar, and on tap are Boddingtons and Flowers IPA, Marston's Pedigree Bitter and Owd Rodger, Ruddles County and Wadworth 6X.

Brewery: Free house
Licensee: James Bennett
Opening hours: 11am-2.30pm, 6-11pm; Sun 12-3pm, 7-10.30pm
Bar food: 11.30am-2pm, 7-9.30pm
Children: Not permitted in bar under 14 years

🍺 LION
Trellech, near Monmouth NP5 4PA. Tel 0600 860322

Trellech

Brewery: Free house
Licensee: Alan and Christine Nixon
Opening hours: 12-2pm (Sat 3pm), 6.30-11pm; closed Mon lunchtime; Sun 12-3pm, 7-10.30pm
Bar food: 12-2pm, 7.30-9.30pm; booking required for Mon and Sun evenings
Children: Welcome anywhere

A chatty atmosphere prevails in this straightforward country pub, a 17th-century building of local red sandstone. Set opposite the village church and decorated with flowers, the Lion has two carpeted bars, with an open fireplace; the Lounge Bar mainly serves as an eating area. Bar food is appropriate to the pub's hearty image: ploughman's (cheddar £2.10 or Stilton £2.40) and brunch (Cumberland sausages, bacon, mushrooms, tomatoes and potatoes (£3.55) offer good value for money, and a full Sunday lunch is served as two (£5.95) or three courses (£6.95). No meals are available unless booked on Sunday and Monday nights, and booking is advised on Thursdays, Fridays and Saturdays. Banks's Mild is available from the keg and Draught Bass and Hook Norton Best Bitter on tap, along with guest bitters. A tarmacked courtyard with a view of the church has tables and benches for outdoor eating or drinking.

🍺 GOOSE AND CUCKOO
Upper Llanover, near Abergavenny NP7 9ER. Tel 0873 880277

Upper Llanover

Brewery: Free house
Licensee: Ann and John Cullen
Opening hours: 11.30am-3pm, 7-11pm; Sun 12-3pm, 7-10.30pm
Bar food: As opening hours (except Thu evening)
Children: Not permitted in bar area under 14 years

It takes a considerable effort to find this pub, which is off the A4042, high above the village along a steep, winding road, but it is well worth it. The low, whitewashed stone building enjoys stunning views of the surrounding mountains and attracts many country walkers as well as visitors from Cardiff and a core of regular customers. This is also an animal lovers' pub: pigs, chickens and a ram are kept in the garden, the goat has a habit of wandering in to eat the flowers arranged in the pretty porchway, and drinkers must compete for seating space with the large and friendly pub dog. Once called the New Inn, the 200-year-old pub's title derives from two women who once ran it, and who insulted each other with the names. The current proprietors are friendly and well versed in the pub's history. A modern bar has been well blended with the one carpeted room, where an old-fashioned stove burns in a brick fireplace. Fresh, wholesome food is available according to demand and season; the 13-bean soup (£1.25) is a speciality. A wide selection of malt whiskies has been introduced, and available on draught are Brains SA, Bullmastiff Best Bitter and a guest beer.

⊛ CROWN AT WHITEBROOK
Whitebrook, near Monmouth NP5 4TX. Tel 0600 860254

Whitebrook

The Crown's proprietors refer to it as an auberge, and this restaurant and hotel prides itself on offering dishes using Welsh ingredients in a French tradition. Set at the edge of the village, in a steep wooded valley near the River Wye, its emphasis is on comfort, with settees and armchairs in the homely lounge and 12 well furnished rooms. As well as the impressive restaurant menu (a set price menu is available at £24 plus VAT), bar 'snacks' are served at lunch time, with items such as ficelles de mer (pancakes filled with crab meat, prawns and pineapple and covered in melted Gruyère) for £4.95, or crevettes à l'ail (king prawns wrapped in bacon and cooked in garlic butter) for £5.75. Standards are high, and the chef is willing to please; any particular requests for off-menu items will be considered. An extensive wine list includes some Welsh labels; at the bar, Whitbread is available on tap. There is a small garden to the rear.

Brewery: Free house
Licensee: Roger and Sandra Bates
Opening hours: 12-2pm, 7-9pm
Bar food: 12-2pm (except Sun)
Restaurant: 12-2pm, 7-9pm; closed to non-residents Sun evening and Mon lunchtimes
Accommodation: (Price per person) £62 for one night; £60 for two nights; £56 for four nights (dinner, bed and breakfast); single occupancy of double room £10 supplement
Children: Welcome anywhere
Credit cards: AMERICAN EXPRESS®, Access, Visa, Diners

GWYNEDD

⊛ PENHELIG ARMS
Aberdovey, near Tywyn LL35 OLT. Tel 0654 767215

Aberdovey

The old cliché 'service with a smile' really does apply to this 18th-century inn overlooking the sea and Dyfi estuary. There is a cheerful, amiable atmosphere here, and a mix of customers - families, local residents and holiday-makers - comes to enjoy the stunning sea views, although there is only a wall to lean against outside. Fresh fish dishes are naturally a speciality, and are chalked up on the blackboard (eg cod £5.95); a range of other simple dishes such as lasagne with salad and chips (£4.75) is expertly prepared. Vegetarian meals are available on request. Tetley Bitter, Felinfoel Double Dragon and Beamish Stout are served at the bar, which has a large open fire and modern decor in keeping with the image of a seaside pub. Seven double rooms and one single offer homely and spacious accommodation, with wonderful outlooks over the estuary towards Aberystwyth.

Brewery: Free house
Licensees: Robert and Sally Hughes
Opening hours: 11am-3pm, 6-11pm; Sun 12-3pm, 7-10.30pm
Bar food: 12-2pm, 7-9.30pm; Sun 12-2pm
Restaurant: 12-2pm, 7-9.30pm
Accommodation: (Price per person) single £36, double £31-£39
Children: In dining area only
Credit cards: Access, Visa

⊕ YE OLDE BULLS HEAD INN
Castle Street, Beaumaris LL58 8AP. Tel 0248 810329

Beaumaris

This old coaching inn, sympathetically upgraded, stands on the site of the original 1472 building, although the present version was erected in 1617. Creaking wooden floors, open fires, a beamed ceiling and cushioned settles all maintain a traditional feel, and there are intriguing items on display, including antique weaponry, an old brass water clock and the town's original ducking stool. Food is served at the bar and in a separate restaurant and is of a particularly high standard. Dishes such as hot pot of seafood (£5.50) or steamed fillet of hake (£4.45) are cooked with skill and imagination from fresh local produce and give very good value for money. Draught Bass and Worthington Best Bitter are served at the bar, and a carefully assembled list of 150 wines includes some excellent choices. Accommodation is offered in ten double and twin rooms and one single, all with antique cast-iron beds.During the summer the courtyard car park doubles as a seating area.

Brewery: Free house
Licensee: D I Robertson
Opening hours: 11am-11pm; Sun 12-3pm, 7-10.30pm
Bar food: 12-2.30pm (except Sun)
Restaurant: 7.30-9.30pm; Sun 12-1.30pm, 7.30-9.30pm
Accommodation: (Price per person) single £42, double £36
Children: Only if accompanied by adults; not permitted in bar area after 8pm
Credit cards: Access, Visa

⊕ SHIP INN
Red Wharf Bay, Benllech LL75 8RJ. Tel 0248 852568

Benllech

Overlooking a bay and natural harbour, this 400-year-old cottage pub is set well away from the main Anglesey coast road and has a busy, nautical atmosphere. Although its decor and facilities are simple, they have quality and character. A small but imaginative range of bar food is on offer; the choice, which changes regularly and is chalked up on a blackboard, includes such dishes as cottage pie (£4.45), home-made broccoli Mornay (£4.65) or sirloin steak (£8.75). Tetley Bitter, Marston's Pedigree Bitter and the pub's own label, Kenneally's, are served at the three bars, with guest beers available in the summer. A sensible wine list is available, and there are 20 choices of malt whisky. Holiday-makers swell the ranks of customers in high season, but this is also a popular local pub. A separate family room caters for children, and a garden looks out over the harbour.

Brewery: Free house
Licensee: Andrew L Kenneally
Opening hours: Summer 11am-11pm; winter 12-3.30pm, 7-11pm; Sun 12-3pm, 7-10.30pm
Bar food: 12-2.15pm, 6-9.15pm; Sun 12-2pm, 7-9pm
Children: In family room only
Credit cards: Access, Visa

Water and Steam

Many attractive pubs today stand on the banks of rivers and canals. The riverside ones reflect the fact that for centuries the quickest, safest and cheapest way to move people and goods about was by river, not by road. The 18th century saw the construction of artificial rivers, the canals, and hostelries quickly sprang up for boatmen and travellers on them too. Again, when the railways spread across the country from the 1840s on, pubs near stations proudly called themselves the Railway or the Railway Arms to cater for the new system.

STAG INN
Cemaes Bay, near Amlwch LL67 0EW. Tel 0407 710281

Cemaes Bay

Claiming to be the most northerly pub in Wales, this popular 200-year-old village pub has a sunny setting at the bottom of the high street, near the harbour. Fishermen form a significant part of the clientele who come to the three bars, where Burtonwood Best Bitter is served on tap. A basic, wholesome menu of bar food offers good value for money with dishes such as garlic mushrooms or breaded Camembert (£2.25 each), broccoli and cheese bake or ham and mushroom tagliatelle (£3.80 each) and apple pie or gâteaux (£1.60 each). An open fire lends a cosy atmosphere to the carpeted lounge, and local photographs and nautical memorabilia decorate the walls. A family room is open to children (until 8.30pm) and pub games include darts, pool and dominoes. An area at the front of the pub is something of a sun trap and has a view of the picturesque village.

Brewery: Burtonwood
Licensee: Andrew Chape
Opening hours: Summer 11am-11pm; winter 11am-3pm, 7-11pm; Sun 12-3pm, 7-10.30pm
Bar food: 12-2.30pm, 6-9.30pm; Sun 12-2.30pm, 7-9.30pm
Children: In family room until 8.30pm only

⊜ SLATERS ARMS
Corris, near Machynlleth SY20 9SP. Tel 0654 761324

Corris

This simple, friendly pub has been operating for 150 years, and blends in with the miners' cottages of the village, which grew up around the slate industry. Set right at the centre of the village, it is surrounded by narrow streets, which makes parking difficult. The two bars are furnished with modern tables and chairs and decorated with local photographs; there is a large, open fireplace. Banks's Bitter and Mild are available on draught. The bar food menu is basic and straightforward: examples include beef hot pot or broccoli and cream cheese pie (£4.30 each), and breaded plaice (£3.20); vegetarian options are always available. Locals and outdoor pursuits enthusiasts form the clientele, and children are made welcome before 8pm. Crib, chess and draughts are all on offer in a separate games room, and there are also electronic games machines but there is no garden.

Brewery: Banks's
Licensee: Peter Cruickshank
Opening hours: 11am-11pm; Sun 12-3pm, 7-10.30pm
Bar food: 11am-9.45pm; Sun 12-3pm, 7-9.45pm
Children: Only until 8pm

TYN-Y-GROES HOTEL
Ganllwyd, near Dolgellau LL40 2NH. Tel 034140 275

Ganllwyd

This attractive, 400-year-old country pub sits on the A470 on the valley floor of Coed-y-Brenin forest. It offers friendly service, well-priced, simple food and a good range of draught beers: Flowers IPA, Boddingtons and Marston's Pedigree Bitter. Welsh 'Chwisgi' (whisky) is also available.

Brewery: Free house
Licensees: Mr and Mrs D A B Ruthwell
Opening hours: 11am-3pm, 6-11pm (Fri and Sat 11am-11pm);

The menu, served from the bar and in a separate restaurant has 'specials' chalked on a blackboard and includes basics such as chicken (£4.95), gammon and eggs (£4.75) and scampi (£4.30), as well as vegetarian dishes. Families, business people, tourists and locals come to enjoy the three bars, which have an open fire and displays of photographs showing the pub through the ages. Three rooms are open to families with children. Accommodation is provided in six double rooms and two single, all with modern, comfortable furnishings; most offer views of the River Mawddach.

Sun 12-3pm, 7-10.30pm
Bar food: 11.30am-2pm, 6.30-9pm; Sun 11.30am-2pm, 7-9pm
Restaurant: 7-9pm (winter Thu-Sun only)
Accommodation: (Price per person) single £21, double £19-£22
Children: In family rooms only
Credit cards: Access, Visa

⊜ QUEENS HEAD
Glanwydden, near Llandudno Junction LL31 9JP. Tel 0492 546570

Glanwydden

Simple, spacious and smart inside, this mid-18th century village pub has an unremarkable pebble-dash exterior; its main attraction is the imaginative range of bar food. The choice changes each day and, although not cheap, offers a particularly high quality for evening meals. Locally caught fish are often used, and there is an excellent choice of desserts. Examples of dishes which may be available are local smoked salmon (£5.95) or green lipped mussels (£4.25) as starters; lemon sole with prawn mousseline (£6.50) or half a fresh Great Orme lobster (£13.95) as main courses; and walnut sponge or strawberry fool (£2.20 each) as desserts. Vegetarian options are always available. Open fires heat the two bars during winter months and draught beers are Ind Coope (Allied) Benskins Best Bitter, Burton Ale and Tetley Bitter. A few tables are set outside the pub, which is at the centre of the small village, between Llandudno and Colwyn Bay.

Brewery: Ansells (Allied Breweries)
Licensee: R F W Cureton
Opening hours: 11am-3pm, 6.30-11pm; Sun 12-3pm, 7-10.30pm
Bar food: 12-2.15pm, 6.30-9pm; Sun 12-2pm, 7-9pm
Children: Not permitted under seven years
Credit cards: Access, Visa

⊜ OLDE BULL INN
Llanbedr-y-Cennin, near Conwy LL32 8JB. Tel 0492 660508

Llanbedr-y-Cennin

One of the oldest drovers' inns in Wales, this cottage pub sits in a tiny hamlet and has wonderful views over the Conwy valley from the patio. Parts of the building date back to the 11th century, and the bar has retained a sense of the past, with exposed beams, an inglenook fireplace with seating and antique furniture, including carved pews. There are also plenty of intriguing items: tables made from beer kegs, and displays of helmets, brasses and whips! Walkers, tourists, families and regulars come to relax in the bar, where Lees GB Mild and Bitter are served on tap, and there are 20 choices of malt whisky. Substantial food is available from the bar and in the separate restaurant: for instance,

Brewery: J W Lees
Licensee: Garry Bullock
Opening hours: 12-3pm, 7-11pm; closed Mon and Tue lunchtime in winter; Sun 12-3pm, 7-10.30pm
Bar food: 12-2pm, 7-9pm
Children: In dining area and family room until 9pm only

home-made steak and kidney pie or cheese and broccoli pie
(£3.95 each), or braised steak and mushrooms (£4.25).
Desserts are £1.50 each and include home-made apple pie or
chocolate fudge cake.

⊜ SUN INN
Llanengan, near Abersoch LL53 7LG. Tel 0758 712660

Llanengan

A friendly, bright atmosphere can be enjoyed in this 17th-
century pub. The black-and-white painted, slate-roofed
cottage sits at the edge of a sprawling village in the heart of
bird-watching country; birdwatchers and ramblers often join
the locals and farmers who visit the two bars, and rare
breeds memorabilia are on display. Although children are
not permitted inside the pub, there is a pleasant garden and
canopied patio where they can play. An excellent bar food
menu changes every day and includes vegetarian options;
examples of dishes include stuffed peppers or sweet and
sour Chinese ribs (both £4.85). Steaks and local lamb are
served during evening hours. Draught beers are Ind Coope
(Allied) Burton Ale and Tetley Bitter. Live entertainment is
provided in winter on Friday or Saturday evenings, and
accommodation is available in a separate house, with an
open spiral staircase and a wood stove, set in parkland with
good views.

Brewery: Free house
Licensee: J M C Evans
Opening hours: Summer 11am-
11pm; winter 11am-3pm,
7-11pm; closed Sun
Bar food: 12-2pm, 6-9pm
Accommodation: (Price per
person) double or twin £15-£25
Children: Not permitted inside;
outdoor play area
Credit cards: Access, Visa

⊜ GRAPES HOTEL
Maentwrog, near Porthmadog LL41 4HN. Tel 076685 208/365

Maentwrog

A wide cross-section of customers forms the clientele of
this 17th-century pub, once a coaching inn. Tourists,
locals and families, covering a wide age range, come to relax
and enjoy the river and valley views. A veranda and garden
take advantage of the open outlook. The two bars, which
have exposed stone walls and two open fires, serve Bass,
Worthington Best Bitter and Boddingtons Bitter, and are
furnished with pews, benches and stools. A bar food menu
and a separate restaurant serve good value, filling meals
such as Stilton and walnut pasta (£2.25), local Welsh lamb
chops (£5.50) and baked trout with prawn sauce (£6.50);
vegetarian dishes are always on offer. Three double rooms
and three single rooms provide accommodation and are
equipped with modern furniture, which is nevertheless
designed to blend well with the character and age of the
building.

Brewery: Free house
Licensee: B Tarbox
Opening hours: 11am-11pm;
Sun 12-3pm, 7-10.30pm
Bar food: 12-2.15pm, 6-9.30pm;
Sun 12-2pm, 7-9pm
Restaurant: Wed-Sat 7-10pm
Accommodation: (Price per
room) single £25, double £50
Children: In dining room and on
veranda only
Credit cards:
AMERICAN EXPRESS®, Access,
Visa

⊕ GEORGE III HOTEL
Penmaenpool, near Dolgellau LL40 1YD. Tel 0341 422525

Penmaenpool

This 1650 inn has a terrace overlooking the Mawddach River and there are fine views towards the Diffwys Mountains. Its two bars have open fires and are decorated with prints and brasses; locals, tourists and business travellers alike come to enjoy the pub's character and its peaceful, out-of-the-way location. Guinness and Marston's Pedigree Bitter are served on tap, and a rare rum, Appleton Estate Gold, is available. A typical menu of country pub food is offered, with dishes such as smoked local trout (£5.50), home-made steak and kidney pie (£4.85) and sirloin steak (£9) offering good value for money. A separate restaurant is open in the evenings. Accommodation is offered in 12 cosy double rooms with good river and mountain views.

Brewery: Free house
Licensees: Mr and Mrs J Cartwright
Opening hours: 11am-3pm, 6-11pm; Sun 12-3pm, 7-10.30pm
Bar food: 12-2.30pm, 7-9pm (except Sat evening and all day Sun)
Restaurant: 7-9pm
Accommodation: (Price per room) £44-£85
Children: Not permitted in bar area under 14 years
Credit cards: AMERICAN EXPRESS®, Access, Visa

⊕ TAFARN TY COCH
Porth Dinllaen, near Morfa Nefyn LL53 6DB. Tel 0758 720498

Porth Dinllaen

Access is not very easy to this busy seaside pub: the nearest parking is at Morfa Nefyn, about three quarters of a mile away, and customers must then walk to the Ty Coch, either along a beach or up a private road to a public footpath, which leads through golf club grounds. The 1823 red-brick building sits right on the beach - there are benches overlooking it - and has three self-catering cottages available. Its bar (open only for restricted periods) has a simple, traditional atmosphere, with benches and cushioned settles and a plain lino floor, and displays of mugs, copperware, lamps and seafaring memorabilia. A basic lunch menu includes meats, pâté or quiche with salad and a roll, ploughman's lunch, with three cheeses, or open prawn roll (all £3.75); there are also baked potatoes with fillings (£1.25 to £1.80) and various pies or pasties (£1). Marston's Burton Best Bitter is served on tap, as is Guinness.

Brewery: Free house
Licensee: Brione S Webley
Opening hours: Etr-Jul and Sep-Oct Mon-Sat 11am-3pm, 6-10.30pm; July and Aug Mon-Sat 11am-10.30pm (Sun 12-4pm (no alcohol served); Nov-Mar Sat 11am-3pm
Bar food: 12-2pm
Accommodation: (Price per cottage per week) from £175
Children: Welcome anywhere; outdoor play area

Skills and Crafts

Inns with names like the Bricklayers Arms and the Masons Arms hark back to the days when groups of craftsmen and tradesmen met regularly in the local hostelry. The trade union movement originally grew up in pubs in this way and a 'local' can mean either a pub or a union branch. Itinerant craftsmen would expect a welcome at these houses, too, and pick up news of work. The Axe and Compasses is a carpenters' badge, the Three (or more) Horseshoes a device of smiths, the Wheatsheaf of bakers and the Beetle and Wedge of builders, while quite a few pubs display the Oddfellows Arms. The Shoulder of Mutton could signify that the landlord doubled as a butcher.

Y LLONG
14 Lombard Street, Porthmadog LL49 9AP. Tel 0766 512990

Porthmadog

A sailing ship sits over the pillared front entrance of this 1824 pub, whose Welsh name means 'The Ship'. This is the oldest pub in the cheerful town of Porthmadog, and is mentioned in maritime accounts of the area. The two bars serve Tetley Dark Mild and Bitter, Ind Coope (Allied) Burton Ale and a guest ale which changes each week. The Lounge Bar, with its wood-burner and large stone fireplace, and the Public Bar, with tiled and wooden flooring, display maritime prints and items, and attract a mix of locals and tourists (there is a 'no leathers' rule). Dark wood decor and leaded windows add to the traditional style. A wide menu is available from the bar and from the restaurant, which opens during evenings only (booking advised on Saturday). Examples of dishes include beef and venison pie (£4.35), lamb with apricot in a spicy sauce (£4.25); and an excellent vegetarian/wholefood choice, including lentil crumble or broccoli and hazelnut bake (each £4.50). Coffee is served all day. Darts and dominoes are available in the bar and in a separate room, and there is an area for families with children but there is no garden.

Brewery: Ansells (Allied Breweries)
Licensee: Robert Jones
Opening hours: 11am-11pm; closed Sun
Bar food: 12-2.15pm, 6.30-9.30pm
Restaurant: 5.30-10.45pm
Children: In family room and restaurant only
Credit cards: Access, Visa

⊜ GROES INN
Tyn-y-Groes, near Conwy LL39 8TN. Tel 0492 650545

Tyn-y-Groes

Pretty gardens and a profusion of flowers add to the attraction of this 14th-century coaching inn, which sits at the edge of the Carneddau Mountains, overlooking the Conwy valley. The pub's character has been well maintained in the four bars, which display jugs, hats, portraits and antique tins. Ind Coope (Allied) Burton Ale, Tetley Bitter and Guinness are served at the bars. During the summer, Pimms, Kir and Cassis are on offer. Dishes available on the bar food menu and in the restaurant include, for example, seafood crêpe (£5.45), home-made steak and kidney pie (£5.75), Dr Finlay's oatmeal settler and old-fashioned apple pudding (£2.25 each). Vegetarian meals are offered, and specialities are chalked up on a blackboard. The pub gardens are open to customers and have beautiful views towards the River Conwy and the hills.

Brewery: Free house
Licensee: D Humphreys
Opening hours: Summer 12-2.30pm, 7-11pm; Sun 12-2.30pm, 7-10.30pm; winter 12-2.30pm, 6.30-11pm; Sun 12-2.30pm
Bar food: 12-2pm, 7-9pm (winter Mon-Sat 12-2pm, 6.30-9pm; Sun 12-2pm)
Restaurant: 12-2pm, 7-9pm (winter Mon-Sat 12-2pm, 6.30-9pm; Sun 12-2pm)
Children: In restaurant only; not permitted under 12 years; outdoor play area
Credit cards: Access, Visa

POWYS

⊜ BEAR INN
Crickhowell, near Abergavenny NP8 1BW. Tel 0873 810408

Crickhowell

Helpful service in relaxing surroundings is offered at this old coaching inn, overlooking the market square in the town centre. Locals and holidaymakers mix well here, whether enjoying a drink or eating in the bar or in one of the three restaurants. An imaginative bar menu, particularly appealing to vegetarians, includes such items as rolled smoked salmon with creamed fresh salmon filling (£3.50), fish stew (£5.50), parsnip and cashew nut bake (£4.75) or peppers stuffed with leek mousse in walnut sauce (£3.95). An extensive wine list is on offer, as well as a wide range of whiskies and ports, and draught beers are Draught Bass, Ruddles County and Best and Courage Webster's. Accommodation is offered in 29 double rooms, built in a new extension overlooking the pub courtyard; four-poster beds are available in two rooms, and one has a jacuzzi.

Brewery: Free house
Licensee: Judy Hindmarsh
Opening hours: 10.30am-3pm, 6-11pm; Sun 12-2pm, 7-10.30pm
Bar food: 11am-2pm, 6-10pm; Sun 12-2pm, 7-9.30pm
Restaurant: 7-9.30pm (lunches by prior arrangment only); Sun 12-2pm (dinners by prior arrangement only)
Accommodation: (Price per room) single £35-£48, double £48-£59
Children: In family room only; outdoor play area
Credit cards: AMERICAN EXPRESS®, Access, Visa

HARP
Glasbury, near Hay-on-Wye HR3 5NR. Tel 0497 847373

Glasbury-on-Wye

Very much a family pub, the Harp offers good value accommodation and food at sensible prices, appealing paricularly to couples with small children and limited budgets. The straightforward bar menu has a 'chips or baked potato with everything' approach; all the food is prepared on the premises, and items include sandwiches from £1, Harp hot-pot for £3.50 or vegetable pastie and chips for £2.25. Housed in an 18th-century building beside the River Wye, the two bars are comfortably furnished with cusioned settles and modern chairs; maps and shipping memorabilia are displayed in the rear bar. Four double rooms provide neat and simple furnishings. A flowered garden and terrace are open to customers at the back of the building. Boddingtons Bitter and Flowers IPA and Original, Draught Bass and Robinson's Best Bitter are available on tap.

Brewery: Free house
Licensee: David and Lynda White
Opening hours: 11am-3pm, 6.15-11pm; Sun 12-3pm, 7-10.30pm
Bar food: 12-2pm, 7-9.30pm (Sat 10pm); Sun 12-2pm, 7-10pm (winter 12-2pm, 7-9pm)
Accommodation: (Price per person) single £18, double £15
Children: Welcome anywhere

⊕ OLD BLACK LION
26 Lion Street, Hay-on-Wye HR3 5AD. Tel 0497 820841

Hay-on-Wye

A good reputation for food draws large evening crowds to this part 13th-, part 14th-century pub fronting the street; this can cause delays and disappointment, as late orders may not be accepted. Typical dishes range from smoked haddock mousse (£3.45) to Mediterranean sea food (£4.35) or home-made steak and kidney pudding (£5.85), and include a mix of homely and more exotic desserts (Tia Maria meringue £2.95, bread-and-butter pudding £2.95). Booking is advised for the separate restaurant. A good wine list is provided, along with four or five malt whiskies, and Draught Bass and Flowers Original are on tap. A mixed crowd of locals and visitors are drawn to the bar, with its low beams and black wood panelling. Accommodation is available in nine double rooms and one single; a minstrel's gallery forms part of one room.

Brewery: Free house
Licensees: John and Joan Collins
Opening hours: 11am-3pm, 6-11pm; Sun 12-3pm, 7-10.30pm
Bar food: 12-2pm, 7-9pm
Restaurant: Times as bar food
Accommodation: (Price per person) double £19.95, single £18.50; single occupancy of double £25
Children: In eating area only
Credit cards: AMERICAN EXPRESS®, Access, Visa

DROVERS ARMS
Howey, near Llandrindod Wells LO1 5PT. Tel 0597 822508

Howey

Despite having a functional and rather uninspiring appearance, this solid Victorian red-brick pub, off the main Llandrindod road near the river, is enjoying a growing reputation for reasonably priced, home-cooked bar food. Good house wines complement the menu, whose dishes include a very popular Stilton and celery soup (£1.85), vegetable samosa (£2.10), steak and mushroom pie (£4.50) and chicken Espagnol (£5.25), with desserts such as golden tart (£1.85) or Death by Chocolate (£1.85). Several vegetarian options are provided. Draught beers are Brains, Castle Eden Ale and Boddingtons. An efficient and friendly atmosphere draws a wide mix of customers to the two bars, which are carpeted and furnished with modern wooden tables and chairs; there is a patio decorated with potted plants and supervised by a volatile cat. Comfortable accommodation is available in one double and one twin room.

Brewery: Free house
Licensees: David and Janet Day
Opening hours: 12-2.30pm, 7-11pm; closed Tue lunchtime; Sun 12-1.30pm, 7-10.30pm
Bar food: 12-1.45pm, 7-9.30pm; Sun 12-1.45pm, 7-9pm
Accommodation: (Price per room) £28-£30
Children: Only if well behaved; not permitted under six years

⊕ LLANERCH
Waterloo Road, Llandrindod Wells LO1 6BG. Tel 0597 822086

Llandrindod Wells

Housed in an attractive 16th-century grey-stone building near the River Ithon, this is a large and accommodating pub with business-like staff. Cushioned settles furnish the two beamed bars, and seating is also available in an extensive garden and orchard. A playground is equipped with swings, a slide and a climbing frame. Children are also well catered for

Brewery: Free house
Licensee: J Leach
Opening hours: 11.30am-2.30pm (Sat 3pm), 6-11pm; Sun 12-2.30pm, 7-10.30pm
Bar food: 12-2.15pm, 6-9pm; Sun

on the bar menu, which offers simple dishes such as Llanerch broth (£1.50), pot meals (eg fisherman's pie, £2.95) and mixed grills (£7.50). Draught Bass, Hancock's HB and a guest beer are served to a clientele of business customers and families. Six double rooms and one twin are available.

12-2.15pm, 7-10pm (except Sun evening in winter)
Accommodation: (Price per person) £18-£22
Children: Welcome except in pool room; outdoor play area
Credit cards: Access, Visa

⊜ RED LION
Llanfair Waterdine, near Knighton LD7 1TU. Tel 0547 528214

Llanfair Waterdine

This pretty, 400-year-old low stone building houses a good example of a cosy country pub. Armchairs, log fires and a wood-burner give a comfy air to the tap room and carpeted lounge, packed with various brasses and rural artefacts. A small enclosed beer garden overlooks the River Teme. Marston's Pedigree, Tetley Bitter, Ansells Pale Ale and Pale Mild (keg) are sold at the bar and a range of malt whiskies is offered. The bar food menu is straightforward at lunchtimes (savoury mince in Yorkshire pudding, £3.95, vegetable curry, £4.30), slightly more adventurous in the evenings (chicken and mushroom fricassée, £4.90, beef in garlic and wine, £5.95). Three double rooms offer country-style accommodation.

Brewery: Free house
Licensees: Mick and Judy Richards
Opening hours: 12-2pm, 7-11pm; closed Tue lunchtime; Sun 12-2pm, 7-10.30pm (may close in future on Mon, Nov-Mar)
Bar food: 12-1.30pm, 7-9pm; Sun 12-1.30pm
Accommodation: (Price per room) £33/£40; single occupancy negotiable

---

WHITE SWAN
Llanfrynach, near Brecon LA3 7BZ. Tel 0874 86276

Llanfrynach

Food takes a high priority in this family-run pub, which sits in the heart of the village, near the church. There is a degree of originality in the choice of menu; Welsh lamb chops (£7.30) and Welsh trout with bacon (£7.20) give a local flavour, and there are less pricey items such as vegetable chilli (£4.70) or baked eggs kindhoven (two eggs on onion and cheese, covered in cream and cheese, £4.30). Although dishes are not cheap, portions are particularly generous. Desserts are perhaps less enterprising than the main meals. Tables in the bar are divided by open wooden partitions; exposed stone walls, flagstone floors and open fires maintain a traditional atmosphere in this late 17th-century building, whose stone exterior is painted white. Flowers IPA and Brains are served at the bar. Seating is provided in a small paddock area decorated with flowers.

Brewery: Free house
Licensee: David Bell
Opening hours: 12-2.30pm, 7-11pm; closed Mon lunchtime; Sun 12-2.30pm, 7-10.30pm
Bar food: 12-2pm, 7-10pm (except Mon evening); Sun 12-1.30pm, 7-9pm
Children: Welcome anywhere; not permitted in garden unless supervised; outdoor play area

VINE TREE
Llangattock, near Crickhowell NP8 1HY. Tel 0873 810514

Llangattock

Popular and well patronised, this is a pub where the emphasis is on food, with a very large blackboard listing a wide choice of items. Examples include stockpot soup (£1.40) or baked stuffed tomato with savoury fish filling (£2.75) for starters, and lemon sole au gratin (£7.95), pork chops in almond and cheese sauce (£6.25) or half a roast duck in a choice of sauces (£9.50) as main dishes. Service here is brisk and no-nonsense, and a large part of the bar, which has an open fire and is partly furnished with West African slate tiles, is now used as a dining area. This is probably a place for an enjoyable meal rather than a quiet, drink or a leisurely evening, though there are pleasant views towards Crickhowell over the River Usk. Draught Bass, Brains, Flowers Original and Boddingtons are all available on tap.

Brewery: Free house
Licensee: I S Lennox
Opening hours: 11am-3pm, 6-11pm; Sun 12-3pm, 7-10.30pm
Bar food: 12-2.30pm, 6.30-10pm; Sun 12-2.30pm, 7-10pm
Children: Welcome anywhere

⊜ RADNOR ARMS
Llowes, near Glasbury HR3 5JA. Tel 0497 847460

Llowes

A remarkable range of freshly cooked dishes is offered at this listed stone building, now more of a restaurant than a pub. Once a drovers' inn, the present building is partly 400 and partly 150 years old, and enjoys stunning views from its valley setting of the Black Mountains and Brecon Beacons. The small, carpeted bar, with an open fire and furnished with cushioned settles brought from a church, is now used mainly as an eating area. Plates painted by local artist Alex Williams are on display. A few examples of dishes include game and brandy soup (£2.20) or lobster terrine (£4.55) as starters; goujons of brill (£9.15), stir-fried chicken with walnuts (£6.95), seafood lasagne (£5.95) or American flat omelette (£5.30) as main courses; and gâteau Veronique - white and dark chocolate with coulis - or whinberry pie (each £2.80) as desserts. Felinfoel and Tetley beers are served on tap; there are also 88 wines and champagnes, 24 malt whiskies and ten ports, as well as speciality herb teas. Outside, customers can enjoy the charming gardens, complete with pergola, a patio and terrace.

Brewery: Free house
Licensees: Tina and Brian Gorringe
Opening hours: 11am-3pm, 6.30-11pm; closed Mon, except BHs; Sun 12-3pm
Bar food: 11am-3pm, 6.30-11pm; Sun 12-3pm
Children: Welcome if well behaved

GRIFFIN
Llyswen, near Glasbury LD3 0UR. Tel 0874 754241

Llyswen

The two bars in this beautiful, creeper-covered 15th-century building, set on a corner site in a riverside village, have really become an annexe to the restaurant. Sandwiches, which had long been a feature, are no longer available; the high-quality dinner menu is, however, available in the bar. Items range from Stilton celery and port terrine (£3.75) or cream of mushroom soup (£2.50) to jugged venison (£8.50) or ratatouille pasta au gratin (£6.75), with a dessert menu including fresh raspberries and home-made sorbets and ices. Boddingtons and Flowers IPA are on tap, and an extensive wine list includes a house wine from the twin auberge in France. Simple and comfortable accommodation is provided in three double, two twin and two single rooms. A garden and patio are open to residents; tables are also set in front of the building.

Brewery: Free house
Licensees: Richard and Di Stockton
Opening hours: Summer 11am-3pm, 6-11pm; winter 12-2.30pm, 7-11pm; Sun 12-3pm, 7-10.30pm
Bar food: 12-2pm, 7-9pm (except Sun)
Restaurant: 12-2pm, 7-9pm; Sun 12-2pm, set lunch at £10.50 only, residents only in evening
Accommodation: (Price per person) single £28.50, double £25
Children: In eating area only
Credit cards:
AMERICAN EXPRESS®, Access, Visa, Diners

◉ HARP INN
Old Radnor, near Presteigne LD8 2RH. Tel 054 421655

Old Radnor

Wonderful views are offered from this renovated 15th-century pub, set on a high hillside by a churchyard and looking out towards Radnor Forest. A large common extends up to the church wall, where children can play quite safely. Antique furniture, including several unspoiled settles, is laid out in the two bars, with flagstone floors and open fires, and a generally friendly atmosphere prevails. A rather narrow range of bar food is available, including granary bread sandwiches (£1.35), home-made soup (£1.75), salmon steak (£6.50) and steak, pepper or Diane (£8). Booking is necessary for the separate restaurant area in high season. Woods Special, Hereford Supreme and Hook Norton are served on tap; a sensible, well priced wine list is offered, as well as eight to ten malt whiskies. Three charming double rooms are available, with outstanding views of the surrounding countryside.

Brewery: Free house
Licensees: Robert and Shirley Pritchard
Opening hours: 12-2pm, 7-11pm; closed Tue lunchtime and all day Mon; Sun 12-2pm, 7-10.30pm
Bar food: 12-1.30pm, 7-10.45pm; Sun 12-1.30pm
Restaurant: Times as bar food
Accommodation: (Price per room) £40
Children: Only if well behaved; outdoor play area

⊜ TRIANGLE INN
Llansantffraed Cwmdeuddwr, Rhayader LD6 5AR. Tel 0597 810537

Rhayader

Small and cosy, this 16th-century weatherboarded pub (with ship-lap timber) gives a very friendly welcome. Its customers range from farmers, factory workers and local professional people to tourists. The views - over the River Wye - are fine, and a short menu offers tasty food at fair prices. Items are changed as they run out; examples include leek soup (£1.20), mixed grill (£6.95), chicken in Pernod on rice or beef in beer (each £3.50); vegetarian options are available. Draught Bass and Welsh Brewers Hancock's HB are served on tap, and there is a good range of whiskies. The two bars are traditionally laid out with settles and copper-topped tables, and decorated with horse-brasses and china plates; because of the low ceiling, darts players must stand in a pit. A patio has tables and chairs overlooking the Wye, and a park with swings and roundabouts is conveniently placed near by.

Brewery: Free house
Licensee: Williams Garlick
Opening hours: 12-3pm, 6.30-11pm; Sun 12-3pm, 7-10.30pm
Bar food: 12-2pm, 6.30-9pm; Sun 12-2pm, 7-9pm
Children: Welcome anywhere; outdoor play area

⊜ STAR INN
Talybont-on-Usk, near Brecon LD3 7NX. Tel 0874 87635

Talybont-on-Usk

Despite its setting, in a nondescript house on a narrow road, backed by a canal, this is a remarkable pub. Its distinctive style, rather Bohemian, is heavily influenced by the landlady; its customers are a mix of canal tradespeople, outdoor pursuits enthusiasts, families and musicians (there is regular blues music on Wednesdays and jazz on Thursdays). The U-shaped, three-bars-in-one arrangement is equipped with open fires and an old bread oven. Draught beers include Draught Bass, Scottish & Newcastle Theakston, Brains, Bullmastiff, Burton Bridge, Smiles, Crown Buckley, Exmoor Gold and Flowers. The food is no-frills, tasty and nourishing, and eaten from cramped tables; Indian dishes are a speciality, and there are always vegetarian options. Examples are chicken in home-made leek and Stilton sauce (£5.50) and beef Madras (£4.50). The atmosphere here is dusty, noisy and welcoming; anyone who walks in is immediately a 'local'. There are plenty of pub games on offer in a separate games room, and a quiz is run regularly. A walled garden by the river is open to customers. Two homely double rooms (one with three beds) are available.

Brewery: Free house
Licensee: Joan Coakham
Opening hours: 11am-3pm, 6-11pm (Sat 11am-11pm); Sun 12-3pm, 7-10.30pm
Bar food: 12-2.15pm, 6.30-9.45pm (Sun from 7pm)
Accommodation: (Price per person) single £20, double £18-£19
Children: Welcome anywhere; outdoor play area
Credit cards: Access, Visa

SCOTLAND

Borders

❖

Central

❖

Dumfries & Galloway

❖

Fife

❖

Grampian

❖

Highland

❖

Lothian

❖

Strathclyde

❖

Tayside

❖

BORDERS

CROW INN
Auchencrow, near Eyemouth TD14 5LS. Tel 08907 61253

Auchencrow

This 18th-century whitewashed building houses a true country pub, set back from the road in a traditional village, which attracts a good mix of customers to its two beamed bars where Broughton Greenmantle and Tennent Special are on draught and a wide range of malt whiskies and liqueurs is stocked. Customers can play darts cards, pool or dominoes in the bars, and outside, as well as the garden, there is a putting green. Bar food offers dishes like deep-fried garlic mushrooms at £1.65 and sole bonne femme at £6.50 and in the evenings a restaurant is open.

Brewery: Free house
Licensee: Christopher Woods
Opening hours: 12-2.30pm, 6-11pm; closed Tue; Sun 12.30-2.30pm, 6-11pm
Bar food: As opening hours until 9pm
Restaurant: Summer, times as bar food, evenings only; winter, times as bar food, weekend evenings only
Children: Not permitted in Public Bar

CLOVENFORDS HOTEL
Clovenfords, near Galashiels TD1 3LU. Tel 0896 85203

Clovenfords

A statue of Sir Walter Scott, surrounded by dried flower pictures and old photographs, gazes down on the broad spectrum of people who frequent this former coaching inn. Anglers and shooting enthusiasts rub shoulders with tourists and locals in the two warm and welcoming bars, where all kinds of entertainment from folk music to recital evenings and a Burns' supper are held. The place has many literary associations, and the owners are keen to promote them. On tap in the bar are Alloa Special and Light, Caledonian 80/-, and a Tetley ale, and there is also plenty of choice from the wine list and range of malt whiskies. The bar menu changes daily, and can include starters like egg mayonnaise at £1.75 and pâté for £1.95. There are main courses such as Whitby scampi for £5.25 and minced beef pie for £4.25, and choices from the sweet menu like apple strudel, or peach crumble, both at £1.75. Seven well furnished rooms offer spacious accommodation. Outside there is a beer garden.

Brewery: Free house
Licensee: Sylvia Hamilton
Opening hours: 11am-12 midnight
Bar food: 12-2pm, 4.30-6.30 (high teas), 7-9.30pm
Restaurant: Times as bar food
Accommodation: (Price per person) single £30, double £22.50
Children: Welcome anywhere; outdoor play area
Credit cards: AMERICAN EXPRESS®, Access, Visa

⚅CASTLE HOTEL
6 The Square, Greenlaw TD16 6UK. Tel 03616 217

Greenlaw

This fine old Georgian coaching inn is set back from the road in the centre of the village. Its two comfortable and welcoming bars are fitted out in country-house style, decorated with old china, photos of the village and local sketches and warmed in winter by open fires. No electronic games or other entertainment disturbs the peaceful atmosphere where customers enjoy Broughton Greenmantle and Alloa Caledonian 80/- on draught and can choose from a range of more than 30 malt whiskies. The bar menu might offer French onion soup at £1.60, savoury pancake at £4.90, or stuffed mussels at £6 and there is also a separate restaurant, for which it is advisable to book. There are eight bedrooms, each equipped with television and telephone and decorated in country style, and a garden with good views.

Brewery: Free house
Licensee: Alistair Appleton
Opening hours: 11am-11pm
Bar food: 12-2.30pm, 6.30-10pm
Restaurant: Times as bar food
Accommodation: (Price per person) £20
Children: Welcome anywhere
Credit cards:
AMERICAN EXPRESS®, Access, Visa, Diners

⚅ TRAQUAIR ARMS HOTEL
Innerleithen , near Peebles EH44 6PD. Tel 0896 830229

Innerleithen

Music, verse and stories are part of the regular entertainment in the carpeted bar at this comfortable ivy-covered hotel. There's a warm welcome from efficient staff, and an interesting menu is on offer for those who want to eat: starters like lentil and mushroom pâté for £2.40, and filo parcels for £2.60, and main dishes such as grilled trout at £5.10, Traquair steak pie for £4.35, and nut and cheese risotto for £3.50. Sweets like cheesecake and steamed ginger pudding are both under £2. On tap in the bar are Broughton Greenmantle Ale and Scottish Oatmeal Stout, Traquair House Ale, and Tartan Special and Mild. There are ten pastel-coloured bedrooms.

Brewery: Free house
Licensees: Mr and Mrs Anderson
Opening hours: 11am-12 midnight; Sun 12.30pm-12 midnight
Bar food: 12-9pm
Restaurant: Times as bar food
Accommodation: (Price per person) single £15, double £27
Children: Welcome anywhere; outdoor play area
Credit cards: Access, Visa

⚅ BLACK BULL HOTEL
Market Place, Lauder TD2 6SR. Tel 0578 722208

Lauder

A great profusion of gleaming horse-brasses decorates the walls of the bar at this 17th-century listed hotel. Here the cosy atmosphere is enhanced by the low lighting and comfortable armchairs, and the friendly staff help to make this a popular place with local country people. Bar food is standard pub fare, with starters like soup at £1.20 and pâté at £2.10, and there are main courses such as steak pie for £4.50, chicken nuggets for £2.80, and scampi at £4.80. Vegetarian dishes can be made to order, and puddings

Brewery: Free house
Licensee: Mr Watters
Opening hours: 11am-12 midnight
Bar food: 12-3pm, 5-9pm
Restaurant: Times as bar food
Accommodation: (Price per person) £17.50-£22.50
Children: Welcome anywhere;

include apple pie and cheesecake, both £2. Broughton Greenmantle Ale is on tap, along with Murphy's Stout, McEwan 80/- and Tartan Special, and the choice of wines and malt whiskies is quite extensive. Outside this large, white-painted inn in the village square is a beer garden with seating, and accommodation is available in 14 comfortable bedrooms.

family room; outdoor play area
Credit cards: Access, Visa

PLOUGH INN
Lilliesleaf, near Melrose TD6 9JD. Tel 08357 271

Lilliesleaf

There's a friendly welcome for both the regular locals and the many visitors who frequent this large, plain hostelry in the village's main street. Inside the spacious Public Bar an open fire, settles and a dartboard create a relaxed ambience, while the Lounge is more conventionally comfortable and cosy with tables and chairs. Paintings by an Edinburgh artist hang on the walls awaiting sale, and and there are several horse-brasses. On tap are McEwan 80/-, 60/- and Export, and Tartan Special, and a reasonable range of malt whiskies. Bar food is both tasty and interesting: the menu offers starters like soup at £1, and crispy coated Camembert for £2.30, and main dishes such as gigot of lamb for £4.75 and lasagne for £4.60. There's a variety of sweets at £1.50. A courtyard outside the late 18th-century coaching inn offers seating in summer, and there are three very attractive double bedrooms.

Brewery: Free house
Licensee: Mr Hannah
Opening hours: 11am-12 midnight
Bar food: 12-2pm, 7-9pm (except Mon)
Accommodation: (Price per person) double £22
Children: Until 8pm in Lounge area only

GREEN TREE HOTEL
41 Eastgate, Peebles EH45 8AD. Tel 0721 20582

Peebles

A solid local trade, swollen by tourists during the season, keeps this comfortable and welcoming hotel-cum-pub busy. The large, white-painted building is set just off the main street, and indoors the carpeted bars offer open fires and relaxing settles in a pleasant atmosphere. Old photographs hang on the walls, and once a month a folk music evening is held here. On tap are Caledonian 80/-, Tennent Special, Guinness and Murphy's, and a regularly changing guest beer. There's also a good number of blended and malt whiskies. Bar food includes starters like home-made soup at £1.20, and breaded mushrooms for £1.75, and there are main dishes like home-made steak pie at £4.25, fried haddock for £3.95, and Hawaiian pork chop for £4.50. Hot fudge delight and chocmint surprise both appear on the sweet menu at £1.75. Accommodation is available in 14 well decorated bedrooms; the garden is for residents only.

Brewery: Free house
Licensee: Mr Edge
Opening hours: 11am-12 midnight
Bar food: 12-2.30pm, 4.30-8pm
Restaurant: Times as bar food
Accommodation: (Price per person) £18.50-£24.50
Children: Welcome anywhere except bar area; outdoor play area
Credit cards: AMERICAN EXPRESS®, Access, Visa, Diners

⊜ TIBBIE SHIELS INN
St Mary's Loch, Selkirk TD7 5NE. Tel 0750 42231

St Mary's Loch

Set as it is on the Southern Upland Way path, this old inn is very popular with the many walkers who converge on this lovely area. It is named after Tibbie Shiels who ran the hostelry for over 50 years last century, and during his famous stewardship many well-known literary figures of the day were frequent visitors to the place. Old prints of some of these literary giants, such as the poets Scott and Hogg, hang on the walls along with pictures of the hilly locality. The bar is snug and cosy with welcoming open fires and low ceilings, and there is plenty of atmosphere. Free loch fishing is available to visitors at this white-painted 18th-century building set amongst trees in six acres of grounds beside St Mary's Loch. The bar food consistently achieves high standards, with main courses like spicy chicken for £3, Yarrow trout at £4.25, and cashew nut loaf for £3. Starters include home-made soup at £1.25, and there are such puddings as chocolate fudge gâteau at £1.75 and Spotted Dick for £1.70. On tap are Broughton Greenmantle Ale, Belhaven 80/- Ale and Tennent Special. Accommodation is available in five pleasantly furnished and spacious rooms. In summer there is seating in the large garden.

Brewery: Free house
Licensees: Mr and Mrs Brown
Opening hours: 11am-12 midnight
Bar food: 12.30-2.30pm, 3.30-8.30pm (except Sun-Wed in winter)
Restaurant: Times as bar food
Accommodation: (Price per person) single £20, double £17
Children: Welcome anywhere; outdoor play area
Credit cards: Access, Visa

⊜WHEATSHEAF
Main Street, Swinton, near Coldstream TD11 3JJ Tel 0890 860257

Swinton

This traditional rural pub looks out over the village green and its garden has open views to the Lammermuir Hills. An across-the-board clientele finds it welcoming and comfortable, but its award-winning restaurant draws in customers from further afield. The two bars serve Broughton Greenmantle and Tennent 70/- beers, as well as a list of 50 wines and numerous malt whiskies. Bar food is also good, with dishes like devilled whitebait (£3.40), Border lamb (£8.75) and braised oxtail (£5.20). Traditional games such as darts , dominoes and pool rub shoulders with electronic games in one of the bars. There are four bedrooms, traditionally furnished in country style.

Brewery: Free house
Licensees: Alan and Julie Reid
Opening hours:11am-3pm, 6-11pm; closed Mon
Bar food:11am-2.30pm, 6-9.30pm (except Sun evening)
Restaurant:12-2.15pm, 6-9.30pm (except Sun evening)
Accommodation: (Price per person) £25
Children: Welcome, but not permitted in the Public Bar after 8pm
Credit cards: Access, Visa

CROOK INN
Tweedsmuir, By Biggar ML12 6QN. Tel 08997 272

Tweedsmuir

The poet Robbie Burns wrote 'Willie Wastle' while staying at this old inn, and the work has been immortalised in the naming of the Public Bar. Flagged floors and an open fire lend a cosy atmosphere and lots of character to this room, and there's also a Lounge Bar. An extension built in the 1930s is pure art deco, and the toilets are worth checking out. Set beside the River Tweed in the heart of the countryside, this inn attracts a mixed crowd with many older people among the hotel guests. Bar food comes in well presented, generous helpings, and offers good value for money: starters like sauté mushrooms in garlic cream, and cruickett egg, both at £2.95, and main courses such as home-made steak pie at £5.25 and Crook grill at £10.50. On tap are Broughton Greenmantle Ale and Scottish Oatmeal Stout, McEwan 80/-, Tartan Special and Guinness. There are lovely views from the eight bedrooms, and as well as two beer gardens there is a putting green in summer.

Brewery: Free house
Licensees: Mr and Mrs Reid
Opening hours: 12-11pm (Sat 12 midnight); Sun 12.30-11pm
Bar food: 12-9pm
Restaurant: 7-9pm
Accommodation: (Price per person) double £26
Children: Welcome anywhere; family room; outdoor play area
Credit cards:
AMERICAN EXPRESS®, Access, Visa, Diners

CENTRAL

⊕ KINGS SEAT
19 Bridge Street, Dollar FK14 7DE. Tel 0259 42515

Dollar

Situated at the centre of the village, with street parking available, this very well maintained pub offers two clean and welcoming Lounge Bars, one with an open fire. A pleasant atmosphere, helpful service and a background of piped music make it the ideal venue for an evening drink or family bar meal, and it also has a lunchtime business clientele. There is no garden. Generously served food is both well cooked and attractively presented, the menu including main dishes like an 8oz peppered sirloin steak ((£9.60) and chicken supreme vol au vent (£6.15) and starters and snacks like like prawn cocktail (£2.35) and avocado savoury (£2.65), with banana split or toffee and butterscotch surprise as puddings. Draught beers include Alloa Special and Export, together with Caledonian 80/- Ale, ABC Best Bitter and guest beers like Jennings Bitter.

Brewery: Free house
Licensee: Daniel McGhee
Opening hours: 11am-2.30pm, 5-11pm (Thu-Sat 12 midnight); Sun 12.30-2.30pm, 6.30-11pm
Bar food: 12-2pm, 5-9.15pm; Sun 12.30-2pm, 6.30-9pm
Children: Welcome in larger Lounge Bar only
Credit cards: AMERICAN EXPRESS®, Access, Visa

⊕ STRATHALLAN HOTEL
Chapel Place, Dollar FK14 7DW. Tel 0259 42205

Dollar

Winner of the Booker Best Pub in Britain award, and 1992 Pub of the Year for both seafood and wine, this well run village pub offers speciality ranges of both malt whiskies and real ales, the latter including Theakston Best Bitter, Belhaven St Andrew's Ale, Ind Coope Burton Ale and Harviestoun Original 80/- , 70/- (Waverley), 85/- (Ptarmigan) and 90/-. A complete cross-section of customers is attracted to two traditional bars where the walls are hung with a collection of original photographs of famous people and where quiz and music nights provide an alternative to the usual amusements of pool and juke box. An excellent restaurant specialising in fish brings in locals as well as tourists with a menu of fresh, tasty and attractively presented dishes that includes many unusual items; a meal beginning with clam chowder (£1.95), for example, might also include Cajun chicken (£7.95) and Orlani Italian ice-cream with fudge sauce (£2.15), and there will always be something to suit the preferences of vegetarians. The garden contains seating for 30 people, there are good car parking facilities, and overnight accommodation is available in completely modernised, well decorated rooms.

Brewery: Free house
Licensee: Patricia Boyd
Opening hours: 11am-2.30pm, 5-12 midnight (Fri and Sat 1am); Sun 12-3pm, 6pm-12 midnight
Bar food: As opening hours until 9pm
Restaurant: 6-11pm
Accommodation: (Price per room) single £30-£35, double £40-£50
Children: Welcome anywhere except in bar later in evening
Credit cards: AMERICAN EXPRESS®, Access, Visa, Diners (restaurant and accommodation only)

⊜ SALMON LEAP INN
19 Main Street, Drymen G63 0BQ. Tel 0360 60357

Drymen

A n original 18th-century coaching inn with 20th-century extensions, set beside the main road at the village centre with a beer garden behind it, this comfortable country pub is popular with backpackers and walkers of the West Highland Way as well as local regulars and family groups. A stuffed pike adorns one of three bars, which have collections of horse-brasses and Clydesdale collars, and piped music provides a relaxing background to such time-honoured pursuits as darts, dominoes and cribbage and the consumption of Younger Tartan Special and McEwan beers. The bar menu (evening meals also being served in a separate restaurant during high season) offers main courses like lasagne (£4.75), salmon steak (£6.95) or a pint of prawns (£5.75) - the selection also featuring a vegetarian option alongside ranges of starters and desserts. Standard bedrooms include a honeymoon suite complete with four-poster bed.

Brewery: Free house
Licensee: James Bryce-Lind
Opening hours: 11am-11pm
Bar food: 11.30am-2.30pm, 6-9pm (Sat 11.30am-9pm); Sun 12.30-9pm
Restaurant: Summer only (Etr-Sep), 6-9.30pm; booking necessary
Accommodation: (Price per room) single from £25, double from £45
Children: Only if dining or accompanying adults; family room

⊜ OLD MILL INN
4-6 Balfron Road, Killearn G63 9NJ. Tel 0360 50001

Killearn

M alt whiskies (particularly those produced by local distillery Glengoyne) are served alongside Tennent Special and 80/- at this village pub - an 18th-century threadmill workshop and cottage - on the main road opposite the church. A garden with seating and a play area makes it popular with local families, and it also attracts backpackers and passing commercial trade to its two beamed bars, one warmed by a log fire in winter. Here, or in the separate restaurant, they can enjoy a largely home-cooked meal - soup at £1.05 perhaps being followed by chilli (£3.85) and hot apple pie (£1.55).Two newly furnished single rooms, one with a veranda overlooking the Campsie Fells, are available for overnight stays.

Brewery: Free house
Licensee: Leslie Carrughers
Opening hours: 11am-11pm
Bar food: 12-2pm, 6-9pm; Sat and Sun 12-9pm
Restaurant: Times as opening hours
Accommodation: (Price per person) single £15-£18
Children: Welcome in Lounge Bar and restaurant areas; outdoor play area

⊜ CLACHAIG HOTEL
Gray Street, Killin FK21 8SL. Tel 0567 820 270

Killin

A ttractively set, overlooking the Falls of Dochart, this village-centre hotel - well maintained, though its building is over 300 years old - has both a large car park and a pleasant garden area with picnic tables and chairs. Very popular with tourists in summer, the small bar also has a regular clientele of local customers (including family groups)

Brewery: Free house
Licensee: John Mallinson
Opening hours: 11am-11pm
Bar food: Summer 12-9.30pm; winter 12-3.30pm, 5.30-9pm
Restaurant: 6.30-9.30pm;

who gather to sample Tartan Special and McEwan 80/- beer, McEwan and Becks lager and Blackthorne cider. Piped music and electronic games augment the traditional pastimes of pool, darts, dominoes and cards, with live music and singing on Friday and Saturday evenings in summer, and the bar menu offers a vegetarian option as well as dishes like roast beef (£4.25) or the regional delicacy of haggis, neeps and tatties (£2.95). Meals are also served in a separate restaurant decorated with illustrations of the history of the McNabb area. Modernised bedrooms provide overnight accommodation.

booking necessary in summer
Accommodation: (Price per person) £18
Children: Welcome anywhere
Credit cards: Access, Visa

⊕ LADE INN
Kilmahog, By Callander FK17 8HD. Tel 0877 30152

Kilmahog

B uilt in the 1930s as a tearoom, this large, isolated pub stands in a rural setting near the river, on the road to the Trossachs, beside the Callander-to-Killin footpath/cycleway.The garden is set with tables and chairs and features a fish pond. Tourists and locals alike appreciate the range of more than 20 malt whiskies served in its two comfortable bars alongside a wine list featuring California, Australia and New Zealand labels; a good selection of bottled beers is also available, and draught beers include Webster's Yorkshire Bitter, Courage Directors, Ruddles County and Younger Tartan Special. The bars and separate restaurant offer a menu which features such regional dishes as haggis Ecosse (£2.35) and wild salmon steak (£7.75). Two pleasantly decorated bedrooms with excellent views are equipped with television and tea-making facilities.

Brewery: Free house
Licensee: Mr David Stirrup
Opening hours: 11am-11pm
Bar food: 12-2pm, 6-9.30pm; Sun 2-5.30pm, 6-9.30pm
Restaurant: Times as bar food
Accommodation: (Price per person) double from £20
Children: Welcome anywhere; half portions available
Credit cards: Access, Visa (restaurant and accommodation only)

⊕ CROSS KEYS HOTEL
Kippen, near Stirling FK8 3DN. Tel 0786 870293

Kippen

M ore than a dozen malts and a good range of wines are sold alongside a selection of draught beers including Younger No 3, Broughton Greenmantle and Guinness at this attractive white-painted hotel on the main street of the village; bottled Old Jock (a strong ale) is also available. Welcoming and homely, it caters particularly well for families - some local, some from the surrounding areas - and is popular with tourists who appreciate the opportunity to relax in its two comfortable bars (which have electronic games as well as pool, darts and dominoes) warmed by open fires. Bar meals include popular choices like home-made steak pie (£4.50) and lasagne (£3.75), old-age pensioners as well as children can be served half portions, and there is

Brewery: Free house
Licensees: Mr and Mrs Watt
Opening hours: 12-2pm, 5.30-10.30pm; Sun 12.30-2pm, 5.30-10.30pm
Bar food: 12-2pm, 5.30-9.30pm; Sun 12.30-2pm, 5.30-9.30pm; high teas 5.30-6pm daily
Restaurant: 12-2pm, 7-8.45pm; Sun 12.30-2pm, 7-8.45pm; à la carte meals in evenings; booking necessary
Accommodation: (Price per

always a vegetarian dish; the restaurant also offers an à la carte menu in the evenings. Three pleasant, well equipped bedrooms look out over Carse of Stirling to the hills beyond and there is an equally pleasant garden.

person) from £19.50
Children: Welcome in family room; not encouraged in bars
Credit cards: Visa (for amounts over £25)

SHERIFFMUIR INN
Sheriffmuir, near Dunblane FK15 0LH. Tel 0786 823285

Sheriffmuir

A pleasant outdoor eating area, children's play equipment and a large car park make this small but efficient moorland inn a popular venue for both locals and tourists in summer. A large wine list is available, as well as a range of real ales and draught beers including Alloa Special 70/- and Arrol's 80/-, Burton Ale, Marston's Pedigree and Guinness. Tea and coffee are served whenever the pub is open, and the comfortable bar offers an extensive and varied menu - a typical meal perhaps comprising home-made pâté with oatcakes (£2.65) followed by local smoked trout salad (£4.95) and hot apple pie (£1.95) - with suitable alternatives for both vegetarians and children. Live entertainment (folk music, for example) is sometimes provided, and maps and pamphlets relating to the Battle of Sheriffmuir are available for those exploring the district. An attractively decorated bedroom has a television and tea-making facilities.

Brewery: Free house
Licensee: Peter Colley
Opening hours: Summer 11am-11pm; winter 12-2.30pm, 5.30-11pm (closed Sat and Sun)
Bar food: 12-2pm, 6-9pm; Sat 12-2.30pm, 6-9.30pm (summer only); Sun 12-2.30pm, 6-9pm (summer only)
Restaurant: Times as bar food; booking necessary at weekends or for large parties
Accommodation: (Price per room) double £38
Children: Welcome except near bar; outdoor play area
Credit cards: Access, Visa

⊕ WOOLPACK INN
Glassford Square, Tillicoultry FK13 6AU. Tel 0259 50332

Tillicoultry

This well maintained black-and-white painted building with shuttered windows - an inn for 250 years - stands near a burn in the oldest part of the village, close to the information centre. A small, beamed bar area hung with military pictures, guns and brasses is made welcoming by an open fire during the colder months, and in its friendly atmosphere all kinds of customers gather to relax over cards, dominoes or electronic games and appreciate the good choice of malts, liqueurs and real ales - draught beers including McEwan Export, Alloa Special and Light, Jennings Bitter, Caledonian 80/- Ale and Guinness. Two rooms are set aside for eating, and bar menus offer good standard main dishes like fried haddock (£3.25), steak pie (£3.55) and braised steak (£3.95), with a range of starters and desserts; a special pensioners' three-course meal is available on Thursdays.There is no garden.

Brewery: Free house
Licensee: Daniel McGhee
Opening hours: 11am-11pm
Bar food: As opening hours
Restaurant: Thu-Sat 12-2pm, 6-9pm; Sun 12.30-3pm
Children: Not permitted in bar area; half portions available; family room

DUMFRIES & GALLOWAY

⊜ FARMERS INN
Main Street, Clarencefield, near Dalton DG1 4NF. Tel 0387 87675

Clarencefield

The real ales are a popular pull at this welcoming old pub, particularly the weekly changing guest beers. The regulars on tap that the beer drinkers come to sample are Caledonian 70/- and 80 /-, and Draught Bass. Many years ago Robbie Burns was reputed to have tasted a less potent brew when he stayed here while 'taking the waters' at the Brow Well. There is still a traditional, rural atmosphere in this early 18th-century coaching inn which once played the role of village shop. Old sporting guns, photographs and paintings by local artists hang comfortably in the homely bar where an open fire adds to the cosiness in winter. Food is fairly standard but offers good value for money, including dishes like home-made steak pie for £3.50, and lasagne or deep-fried chicken nuggets with dip, both at £3.40. Starters like spicy lattice potatoes with garlic mayonnaise dip cost £1.35, and apple pie with cream or ice cream at £1.15 makes a tasty sweet. There is always a vegetarian dish on the menu, and on summer Sundays afternoon tea is served. A small beer garden at the front of this village centre inn offers some seating, and accommodation is available in two comfortable, modern bedrooms with central heating.

Brewery: Free house
Licensee: Colin Pearson
Opening hours: 11am-2.30pm, 6-11pm (Fri 12 midnight); Sat and Sun 11am-11pm
Bar food: 12-2pm, 7-9pm
Accommodation: (Price per person) £12
Children: Welcome only if eating; family room

⊜ GLOBE INN
56 High Street, Dumfries DG1 2JA. Tel 0387 52335

Dumfries

This is the inn where Robert Burns used to while away the hours, and the wood-panelled Snug Bar is a living museum in his memory. The Burns connections have made this one of Scotland's most famous pubs, and there are plenty of Burns memorabilia and pictures of the annual festival to captivate even the most casual fan of his poetry. Tourists and visitors mingle with regulars in the two bars, and on tap are real ales from Maclay and Scottish Brewers. There are also about 35 malt whiskies. Bar food is tasty and plentiful, with starters like smoked mackeral pâté at £1.80, and exciseman's prawns for £2.40. How towdie is chicken Scottish style, howff special is beefburgers with relish, and these dishes and the traditional haggis are all under £4. This early 17th-century pub is up a narrow alleyway off the main street in the town centre, and a courtyard provides a suntrap with tables and chairs.

Brewery: Free house
Licensee: Maureen McKerrow
Opening hours: 11am-11pm
Bar food: 12-3pm (except Sun)
Restaurant: 6-9pm (except Sun) in summer by arrangement
Children: Welcome anywhere; own menu available

◉ COURTYARD
High Street, Eaglesfield, near Lockerbie DG11 3PQ. Tel 04615 215

Eaglesfield

This former drapery shop has only been a pub since 1985, but already it is gaining a reputation for its thoughtful and inventive food. Dishes like collops of venison with cranberry and Drambuie sauce, and sautéd duck breast with a winterberry cassis are both £7.95, and mild chicken and mango curry with brown rice and cashew nuts is £5.95. Starters include falafel with piquant sauce at £2.40, and courgette and spinach terrine with crusty Italian toast for £2.45. To complement the food there are wines from several different countries, and on tap are Murphy's, McEwan Pale Ale and Younger Tartan Special. There are also nearly 40 malt whiskies. Old books and pictures, and local historical artefacts make interesting displays in the relaxing bar with its pointed sandstone walls. Outside this village-centre country pub a small and intimate courtyard provides seating. There are three comfortable bedrooms.

Brewery: Free house
Licensee: Michael Mason
Opening hours: 12-2.30pm, 6.30-11pm (Sat and Sun 12 midnight); closed Mon
Bar food: 12-2pm
Restaurant: 7-9pm (by arrangement only)
Accommodation: (Price per person) £12.50; children £5
Children: Not permitted under 14 years in Public Bar; family room; outdoor play area
Credit cards: Access, Visa

◉ STEAM PACKET HOTEL
The Quay, Isle of Whithorn DG8 8LL Tel. 09885 334

Isle of Whithorn

Mementoes of the old steam packet era and maritime artefacts make a fascinating historical display at this old harbourside hotel. Yachtsmen and sailing types as well as local regulars make a beeline for the two atmospheric bars - one of traditional stone with open solid-fuel stove, the other with photographs and a strongly seafaring flavour. Dominoes and pool are available here, and there are occasional folk nights. Seafood is high on the menu as might be expected, and live lobsters are kept in a tank for personal selection. Shellfish bisque at £2.60 and rollmop herrings at £1.75 are typical starters, followed by main dishes like poached salmon steak with Hollandaise sauce for £8, and scallops or whole grilled Dover sole both for £9.50. Vegans and vegetarians are also catered for without any previous notice being required. On tap are Younger Tartan Special, McEwan Pale Ale and 80/-, Tennent 70/- and Guinness. The wine list is also comprehensive, and there are 24 malt whiskies. This traditional 18th-century quayside building has a flower garden and patio with benches, and five basic bedrooms offer accommodation.

Brewery: Free house
Licensee: John Scoular
Opening hours: 11am-11pm; Sun 12-11pm
Bar food: 12-2pm; 7-9.30pm
Restaurant: 7-9.30pm
Accommodation: (Price per person) £22.50
Children: Not permitted in Public Bar; family room; outdoor play area; own menu available
Credit cards: Access, Visa

🍺 BALMORAL HOTEL
High Street, Moffat DG10 9DL. Tel 0683 20288

Moffat

There's a bustling, efficient atmosphere in this cosy, down-to-earth pub in the centre of the historic village of Moffat. This enthusiasm in no way detracts from the traditional bar as a place to relax, and exposed wooden beams add to its pleasant old-world feel. Horns and guns are on display, and from time to time folk musicians come along to entertain the mixed clientele of families, locals and business people. On tap are Broughton Greenmantle Ale and Scottish Oatmeal Stout, and Tennent 70/-, and there's a good selection of wines and malt whiskies. The food is delicious and promptly served, and includes bar meals like scampi and chilli con carne both at £4.20, and trout for £4.80, all offering very good value for money. There is usually a vegetarian dish on the menu. This 18th-century black-and-white coaching inn offers traditional, comfortable accommodation in 16 neat and tidy bedrooms.

Brewery: Free house
Licensee: John Graham
Opening hours: 11am-2.30pm, 5.30pm-11pm
Bar food: 12-2pm, 6-9pm
Restaurant: 6-9pm
Accommodation: (Price per person) single £24-£32, double £20-£24
Children: Welcome anywhere; family room
Credit cards: Access, Visa

🍺 GEORGE HOTEL
High Street, Moniaive DG3 4HN. Tel 08482 203

Moniaive

One of the oldest pubs in Scotland and the oldest in the county, the George dates back to 1624 and has many interesting original features still intact. The Tramp's Hole on the fireplace is where villagers used to leave money for passing itinerants, and there is also the old covenanters' hiding hole. Flagged floors and original old beams in the bars provide reminders of those bygone days, and photographs of local historical importance hang on the walls. Rural artefacts are displayed, and an open fire keeps the atmosphere cheerful in winter. On tap are McEwan Tartan, Belhaven 60/-, 70/- and 80/-, Guinness and Murphy's, and a choice of 36 malt whiskies is offered. The food is reasonably priced, and includes haggis at £2.25, chicken and mushroom pie at £2.95, and scampi for £3.25. A colourful garden contains tables and chairs at this riverside, village-centre pub, and there are three double bedrooms.

Brewery: Free house
Licensee: Frederick Payne
Opening hours: 11am-11pm; Sun 12-11pm
Bar food: As opening hours
Accommodation: (Price per person) £15
Children: Welcome anywhere until 8.30pm

🍺 CRIFFEL INN
The Square, New Abbey, near Dumfries DG2 8BX. Tel 038785 244/305

New Abbey

Children are made to feel at home in the unassuming atmosphere of this pub whose friendly owner is a steam engine enthusiast. Toys and books are kept handy in the bar for small visitors, and there is a large collection of model

Brewery: Free house
Licensee: Herries McCulloch
Opening hours: 11.30am-2.30pm, 5.30-11pm; Sun 12-

steam engines which are exhibited. This is an unpretentious, welcoming sort of place with a no-nonsense, old-fashioned decor and a relaxed ambience. It goes without saying that families are regular customers along with country locals, and there's a beer garden outside the colourful Victorian building which is popular with both. Good, honest fare is served here, offering excellent value for money: egg mayonnaise at £1.35 and home-made soup for 95p are tasty starters, and main dishes include roast beef and Yorkshire pudding, gammon steak and pineapple, and home-made quiche, all £3.90. Puddings like fruit melba and banana split both cost £1.40. Broughton Best Bitter, McEwan 70 /- and a Belhaven real ale are on tap, and bottled Broughton Old Jock Beer and Greenmantle Extra are also for sale. Around 85 whiskies offer a dazzling choice for lovers of the 'wee dram'. Accommodation is available in five comfortable bedrooms.

2.30pm, 6.30- 11pm
Bar food: 12-2pm, 4.30-7pm
Restaurant: Times as bar food
Accommodation: (Price per person) single £9.50, double £17.50- £19.50
Children: Welcome anywhere; outdoor play area
Credit cards: Access, Visa

⚜ CREEBRIDGE HOUSE
Minnigaff, Newton Stewart DG8 6NP. Tel 0671 2121

Newton Stewart

Once the home of an earl, and a former shooting lodge, this old hotel still offers elegant and gracious accommodation and food of a very high quality. A grand piano, antique furniture, ornate mantles and grand log fires reflect its aristocratic heritage which dates back to 1760, before it was turned into a comfortable hotel in 1920. It attracts a mixed clientele, not least for the very tasty and imaginative meals which are prepared and served here. Starters include chicken liver pâté with oatcakes at £2.65, and soup for £1.65, and there are main courses like loin of lamb with sweet herb crust for £8.20, collops of venison with cranberry and Drambuie sauce for £7.95, and chicken and mango curry with brown rice, coconut and cashew nuts for £5.95. To wash it all down are real ales like Theakston XB, Flowers Original, Tennent Export and Guinness, as well as a guest beer. There are several traditionally styled bedrooms.

Brewery: Free house
Licensee: Chris Walker
Opening hours: 11am-2.30pm, 6-11pm
Bar food: 12-2pm, 6-9pm; Sun 12.30-2pm, 7-9pm
Restaurant: 7-8.30pm
Accommodation: (Price per person) £27.50-£35
Children: Welcome anywhere until 10pm; family room
Credit cards: Access, Visa

Quoits

Throwing a ring over a low post in the ground is the basis of a pastime which was repeatedly forbidden by law from the 14th century on and at some unknown date became a popular pub game. Clubs were competing in Scotland and the North of England before 1850. The game has always been especially strong in the North East, where a standard throwing distance of 11 yards emerged, but 18 yards is the pitch length in East Anglia. The game is subtler and more elaborate than might be supposed, as is the allied pastime of throwing horseshoes.

CROWN HOTEL
North Crescent, Portpatrick DG9 8SX. Tel 077681 261

Portpatrick

There is not too much evidence left of the converted fishermen's cottages dating from 1800 which have been transformed into this very smart, upmarket hotel. The maritime connection of this harbourside building remains in the seafaring displays throughout, but there are also copper pans and brasses, and pictures of aircraft everywhere. A wide range of customers, from tourists, locals and business people keeps the place busy, but no matter how rushed the staff become there is always an air of welcome. McEwan 80/-Export and Tartan Special are on tap along with Guinness, and there's a good wine list. Bar food leans heavily on the fruits of the ocean, with dishes like prawn breval with boiled potatoes at £7.60, seafood pancake for £7.65, and seafood platter costing £18.50. A red-brick courtyard provides some seating, and there is accommodation in 12 bedrooms.

Brewery: Free house
Licensee: Bernard Wilson
Opening hours: 11am-11.30pm; Sun 12-11pm
Bar food: 12-2.30pm, 6-10; Sun 12-2.30pm, 6.30-10pm
Restaurant: Times as bar food
Accommodation: (Price per person) single £33, double £31
Children: Welcome anywhere; family room
Credit cards: Access, Visa

FIFE

ABERDOUR HOTEL
High Street, Aberdour, near Dumfermline KY3 0SW. Tel 0383 860325

Aberdour

This neat, black-and-white painted hotel with traditional stables and courtyard has stood at the centre of the village for 200 years, but there has been an inn on the site since 1648. Small and well run, it attracts mainly local and business customers to its roomy, comfortably furnished bar enlivened by piped music and electronic games as well as the time-honoured pursuits of dominoes and cards; every couple of weeks, on Friday evenings, there will also be live rock and roll music. Draught beers include Theakston Best Bitter, McEwan 80/-, Younger Tartan Special, Broughton Greenmantle 80/- and Guinness, while an extensive wine list accompanies menus comprised largely of straightforward dishes like deep-fried breaded haddock at £3.80 and beef and ale pie or gammon steak, both at £4.50. Bedrooms in traditional style offer television (including Sky) and tea-making facilities.

Brewery: Free house
Licensee: Russell Kelly
Opening hours: 11am-11pm
Bar food: 12-2pm, 6-9pm
Restaurant: 6-9pm
Accommodation: (Price per person) double from £22.25; family room available
Children: Welcome anywhere, but not in the bar after 8pm
Credit cards: AMERICAN EXPRESS®, Access, Visa

CRAWS NEST HOTEL
Pittenweem Road, Anstruther KY10 3DA. Tel 0333 310691

Anstruther

This well kept hotel within easy reach of the sea offers both a pleasant garden and ample car parking facilities despite its town-centre setting. Housed in a large 18th-century building, it is perhaps more impersonal than many smaller pubs, but the three bars (with their darts, pool, electronic games and piped music) attract an across-the-board clientele; a superior wine list and range of malt whiskies supplement the comprehensive choice of bottled beers (Broughton Greenmantle for example), while draught beverages include McEwan 80/-, Younger Tartan Special and Guinness. Meals are served both in the bar and the separate restaurant - a typical meal comprising smoked halibut salad (£2.65), roast beef (£4.50) and banana sundae (£2) - and a dinner-dance is held on Saturday evenings. Fifty well equipped bedrooms are available, two with four-poster beds.

Brewery: Free house
Licensee: Ian Birrell
Opening hours: 11am-11pm
Bar food: 12-2pm, 6-10-9.30pm
Restaurant: 12.15-1.45pm, 7-8.45pm; booking necessary
Accommodation: (Price per room) double £68-£86
Children: Welcome anywhere
Credit cards: AMERICAN EXPRESS®, Access, Visa, Diners

MELDRUMS HOTEL
Main Street, Ceres, near Cupar KY15 5NA. Tel 033482 286

Ceres

A large range of malt whiskies, together with Younger Tartan Special, Guinness and McEwan lager on draught, is served at this very well maintained hotel which stands in the village centre, welcoming a clientele made up of businessmen as well as families and local regulars; pots of flowers help to create an attractive exterior, the small garden is set with benches, and a stream runs to one side of the building. In the cosy, open-fired bar with its comfortable chairs and piped music, you can play dominoes and choose a meal from the bar menus ranging from a ploughman's (£3.25) to roast beef and Yorkshire pudding (£4.50), with a choice of starters and puddings. Overnight accommodation is provided in rooms equipped with television and tea-making facilities.

Brewery: Free house
Licensee: Anne McKinnon
Opening hours: 12-3pm, 5-11pm
Bar food: 12-2pm, 6-9pm
Restaurant: 7-9pm; booking necessary
Accommodation: (Price per room) single from £29, double from £42
Children: Welcome anywhere
Credit cards: Access, Visa

OLD RECTORY INN
West Quality Street, Dysart KY1 2TA. Tel 0592 51211

Dysart

An 18th-century building, set in a large, Georgian-style garden with a friendly rabbit to keep children interested, at the heart of a village near the sea, this busy pub offers limited parking space on waste ground opposite. Primarily a place for eating, it features an extensive range of wines at all price levels, but draught beers are restricted to McEwan 80/-, and there are also McEwan and Tennent lagers on draught.

Brewery: Free house
Licensee: David North
Opening hours: 11.30am-3pm, 6.30-11pm
Bar food: As opening hours
Restaurant: Times as bar food; booking essential

Food is excellent - the same varied selection being served in bar and restaurant - and dishes like green pea soup with smoked sausage (£1.25), roast leg of lamb (£4.50) and pineapple upside-down pudding represent good value for money. The beamed bar with its flagged floor, wood-burning stove and cushioned settles is undisturbed by any form of entertainment; landlord and staff are welcoming and attentive.

Children: Welcome anywhere; outdoor play area
Credit cards: AMERICAN EXPRESS®, Access, Visa

⊛ SHIP INN
The Toft, Elie KY9 1DT. Tel 0333 330246

Elie

A typical 19th-century fisherman's inn, and larger than its external appearance would suggest, this seaside pub has very pleasant restaurants - with wonderful sea views from upstairs - as well as its small, traditional bar with flagged floors, old oak beams and open fires where locals congregate to play old-fashioned games like dominoes, Shut the Box and Captain's Mistress whilst enjoying draught beers such as Younger Tartan Special, Belhaven 80/-, Courage Directors and Guinness. Delicious, attractively presented, value-for-money food has earned the Ship a well deserved reputation, a typical meal perhaps following smoked peppered mackerel at £1.95 with lamb, rosemary and tomato (£4.95) and chocolate fudge cake (£3.25); a list of some 30 wines offers a suitable accompaniment to any selection. An outside bar and barbecue area operate in July and August.

Brewery: Free house
Licensee: Richard Philip
Opening hours: 11am-11pm
Bar food: 12-2.30pm, 6-9pm (Fri and Sat 9.30pm)
Restaurant: Times as bar food; booking necessary in one restaurant
Children: Welcome in restaurants and Lounge Bar
Credit cards: Access, Visa

⊛ KETTLEBRIDGE INN
Cupar Road, Kettlebridge, near Glenrothes KY7 7QD. Tel 0337 30232

Kettlebridge

B usy and well run, set on the main road through the village, this small, 180-year-old pub attracts tourists as well as regulars during the summer months - not least by an array of real ales that won it third place in the CAMRA ratings and includes Belhaven 60/-, 80/- and St Andrew's ales, a guest ale and Murphy's Stout; Belhaven lager, Scrumpy Jack cider and a selection of bottled Continental beers are also on sale. Both the beamed bar and the restaurant are warmed by open fires, and customers can choose from a selection of popular dishes like chicken Kiev (£5.95), steak pie and lasagne (both at £3.95); a choice of starters and desserts is available. On warmer days meals may be taken on the terrace. Pleasant overnight accommodation furnished in country style is well equipped

Brewery: Free house
Licensee: James M Aikman
Opening hours: 11am-2.30pm, 5-11pm; Fri-Sun 11am-11pm
Restaurant: 12-2pm, 7-8.30pm (except Mon evening); Sun 12.30-2pm, 7-8.30pm
Accommodation: (Price per person) single or double from £15
Children: Not permitted in bar; welcome in restaurant; half portions available
Credit cards: Access, Visa (for meals only)

⊛ HOFFMANS
435 High Street, Kirkcaldy KY1 2SG. Tel 0592 204584

Kircaldy

Overlooking Kircaldy harbour from the main road, Hoffmans features an interior far pleasanter that its exterior suggests. A pub to visit for meals rather than just for a drink, it offers a very varied menu of home-cooked dishes: duck liver pâté at £1.65, for example, might be followed by chilli con carne, bacon and pepper flan or spiced lamb and couscous (all at £3.75), with peach and plum crumble (£1.50) to complete the meal. Draught beers include McEwan 80/-, Younger No 3 and Guinness, with a range of malt whiskies and a superior wine list also available.

Brewery: Free house
Licensee: Jan Hoffman
Opening hours: 11am-11pm; closed Sun
Bar food: Wed-Sat 12-2pm, 7.30-9.30pm; Mon and Tue 12-2pm
Children: Welcome anywhere

GRAMPIAN

⊛ TOWIE TAVERN
Auchterless, near Turriff AB53 8EP. Tel 0884 201

Auchterless

This attractive pub on the main Aberdeen-to-Banff road (near Towie-Barclay castle) dates from 1804, but there was an inn on the site long before this. Set in the depths of the countryside, it offers its clientele - business folk, locals and families - ample parking space and the choice of two comfortable, attractively furnished bars; some lovely wood from an old church has been used in the making of the chairs, and the walls are hung with fishing rods as well as prints and plates. Over 60 wines and a large selection of malt whiskies are on sale here, as well as a wide range of bottled beers and lagers, with Guinness and McEwan on draught; the meals served in the bars and three separate dining rooms cater for all tastes, including dishes for both vegetarians and children, and a feature of Sunday evenings is the serving of free stovies - a traditional Scots potato dish.

Brewery: Free house
Licensees: Eileen and Douglas Pearson
Opening hours: 11am-2.30pm, 6-11pm; Sun 12.30-2.30pm, 5-11pm
Bar food: 12-2pm, 6-9pm; Sun 12-2pm, 5-8.30pm (6pm in winter)
Restaurant: Times as bar food
Children: Welcome anywhere
Credit cards: Access, Visa

Royal State

The Crown is one of the commonest inn names, for patriotic reasons and sometimes because the inn stood on royal land. The Rose and Crown celebrates Henry VII's achievement in ending civil war by reconciling the rival roses of York and Lancaster in the crown. The King's Head, King's Arms and Queen's Arms are equally familiar, often with Henry VIII on the sign, roughly after Holbein. Elizabeth I, the Georges, Queen Victoria and Prince Albert make their appearances, too, and many pubs are named after children of George III or Queen Victoria (the Duke of York, Duke of Clarence, Duke of Edinburgh, etc). Others honour the Prince of Wales or his badge of the Feathers, while the Fleur de Lys recalls the fact that down to 1801 the kings of England claimed to be kings of France as well.

⊕ CROWN AND ANCHOR
Findhorn, near Forres IV36 0YF. Tel 0309 690243

Findhorn

One hundred and ten malt whiskies and more than 35 foreign bottled beers (Mexican, Spanish, Japanese, German and Dutch, for example) are available at this black-and-white 18th-century coaching inn - a solid building not picturesque in itself but beautifully set in a popular yachting and fishing area, looking out over the marina and Findhorn Bay. Beers are also an attraction, with seven real ales on draught including Murphy's, Beamish and Guinness stouts as well as Tennent 70/-. Two beamed bars adorned with old prints have electronic games and piped music (with live music on Sundays) and serve a good range of home-cooked dishes, a typical meal consisting of mushroom and garlic dip (£1.70), sirloin steak (£8.75) and apple pie with ice cream (£1.50). Six bedrooms, furnished in old-fashioned style, are available for overnight stays.

Brewery: Free house
Licensee: George Burrell
Opening hours: 11am-11pm
Bar food: As opening hours
Accommodation: (Price per person) single from £17, double from £16
Children: Welcome anywhere

⊕ GORDON ARMS
High Street, Fochabers IV32 7DH. Tel 0343 820508

Fochabers

Overlooking the town's high street, but boasting ample car parking space and a small garden, this 200-year-old coaching inn attracts all comers. Two comfortable, unobtrusively stylish bars feature a large open fire, a stained-glass window, copper tables and a collection of old prints; electronic games and pétanque provide entertainment, and quiet background music creates a relaxed atmosphere. A standard range of beverages is augmented by an extensive wine list with examples from all over the world and a choice of 30 malt whiskies. Bar food, like that served in the separate restaurant, is both excellent in quality and attractively presented, rollmop herring salad (£2) perhaps being followed by grilled lamb cutlet garni (£4.50) and fruit cheesecake (£2.10), for example. Modern accommodation includes two rooms with four-poster beds.

Brewery: Free house
Licensee: Mr Raul Suarez
Opening hours: 11am-2.30pm, 5-11pm
Bar food: 12-2.30pm
Restaurant: 12-2.30pm, 5-9.30pm
Accommodation: (Price per room) single £35 (£42 inc dinner), double £55 (£70 inc dinner)
Children: Welcome if accompanied by adult; family room
Credit cards:
AMERICAN EXPRESS®, Access, Visa

⊕ GORDON ARMS
Main Street, Kincardine O'Neil AB34 5AA. Tel 03398 84236

Kincardine O'Neil

Forty malt whiskies and a range of mainly French organic wines can be sampled here, while bottled Elephant Beer and a selection of premium lagers supplement the real ales available on draught, Theakston Best Bitter and a number of guest beers (Courage Directors and Boddingtons, for example). Customers of all types and ages gather in the two spacious bars to play darts, dominoes and electronic games - or to enjoy live entertainment on special occasions like Burns' Night or Hogmanay. Generously served bar meals are good, and the extensive menu contains an excellent vegetarian choice. A typical meal might be garlic mushrooms (£1.90), followed by either home-made beefsteak pie (£3.95) or curried tofu with rice (£4.50), with Kincardine pancakes (£1.95) to finish. Attractively set on the main street of the the historic Royal Deeside village, this character Victorian coaching inn provides an excellent base from which to explore the area, its spaciously airy bedrooms offering clean and comfortable accommodation.

Brewery: Free house
Licensee: Bryn Wayte
Opening hours: 11am-11pm
Bar food: 12-2.15pm, 5-9pm
Accommodation: (Price per person) single from £25, double from £20
Children: Permitted in large bar only
Credit cards:
AMERICAN EXPRESS®, Access, Visa

⊕ GRANT ARMS
The Square, Monymusk, AB51 7HJ. Tel 04677 226

Monymusk

The main building in the historic village's square, its Bennachie Lounge named after a famous nearby hill, this 19th-century hunting and fishing hotel (rebuilt in 1922) offers two simply furnished bars, conventionally adorned with fishing rods and deer antlers. Between 40 and 50 malt whiskies are on sale, and a wide range of bottled beers and lagers supplements Younger No 3 and McEwan 80/- and Export on draught. The bar menu offers a wide range of dishes, from home-made soup (£1.35), chicken liver pâté and oatcakes (£3.25) to coq au vin and fresh haddock cooked in beer (both at £4.25), or a vegetarian dish of the day (£4.75). The brandied apricot crêpe with hot apple sauce makes a delicious end to a meal. Live entertainment is provided occasionally, but an across-the-board clientele usually contents itself with such amusements as darts, dominoes and electronic games; in summer the courtyard - hemmed in by chalets on two sides - doubles as a tea garden. The 15 bedrooms offer a reasonable standard of comfort.

Brewery: Free house
Licensees: Mr and Mrs C Hart
Opening hours: 11am-3pm, 5-11pm; (Fri 11.30pm, Sat 11.45pm); Sun 12.30-11pm
Bar food: 12-2pm, 6-9pm; Sun 5-8.30pm
Restaurant: 12-2.30pm, 6.30-8.30pm (9.30pm at weekends)
Accommodation: (Price per person) single £35, double £54-£59
Children: Welcome until 8pm
Credit cards:
AMERICAN EXPRESS®, Access, Visa

⊜LAIRHILLOCK INN
Netherley, near Stonehaven AB3 2QS. Tel 0569 30001

Netherley

Sixty malt whiskies, a good wine list and a wide selection of bottled Continental beers and lagers are available at this attractive, modernised, 200-year-old coaching inn in the depths of the country; draught beers feature a guest ale each week - the range including Courage Directors, Thwaites Craftsman Bitter, McEwan Export and Gibbs Mew - and the establishment is renowned for its totally fresh bar food. No frozen products or chips are to be found here: instead you might enjoy crêpe fruit de mer (£3.95) followed by duck Creole (£8.75) and the traditional clootie dumpling (£2.15). Customers from miles around collect in the two beautifully furnished bars, one warmed by an open fire, to enjoy such traditional pursuits as darts and dominoes.

Brewery: Free house
Licensees: Frank and Anne Budd
Opening hours: 11am-3pm, 5-12 midnight
Bar food: 12-2pm, 6.30-9.30pm (10pm weekends)
Restaurant: 7pm-12 midnight; Sun 12-3pm, 7-9.45pm
Children: Welcome in conservatory and restaurant
Credit cards: AMERICAN EXPRESS®, Access, Visa, Diners

⊜UDNY ARMS
Main Street, Newburgh AB41 0BL. Tel 03586 89444

Newburgh

Popular with fishermen and birdwatchers as well as businessmen and family groups, this 100-year-old pub stands in the town's main street, beside the River Ythan. Both bars have a chintzy, country atmosphere, and the Café Bar offers television as well as darts, dominoes and cards; a model and picture of a lifeboat mark the fact that Newburgh once had a lifeboat station. Menus include both a vegetarian dish - creamed cheese and herbs at £3.65, for example - as well as reflecting the specialities of the area in Orkney oysters (£6.95) and cold salmon with prawns and salad (£6.50). An extensive wine list features Australian, Chilean and South African wines, and on draught are McEwan Export and Murphy's Stout are available on draught. A large conservatory and patio are used in summer and bedrooms furnished with antiques are provided for overnight guests.

Brewery: Free house
Licensees: Mr and Mrs D Craig
Opening hours: Cocktail Bar 12-2.30pm, 6-11pm; Café Bar 4-11pm
Bar food: 12-2pm (except Sun)
Restaurant: 6.30-9.30pm; Sun 6-9pm
Accommodation: (Price per person) single from £45.50, double from £56 (£45 at weekends)
Children: Welcome with parents in Café Bar; family room
Credit cards: AMERICAN EXPRESS®, Access, Visa

⊜PENNAN INN
Pennan, near Macduff AB43 4JB. Tel 03466 201

Pennan

One hundred and sixty malt whiskies are offered by this tiny pub, a converted 18th-century fisherman's cottage spectacularly set at the foot of steep cliffs on the quayside where the film *Local Hero* was shot. The range of draught beers is more modest, however, being confined to Belhaven Special and Drybroughs Heavy and Skol lager. Meals are

Brewery: Free house
Licensees: Norrie and Pat Grierson
Opening hours: 11am-11pm
Bar food: 12.30-2pm, 5.30-6.30pm

served both in the small, crowded bar - warmed by an open fire, hung with old local fishing pictures and displaying an unusual collection of blow lamps - and in a separate restaurant which was once the net store. Food is home-cooked, and menus include local specialities like fresh crab (served with salad and chips at £5.75) and jumbo prawns (£5.50). The seven simply furnished bedrooms have kept the atmosphere of the old fishing village, but there is no garden.

Restaurant: From 7pm; reservations required
Accommodation: (Price per person) single from £35, double from £20
Children: Welcome anywhere
Credit cards: AMERICAN EXPRESS®, Access, Visa

HIGHLAND

⊜ APPLECROSS INN
Applecross, near Lochcarron IV54 8LR. Tel 05204 262

Applecross

Mammoth portions of very fresh produce - especially locally caught seafood - is one of the great draws here, and a very mixed clientele from the young and lively to locals and tourists come to enjoy it. Once a temperance hotel with a history going back about 150 years, it has no such restrictions on alcohol these days, and several malt whiskies are backed up by draught McEwan Export and 80/-, and Guinness. The delicious food on the bar menu includes dressed crab salad for £5.95, queen scallops with rice at £5.25, and local haddock for £4.25. A vegetarian choice always appears on the menu, and afternoon tea is served. Seating is available in a garden and pation behind the hotel, and there are four comfortable bedrooms.

Brewery: Free house
Licensee: Judith Fish
Opening hours: 11am-11pm; closed Sun in winter
Bar food: As opening hours until 9pm
Restaurant: 7-8.30pm
Accommodation: (Price per person) £18.50
Children: Welcome anywhere

⊜ LOCK INN
Canalside, Fort Augustus PH32 4AU. Tel 0320 6302

Fort Augustus

Set beside a lovely clear canal in the village centre, this small sandstone pub has also seen service as a bank and later a post office. Its identity as a cosy and atmospheric drinking house is now firmly established, and it is a rarity in Scotland where that function is usually filled by hotel bars. Beer barrels provide the seating in the bar, with its stone walls and open fire, and old photographs of Fort Augustus hanging up. Folk music is played here. McEwan 80/- and Tartan Special are on tap, and there are several malts to sample. Snacks only are served at lunchtime, but in the evenings the wider bar menu includes such traditional Scottish dishes as haggis and clapshot for £3.10.

Brewery: Free house
Licensee: James MacLennan
Opening hours: 11am-11pm; Thu-Sat 11am-1am
Bar food: 12-3pm, 6-8.30pm
Children: Not permitted under 14 years and there is no garden
Credit cards: AMERICAN EXPRESS®, Access, Visa

⊜ BADACHRO HOTEL
Gairloch, near Poolewe IV21 2AA. Tel 044583 255

Gairloch

Yachtsmen, Highland tourists and locals all frequent this welcoming hotel which overlooks Loch Maree in the tiny village of Gairloch. More of a pub with rooms than a hotel, there's a lovely atmosphere in the bar where lots of oak is in evidence from the exposed beams to the benches. Low ceilings and an open fire complete the cosy picture. This listed whitewashed building is over 200 years old, and it nestles comfortably beside the old pier. A small garden with a couple of marble tables has views out over the sea. Bar food is served every day in the summer, and there are dishes like fisherman's pie for £2.90, and Gairloch prawns for £4.75. On tap are McEwan Export and Tennent 70/-, and there's a range of malt whiskies. Two small but very homely bedrooms offer accommodation.

Brewery: Free house
Licensee: Sheila King
Opening hours: Summer 12-2.30pm, 5-11pm; winter, Wed, Fri and Sat only 5-11pm
Bar food: As opening hours in summer only
Accommodation: (Price per person) £15; children under 12 years not permitted
Children: Welcome until 8pm

⊜ OLD INN
Gairloch, near Poolewe IV21 2BD. Tel 0445 2006

Gairloch

This traditional old coaching inn is in a lovely setting beside a river close to Gairloch Harbour but away from the main village. Anglers join tourists and families in the oak-panelled bar where an open fire creates a cosy feel even on the coldest Scottish winter days. The welcome at this family-run hotel is also warm and friendly even when the fire is not burning. Food is of an excellent quality and offers good value: starters like prawn cocktail and potato skins are £2,75, and there are main dishes such as turkey nuggets at £4.95, local herring for £11.50. Apple pie and cheesecake are both £2.25. As well as the bar food there is a bistro in the summer months and a restaurant open all year round. On tap are Younger No 3, Draught Bass, Tennent 70/-, Export and Light, Guinness and Beamish. Several different malt whiskies are on sale. Accommodation is available in 13 bedrooms.

Brewery: Free house
Licensee: David Carruthers
Opening hours: 11am-12 midnight; Sat 11am-11.30pm; Sun 11am-11pm
Bar food: As opening hours
Restaurant: 6.30-9.30pm
Accommodation: (Price per person) £27.50-£36.50
Children: Welcome anywhere
Credit cards:
AMERICAN EXPRESS®, Access, Visa

⊜ CLACHAIG INN
Glencoe, near Ballachulish PA39 4HX. Tel 08552 252

Glencoe

The magnificent mountain scenery around the site of the Massacre of Glencoe provides the setting for this famous old coaching inn. Its reputation is spread far and wide, and this 300-year-old inn has become almost a legend amongst mountaineers. Climbers and walkers as well as many other visitors feel at home amongst the marvellous collection of

Brewery: Free house
Licensee: Peter Daynes
Opening hours: 11am-11pm (Fri 12 midnight, Sat 11.30pm); Sun 12.30-11pm
Bar food: As opening hours

mountaineering photographs, and huge log fires provide a roaring welcome in the two stone-flagged bars. Real ales on tap here are Younger No 3, Alloa Arrol's 80 /-, Ind Coope Burton Ale, as well as Guinness, Murphy's and various guest beers. There is also a huge selection of malt whiskies. Bar food is mainly snacks, but only fresh produce is used, and portions are generous. As well as a large range of filled baked potatoes for £1.90 there are toasties at 75p, and a home-made vegetarian soup for 95p. At weekends the friendly atmosphere is enlivened when folk musicians entertain the customers, in late January there is a beer festival, and when the entertainment ceases there are always the stunning views to admire. Nineteen cosy, old-fashioned single bedrooms offer comfortable accommodation.

Restaurant: 6.30-9pm
Accommodation: (Price per person) £18-£24
Children: Permitted in Lounge Bar only
Credit cards: Access, Visa

⊜ GLENELG INN
Glenelg, By Kyle of Lochalsh IV40 8DJ. Tel 059982 273

Glenelg

Set in its own grounds overlooking the Isle of Skye, the spacious bar of this old coaching inn basks in plenty of natural light. This special place has a great atmosphere but is never uncomfortably busy, attracting mainly families and tourists, and there is regular live entertainment, often impromptu. There's a fine range of malt whiskies, and on tap are McEwan Export and Guinness. Highly recommended bar food includes dishes such as beef in red wine for £4.50 and salmon steaks at £5. The bar is closed on Sundays but the separate restautant is open on a Sunday evening. Six very luxurious bedrooms offer comfortable accommodation, and outside there's a pleasant patio with a wonderful view overlooking the sea.

Brewery: Free house
Licensee: Christopher Main
Opening hours: 12-2.30pm, 5-11.30pm; closed Sun
Bar food: 12.30-2pm, 6.30-9pm
Restaurant: 7-9pm (inc Sun)
Accommodation: (Price per person, inc dinner) £45-£75
Children: Welcome until 8pm; half portions available; family room
Credit cards: Access, Visa

STAGE HOUSE
Glenfinnan, By Fort William PH37 4LT. Tel 0397 83246

Glenfinnan

Set on the main road to the Western Isles between Fort William and Mallaig, this 17th-century staging inn enjoys a striking mountain setting. The traditional old building in the heart of the rugged countryside offers two quite different bars inside - a modern Lounge and a more old-fashioned Public Bar. Pine rafters look down on cushioned benches and chairs, and there is a vast collection of miniature whiskies. On tap are Marston's Pedigree Bitter, Dryburroughs Heavy Ale, Alloa Export and Guinness, and several malt whiskies are on sale. The bar menu offers starters such as prawn hoaggies at £3.55 and smoked salmon

Brewery: Free house
Licensees: Robert and Carole Hawkes
Opening hours: 11am-2.30pm, 5-11pm; Sat and Sun 11am-11pm
Bar food: 11am-2.30pm, 5-9pm
Restaurant: 6.30-8.30pm
Accommodation: (Price per person) £27.50; children under three years not permitted

salad for £3.25. Main dishes include scampi at £5.65, and haddock or a chicken quarter for £4.95. Apple pie and ice cream with shortbread are both £1.95. Accommodation is available in six double and three single modern bedrooms.

Children: Welcome anywhere
Credit cards: Access, Visa

⊜ CLUANIE INN
Glen Moriston, Kyle of Lochalsh IV3 6YW. Tel 0320 40238

Glen Moriston

There's an intimate atmosphere in this small, cosy inn thanks to some subdued lighting and comfortable furnishings. Outside, the large, isolated building is dwarfed by its impressive mountain surroundings, but inside it's all warm and welcoming, offering a good place to relax. Set on the main Fort William to Kyle of Lochalsh road, hillwalkers and tourists journeying to the Isle of Skye most often find their way to this remote place which was once a coaching inn and still carries out a similar function: small but cosy bedrooms provide homely and comfortable accommodation for travellers. Freshly prepared food served in generous portions is available in the bar, with roast of the day for £5.20, and home-made steak pie or haddock for £4.95. Sweets from the trolley cost from £1.95. McEwan Export and Murphy's are on draught, with a good range of island malts for sale. A courtyard offers some outdoor seating.

Brewery: Free house
Licensee: John Clinton
Opening hours: 11am-11pm
Bar food: As opening hours
Restaurant: 6-8.30pm (except Sun)
Accommodation: (Price per person) £26.50-£35.50
Children: Welcome anywhere; family room; own menu available
Credit cards: Access, Visa

Glenmoriston Arms Hotel, Invermoriston, *see page 476*

⊜ KYLESKY HOTEL
Kylesky, By Lairg IV27 4HW. Tel 0971 50 2231

Kylesky

This used to be the Kylesky ferry house, although nobody is sure about how old it is, and it still caters to the needs of fishermen, yachtsmen and the many tourists attracted to this magnificent location. Set right beside the Highland sea loch of Glencoul, it has superb views up the water to the mountains beyond. This appealing, low white building has an equally lovely atmosphere inside, where subdued lighting, an open fire and wood panelling create a pleasant place to relax. There are seven traditional cosy rooms furnished in keeping with the rest of the hotel which make staying overnight or longer a delightful option. In the bar McEwan Export and Tennent 80/- are on draught, and bar meals are served all day. Dishes include grilled langoustine and chicken tikka for £5.75, omelettes for £3.75, and there are starters like baked mussels and prawns for £3.25, and terrine of venison at £2.50.

Brewery: Free house
Licensee: M Klein
Opening hours: 11am-11pm
Bar food: As opening hours
Restaurant: 6.30-9pm (booking advised)
Accommodation: (Price per person) single £20-£23, double £38-£40
Children: Welcome anywhere
Credit cards: Access, Visa

⊜ GLENMORISTON ARMS HOTEL
Invermoriston, near Fort Augustus IV3 6YA. Tel 0320 51206

Invermoriston

Backed by a wooded hillside and close to Loch Ness, this traditional whitewashed building is in a very attractive setting. There's a relaxed, old-world atmosphere in the two bars, mingled with a strong sporting influence which comes from the wall-mounted antique guns and fishing rods. Antlers and old prints also adorn the walls. This old coaching inn, dating back about 200 years, is close to the main road in the tiny village of Invermoriston, and there is a pleasant and well kept garden on two sides. Platter of prawns at £2.25 and soup for £1.40 are two of the starters on the bar menu, and main courses include dishes like steak and ale pie at £4.75, aubergine mousaka for £4.25, and haddock at £4.50. There is always a vegetarian choice. McEwan 80 /- and Tartan are on draught, and there are about 100 malt whiskies for sale. Accommodation is available in eight pretty double bedrooms.

Brewery: Free house
Licensee: Alan Draper
Opening hours: 11am-11pm
Bar food: 12-2pm, 5.30-8.30pm
Restaurant: 6.30-8.30pm
Accommodation: (Price per person) £29.50
Children: In Lounge Bar only
Credit cards: Access, Visa

CRASK INN
Lairg IV21 4AB. Tel 054981 241

Lairg

A well-worn former drovers' inn whose remote setting by Loch Shin is one of its attractions. Bare and lonely Sutherland moors and hills surround the isolated old coach house, built in two-storey traditional style. Shooting sportsmen frequent this late 18th-century inn during the season, and it also draws in anglers, hill walkers and tourists. Indoors there's a comfortable and unsophisticated mixture of old and new, and paintings and photographs of the striking local scenery cover the walls. The bar food served here is good standard pub fare, and the portions are generous. Dishes like mince and tatties are £3.25, boozy venison is £4.25, king prawns cost £6.75, and sirloin steaks £8. Starters include soup of the day for 95p, and there are desserts like sticky toffee pudding and Eve's pudding both for £1.25. McEwan Export is on tap. Three simple bedrooms offer basic accommodation.

Brewery: Free house
Licensee: Susan Hayhurst
Opening hours: 11am-11pm
Bar food: As opening hours
Accommodation: (Price per person) single £25, double £17
Children: Welcome anywhere

LEWISTON ARMS HOTEL
Lewiston, near Drumnadrochit IV3 6YN. Tel 04562 225

Lewiston

Hanging flower baskets make a splash of colour against the whitewashed walls of this traditional long building. Set in a quiet street off the main road, this old drovers' inn dates from 1730. It is run along solid, old-fashioned lines by a pleasant couple, and on Sunday evenings a Scottish singer entertains the customers. Few drovers frequent the two oak panelled bars these days, having given way in large part to tourists and locals. Bar food includes reliable dishes like chicken, ham and leek pie, and cold roast, both costing £4.50, and fish and chips at £3.50. Starters include home-made soup at £1, and chicken liver pâté for £3. McEwan Export and Murphy's are on draught, and several malt whiskies are available. There's a large, well kept garden to the rear of the hotel, and nine homely and very comfortable bedrooms with low ceilings provide old-fashioned accommodation.

Brewery: Free house
Licensees: N J and H W Quinn
Opening hours: 11am-11pm
Bar food: 12.30-2.30pm, 6.30-9pm
Restaurant: 7-9pm
Accommodation: (Price per person) £22.50
Children: Not in Public Bar; outdoor play area
Credit cards: Access, Visa

PLOCKTON HOTEL
Harbour Street, Plockton, By Kyle of Lochalsh IV52 8TN. Tel 059984 274

Plockton

Palm trees on the foreshore of this 18th-century traditional building fronting the sea bear visual testimony to the temperate climate of this picturesque bay. Inside it's all warm and welcoming too, with dimmed lighting and brass

Brewery: Tennent
Licensee: Tom Pearson
Opening hours: 12-2.30pm, 5pm-12 midnight

fittings creating a pleasant atmosphere in the bars. Tourists during the seasons and locals during quieter times enjoy the Scottish and Irish folk music that is played every Thursday evening at this pub, known in the area as the Black House. A real ale from Maclays is on tap here with Tennent 70/- and 80/- ,and 14 different malts are on sale. Clear langoustine soup at £1.50 and Talisker whisky pâté for £2.50 make original starters, and main dishes include sizzler steak platter for £8.95, local queen scallops for £8.50, and hot pot at £4.25. Sweets cost from £1.50. A beer garden offers seating facing the bay, and accommodation is available.

Bar food: 12-2pm, 6-10pm; Sun 12.30-2.30pm, 6-9pm
Accommodation: (Price per person) £20-£22.50
Children: Welcoke except in Public Bar; family room; own menu available

---

@ COACH HOUSE INN
Stoneyfield, near Inverness IV1 2PA. Tel 0463 230244

Stoneyfield

There's a pleasant atmosphere inside this traditional single-storey inn, with its oak rafters, whitewashed walls, old timbered seating and tables, and cushioned settles in the bar. Set in the countryside just off the main road, it attracts many business and commercial customers, and at bar meal times it gets very busy. The freshly cooked food comes in large helpings, and offers good value for money. Dishes like highwayman steak come at £9.85, with beef Stroganoff at £10.75, and gammon steak for £4.75. Starters include Dornoy Firth mussels for £3.60, and seafood salad at £2.25. Puddings like home-made apple pie and cheesecake cost £1.50. On tap are McEwan Tartan and Export, Younger 80/- and Guinness, and afternoon tea can also be served. A patio off the bar provides a paved beer garden, and accommodation is available in five old-fashioned but comfortable bedrooms.

Brewery: Free house
Licensee: A Torrance
Opening hours: 11am-11.30pm
Bar food: 11.30am-2.30pm, 6.30pm-9.30pm
Restaurant: 7.30-9.30pm
Accommodation: (Price per person) single £27.50, double £40
Children: Not permitted after 7.30pm
Credit cards: Access, Visa

Coaching Days

The traditional English inn reached its apogee in the coaching age in the 18th century. This was the period of the capacious Georgian inn of popular nostalgia, with its jovial, welcoming landlord and army of maids, tapsters, ostlers and pot-boys. Here the stagecoaches halted to change horse, while the passengers went inside to warm themselves by a roaring fire, eat and drink and clean up. The best inns were social centres for affluent locals, tastefully furnished and lavishly provided with clocks, mirrors and barometers. In the second half of the century the smartest ones began to call themselves 'hotels', French-style.

Wine drinking had fallen off by this time and the old-style tavern disappeared, but the alehouses were growing far more comfortable. Some of them now called themselves taverns and from the late 17th century the term 'public house' came in. Some were now purpose-built, instead of being ordinary dwelling houses. The bigger ones had upstairs lodging rooms, decently furnished, and games rooms for shove halfpenny, billiards or bagatelle. They sold simple food - pies, bread and cheese, buns - eaten in a thick fug of tobacco smoke, and you could buy all sorts of things in the bar from small traders, from butter to gloves or pens.

⊕ MOREFIELD HOTEL
North Road, Ullapool IV26 2TS. Tel 0854 612161

Ullapool

Seafood is the speciality of this modern hotel set in the middle of a new housing estate with distant views of Loch Broom from its car park. Starters like west coast seafood chowder at £2.95 and mussels for £2.75 are part of the attraction of this place, and scampi tails makes a delicious main dish at £5.75. Meat also features on the bar menu, with choices like fillet of pork Hawaiian for £5.75, and starters such as pâté for £2.25. Sweets like ices and sorbets are offered, and a vegetarian choice always appears on the menu. There's a good range of malt whiskies on sale, and McEwan 80/- and Export are on tap. Inside the bar there are photographs of local scenes on the walls, and many tourists and business people come here as well as locals. Outside there's a small walled patio with tables and chairs, and several fairly basic, modern bedrooms are available for accommodation.

Brewery: Free house
Licensee: D Smyrl
Opening hours: 11am-2.30pm;, 5-11pm
Bar food: 12-2pm, 5.30-9.30pm
Restaurant: 6-9.30 (except Mon)
Accommodation: (Price per person) £20
Children: Welcome anywhere
Credit cards: Access, Visa

⊕ CEILIDH PLACE
West Argyll Street, Ullapool IV26 2TY. Tel 0854 612103

Ullapool

Vegetarians are particularly well catered for at this trendy rose-covered pub, although fish and meat eaters are by no means neglected. The lively and interesting atmosphere makes it a good place to linger, and depending on the season there's either a crowd of young locals here or a mixture of youthful tourists and locals. There's a separate clubhouse which is known throughout Scotland for its folk music events. In the two oak-panelled bars there's a great range of cask malt whiskies, and McEwan Export is on draught. Italian mushroom casserole at £4.25 and lentil lasagne for £3.25 are two examples of vegetarian dishes on the menu, and there is also haggis at £3.85, and fish and chips for £3.80. Set in a quiet street close to the town centre and overlooking the sea loch, this popular pub has several modern, comfortable bedrooms, and set amongst the roses outside is a pleasant patio with tables and chairs.

Brewery: Free house
Licensee: Jean Urquhart
Opening hours: 11am-12 midnight; Sun 12.30-2.30pm, 6.30-11.30pm
Bar food: As opening hours
Restaurant: 6-9.30pm
Accommodation: (Price per person) £30-£43
Children: Not permitted around bar area
Credit cards:
AMERICAN EXPRESS®, Access, Visa, Diners

LOTHIAN

GREY HORSE INN
Main Street, Balerno, near Edinburgh EH14 7EH. Tel 031-449 3092

Balerno

This 'wee gem' of a 19th-century village pub has been in the same family for many years, and the sense of continuity is part of its character. The delightful owner, Mrs Brow, keeps her customers in order and they love it - no swearing or stamping of feet is allowed here! The wood-panelled bar is quite unspoilt, and offers cosy and comfortable seating for the country regulars and others who frequent the place. A fine collection of old brewery mirrors enlivens the walls, and customers have to ring a bell to enter the Lounge. On tap here are Belhaven 60/- and 80/-, and there are several bottled beers. There is no bar food.

Brewery: Free house
Licensee: Mrs Brow
Opening hours: 11am-2.30pm, 5-11pm; closed Sun
Children: Not permitted under 14 years

⊕ BLACKNESS INN
The Square, Blackness, By Linlithgow EH49 7NL. Tel 0506 834252

Blackness

Long winding country roads lead down to the tiny village of Blackness where this pub sits on the Forth of Forth. It is famous for its haddock, and that fish features on the bar menu along with four or five starters, and main dishes like lasagne, steak pie and steaks. To wash it all down there's Ind Coope Burton Ale and Maclays 80/- Export, plus several bottled beers. Open fires create a cosy, comfortable atmosphere in the Lounge Bar and the Public Bar, and old local photographs adorn the walls. Outside there is a beer garden and barbecue, and five basic bedrooms offer overnight accommodation.

Brewery: Alloa
Licensee: Jim Slavin
Opening hours: 11am-2.30pm, 6-11pm; Sun 12.30-11pm
Bar food: 12-2pm, 6.30-10pm; Sun 5.30-10pm
Accommodation: (Price per person) £16
Children: Not permitted under 14 years in bar

⊕ CASTLE INN
Dirleton, near Edinburgh EH39 5EP. Tel 062085 221

Dirleton

This attractive old coaching inn is set opposite Dirleton Castle, with the village green laid out in front. The white-washed pub draws in all types of customers, from tourists to locals and business people, and often at weekends an accordian player adds to its appeal. There is a huge choice of bottled beers to sample, and in addition McEwan 80/- and 70/- are on tap. There are also several malt whiskies. Food is served all day, and the menu includes starters like butterfly-style breaded prawns at £1.75, and lentil soup for 90p. Also featured are main dishes like deep-fried scampi at £3.50,

Brewery: Free house
Licensee: Douglas Stewart
Opening hours: 11am-2.30pm, 5-11pm (Fri and Sat 11am-12 midnight); Sun 11am-11pm
Bar food: As opening hours
Accommodation: (Price per person) £19-£22
Children: Not permitted under 14 years in bar; outdoor play area

grilled sirloin steak for £8, and chicken in white wine sauce for £4.75. Banana split and steamed treacle sponge with custard are under £2. Eight twin and single bedrooms offer simple modern accommodation, and a garden outside the inn makes the most of its lovely situation.

Credit cards: Access, Visa

⊕ BENNETS BAR
8 Leven Street, Edinburgh EH3 9LG. Tel 031-229 5143

Edinburgh

This beautiful pub with lovely stained-glass windows is one of Edinburgh's best known. Situated next to the King's Theatre in a busy main street, the pub's traditional bars are never short of customers. Inside the decor is as attractive as the outside of the 19th-century building, and an open fire adds to the comfortable ambience and character. Over 100 malt whiskies are on sale here, and McEwan 80/- and Caledonian 70/- are on tap. Food is basic and good value, and includes soup for 90p, and chef's pâté at £1.75. Jumbo sausage is £2.25, lasagne £2.95, and scampi £3.95, and there are selections of salads. There is no garden.

Brewery: Scottish & Newcastle
Licensee: W Eaton
Opening hours: 11am-11pm; Sun 7pm-12 midnight
Bar food: 12-2pm
Children: Only in Lounge at lunchtime
Credit cards: Access, Visa

⊕ GUILDFORD ARMS
1-5 West Register Street, Edinburgh EH21 2AA. Tel 031-556 4312

Edinburgh

The fine architecture of this 18th-century pub includes a famous ceiling and galleried alcove above the bar. Positioned just off Princes Street in the city centre (there is no garden), it attracts a mixed crowd, especially in the evenings. But this is mainly a drinking man's pub, and children are not welcome here. The bar is comfortable, with stools and bench seating, and on tap are ten cask-conditioned beers and two English guest ales. Orkney Dark Island, Caledonian 80/- and Belhaven 80/- are just a few of the regulars. Snacks are served all day, with full meals at lunchtime only, including chilli con carne and roast chicken.

Brewery: Free house
Licensee: Gary Fletcher
Opening hours: 11am-11pm (Fri and Sat 11am-12 midnight); Sun 12.30-11pm
Bar food: 12-2pm

⊛ TATTLER
23 Commercial Street, Leith, Edinburgh EH6 6JA. Tel 031-554 9999

Edinburgh

Dimly lit bars with wooden chairs and benches, comfy couches and cosy corners makes this Victorian pub a very popular venue. Situated on a prominent corner near the harbour and the river, the Tattler is rapidly becoming a well known eating and drinking house within easy distance of the centre of Edinburgh. All kinds of people find their way into the pleasant atmosphere of the two bars, and on Saturday evenings a pianist entertains the customers. Caledonian 80/- ale is on tap, and there is a good wine list to complement the food. Haddock Mornay, barbecued spare ribs and prawn and haddie are some of the choices on the bar menu, and there are tempting sweets like bread-and-butter pudding, strawberries and cream, and profiteroles to finish off with. At least one vegetarian dish is always available on the menu No outside seating is available.

Brewery: Free house
Licensees: Mr and Mrs Thomson
Opening hours: 10.30am-11pm (Fri and Sat 10.30am-12 midnight); Sun 11.30am-11pm
Children: Welcome anywhere except standing at bar

⊛ TWEEDALE ARMS
High Street, Gifford, near Haddington EH41 4QU. Tel. 062081 240

Gifford

The 17th-century Tweedale Arms inn is the oldest building in the village of Gifford, where most of the other properties date from about 100 years later. This long, low, whitewashed building harbours a pleasant atmosphere inside its three cosy bars, with their low ceilings, open fires and comfy sofas. There's an interesting collection of miniatures, and the traditional game of dominoes is played here. Locally smoked Scottish salmon is on the bar menu at £4.25, with deep-fried mushrooms and garlic dip for £2.75, and main dishes include lasagne with side salad, and curried lamb Madras, both at £4.50. Various salads cost £5. There's a good wine list and an interesting range of malt whiskies, and on tap is McEwan 80/- and Guinness. Set deep in the countryside overlooking the village green, there are two gardens at the back of the pub, and several bedrooms offer accommodation.

Brewery: Free house
Licensee: Christopher Cook
Opening hours: 11am-11pm
Bar food: 12-2pm, 7-9pm
Restaurant: Times as bar food
Accommodation: (Price per person) single £47.50, double £60
Children: Welcome anywhere, but very young children in Lounge only after 8pm; outdoor play area
Credit cards: AMERICAN EXPRESS®, Access, Visa

⊛ FOUR MARYS
65 High Street, Linlithgow EH49 7AZ. Tel 0506 842171

Linlithgow

Mary Queen of Scots memorabilia is displayed in this old coaching inn which was named after the old Scottish folk song 'Yestreen I Had Four Marys'. Part of the walls of this historic building date back to 1650, and the pub is set opposite the even older and beautiful Linlithgow Palace

Brewery: Free house
Licensee: Mr Scott
Opening hours: 12-2.30pm, 5-11pm (Fri 12 midnight); Sat 11am-12pm

which was the birthplace of Queen Mary in 1542. Low ceilings, stone walls and old wooden benches vouch for the bar's antiquity, and in this comfortable and pleasant atmosphere country regulars and business people rub shoulders. On tap are ten real ales including Broughton Scottish Oatmeal Stout and Greenmantle Ale, and Robinson Best Bitter, and there are over 80 malt whiskies. Draught beers are changed constantly. Bar food includes dishes like fried fillet of haddock, and lasagne, both at £4.50, and haggis and neeps at £3.75. Puddings range from £1.50 to £2.45, and there is usually a vegetarian choice on the menu.

Bar food: As opening hours
Children: Welcome anywhere except bar
Credit cards: AMERICAN EXPRESS®, Access, Visa

⊕ HABBIES HOWE
Nine Mile Burn, Penicuik, near Edinburgh EH26 9LZ. Tel 0968 676969

Nine Mile Burn

Sketches of local characters line the whitewashed walls of this lovely old pub which dates back to the 14th century. Nestling in the peaceful Pentland Hills, it is nevertheless not particularly quiet inside where a lively and interesting crowd gathers. Occasionally folk singers come along to perform. The two bars are unspoilt and full of atmosphere, with their low ceilings and basic wooden benches. Locally brewed Broughton Greenmantle Ale is on tap, along with Tennent 80/- and Guinness, and several bottled beers are on sale. The speciality of the house is steaks, and the bar menu carries other dishes like Guinness and pepper stew, and baked yoghurt chicken. Cheesecakes, gâteaux and ice creams make tasty sweets. At weekends the place is open for afternoon tea, and there's a separate restaurant with exposed beams. There are attractive gardens and terraces outside, and accommodation is provided in four bedrooms.

Brewery: Free house
Licensee: L Wilson
Opening hours: 11am-11pm
Bar food: 12-2pm, 7-9pm
Restaurant: As opening hours
Accommodation: (Price per person) £20
Children: Welcome in separate children's area; outdoor play area
Credit cards: Access, Visa

HAWES INN
Newhalls Road, South Queensferry EH30 9TA. Tel 031-331 1990

South Queensferry

This historic inn features in works by Sir Walter Scott and *Kidnapped* by Robert Louis Stevenson who wrote the book while staying in one of the rooms. Both men are immortalised here as well as in their published works, and information about them shares space with ferry and Forth railway bridge memorabilia. This traditional Scottish coaching inn stands beneath the splendid bridge, and enjoys a fascinating history going back to the 17th century. The bars are comfortable with dim lighting and open fires, and are often full of tourists as well as local families and regulars. The atmosphere is friendly, and both the food and drink sides are run by the owners in a well organised manner. On

Brewery: Alloa
Licensee: C Parvin
Opening hours: 11am-11pm (Fri and Sat 11am-11.45pm); Sun 12.30-11pm
Bar food: As opening hours
Restaurant: 12-2.30pm, 6.30-10pm
Accommodation: (Price per person) single £34, double £51
Children: Welcome in family room

tap are Ind Coope Burton Ale and Alloa Arrols 70/- and 80/-ales. There are also guest beers every two weeks. Food is well priced, with home-made steak pie, haddock and chips, and crofter's pie all costing £3.95, and there is a salad bar. Outside the attractive whitewashed building on South Queensferry's main street a courtyard offers seating overlooking the Forth Bridge, and there is also a garden. Seven tastefully decorated and comfortable bedrooms, one with a four-poster bed, provide beautiful accommodation.

Credit cards:
AMERICAN EXPRESS®, Access, Visa, Diners

STRATHCLYDE

⊜ARDENTINNY HOTEL
Ardentinny, near Dunoon PA23 8TR. Tel 036981 209

Ardentinny

In a beautiful wooded setting on the shores of Loch Long, this fine, early 18th-century hotel, once an old droving inn, is surrounded by the Argyll Forest Park and its gardens stretch down to the shore, making it a popular calling-in place for yachtsmen as well as locals and tourists. There are two bars: the Lauder Bar takes its name from the well known singer Sir Harry Lauder, who lived in Ardentinny, and, apart from memorabilia devoted to his memory, has a nautical feel about the decor; the Viking Bar has a beamed ceiling, open fire and opens out on to a patio leading into the gardens. Draught beers include McEwan Export, Webster's Yorkshire Bitter and Guinness, and in the Lauder Bar darts, dominoes and kalaha can be played. The bar menu is well above average, as is the wine list, with dishes like seafood pancakes, mussels meunières with garlic bread, croissants filled with local prawns, venison sausages, and Musselburgh pie (mussels with beef and cheesy potatoes) ranging in price from £4.25 to £6.75. There is also a separate restaurant (booking advisable), where a non-smoking room is available, for evening meals. The 11 comfortable, well equipped bedrooms all have either forest or loch views.

Brewery: Free house
Licensee: John Horn
Opening hours: 12 noon-11pm; closed 1 Nov-15 Mar
Bar food: 12-2.30pm, 6-9.30pm (Sat, 12-3pm, 6-10pm); Sun 12 noon-9.30pm
Restaurant: 7.15-9.15pm
Accommodation: (Price per person) single £25-£41, double £25-£39
Children: Welcome anywhere; outdoor play area
Credit cards:
AMERICAN EXPRESS®, Access, Visa, Diners

⊜ OLD RACE COURSE HOTEL
2 Victoria Park, Ayr KA7 1TE. Tel 0292 262873

Ayr

A central open fire is the cosy focus of the bar in this Victorian pub set in its own grounds. Tables and chairs spaced around the carpeted floor encircle the fire, and photographs of racehorses - winners of the Ayr Gold Cup - grace the walls. Bar food is well cooked and served in

Brewery: Free house
Licensees: Mr and Mrs Nichols
Opening hours: 11am-12 midnight (Fri and Sat 12.30pm)
Bar food: 12-2.30pm, 4.30-9pm

generous proportions, and a popular innovation is the half portions which are available to pensioners as well as children. On the menu are starters like smoked salmon at £3.95 and melon boat for £2.35, and main courses such as game pie or venison and pheasant casserole, both at £5.45, and seafood platter for £5.25. Home-made cheesecake and raspberries in Drambuie are under £2. High teas are also served in the early evening. On tap are Younger Tartan Special, McEwan No 3 and Export, Guinness, and real ales from Theakston. Thirteen spacious and attractive bedrooms offer accommodation, and there is seating in the garden in the summer.

(Fri-Sun 10pm)
Restaurant: Times as bar food
Accommodation: (Price per person) £28-£30
Children: Welcome anywhere; family room; half portions available
Credit cards: AMERICAN EXPRESS®, Visa

⊜ FINLAYSON ARMS
Coylton, near Ayr KA6 6JT. Tel 0292 570298

Coylton

Attractive window shutters and hanging baskets of flowers brighten the entrance to this hotel-cum-pub in the village's main street. Golfers on package holidays swell the ranks of the locals and tourists who enjoy the homely atmosphere here, and the Lounge Bar in particular is comfortable and cosy. Robert Burns memorabilia pays tribute to the Scottish poet. On tap are Broughton Greenmantle Ale, Courage Bitter, Tennent Caledonian Special and Light, and Guinness, and there are 40 malt whiskies. Bar food is excellent, and the menu offers dishes like gammon steak at £5.50, home-made steak and kidney pie for £4.45, and scampi at £5.60. Starters include soup at 95p and pâté at £2.80, and there are puddings like apple cake and ice cream for £1.70. Vegetarian dishes can be made to order. A beer garden offers shaded seating, and there are nine pleasantly furnished bedrooms.

Brewery: Free house
Licensees: Mr and Mrs Munro
Opening hours: 11am-2.30pm, 5pm-12 midnight (Fri 1am); Sat 11am-1am; Sun 12.30-12 midnight
Bar food: 12-2pm, 6-8pm
Restaurant: Times as bar food
Accommodation: (Price per person) £24
Children: Welcome anywhere; own menu available; outdoor play area
Credit cards: AMERICAN EXPRESS®, Access, Visa

⊜CRINAN HOTEL
Crinan, By Lochgilphead PA31 8SR. Tel 054683 261

Crinan

An imposing late 19th-century building in the Scottish baronial style, this hotel stands in the village on the edge of the sea. Its Public Bar mirrors its setting with a nautical theme to the decor and a collection of marine artefacts. Its clientele is mostly local, but tourists do find it out in summer. Guinness and Tennent 70/- and 80/- beers are on draught, there is an excellent wine list and a large number of local malt whiskies. Bar meals might feature soup, marinated local herring, mussels, trout or steak and kidney pie, all, apart from the soup, costing between £3.50 and £5. There is another bar associated with the hotel, and also a

Brewery: Free house
Licensee: Mr NA Ryan
Opening hours: Summer 11am-11pm; winter 11am-2.30pm, 5-11pm
Bar food: As opening hours
Restaurant: Seafood, Tue-Sun, 8pm (one sitting only); Westwood Room, 7-9pm
Accommodation: (Price per person) single £75, double £50-

rooftop bar for the restaurants, of which there are two, one devoted to seafood; booking is advisable for both. There is also a coffee shop and outside a large patio where meals can be served in warm weather. Bedrooms are all individually decorated by Scottish artist Francis McDonald, have sea views and are equipped with television and phone.

£70
Children: Not permitted in Public Bar; family room
Credit cards:
AMERICAN EXPRESS®, Access, Visa

⊛ FENWICK HOTEL
Ayr Road, Fenwick, By Kilmarnock KA3 6AU. Tel 05606 478

Fenwick

Staff are very friendly and welcoming at this recently refurbished country pub that stands alone just outside the village of Fenwick. Set on the main A77, it attracts a passing trade as well as regular locals, and the smart carpeted interior offers comfortable cushioned seating on pine chairs, and extra warmth in winter from an open fire. Old photographs of the area offer a nostalgic touch, and on the last Sunday of each month country and western music is played live. Chicken with curry sauce at £4.90 and scampi at £4.95 are typical main dishes, and there are starters like deep-fried mushrooms for £2.95 and home-made pâté for £2.50. Sweet choices are changed daily. On tap are McEwan Export, Younger Tartan Special, Guinness and Murphy's, and there is a wide selection of bottled beers. Ten bedrooms offer king-sized, pastel-coloured accommodation, and there's a garden with tables and benches.

Brewery: Free house
Licensees: Mr and Mrs Dickson
Opening hours: 11am-12 midnight
Bar food: 12pm-10pm
Restaurant: Times as bar food
Accommodation: (Price per person) single £25-£40, double £34-£46
Children: Welcome anywhere; own menu available; outdoor play area
Credit cards: Access, Visa

UBIQUITOUS CHIP
12 Ashton Lane, off Byres Road, Glasgow G12 8SJ. Tel 041-334 5007

Glasgow

A converted 19th-century dairy houses this pub in a bustling, self-contained complex off the main thoroughfare. Noted for the excellence of its food and wines, the pub attracts a wide range of people from university students and BBC staff to business people and families. Many of the original features have been retained, in particular an impressive gantry, and there are tiled floors and an open fire. Wine certificates and large batiks decorate the walls. Outside in a stunning enclosed courtyard is a small pond and luxuriant exotic greenery. Bar food is served in the dining area, and includes starters like vegetarian haggis, neeps and tatties for £2.75, and chicken wings with salad for £3.95. Grilled shark at £ 7.95 appears on the menu, along with chicken casserole for £4.05, and grilled Scotch chops for £5.15. Bread pudding with cream costs £2.15, and home-made carrot cake is 95p. On tap are Caledonian 70/- and 80/-.

Brewery: Free house
Licensee: Ronald Clydesdale
Opening hours: 11am-11pm (Fri and Sat 12 midnight); Sun 12.30-11pm
Bar food: As opening hours
Restaurant: 12-2.30pm, 5.30-11pm; Sun 6.30-11pm
Children: In restaurants only
Credit cards:
AMERICAN EXPRESS®, Access, Visa, Diners

KILBERRY INN
Kilberry, By Tarbet PA 29 6YD. Tel 08803 223

Kilberry

This old converted crofter's cottage lies in the depths of the countryside about a mile from the sea. Beautifully maintained, it has preserved the thick white-painted walls and red tin roof so characteristic of such cottages, and the one bar has a beamed ceiling, an elmwood bar and tables and an open fire for warmth. Families and tourists flock here for the food and the setting rather than the choice of beer on draught, which is limited to Younger Tartan Special, but Broughton Greenmantle and Old Jock are available in bottles, and there is a good choice of malt whiskies. Bar meals start with home-made soup at £1.75, smoked haddock mousse with home-baked bread at £3.75 or oak-smoked venison at £3.95, and main courses might be sausage or salmon pie or chicken with cheese and pineapple, all at around £7 to £8, and puddings cost £2.95. Customers can also buy home-made jams and chutneys.

Brewery: Free house
Licensee: John Leadbeater
Opening hours: 12-2pm, 5.30-11pm; closed Sun, mid Oct-New Year, and 2nd week Jan-Easter
Bar food: 12-2pm, 7-9pm
Children: Not permitted in bar under 14 years; family room
Credit cards: Access, Visa

⊜ BRUCE HOTEL
Harbour Road, Maidens KA26 9NP. Tel 0655 31401

Maidens

Its setting, overlooking the harbour, is the factor that makes this large, friendly, 1950s hotel so popular with the business people, locals and tourists who throng its three comfortable bars. Among the beers on draught are Tennent Special and 80/-, Younger Tartan Special and Guinness and there is a wide choice of bottled beers and malt whiskies. Darts, pool and dominoes offer entertainment, and there are occasional folk-music evenings. Bar food consists of standard favourites like fillet of sole, liver and bacon and lamb cutlets, at prices ranging from £3.95 to £4.85 and there is also a separate restaurant, for which booking is advisable at weekends. For overnight or holiday stays there are nine comfortable bedrooms.

Brewery: Free house
Licensee: Mr G Justice
Opening hours: 11am-11pm
Bar food: 12-2.30pm, 6-9pm
Restaurant: Times as bar food
Accommodation: (Price per room) double £45
Children: Welcome anywhere
Credit cards: Visa (restaurant and accommodation only)

⊜ OBAN INN
1 Stafford Street, Oban PA34 5NJ Tel 0631 62484

Oban

Dating back to the 18th century, this lively, hospitable pub by the harbourside overlooking the bay may well be the oldest one in this popular west-coast port. It is a firm favourite with its local customers, particularly the young, but in summer tourists predominate in its ground-floor Public Bar and upstairs Lounge Bar - the latter featuring old stained-glass windows from a former church. Beers include

Brewery: Scottish & Newcastle
Licensee: Jeanette Boyd
Opening hours: 11am-11pm
Bar food: 12-2.30pm
Children: Welcome in Lounge Bar at mealtimes

Theakston Best Bitter, McEwan 80/- and Export and Guinness and there is an excellent range of malt whiskies, including Oban Malt. Bar meals are served in the Lounge Bar at lunchtime and dishes include the standard favourites such as steak pie, scampi, and chicken Kiev at prices from £3.50 to £4.

LORD LOUNSDALE
37 Lounsdale Road, Paisley PA2 1PC. Tel 041 889 6263

Paisley

Horses are the focus of this modern pub just outside the centre of Paisley, and everywhere you look there are reminders of this great fascination. The two L-shaped bars are named Stable and Hayloft, and both are decorated with saddles, horse brasses, riding tack and heavy-horse artefacts. Pictures of horses line the walls. This equine atmosphere attracts a mainly local clientele, and staff here are easy-going and friendly. On tap are Draught Bass, Tennent Special and 80/-, and Guinness, and the food is standard pub fare: starters like garlic bread at £1.20, prawn platter for £2.35, and chicken wings at £1.95, and such main dishes as steak pie for £6.50, lasagne at £3.35, and scampi at £3.95. Puddings might be chocolate fudge cake and cheesecake both for under £2. There is seating in the beer garden.

Brewery: Tennent
Licensee: Andrew Maxwell
Opening hours: 11am-12 midnight; Sun 12.30-11pm
Bar food: 12-9pm
Restaurant: 12-10pm
Children: In restaurant only until 8pm
Credit cards:
AMERICAN EXPRESS®, Visa

⊕ WHEATSHEAF INN
Main Street, Symington K1 5QB. Tel 0563 830307

Symington

A lovely old conservation village is the setting for this black-and-white 16th-century inn. The interesting and well cooked food attracts many people from the south side of Glasgow which is just half an hour's drive away, and several locals regularly use the two bars. Both rooms have open fires and dark wooden furniture, and while the 'English-style' Lounge is carpeted, the Public Bar has a quarry-tiled floor. Paintings by a local artist are on sale in the gallery. Some of the main dishes which have put this inn on the map are Scottish salmon with fresh lime, and loin of Scottish venison, both at £5.25, and grilled Ayrshire ham steak for £4.95. Starters include home-made pâté with Cognac at £2.50, prawns with Marie-Rose sauce for £3.50, and home-made soup at £1.20. Sticky toffee pudding and fresh pineapple with Grand Marnier are popular sweets at £2.25. On tap are Belhaven Best Bitter, 60/- and 80/- Ales, Guinness and Murphy's Stout.

Brewery: Belhaven
Licensee: Hamilton Thompson
Opening hours: 11am-2.30pm, 5pm-12 midnight
Bar food: 12-2pm, 5-10pm
Restaurant: Times as bar food
Children: Welcome in restaurant only; outdoor play area
Credit cards: Access, Visa

⊕ STATION TAP
Old Station Brewery, Taynuilt PA38 1JE. Tel 08662 246

Taynuilt

This well named pub is housed in a converted Victorian listed building that is part of the still active railway station and customers can sit out on the platform to watch the trains go by. The one bar, although simply furnished, has lots of character and is not surprisingly decorated with collections of railway memorabilia and posters. The pub has a flourishing local trade all year round, supplemented by tourists in the summer, who are attracted both by the unique atmosphere and by the strong beers brewed on the premises by West Highland Brewers - Highland Heavy, Highland Severe and Old Station Porter. There is also Guinness on draught and a satisfying range of malt whiskies. Bar food is not elaborate, but offers good value - soup at £1, venison stew or baked potato and haggis at £2, venison burger at £1. There is usually live folk music at weekends.

Brewery: Free house
Licensees: Mr and Mrs Saunders
Opening hours: Summer 11am-12 midnight or 1am; winter 11am-3pm, 5pm-12 midnight (11.30pm if not busy)
Bar food: 11am-12 midnight
Children: Welcome anywhere until 8pm

⊜TAYVALLICH INN
Tayvallich, near Lochgilphead PA31 8PR. Tel 05467 282

Tayvallich

This small, single-storey, modern building has an enviable position on the edge of Loch Sweene with an attractive patio for outdoor eating and drinking. The one bar is light and airy, with pine furniture, and attracts a lot of young people as well as families and local regulars. Beers include Alloa Drybroughs Heavy, Tetley Drum and Guinness and there is a large wine list. The bar menu offers a good choice of fish and shellfish - mussels, scallops, smoked salmon - as well as meat dishes and snacks like soup and pâté. Prices range from £1.25 for soup to £7.95 for scallops. There is a separate restaurant (booking advisable).

Brewery: Free house
Licensee: John Grafton
Opening hours: 11am-2.30pm, 5-11pm (Fri and Sat 1am); closed Mon in winter
Bar food: 12-2pm, 6-8.30pm
Restaurant: Summer 7-9pm; winter Fri and Sat only
Children: Welcome anywhere until 8pm accompanied by adult
Credit cards: Access, Visa

From Gin Shop to Gin Palace

As the alehouses moved further up in the world in the 18th century, new drinking-houses filled the vacant space at the foot of the social ladder. These were the gin shops (or dram shops, for brandy). Gin was cheap and strong it was adulterated with anything from turpentine to sulphuric acid, and in the slums of London and other towns the poor could get 'drunk for a penny, dead drunk for twopence' as the slogan went, in squalid cellars, hovels and back alleys. The scenes of drunkenness and degradation - vividly depicted in Hogarth's 'Gin Lane' - were so appalling that Parliament moved decisively in the 1750s to make spirits more expensive.

Following a sharp rise in beer prices at the end of the century, gin made a comeback in the industrial slums and from the 1820s on the distillers made a bid for working-class custom by opening gin palaces of ostentatious grandeur. The brewers followed this lead, hence the creation of magnificent Victorian and Edwardian pubs opulently provided with mahogany panelling, tiles and gilt, engraved mirrors and decorated glass, ornate gas lamps and richly elaborate ceilings. A few of them survive as reminders of vanished splendour.

TAYSIDE

ALMONDBANK INN
29-31 Main Street, Almondbank PH1 3NJ. Tel 0738 83242

Almondbank

A cockatiel provides lively entertainment in this cosy, homely inn overlooking the River Almond. Dating back to the 18th century, the well known hostelry attracts plenty of tourists as well as locals, and with its carpeted floors and cushioned sofas it makes a comfortable place to relax. Friendly staff help to enhance the convivial atmosphere. A very extensive bar menu offers only freshly cooked food, including such main courses as home-made steak and onion pie for £3.85, chicken supreme at £4.65, and scampi for £4.35. Starters include fresh breaded mushrooms with sauce for £2.75, fresh melon and prawn cocktail at £3.50, and soup for £1.15, and there are sweets like banana split at £2.15 and apple tart for £1.85. There's an extensive wine list to complement the food, and on tap are Broughton Greenmantle Ale, Tennent 70/- and Guinness. A garden next to the river offers seating in the summer.

Brewery: Free house
Licensees: Mr and Mrs Lindsay
Opening hours: 11am-2.30pm, 5-11pm (Fri and Sat 11am-11.30pm); Sun 12.30-11pm
Bar food: 12-2.15pm, 5-8.30pm (Fri and Sat 6.30-10pm)
Restaurant: Times as bar food
Children: Not permitted under 14 years in bar; own menu available; family room
Credit cards: Access, Visa

☻ ALYTH HOTEL
6 Commercial Street, Alyth PH11 8AF. Tel 08283 2447

Alyth

This 18th-century inn is right at the centre of village life in Alyth, and the landlord works hard to keep it that way. There's a warm and friendly welcome for everyone from local country people to tourists, whether alone or as one of a large coach party, and walkers are especially well received. Saturday night is usually Scottish music night at this stone-built hotel, when piped music gives way to the real thing, and session folk musicians are welcome at any time to entertain the customers. Once a month the local folk club also meets here. The bar food is good traditional Scottish fare, with dishes like haggis and steak pie featuring on the menu every day. Afternoon tea and high tea are also served. On tap are Tennent 70/-, plus one changing heavy ale such as Tennent 80/- or Alloa Export, plus Guinness, and there's a good selection of speciality malts. Accommodation is available in eight rooms decorated in restful colours.

Brewery: Free house
Licensees: Graham and Alison Marshall
Opening hours: 12-11pm (Fri and Sat 11.45pm); Sun 12.30-11pm
Bar food: 12-9pm
Restaurant: Times as bar food
Accommodation: (Price per person) £15-£30
Children: Welcome anywhere; family room
Credit cards: Access, Visa

⏣ OLD BREWHOUSE
3 High Street, Arbroath DD11 1BH. Tel 0241 79945

Arbroath

Banknotes from every part of the globe decorate the bar of this harbourside pub which was once the town's customs house. The Grade-1 listed 16th-century building is the haunt of a mixture of locals, business people and tourists, and in the summer they take their drinks out on to the harbour wall which takes the place of a beer garden. The award-winning bar food offers good value for money, and includes a daily changing vegetarian dish. In addition the menu offers starters like deep-fried mushrooms at £1.85 and frogs' legs for £2.65, and there are main choices such as Arbroath smokie for £4.55, silver darlings (herrings) for £3.95, and chilli at £4.45. Clootie dumplings and sticky toffee pudding are both under £2. There's a good selection of fruit wines, including strawberry hock and champagne, and on tap are McEwan 70/- and 80/-, and Guinness. Live country music is played in the bar every Saturday night.

Brewery: Free house
Licensees: Mr and Mrs Stewart
Opening hours: 11am-2pm, 5-11pm
Bar food: 11.45am-2pm, 6-9.30pm
Restaurant: 7-9.30pm
Children: Welcome, but not in Public Bar
Credit cards: Access, Visa

⏣ AUCHMITHIE HOTEL
Auchmithie, By Arbroath DD11 5SQ. Tel 0241 73010

Auchmithie

This rambling hotel set in a small village high up on the top of a cliff was built as a coaching inn in 1885. Nowadays this cosy and welcoming family-run place attracts several older locals as well as tourists, and from the white-painted building they can enjoy superb views out to sea. McEwan 80/- and Tartan Special as well as Murphy's Stout are on tap in the bar, where seating is on a mixture of chairs and settles, and there are plenty of wines to choose from. Bar food is all home-made, and the choice of dishes available all day is quite considerable: starters like spare ribs are £2.15 and smoked mackerel costs £2.20, while main courses include smokies at £4.60, fisherman's pie at £4.80, and 'surf and turf' for £8.25. There are sweets such as filled pancakes for £2.10 and cheesecake at £2.50, and a vegetarian choice is always on the menu. Six bedrooms offer pleasant accommodation, some with sea views.

Brewery: Free house
Licensee: Arthur Watt
Opening hours: Summer 11.30am-12 midnight (Sun from 12 noon); winter 6pm-12 midnight; Sat and Sun 11.30am-12.30am
Bar food: 12-10pm (winter 6-10pm except Sat and Sun)
Restaurant: Times as bar food
Accommodation: (Price per person) double £30-£35
Children: Welcome anywhere except Lounge Bar
Credit cards: Access, Visa

Shove Halfpenny
The game is still played with pre-decimal halfpennies, lovingly preserved, but is not as popular and widespread in pubs as it used to be. It is a scaled-down version of shuffleboard, which involved propelling flat metal discs along a smooth wooden table up to 30ft long. Down to the First World War a playing area was often drawn in chalk on the bar or a tabletop, but today a special wooden or slate board is used, 24 inches long by 15 inches wide. As usual, the house rules vary in detail from one pub to another.

⬤ OLD SMIDDY
The Cross, Errol PH2 7QW. Tel 0821 642888

Errol

A reproduction forge dominates the bar of this former smithy, and horseshoes as well as agricultural implements and artefacts decorate the room. The small neat building was converted as recently as 1989, and there's a cosy, intimate atmosphere which appeals to a wide range of people. Regular folk evenings attract their own following, but parking around this village square pub is limited. The well presented food offers excellent value for money, and the portions are generous; on Sundays a traditional Scottish high tea is served instead of dinner. The menu offers starters like soup for £1.30, and Orkney herring at £2.45, and there are main dishes such as North Sea chowder for £5.50, haddock at £5.10, and steak for £8.70. Puddings include apple pie at £2, and banana split for £2.40. Cairn O'Mhor fruit wines and a wide range of malt whiskies are on sale, as well as draught Belhaven 80/- and Best, and Murphy's Stout.

Brewery: Free house
Licensee: Mr Knight
Opening hours: 11am-2.30pm, 5-11pm (Fri and Sat 11.45pm); Sun 12.30-11pm
Bar food: 12-2pm, 5-9pm; Sun 12-2pm, 4-7pm
Children: Welcome anywhere; half portions available
Credit cards: Access, Visa

⬤ TORMAUKIN HOTEL
Glendevon, By Dollar FK14 7JY. Tel 0259 781252

Glendevon

A small hamlet is the rural setting for this well kept and attractive 18th-century hotel. In the summer there's seating outside on a paved patio, while in the bar open fires and a cushioned settle create a cosy and comfortable atmosphere. Prints and a collection of plates adorn the walls, and service from the friendly staff is helpful and efficient. There's a good choice of tasty food from the bar menu, and starters include soup at £1.50, and deep-fried mushrooms in batter for £2.75. Main dishes might be fettucini carbonara or spinach and mushroom lasagne, both at £5.55, and venison sausages for £5.25, while desserts like summer fruit pie with cream, and duo of fruit sorbets cost under £2.50. On tap are Harviestoun Original 80/-, Ind Coope Burton Ale, Alloa Export and Guinness. Traditional accommodation is available in ten bedrooms with pine furniture and exposed beams.

Brewery: Free house
Licensee: Marianne Worthy
Opening hours: 11am-11pm; Sun 12-11pm
Bar food: 12-2pm, 5.30-9.30pm; Sun 12-9.30pm
Restaurant: 6.30-9.30pm
Accommodation: (Price per person) single £45, double £30
Children: Not permitted under 14 years in bar after 6.30pm; family room available for eating
Credit cards: AMERICAN EXPRESS®, Access, Visa

Top of the Tree

Pubs called the Royal Oak were originally named in loyal remembrance of the day in 1651 when the youthful King Charles II hid in an oak tree at Boscobel in Shropshire, while Roundhead soldiers unsuccessfully searched the woods for him. The Royal Oak sign often shows simply the oak tree, or the king is shown perched among the branches - in plain view from all directions, but conventionally accepted as invisible to the purblind Roundheads. Sometimes, more subtly, the tree has a large crown among the foliage. Rarer variants include the king holding an oak spray with acorns, or acorns below a crown.

⊜ AILEAN CHRAGGAN HOTEL
Weem, By Aberfeldy PH15 2LD. Tel 0887 820346

Weem

The clientele changes according to the season at this large and roomy hotel above the River Tay, but the standard of comfort manages to remain the same all year round. Lounge chairs and sofas make the carpeted bar a pleasant place to relax, and good food is available here at mealtimes. Starters include chicken liver pâté at £2.95, and rollmop herrings at £2.85, and there are main dishes like fillet of salmon for £6.95, herring in oatmeal at £4.95, and chicken casserole for £5.50. Sweets include banana split at £3.25, and cream meringue for £2.85, and there is always a vegetarian choice. There's a huge range of malt whiskies, including the local Aberfeldy label, and on tap are Tartan Special and Murphy's Stout. Three double bedrooms offer comfortable accommodation with views over the river and the hills, and the same view can be enjoyed from the large garden which has seating.

Brewery: Free house
Licensee: Mr Gillespie
Opening hours: Summer 11am-11pm; winter 11am-2.30pm, 5-11pm
Bar food: 12-2pm, 6.30-9.30pm
Restaurant: 12-2pm, 6.30-9.30pm
Accommodation: (Price per person) double £26
Children: Welcome anywhere; outdoor play area
Credit cards: Access, Visa

PUBS WITH OVERNIGHT ACCOMMODATION

Bedfordshire
Houghton Conquest Knife and Cleaver
Woburn Bell Inn

Berkshire
Boxford Bell
East Ilsley Swan
Hamstead Marshall White Hart
Hungerford Bear
Kintbury Dundas Arms
Sonning Bull
Yattendon Royal Oak

Buckinghamshire
Fawley Walnut Tree
Hambleden Stag and Huntsman
Wooburn Common Chequers Inn
West Wycombe George and Dragon
Holywell Old Ferry Boat Inn
Mepal Three Pickerells
Stilton Bell Inn

Cheshire
Barthomley White Lion Inn
Brereton Green Bears Head
Chester Ye Olde Kings Head
Cholmondeley Cholmondeley Arms
Higher Burwardsley Pheasant Inn
Nantwich Bowling Green

Cornwall
Bodinnick Old Ferry Inn
Cadgwith Cove Inn
Goldsithney Crown
Lostwithiel Royal Oak Inn
Mousehole Ship
Nancenoy Trengilly Wartha Inn
Pendoggett Cornish Arms
Port Gaverne Port Gaverne
St Mawes Rising Sun
St Mawgan Falcon Inn
Tregadillett Eliot Arms

Cumbria
Appleby in Westmorland Royal Oak Inn
Askham Punch Bowl Inn
Barngates Drunken Duck
Bouth White Hart
Braithwaite Coledale Inn
Brampton Abbey Bridge Inn
Buttermere Bridge Hotel
Cartmel Fell Masons Arms
Casterton Pheasant
Dent Sun Inn
Elterwater Britannia Inn
Eskdale Green Bower House
Faugh String of Horses
Floriston Metal Bridge Inn
Garrigil George and Dragon
Gosforth Wasdale Head Inn
Hesket Newmarket Old Crown
Kirkby Lonsdale Snooty Fox Tavern
Loweswater Kirkstile Inn
Lowick Green Farmers Arms
Near Sawrey Tower Bank Arms
Troutbeck Mortal Man
Ulverston Bay Horse Inn

Derbyshire
Castleton Ye Olde Nags Head
Hurdlow Bull I' Th' Thorn
Kirk Ireton Barley Mow

Over Haddon Lathkil Hotel
Tideswell George Hotel

Devon
Branscombe Masons Arms
Dalwood Tuckers Arms
Doddiscombleigh Nobody Inn
Exminster Turf
Hatherleigh Tally Ho
Haytor Vale Rock Inn
Horndon Elephants Nest
Iddesleigh Duke of York
Kingskerswell Barn Owl Inn
Knowstone Masons Arms
Lynmouth Rising Sun
North Bovey Ring of Bells
Slapton Tower Inn
South Zeal Oxenham Arms
Stockland Kings Arms Inn
Thelbridge Thelbridge Cross Inn

Dorset
Abbotsbury Ilchester Arms
Bridport George Hotel
Cerne Abbas New Inn
Cranborne Fleur De Lys
Evershot Acorn Inn
Farnham Museum Hotel
Milton Abbas Hambro Arms
North Wootton Three Elms
Piddletrenthide Poachers Inn
Powerstock Three Horseshoes Inn
Tarrant Monkton Langton Arms

Co Durham
Barnard Castle Red Well Inn
Blanchland Lord Crewe Arms
Cotherstone Fox Hounds
Greta Bridge Morritt Arms Hotel
Romaldkirk Rose and Crown Inn

Essex
Colchester Peldon Rose
Dedham Marlborough Head Hotel
Horsley Cross Cross Inn
Rickling Green Cricketers Arms
Tillingham Cap and Feathers

Gloucestershire
Bledington Kings Head
Blockley Crown Inn
Clearwell Wyndham Arms
Coln St Aldwyns New Inn
Ewen Wild Duck Inn
Ford Plough
Great Rissington Lamb Inn
Joyford Dog and Muffler
Kingscote Hunters Hall Inn
Newland Ostrich Inn
North Cerney Bathurst Arms
North Nibley New Inn

Hampshire
Beauworth Milburys
Cheriton Flower Pots
Droxford White Horse
Emery Down New Forest Inn
Winchester Wykeham Arms

Hereford & Worcester
Brimfield Roebuck
Carey Cottage of Content
Hanley Castle Three Kings

Knightwick Talbot
Pembridge New Inn
Ruckhall Common Ancient Camp
Shobdon Bateman Arms
Whitney on Wye Rhydspence Inn
Woolhope Butchers Arms

Hertfordshire
Ayot St Lawrence Brocket Arms

Humberside
Bishop Wilton Fleece Inn

Isle of Wight
Chale Wight Mouse Inn
Seaview Seaview Hotel

Kent
Brenchley Rose and Crown
Eastling Carpenters Arms
Groomsbridge Crown
Lenham Harrow Inn
Smarden Bell, Chequers

Lancashire
Slaidburn Hark to Bounty Inn
Whitewell Inn at Whitewell

Leicestershire
Empingham White Horse
Glooston Old Barn
Hallaton Bewicke Arms
Market Overton Black Bull
Waltham-on-the-Wolds Royal Horseshoes

Lincolnshire
Aswarby Tally Ho Inn
Donington-on-Bain Black Horse
Grimsthorpe Black Horse Inn
Heckington Nags Head
Raithby by Spilsby Red Lion Inn
Skendleby Blacksmiths Arms
Stamford George of Stamford
Tetford White Hart

Norfolk
Blickling Buckinghamshire Arms
Burnham Market Hoste Arms
East Barsham White Horse Inn
Ingham Swan
Scole Scole Inn
Snettisham Rose and Crown
Sutton Staithe Sutton Staithe Hotel
Thornham Lifeboat Inn
Warham Three Horseshoes
Winterton-on Sea Fishermans Return
Wolterton Saracens Head

Northamptonshire
Ashby St Ledgers Olde Coach House
Blakesley Bartholomew Arms
East Haddon Red Lion
Marston Trussell Sun Inn

Northumberland
Chatton Percy Arms
Embleton Cottage Inn
Long Framlington Granby
Seahouses Olde Ship
Seaton Sluice Waterford Arms
Stannersburn Pheasant Inn

Nottinghamshire
Blyth Angel Inn

Oxfordshire
Asthall Maytime Inn
Burford Lamb
Charlbury Bell
Clanfield Clanfield Tavern
Clifton Hampden Barley Mow
Dorchester on Thames George
Great Tew Falklands Arms
Moulsford -on-Thames Beetle and Wedge
Shipton-under-Wychwood Lamb Inn
Shaven Crown

Shropshire
Cardington Royal Oak
Hopton Wafers Crown Inn
Much Wenlock Talbot Inn
Norton Hundred House Hotel
Shrewsbury Castle Vaults
Wenlock Edge Wenlock Edge Inn

Somerset
Hinton St George Poulett Arms
Kilve Hood Arms
Luxborough Royal Oak
Montacute Kings Arms Inn
Priddy New Inn
Rudge Full Moon
Stoke St Gregory Rose and Crown
Withypool Royal Oak

Staffordshire
Black Lion Inn

Suffolk
Barwell Six Bells Inn
Chelsworth Peacock Inn
Dunwich Ship Inn
Lavenham Angel
Long Melford Bull
Orford Jolly Sailor
Shadingfield Fox Inn
Southwold Crown
Stoke by Nayland Angel Hotel
Thornham Magna Four Horseshoes

Surrey
Chiddingford Crown Inn
Coldharbour Plough

Sussex
Burwash Bell Inn
Cuckfield Kings Head
Fletching Griffin Inn
Firle Ram Inn
Hartfield Anchor Inn
Hastings Stag Inn
Mayfield Rose and Crown
Petworth Angel Hotel
Tillington Horseguards

Tyne & Wear
Matfen Black Bull

Warwickshire
Ilmington Howard Arms
Shipston-on-Stour White Bear
Wilmcote Swan House Hotel

Wiltshire
Axford Red Lion Inn
Ebbesbourne Wake Horseshoe
Ford White Hart
Hindon Lamb Inn
Horningsham Bath Arms
Lacock Red Lion
Little Bedwyn Harrow Inn
Stourton Spread Eagle

Wootton Rivers Royal Oak

Yorkshire (North)
Carlton Foresters Arms
Coxwold Fauconberg Arms
East Witton Blue Lion
Horsehouse Thwaites Arms
Hubberholme George Inn
Keld Tan Hill Inn
Lastingham Blacksmiths Arms
Osmotherley Three Tuns
Pickhill Nags Head
Rosedale Abbey Milburn Arms
Starbotton Fox and Hounds
Thornton Watlass Buck Inn
Wass Wombwell Arms
Wath in Nidderdale Sportsmans Arms
York Black Swan

Yorkshire (South)
Hatfield Woodhouse Green Tree Inn

Yorkshire (West)
Shelley Three Acres Inn

WALES
Clwyd
Dolywern Golden Pheasant Hotel
Erbistock Boat Inn
Llanarmon Dyffryn Ceiriog West Arms Hotel
Llangedwyn Green Inn
Llangollen Britannia Inn
Llansannan Red Lion

Dyfed
Carew Carew Inn
Dinas Cross Freemasons Arms
Mathry Farmers Arms
Nevern Trewern Arms
Pisgah Halfway Inn
Newchapel Ffynone Arms
Pelcomb Bridge Rising Sun

Gwent
Abergavenny Llanwenarth Arms
Llanfihangel Crucorney Skirrid
Llanthony Abbey Hotel
Raglan Beaufort Arms Hotel
Whitebrook Crown at Whitebrook

Gwynedd
Aberdovery Penhelig Arms
Beaumaris Ye Olde Bulls Head Inn
Ganllwyd Tyn Y Groes
Llanengan Sun Inn
Maentwrog Grapes Hotel
Penmaenpool George III Hotel
Porth Dinllaen Tafarn Ty Coch

Powys
Crickhowell
Bear Inn
Glasbury-on-Wye Harp
Hay-on-Wye Old Black Lion
Howey Drovers Arms
Llandrindod Wells Llanerch
Llanfair Waterdine Red Lion
Llyswen Griffin
Old Radnor Harp Inn
Talybont -on-Usk Star Inn

SCOTLAND
Borders
Clovenfords Clovenfords Hotel

Greenlaw Castle Hotel
Innerleithen Traquair Arms Hotel
Lauder Black Bull
Lilliesleaf Plough Inn
Peebles Green Tree Hotel
St Marys Loch Tibbie Shiels Inn
Swinton Wheatsheaf
Tweedmuir Crook Inn

Central
Dollar Strathallan Hotel
Drymen Salmon Leap Inn
Killearn Old Mill Inn
Killin Clachaig Hotel
Kilmahog Lade Inn
Kippin Cross Keys Hotel
Sheriffmuir Sheriffmuir Inn

Dumfries & Galloway
Clarencefield Farmers Inn
Eagles Field Courtyard
Isle of Whithorn
Steam Packet Hotel
Moffat Balmoral Hotel
Moniaive George Hotel
New Abbey Criffel Inn
Newton Stewart Creebridge House
Portpatrick Crown Hotel

Fife
Aberdour Aberdour Hotel
Anstruther Craws Nest Hotel
Ceres Meldrums Hotel
Kettlebridge Kettlebridge Inn

Grampian
Findhorn Crown and Anchor
Fochabers Gordon Arms
Kincardine O'Neil Gordon Arms
Monymusk Grant Arms
Newburgh Udny Arms
Pennan Pennan Inn

Highland
Applecross Applecross Inn
Gairloch Badachro Hotel Old Inn
Glencoe Clachaig Inn
Glenelg Glenelg Inn
Glenfinnan Stage House
Glen Moriston Cluanie Inn
Invermoriston Glenmoriston Arms Hotel
Kylesky Kylesky Hotel
Lairg Crask Inn Kylesky Hotel
Lewiston Lewiston Arms Hotel
Plockton Plockton Hotel
Stoneyfield Coach House Inn
Ullapool Morefield Hotel Ceildh Place

Lothian
Blackness Blackness Inn
Dirleton Castle Inn
Gifford Tweedale Arms
Nine Mile Burn Habbies Howe
South Queensferry Halles Inn

Strathclyde
Ardentinny Ardentinny Hotel
Ayr Old Race Course Hotel
Maidens Bruce Hotel

Tayside
Alyth Alyth Hotel
Authmithie Authmithie Hotel
Glendevon Tormankin Hotel
Weem Ailean Chraggan Hotel

PUBS WHICH ACCEPT CREDIT CARDS

Avon
Bathford — Crown
Oldbury-on-Severn — Anchor Inn

Bedfordshire
Houghton Conquest — Knife and Cleaver
Odell — Mad Dog
Old Warden — Hare and Hounds
Radwell — Swan
Shillington — Musgrave Arms
Steppingly — French Horn
Turvey — YeThree Fyshes

Berkshire
Boxford — Bell
Burghclere — Carpenters Arms
Chaddleworth — Ibex
East Ilsley — Swan
Hamstead Marshall — White Hart
Hungerford — Bear
Kintbury — Dundas Arms
Lower Inkpen — Swan
Sonning — Bull
West Ilsley — Harrow
Yattendon — Royal Oak

Buckinghamshire
Fawley — Walnut Tree
Fingest — Chequers Inn
Frieth — Yew Tree
Hambleden — Stag and Huntsman
Ley Hill — Swan
Little Hampden — Rising Sun
Preston Bissett — Old Hat
Wooburn Common — Chequers Inn
West Wycombe — George and Dragon

Cambridgeshire
Abbotsley — Jolly Abbot
Bartlow — Three Hills
Fowlmere — Chequers
Holywell — Old Ferry Boat Inn
Horningsea — Plough and Fleece
Mepal — Three Pickerells
Stilton — Bell Inn

Cheshire
Audlem — Shroppie Fly
Brereton Green — Bears Head
Chester — Ye Olde Kings Head
Cholmondeley — Cholmondeley Arms
Higher Burwardsley — Pheasant Inn
Knolls Green — Bird in Hand
Lower Peover — Bells of Peover
Macclesfield Forest — Stanley Arms
Nantwich — Bowling Green
Rainow — Cheshire Hunt

Cleveland
Saltburn — Ship
Stainton — Stainton Inn

Cornwall
Bodinnick — Old Ferry Inn
Chapel Amble — Maltsers Arms
Goldsithney — Crown
Lostwithiel — Royal Oak Inn
Mylor Bridge — Pandora Inn
Nancenoy — Trengilly Wartha Inn
Pendoggett — Cornish Arms
Polkerris — Rashleigh Inn
Port Gaverne — Port Gaverne Hotel
St Mawes — Rising Sun
St Mawgan — Falcon Inn

Cumbria
Appleby in Westmorland — Royal Oak Inn
Askham — Punch Bowl Inn
Barngates — Drunken Duck
Braithwaite — Coledale Inn
Brampton — Abbey Bridge Inn
Casterton — Pheasant
Dent — Sun Inn
Elterwater — Britannia Inn
Eskdale Green — Bower House
Faugh — String of Horses
Floriston — Metal Bridge Inn
Gosforth — Wasdale Head Inn
Hesket Newmarket — Old Crown
Loweswater — Kirkstile Inn
Lowick Green — Farmers Arms
Melmerby — Shepherds Inn
Near Sawrey — Tower Bank Arms
Threlkeld — White Horse
Ulverston — Bay Horse Inn

Derbyshire
Birchover — Druid Inn
Castleton — Ye Olde Nags Head
Over Haddon — Lathkil Hotel
Shardlow — Malt Shovel
Tideswell — George Hotel

Devon
Branscombe — Masons Arms
Dalwood — Tuckers Arms
Dartmouth — Cherub
Doddiscombleigh — Nobody Inn
Hatherleigh — Tally Ho
Haytor Vale — Rock Inn
Kingskerswell — Barn Owl Inn
Kingsteignton — Old Rydon Inn
Lynmouth — Rising Sun
Peter Tavy — Peter Tavy Inn
Rattery — Church House Inn
Rockbeare — Jack in the Green
South Zeal — Oxenham Arms
Thelbridge — Thelbridge Cross Inn
Weston — Otter

Dorset
Abbotsbury — Ilchester Arms
Bridport — George Hotel
Cerne Abbas — New Inn
Cranborne — Fleur De Lys
Evershot — Acorn Inn
Farnham — Museum Hotel
Kingston — Scott Arms
Langton Herring — Elm Tree
Milton Abbas — Hambro Arms
Piddletrenthide — Poachers Inn
Plush — Brace of Pheasants
Powerstock — Three Horseshoes Inn
Tarrant Monkton — Langton Arms
Trent — Rose and Crown

Co Durham
Barnard Castle — Red Well Inn
Blanchland — Lord Crewe Arms
Cotherstone — Fox Hounds
Fir Tree — Duke of York
Greta Bridge — Morritt Arms Hotel

Essex
Clavering — Cricketers
Colchester — Peldon Rose
Dedham — Marlborough Head Hotel
Elsenham — Crown
High Roding — Black Lion
Horndon on the Hill — Bell
Horsley Cross — Cross Inn
North Fambridge — Ferryboat Inn
Paglesham Eastend — Plough and Sail
Rickling Green — Cricketers Arms
Saffron Walden — Eight Bells

Gloucestershire
Apperley — Farmers Arms
Bibury — Catherine Wheel
Blockley — Crown Inn
Clearwell — Wyndham Arms
Cockleford — Green Dragon
Coln St Aldwyns — New Inn
Eastleach Turville — Victorian Inn
Ewen — Wild Duck Inn
Ford — Plough
Great Rissington — Lamb Inn
Joyford — Dog and Muffler
Kingscote — Hunters Hall Inn
Newland — Ostrich Inn
North Cerney — Bathurst Arms
North Woodchester — Royal Oak
Shuthonger — Crown
South Woodchester — Ram Inn

Greater Manchester
Manchester — Mr Thomas's Chop House

Hampshire
Beauworth — Milburys
Boldre — Red Lion
Bramdean — Fox
Buriton — Five Bells
Bursledon — Jolly Sailor
Chalton — Red Lion
Chilbolton — Mayfly
Droxford — White Horse
Ellisfield — Fox
Emery Down — New Forest Inn
Langstone — Royal Oak
Longparish — Plough
Lower Wield — Yew Tree
Mortimer West End — Red Lion
Ovington — Bush Inn
Rotherwick — Coach and Horses
Upton Grey — Hoddington Arms
Well — Chequers
Whitsbury — Cartwheel

Hereford & Worcester
Bewdley — Little Pack Horse
Brimfield — Roebuck
Carey — Cottage of Content
Fownhope — Green Man Inn
Great Malvern — Bluebell
Hanley Castle — Three Kings
Kidderminster — Little Tumbling Sailor

Knightwick	Talbot
Ombersley	Kings Arms
Ruckhall Common	Ancient Camp
Sellack	Lough Pool Inn
Shobdon	Bateman Arms
Whitney-on-Wye	Rhydspence Inn
Wyre Piddle	Anchor

Hertfordshire

Ashwell	Bushel and Shrike
	Rose and Crown
Ayot St Lawrence	Brocket Arms
Datchworth	Horns
Old Knebworth	Lytton Arms
Watton at Stone	George and Dragon

Humberside

Beverley	White Horse Inn (Nellie's)
Etton	Light Dragoon
Skidby	Half Moon
South Dalton	Pipe and Glass

Isle of Wight

Chale	Wight Mouse Inn
Niton	Buddle Inn
Seaview	Seaview Hotel
Shalfleet	New Inn

Kent

Chiddingstone	Castle Inn
Chilham	White Horse
Eastling	Carpenters Arms
Groomsbridge	Crown
Ickham	Duke William Inn
Ightham Common	Harrow
Ivy Hatch	Plough
Lamberhurst	Brown Trout
Lenham	Harrow Inn
Penshurst	Spotted Dog
Pett Bottom	Duck Inn
Ringlestone	Ringlestone Inn
Smarden	Bell
	Chequers
Snargate	Red Lion Inn
Stowting	Tiger Inn
Teynon	Ship Inn

Lancashire

Downham	Assheton Arms
Whitewell	Inn at Whitewell
Woodplumpton	Plough at Eaves

Leicestershire

Empingham	White Horse
Glooston	Old Barn
Hallaton	Bewicke Arms
Market Overton	Black Bull
Old Dalby	Crown Inn
Redmile	Peacock
Sibson	Cock Inn
Sileby	White Swan

Lincolnshire

Aswarby	Tally Ho Inn
Grimsthorpe	Black Horse Inn
Heckington	Nags Head
Lincoln	Wig and Mitre
Raithby by Spilsby	Red Lion Inn
Stamford	George of Stamford

London (Central)

EC1	Fox and Anchor
EC4 Black Friar	Ye Olde Cheshire Cheese
SW1	Grouse and Claret
SW1	Grenadier
SW3	Coopers Arms
W1	Red Lion
	Guinea
WC1	Museum Tavern
	Cittie of York
	Lamb
WC2	Sherlock Holmes
	Freemasons Arms

London (East)

E1	Prospect of Whitby
E14	Grapes

London (South)

SE1	Anchor George
	Trafalgar Tavern
SE10	Yacht Tavern
SE16	Famous Angel
	Mayflower
SW6	White Horse
SW18	Ship Inn
	Adam and Eve

London (North)

N6	Flask
NW3	Spaniards Inn

London (West)

W4	Bulls Head
	City Barge
W6	Rutland Ale House

Norfolk

Blickling	Buckinghamshire Arms
Brancaster Staithe	Jolly Sailors
Burnham Market	Hoste Arms
East Barsham	White Horse Inn
Ingham	Swan
Reedham	Reedham Ferry Inn
Salhouse	Lodge
Scole	Scole Inn
Snettisham	Rose and Crown
Sutton Staithe	Sutton Staithe Hotel
Swanton Morley	Darbys
Thompson	Chequers
Thornham	Lifeboat Inn
Wolterton	Saracens Head

Northamptonshire

Ashby St Ledgers	Olde Coach House
East Haddon	Red Lion
Fotheringhay	Falcon Inn
Lamport	Lamport Swan
Marston Trussell	Sun Inn
Nassington	Black Horse
Wilbarston	Fox Inn

Northumberland

Carterway Heads	Manor House Inn
Embleton	Cottage Inn
Long Framlington	Granby
Seahouses	Olde Ship
Warenford	Warenford Lodge

Nottinghamshire

Colston Bassett	Martin Arms Inn
Hoveringham	Reindeer Inn
Laxton	Dovecote Inn

Oxfordshire

Asthall	Maytime Inn
Burford	Lamb
Charlbury	Bell
Clanfield	Clanfield Tavern
Clifton Hampden	Barley Mow
Dorchester-on-Thames	George
Longworth	Blue Boar
Lower Wolvercote	Trout
Maiden Grove	Five Horseshoes
Moulsford-on-Thames	Beetle and Wedge
Oxford	Turf Tavern
Shipton under Wychwood	Lamb Inn
	Shaven Crown
Spriggs Alley	Sir Charles Napier
Steeple Aston	Red Lion

Shropshire

Bridgnorth	Down Inn
Hopton Wafers	Crown Inn
Much Wenlock	Talbot Inn
Norton	Hundred House Hotel
Pulverbatch	White Horse
Wenlock Edge	Wenlock Edge Inn

Somerset

Ashcott	Ashcott Inn
East Woodlands	Horse and Groom
Hinton St George	Poulett Arms
Kilve	Hood Arms
Knapp	Rising Sun
Montacute	Kings Arms Inn
Over Stratton	Royal Oak
Staple Fitzpaine	Greyhound
Stoke St Gregory	Rose and Crown
Withypool	Royal Oak

Staffordshire

Fradley	Swan
Tatenhill	Horseshoe Inn

Suffolk

Barwell	Six Bells Inn
Bury St Edmunds	Linden Tree
Halesworth	Cratfield Poacher
Horringer	Beehive
Lavenham	Angel
Long Melford	Bull
Pettistree	Three Tuns
Rede	Plough
Shotley	Bristol Arms
Southwold	Crown
Stoke-by-Nayland	Angel Hotel
Thornham Magna	Four Horseshoes
Westerfield	Swan
Woodbridge	Cherry Tree

Surrey

Bletchingley	Whyte Harte
Chiddingfold	Crown Inn
East Clandon	Queens Head
Elstead	Woolpack
Friday Street	Stephen Langton
Long Ditton	City Arms
Outwood	Bell Inn
Shere	White Horse
Thursley	Three Horseshoes
West Clandon	Onslow Arms
Woking	Bleak House

Sussex

Bucks Green	Fox
Burwash	Bell Inn
Byworth	Black Horse
Chilgrove	White Horse
Compton	Coach and Horses
Cousley Wood	Old Vine
Cuckfield	Kings Head
Ewhurst Green	White Dog Inn
Firle	Ram Inn

Fletchling — Griffin Inn
Fulking — Shepherd and Dog
Hartfield — Anchor Inn
Hooksway — Royal Oak
Kingston — Juggs Arms
Lickfold — Lickfold Inn
Lodsworth — Halfway Bridge Inn
Mayfield — Rose and Crown Inn
Nuthurst — Black Horse
Oving — Gribble Inn
Petworth — Angel Hotel

Tyne & Wear
Matfen — Black Bull
New York — Shiremoor House Farm

Warwickshire
Alderminster — Bell
Alveston — Ferry
Broom — Broom Tavern
Edge Hill — Castle Inn
Ilmington — Howard Arms
Lowsonford — Fleur De Lys
Priors Marston — Holly Bush
Shipston-on-Stour — White Bear
Wilmcote — Swan House Hotel

West Midlands
Kinver — Whittington Inn
Netherton — Little Dry Dock
Stone Cross — Manor House
Tipton — Mad O'Roukes Pie Factory

Wiltshire
Axford — Red Lion Inn
Beckhampton — Waggon and Horses
Brinkworth — Three Crowns
Castle Combe — White Hart
Charlton — Horse and Groom
Ford — White Hart
Hindon — Lamb Inn
Horningsham — Bath Arms
Lacock — Red Lion
Little Bedwyn — Harrow Inn
Lower Chute — Hatchet
Pitton — Silver Plough
Ramsbury — Bell Inn
Rowde — George and Dragon
Stourton — Spread Eagle
Wootton Rivers — Royal Oak

Yorkshire (North)
Asenby — Crab and Lobster
Carlton — Foresters Arms
Coxwold — Fauconberg Arms
East Witton — Blue Lion
Harome — Star Inn
Hetton — Angel
Hutton-le-Hole — Lion
Moulton — Black Bull
Osmotherley — Three Tuns
Pickhill — Nags Head
Rosedale Abbey — Milburn Arms
Thornton Watlass — Buck Inn
Wass — Wombwell Arms
Wath in Nidderdale — Sportsmans Arms
York — Black Swan
Yorkshire (South)
Cadeby — Cadeby Inn
Hatfield Woodhouse — Green Tree Inn
Ulley — Royal Oak
Wadsworth — Fox and Hounds
Yorkshire (West)
Bardsley — Bingley Arms

Heath Common — Kings Arms
Heckmondwike — Old Hall
Ledsham — Chequers
Leeds — Whitelocks
Lees Moor — Quarry House Inn
Ripponden — Old Bridge Inn
Shelley — Three Acres Inn

WALES
Clwyd
Betws Yn Rhos — Ffarm Hotel
Bodfari — Dinorben Arms
Cilcain — White Horse Inn
Dolywern — Golden Pheasant Hotel
Erbistock — Boat Inn
Llanarmon — Dyffryn Ceiriog West Arms Hotel
Llangedwyn — Green Inn
Llangollen — Britannia Inn
Llanynys — Cerrigllwydion Arms
Rhewl — Sun Inn

Dyfed
Abergorlech — Black Lion
Lamphey — Dial Inn
Llanddarog — Butchers Arms
Llandybie — Red Lion
Nevern — Trewern Arms
Pontargothi — Salutation Inn

Glamorgan
Alltwen — Butchers Arms
Caerphilly — Court House
East Aberthaw — Blue Anchor
Llangeinor — Llangeinor Arms
Llangynwyd — Old House/Yr Hendy
Oldwalls — Greyhound Inn
Swanbridge — Captains Wife

Gwent
Abergavenny — Llanwenarth Arms
Raglan — Beaufort Arms Hotel
Whitebrook — Crown at Whitebrook

Gwynedd
Aberdovey — Penhelig Arms
Beaumaris — Ye Olde Bulls Head
Benllech — Ship Inn
Glanwydden — Queens Head
Llanengan — Sun Inn
Maentwrog — Grapes Hotel
Penmaenpool — George III Hotel
Porthmadog — Y Llong
Tyn y Groes — Groes Inn

Powys
Crickhowell — Bear Inn
Hay on Wye — Old Black Lion
Llandrindod Wells — Llanerch
Llyswen — Griffin
Talybont-on-Usk — Star Inn

SCOTLAND
Borders
Clovenfords — Clovenfords Hotel
Greenlaw — Castle Hotel
Innerleithen — Traquair Arms Hotel
Lauder — Black Bull
Peebles — Green Tree Hotel
St Marys Loch — Tibbie Shiels Inn
Swinton — Wheatsheaf
Tweedsmuir — Crook Inn

Central
Dollar — Kings Seat

Strathallan Hotel
Killin — Clachaig Hotel
Kilmahog — Lade Inn
Kippen — Cross Keys Hotel
Sheriffmuir — Sherifmuir Inn

Dumfries & Galloway
Eaglesfield — Courtyard
Isle of Whithorn — Steam Packet Hotel
Moffat — Balmoral Hotel
New Abbey — Criffel Inn
Newton Stewart — Creebridge House
Portpatrick — Crown Hotel

Fife
Aberdour — Aberdour Hotel
Anstruther — Craws Nest Hotel
Ceres — Meldrums Hotel
Dysart — Old Rectory Inn
Elie — Ship Inn
Kettlebridge — Kettlebridge Inn

Grampian
Auchterless — Towie Tavern
Fochabers — Gordon Arms
Kincardine O'Neil — Gordon Arms
Netherley — Lairhillock Inn
Newburgh — Udny Arms
Pennan — Pennan Inn

Highland
Fort Augustus — Lock Inn
Gairloch — Old Inn
Glencoe — Clachaig Inn
Glenfinnan — Stage House
Glen Moriston — Cluanie Inn
Invermoriston — Glenmoriston Arms
Glenelg — Glenelg Inn
Kylesku — Kylesky Hotel
Lewiston — Lewiston Arms Hotel
Stonyfield — Coach House Inn
Ullapool — Morefield Hotel
Ceilidh Place

Lothian
Dirleton — Castle Inn
Edinburgh — Bennets Bar
Gifford — Tweedale Arms
Linlithgow — Four Marys
Nine Mile Burn — Habbies Howe
South Queensferry — Halles Inn

Strathclyde
Ardentinny — Ardentinny Hotel
Ayr — Old Race Course Hotel
Coylton — Finlayson Arms
Crinan — Crinan Hotel
Fenwick — Fenwick Hotel
Glasgow — Ubiquitous Chip
Kilberry — Kilberry Inn
Maidens — Bruce Hotel
Paisley — Lord Lounsdale
Symington — Wheatsheaf Inn
Tayvallich — Tayvallich Inn

Tayside
Almondbank — Almondbank Inn
Alyth — Alyth Hotel
Arbroath — Old Brewhouse
Authmithie — Authmithie Hotel
Errol — Old Smiddy
Glendevon — Tormankin Hotel
Weem — Ailean Chraggan Hotel

INDEX OF PUBS

INDEX OF PLACES

NOTES